Psychology: A Study of a Science

STUDY II. EMPIRICAL SUBSTRUCTURE
AND RELATIONS WITH OTHER SCIENCES

Volume 4. Biologically Oriented Fields: Their Place in Psychology and in Biological Science

PSYCHOLOGY: A STUDY OF A SCIENCE

THE SERIES

STUDY I. CONCEPTUAL AND SYSTEMATIC

Volume 1. Sensory, Perceptual, and Physiological Formulations

CONTRIBUTORS: *Albert A. Blank, James J. Gibson, C. H. Graham, D. O. Hebb, Harry Helson, J. C. R. Licklider, Clifford T. Morgan, Kenneth N. Ogle, M. H. Pirenne and F. H. C. Marriott, Leo Postman and Edward C. Tolman, W. C. H. Prentice*

Volume 2. General Systematic Formulations, Learning, and Special Processes

CONTRIBUTORS: *Dorwin Cartwright, Douglas G. Ellson, W. K. Estes, F. C. Frick, Edwin R. Guthrie, Harry F. Harlow, R. A. Hinde, Arthur L. Irion, Frank A. Logan, Neal E. Miller, B. F. Skinner, Edward C. Tolman*

Volume 3. Formulations of the Person and the Social Context

CONTRIBUTORS: *Solomon E. Asch, Raymond B. Cattell, Franz J. Kallmann, Daniel Katz and Ezra Stotland, Paul F. Lazarsfeld, Henry A. Murray, Theodore M. Newcomb, Talcott Parsons, David Rapaport, Carl R. Rogers, Herbert A. Thelen*

STUDY II. EMPIRICAL SUBSTRUCTURE
AND RELATIONS WITH OTHER SCIENCES

Volume 4. **Biologically Oriented Fields: Their Place in Psychology and in Biological Science**

CONTRIBUTORS: *Fred Attneave, Paul R. David and Laurence H. Snyder, R. C. Davis, I. T. Diamond and K. L. Chow, C. H. Graham and Philburn Ratoosh, William H. Ittelson, Robert B. Livingston, Carl Pfaffmann, Karl H. Pribram, Floyd Ratliff, W. A. Rosenblith and Eda B. Vidale, Burton S. Rosner, Gerhardt von Bonin, Karl Zener and Mercedes Gaffron*

Volume 5. **The Process Areas, the Person, and Some Applied Fields: Their Place in Psychology and in Science**

CONTRIBUTORS: *D. E. Berlyne, Irvin L. Child, Paul M. Fitts, Norman Guttman, Ernest R. Hilgard, Douglas H. Lawrence, Robert W. Leeper, Daniel R. Miller, Leo Postman, Eliot H. Rodnick, Julian B. Rotter, Nevitt Sanford, W. N. Schoenfeld and W. W. Cumming, Franklin V. Taylor*

Volume 6. **Investigations of Man as Socius: Their Place in Psychology and the Social Sciences**

CONTRIBUTORS: *Kenneth J. Arrow, Donald T. Campbell, David French, A. Irving Hallowell, Alex Inkeles, George Katona, William W. Lambert, Robert E. Lane, F. G. Lounsbury, Charles E. Osgood, Muzafer Sherif, Herbert A. Simon, George and Louise Spindler, James Tobin and F. Trenery Dolbear, Jr.*

POSTSCRIPT TO THE STUDY
(*This title in preparation*)

Volume 7. **Psychology and the Human Agent** (*by Sigmund Koch*)

Psychology: A Study of a Science

STUDY II. EMPIRICAL SUBSTRUCTURE
AND RELATIONS WITH OTHER SCIENCES

Volume 4. Biologically Oriented Fields: Their Place in Psychology and in Biological Science

Edited by Sigmund Koch

DUKE UNIVERSITY

McGRAW-HILL BOOK COMPANY, INC.   1962

New York   San Francisco   Toronto   London

PSYCHOLOGY: A STUDY OF A SCIENCE was made possible by funds granted by the National Science Foundation to the American Psychological Association, and carried out under the sponsorship of the latter organization. Neither agency, however, is to be construed as endorsing any of the published findings or conclusions of the study.

THE MAPLE PRESS COMPANY, YORK, PA.

3 4 5 6 7 8 9–MP–9 8 7 6

35274

PREFACE

When one looks back over the history of science, the successes are likely to be stressed and the failures forgotten. Thus one tends to see science as starting with a sure sense of direction and progressing neatly to its present form; or so it is for the older and well-established branches of science but not for psychology. Psychology has not one sure sense of direction but several quite unsure directions. Growth is erratic, and there is much casting about for the most crucial problems and the most powerful methods. These apparent differences between psychology and the older branches of science may result from the difficulty of developing a science of man; it is perhaps significant that many of the problems of psychology were not attacked by the methods of science until so late a date in history. Or the differences may be an illusion resulting from the much closer view we have of the beginning struggles to develop a science of psychology than we now have of the beginning efforts in the older sciences.

Certainly psychology has its problems, and they are not easy. Nevertheless, knowledge has grown rapidly in the short history of man's efforts to develop a science of behavior, and the time seems appropriate for a major effort to examine the progress that has been made in attempting to find a way, or ways, to the attainment of the explanatory power that we like to think of as characteristic of science. A growing body of empirical information, a serious concern over methodological issues, and a variety of efforts to bring a selected body of fact into the organizing framework of theory all emphasize the need for that line of questioning—always going on in science—which explores the shape of knowledge, the range and inner connections of the ideas through which it has been developed and organized, the changing substructures of empirical data, and their emerging relations to each other and to the findings of other sciences. The seven volumes of *Psychology: A Study of a Science* are a response to this need.

The first three volumes, which bear the collective title *Study I. Conceptual and Systematic,* are concerned with many of the systematic formulations of recent and current influence which psychologists have developed to account for the phenomena in which they are interested. Each systematic position is analyzed by its originator, or a person connected with its development, in a way which gives attention to the problems it seeks to solve, the empirical basis on which it rests, its degree of success, and its relations to other formulations.

A second set of three volumes, collectively called *Study II. Empirical Substructure and Relations with Other Sciences,* inquires, again through the efforts of creatively active investigators, into the organization of various fields of empirical knowledge, the relations of one to another, and to work going forward in other sciences. It also examines such problems in reverse through the participation of social and biological scientists who consider the relations of their own special fields to various parts of psychology.

Volume 7—*Psychology and the Human Agent*—will present the Study Director's view of certain problems of psychological inquiry in the light of the findings of the project.

Primary credit for the initiation of these studies goes to the Association's Policy and Planning Board, which decided in 1952 that the time had come for a thorough and critical examination of the status and development of psychology. The National Science Foundation agreed upon the desirability of such an undertaking and has generously supported the effort. When funds from the National Science Foundation were found to be insufficient for all of the expenses of the studies, the American Psychological Association provided the supplementary funds necessary to complete the work.

From the beginning, the study was divided into two parts. One part dealt with the education of psychologists and the factors conducive to research productivity in psychology. That part was directed by Professor Kenneth Clark of the University of Minnesota—now Dean Clark of the University of Colorado—who has reported the findings in *America's Psychologists: A Survey of a Growing Profession,* published by the American Psychological Association in 1957.

The other part, the part with which the present series of volumes is concerned, has dealt with the substance of psychological thought and data. Professor Sigmund Koch of Duke University has been responsible for this part of the study. Working closely with him has been a panel of consultants consisting of Lyle H. Lanier, Howard H. Kendler, Conrad G. Mueller, and Karl E. Zener. These men, but chiefly Dr. Koch, have planned, organized, interpreted and edited the work, and successfully enlisted the cooperation of the approximately 80 authors whose original papers constitute the basic material of the series.

In the background, at a safe distance from the labors that have sometimes engulfed Dr. Koch, his panel of consultants, and the primary authors, has been a steering committee on which I had the pleasure of serving as chairman, and having as colleagues Clarence H. Graham, Lyle

H. Lanier, Robert B. MacLeod, Eliot H. Rodnick, M. Brewster Smith, and Robert L. Thorndike. The steering committee helped to make administrative arrangements and helped to decide on the scope of the studies, but takes no credit for their successful completion.

In the preface to *America's Psychologists* we have already acknowledged our gratitude to Kenneth Clark and his collaborators who helped to produce that volume. It is our final pleasant duty to express our thanks to Duke University for making Dr. Koch's time available; to the National Science Foundation for its necessary and generous financial support and for the counsel and support of John T. Wilson, Assistant Director for the Biological Sciences; to Lyle H. Lanier, Howard H. Kendler, Conrad G. Mueller, and Karl E. Zener for their critical and devoted help; to all the authors whose names appear on the title pages for their original contributions; and—most of all—to Sigmund Koch for directing and driving through to completion what we hope will be an oft-consulted aid to the scholars and research workers who are striving to increase the rigor and further the development of scientific psychology.

Dael Wolfle, CHAIRMAN
STEERING COMMITTEE
POLICY AND PLANNING BOARD

CONTENTS

Preface v
    Dael Wolfle

Introduction to Study II xi
    Sigmund Koch

Some Interrelations between Psychology and Genetics . . . 1
    Paul R. David and Laurence H. Snyder

How Man Looks at His Own Brain: An Adventure Shared by
Psychology and Neurophysiology 51
    Robert B. Livingston

Brain and Mind 100
    Gerhardt von Bonin

Interrelations of Psychology and the Neurological Disciplines . 119
    Karl H. Pribram

Biological Psychology 158
    I. T. Diamond and K. L. Chow

Experiment and Theory in Physiological Psychology 242
    R. C. Davis

Psychophysics and Neurophysiology 280
    Burton S. Rosner

A Quantitative View of Neuroelectric Events in Relation to Sensory Communication 334
    W. A. Rosenblith and Eda B. Vidale

Sensory Processes and Their Relation to Behavior: Studies on the
Sense of Taste as a Model S-R System 380
    Carl Pfaffmann

Some Interrelations among Physics, Physiology, and Psychology
in the Study of Vision 417
    Floyd Ratliff

Notes on Some Interrelations of Sensory Psychology, Perception, and Behavior 483
C. H. Graham and Philburn Ratoosh

Perceptual Experience: An Analysis of Its Relations to the External World through Internal Processings 515
Karl Zener and Mercedes Gaffron

Perception and Related Areas 619
Fred Attneave

Perception and Transactional Psychology 660
William H. Ittelson

Name Index 705

Subject Index 717

INTRODUCTION TO STUDY II

Psychology: A Study of a Science is a report of the inquiries of many men into the status and tendency of psychological science. There were two major contexts of inquiry: *Study I* sought analytic understanding of many systematic formulations of current influence, while *Study II* sought insight into the structure, mutual interrelations, and associations with other sciences of the main empirical areas in which psychological research proceeds. The findings of *Study I. Conceptual and Systematic* have already been published as the first three volumes of *Psychology: A Study of a Science*. This fourth volume, along with the fifth and sixth, comprise *Study II. Empirical Substructure and Relations with Other Sciences*. A postscript volume by the Study Director completes the series.

Many motives can bring—and apparently have brought—readers to the series. It can be approached as a group of handbooks, textbooks, or as an encyclopedia; as a complement to the education of the student and a supplement to that of the advanced worker; as a repository of remedial reading for the repentant specialist or the overdiffuse generalist; as a guide to the recent history of the science; as a source work for the comparative analysis and assessment of theory, method, research strategies; as a detailed index to the emerging structure of the science; as data for the mapping of research within special fields and of cross-field interrelations; as an aid to inferences concerning the achievements, shortcomings, trends, prospects of our science. There is much in this Study that can nourish all such motives, as indeed many others. But first and foremost the Study is a *study* with its own milieu of aims, values, methods, questions—its own biography. Most of that biography was set forth in Volume 1, which contains the General Introduction to the Series (pages 1–18) and an Introduction to Study I (pages 19–40). The present Introduction to Study II will complete the story—happily with some dispatch because of the availability of the material just cited.

Each *study, volume, essay* is a self-contained unit which may be read with profit. But a nice appreciation of any of the units demands that it be seen in relation to the total Study. Study II, for instance, differs in problematic incidence from Study I, but it is animated by similar values and is not without overlap in subject matter, the difference between the "systematic" and the "empirical" being, after all, something less than absolute. Moreover, the two studies were designed so as to complement each other in certain respects—some of them obvious and some perhaps not immediately apparent. For instance, substantive areas thinly sampled in Study I were somewhat more fully represented in Study II. Again, systematic influence—necessarily one of the stronger selective criteria for contributors to Study I—resulted in a high proportion of senior contributors; the differing incidence of Study II made it possible to invite a larger proportion of younger investigators (though we make no claim to the satisfaction of "New-Frontier" standards). Points such as these are easily clarified in the present introduction. But if the reader is fully to realize any of the varied aims which may bring him to this Study, it is well that he see it in the first instance *as* a study, bearing its full burden of identity. For *that,* the reader must see this Introduction to Study II in relation to the introductions in Volume 1.

In this introduction, we consider briefly (1) the plan of the over-all Study, (2) the history and rationale of Study II, (3) the factors determining the composition of the contributor group and the coverage of this study, and (4) certain anticipations concerning the character of the findings.

RÉSUMÉ OF DESIGN OF "PSYCHOLOGY: A STUDY OF A SCIENCE"

For the immediate orientation of the reader, the next few paragraphs are given over to a résumé of the Study's plan.

Study I. Conceptual and Systematic

This study involved the intensive analysis of thirty-four "systematic formulations" of widely varying type and subject-matter reference, and all of established influence in recent psychology. A systematic formulation was defined quite generally as "any set of sentences formulated as a tool for ordering knowledge with respect to some specified domain of events, or furthering the discovery of such knowledge": in applying this definition, care was taken that no formulation be precluded by nonconformity to standardized conceptions of the nature of "theory." Since each systematic formulation is the end product of a human effort to see and state order in a given domain, each analysis was made either by the originator(s) of the formulation in question or (in a few cases) by individuals creatively associated with the *development* of formulations of which they were not the primary authors.

Each systematist was invited to approach his work with certain common *themes of analysis* in mind. These were designed to invite a convergence of insight on problems of systematization which had emerged from the practice of the past three decades, more or less. Some of the suggested problems had been conspicuous in previous "metasystematic" discussion, but required, in our opinion, exposure to a wider range of systematically schooled sensibilities. Others were problems that seemed critically posed by recent systematic work, yet ones which had received little or no explicit attention.

The dominating hope was for analyses that might illumine the relations between the creative *processes* of systematizing and their publicly expressed *products*. It was thus hoped that the atmosphere of the study might encourage as much concern with background influences, orienting presuppositions, and working methods as with conceptual content, research achievements, and prospects. It was felt that analysis of this order could itself have creative consequences; reflective scrutiny of the extent and depth envisaged means *re*thinking. The primary intent of the discussion themes (and indeed, the constant aim of editorial effort) was to realize an atmosphere that might invite such emphases. Authors were requested to make explicit reference to the themes in their writing only to an extent they deemed appropriate or congenial. The use of the themes for facilitating the collation of findings was thus a secondary, if still important, aim. As matters turned out, most authors adhered to them sufficiently to give the reader an excellent purchase for the detection of similarities and differences on key issues.

The grounds for the selection of the thirty-four formulations included in Study I are given in Volume 1 (pages 21–27). The aim was a reasonably balanced diversification of formulations (as judged by many consultants) with respect to (1) subject-matter reference, and (2) conceptual and methodological "type." Many significant formulations that we would have wished to represent in the original list were excluded by spatial and other arbitrary restrictions. Nor was it possible to include in the final domain all formulations originally chosen. Though the proportion of inclusions is remarkable, there were some individuals who could not participate. We do not, then, claim "representativeness" even in an informal and impressionistic sense. We do, however, claim sufficient diversity to extend markedly the range of formulations which in recent years have been given sustained analytic attention.

Study II. Empirical Substructure and Relations with Other Sciences

This study seeks increased understanding of the internal structure of psychological science and its place in the matrix of scientific activity. A large number of distinguished investigators in psychology proper and in related biological and social sciences were invited to write papers which examine the organization of empirical knowledge within subareas

of these disciplines and chart their cross-connections. Psychologist contributors were asked to consider the relations between their own fields
of special competence and the rest of psychology and, if they wished, to
inquire also into relations with relevant segments of other sciences. Social
and biological scientists were asked to examine the relations between
their own fields and psychology.

All who were invited are individuals whose research interests have
bridged conventionally discriminated fields of knowledge. Each was asked
to place special emphasis on those "bridging problems" which had been
central in his own research experience. As in the case of Study I, certain
common themes of analysis were proposed. The "themes" for Study II
comprise a detailed breakdown of the senses in which questions of
"mapping" subject-matter structure and exploring field interrelations
might be entertained. The analytic themes were intended to play rather
different roles in the two studies. Because in Study I the analytic unit
was typically a circumscribed "systematic formulation," it was reasonable
to encourage adherence to the themes in some degree. In Study II, the
scope of the topics made it impossible for any author to embark on more
than a few of the many analytic directions that could be pursued in
considering subject-matter interrelations. The analytic themes were thus
offered primarily as an illustrative check list in the hope that concrete
and differentiated questioning might be encouraged, and that certain
perhaps promising modes of analysis of a sort not often carried out be
at least considered.

Though the topography of a science is too vast and labile for comprehensive or final mapping, this very fact makes it more important to assay
the contours of knowledge as best we can. Study II exploits the only
resource available in such problems—individual vision. It assumes that
a pool of expert, specialized minds can give insight of a sort not ordinarily
available into the emerging structure of a science. Forty-two essays have
been contributed by forty-nine authors (counting collaborators) whose
interests have signally spanned subdivisions of psychology, or of social or
biological science on the one hand, and psychology on the other. Just as
in the case of Study I, contributors and topics are not meant to be
"representative"—whatever that can mean—of their respective populations: the intention is to extend the range of areas which have been
considered from a perspective like that of Study II, the range of sensibilities which have been trained on such interrelational questions, and the
range of analytic approaches that have been made. The hope is that the
study will not only extend knowledge of the developing structure of our
science, but will highlight the importance of explicit questioning concerning the articulation of knowledge and recommend to the reader, by
the rhetoric of its insights, the habit of such questioning.

Psychology and the Human Agent

This volume is a postscript to the Study, representing certain views formed by the director in its course. The book (1) records those attitudes toward *a* science and science which necessarily color the spirit of the Study, (2) constructs trends from the massive findings of the two group studies, and (3) considers, in the light of the Study's premises and apparent trends, certain problems of psychological inquiry suggested by the practice of the past several decades.

HISTORY AND RATIONALE OF STUDY II

Psychology: A Study of a Science is the result of a project sponsored by the American Psychological Association and subsidized jointly by the National Science Foundation and the sponsoring organization. The project, known as "Project A of the APA Study of the Status and Development of Psychology," was inaugurated in the fall of 1952. It, and a separately administered sister project ("Project B") had their origin in proposals of the Association's Policy and Planning Board concerning the desirability of a series of investigations into psychological knowledge and the institutional and occupational arrangements which had evolved in its pursuit. It was the Board's energetic advocacy of such a program (especially under the chairmanship of Lyle H. Lanier in 1951–1952) that eventuated in the constitution of the two projects: Project A to be concerned with the "methodological, theoretical, and empirical status of psychological science," and Project B with "occupational, educational, and institutional problems."

Kenneth Clark served as Director of Project B (and has already reported its results in his book, *America's Psychologists*[1]). The present editor served as Director of Project A. Both projects profited from the counsel of an advisory committee under the chairmanship of Dael Wolfle. Each director also had the advice of a panel of consultants. Dr. Wolfle has described the relations of these groups to the project in his *Preface*.

Certain of the stages in the process of translating the general mandate for the project into the detailed plan for *Psychology: A Study of a Science* have been described in the General Introduction to the series (Volume 1, pages 6–14). Let it suffice here to reduce an intricate story to a few words.

From the beginning it was decided to proceed gradually: to set no plan into action until it was clear that it could stir a reasonable community of imaginations, and until there was at least some evidence for its practicability. After a lengthy planning process involving an intricate

---

[1] K. E. Clark, *America's Psychologists: A Survey of a Growing Profession*, Washington, American Psychological Association, 1957.

give-and-take between the director, the committee, panel, and selected consultants, the investigation that was to become *Study I. Conceptual and Systematic* was launched in the fall of 1953. Further planning concerning Study II and, to some extent, the more slender venture of the director's book continued through October, 1954. The present study was initiated at that time.

In planning, it was felt important to arrive at relatively limited, if still challenging, objects of study: to avoid the kind of grandiosity on which group investigations can so easily founder. Moreover, objects of inquiry were sought which might most profit from the circumstances of group inquiry. If grandiosity was thus held under control, exuberance was another matter! Many such objects suggested themselves during the planning, too many. Their range is barely suggested in the discussion of "rationale" given in the Volume 1 general introduction (pages 7–14). The ideas for the present study (as those for Study I) thus represent a selection from a wide array of possibilities.

Among the many types of questions that can be asked about a science, none could well be more important than those concerning the relations among its chief fields of inquiry and its interpenetrations with other disciplines concerned with overlapping objects of study. Yet in psychology few questions have been pursued with less vigor. It has long been a platitude to lament the growing specialism and insulation of research areas in our science. But the lament has occasioned not much more than discomfort and perhaps not enough of that.

Nevertheless, the investigator who wishes to environ his work with meaning has necessarily held certain beliefs about such matters. These, however, have often been so thin as to be tantamount to a brushing aside of the type of problem they address. Thus, for instance, it has been fairly fashionable to assume that the traditional, so to say, "process fields" of psychology (as e.g., perception, learning, motivation) are essentially chapter headings, having no systematic significance. The frequent corollary is that whatever is viable in the various fields will somehow be integrated in some future theory. But whether a theory can integrate research in diverse and largely insulated fields without the theorist keeping carefully in view from an early stage the detailed relations which obtain among them is not often considered. Certainly those theorists of the recent past who assumed that all significant problems of psychology could be solved via postulates local to a single research area have not in the results of their work increased confidence in such a position.

The relatively superficial concern with interrelationship issues often reflects a judgment that such problems cannot be solved within the terms given by the state of psychology. It is held that the main areas distinguished by convention are essentially distinctions of investigative convenience and with this it is usual to presume that analysis would show each such field to be a loose congeries of research findings having little rational coherence. But since the analysis is almost never made, it is impossible to test the *coherence* of field boundaries and thus arrive at more significant organizations. *Psychology: A Study of a Science* has constantly emphasized a view which sees most things in science as an uneven compound of the rational and extrarational, but certainly the relative proportion may be made to vary.

There is no way out of it. Even were the "field" distinctions wholly ones of "convenience," it would be well to know whether and to what extent they *are* convenient. But one can doubt the story to be that simple. The rather crassly defined fields into which convention parcels psychological knowledge could be distinctions of convenience, yet not of *mere* convenience. Certainly if we trace fields like perception, learning, cognition, motivation, emotion, into the history of psychology, near or remote, it becomes clear that such fields were premised on analyses of psychological phenomena meant to have systematic and even a crude ontological significance. The late nineteenth-century psychologists who talked about cognition, conation, and affection, for instance, thought they were talking about dimensions of analysis which in some sense fitted psychological phenomena and were adequate to them. The conventionalist and nominalist sensibility of recent psychology prefers to see its subareas as collections of functional relationships among characteristic (but often not character*ized*) classes of variables. It is perhaps this nominalism which, at some level in the inquirer's personality, has supported the rather nonchalant attitude toward interrelational problems. But, whether these collections of functional relationships are seen as having "functional," systematic, or even ontological force or not, their relation must be taken seriously if we are to have a meaningful science. Plural inquiries must stand in some kind of relationship if we are to have a science. If they stand in none, we have no science.

Despite such tendencies to evade interrelational problems, they have not been bypassed. They cannot be. They are constantly thrust upon us by the exigencies of research planning, pedagogy, and administration. The upshot is that we are content with superficial levels of analysis and cognitively thin stereotypes. For example, it has not in recent memory been rare for a theorist to champion either a "purely behavioral" or a "physiological" frame of reference for his concepts and translate this preference into the grain of an ambitious theory *before* essaying detailed analysis of actual and possible relations between physiology and psychology. Indeed, there have been cases when, say, a dogmatic "empty organism" approach has become an embarrassment after the "purely behavioral" theory begins to generate psychophysiological analyses and re-search.

To pursue the area of this illustration a bit further: For a long time in recent history, consideration of relations between psychology and physiology was left pretty much to philosophers of science, a group not eminently qualified in either field. The philosophers proceeded from a context established by the traditional "mind-body problem." For a period —coinciding with the hegemony of positivism—of some twenty-five years, it was something of a fashion to show that this problem becomes meaningful only upon translation into questions concerning the relations between the "language systems" of psychology and physiology. But actual analysis of these relations, if not eschewed, was approached in a way that could yield little of value to the empirical scientist. In effect, the philosophers called for an analysis they did not make, while the psychologists posited stereotypes (e.g., "All explanations must come from physiology," "No explanations can come from physiology," "Psychological laws are derivable in principle from physiology but psychology must first develop at its own level") for which they did not even *invite* analysis. In the course of what discussion took place, the issue was addressed in hope-lessly global form: e.g., *prescriptions* recommending some desirable future relationship between the two disciplines were not distinguished from *de-scription* of extant relations, or either of these from *prediction,* based on apparent trends, of probable future relations. Again, much of the discussion seemed to presume that the relations of psychology to the biological sciences *in general* would be established once the matter was got straight for physiology: that specific relations with other biological disciplines need not be considered.

The century has seen considerably more attention given to relations of psychology and the social sciences than to its relations with the biological sciences. Much of this has come from within the social sciences where, for obvious historical reasons, the need to establish identity is great and where psychology is readily seen as some kind of base line against which a *persona* may be traced. And social psychology, a specifically twentieth-century product, has perforce faced the same problem in reverse. But here, too, thinking has tended to be dominated by stereotype. For instance, it is often claimed that psychology and sociology deal with behavior at different levels of abstraction, independently of efforts to specify the formal or contentual characteristics of the abstractive levels in question. Assumptions may be made to the effect that it *is* or *is not* legitimate to transfer concepts from a psychological to a sociological (or political-science, or anthropological) context, or vice versa, with little clear analysis of the grounds for the one belief or the other. Again, much enthusiasm has gone into programs toward the "interdisciplinary" integration of psychology and the social sciences, with little prior exploration of the nature and degree of integration of the relevant sciences taken separately.

But questions concerning interrelations among the *subparts of psychology* have been slighted even more than those concerning relations with its bordering sciences. Conventionally discriminated areas of psychological science are variously held to be supplementary, independent, reducible one to the other, related according to one or another set of "bridging laws" or improperly subdivided, but such positions are rarely backed up by intensive analyses of the areas in question. Not seldom, workers in a given field are victims of an irresistible tendency to see their specialty as embracing the entire science; in the embrace, the rest of the science is often squeezed to death. Students of sensory process have been known to see no room for perceptual process; of learning, no room for either; of all, none for personality; of personality, none for all: men are easily drugged by the grandeur of their solipsisms. And in each such area there are subareas and sub-subareas within which solipsisms of descending magnitude may be achieved.

Crosscutting such substantive areas, discriminations such as the "pure" versus the "applied" figure with increasing importance in recent history, especially with the growth of vast professional groupings like the clinical. Here again it can be said that though many dogmas exist with regard to interrelations—of knowledge, training, professional roles, etc.—these dogmas have not often been backed by sustained and differentiated analysis.

The preceding account of certain of the circumstances which invite a study like this may impress the reader as rather more bleak than it need be. For instance, especially over the last ten or fifteen years, a number of research clusters which relate variables usually assigned to discrete fields have become conspicuous. There was the "new look" in perception and, more generally, the cluster of concerns with relations between motivational and perceptual variables. Another cluster has involved relations between perception and personality. Perhaps most conspicuous has been a massive concentration of interest—heavily documented in the present study but certainly evident outside it—in relations between perception and learning. This increase of interstitial interest no doubt announces a changing atmosphere and is certainly encouraging. But the depth of the earlier neglect and the thinness *still* of the present interest could not well be better documented than by the *character* of the newer interstitial research. The research that has been done on the relations of motivational and perceptual variables, or perceptual and so-called "personality variables," however valuable, has by and large involved narrow and adventitiously selected sets of variables and has been correlated with few far-reaching or searching examinations of relations between the fields from which they derive. As for the present interest in learning-perception relations, this admirable development, it must be recalled, occurred only after the field of perception itself had been all but legislated out of existence (at least in this country) for a period of roughly thirty years. Learning had *preempted* perception during the hegemony of behaviorism and neobehaviorism; neo-neobehaviorism, in willing peception back to life, is at the same time drawing attention to what can happen in the history of a science as a result of piecemeal viewing.

Words like "fields," "areas," "research clusters," "disciplines," are deceptive. The terms in which we talk about the architecture of knowledge inevitably suggest knowledge to be more architectonic than it is. Study II supposes that more explicit and intensive interest in the emerging structure of psychology is desirable. But it is well that an investigation into the "structure" of knowledge commence with a profound appreciation of the limits upon any such enterprise.

The study does not, for instance, suppose that everything that has been or is being done in psychology can fall into place, or in some way be "salvaged," in the terms of some happy and even-tempered interrelational scheme. Far from it—much that happens in a science is expendable (would that we knew precisely what!); much that is not expendable may fall at a given time into no orderly relations with any consistent map. The study does not presume that what is currently called psychology is best regarded as a single cohesive field of knowledge; rather, it stresses the importance of asking at all times penetrating questions about the degree of integration or fractionation of the field relative to prevailing definitions. The study does not even suppose that all *significant* knowledge need now or ever fall into one systematic or rational pattern; nothing says that differing universes of discourse, or even disparate "levels" of analysis must be commensurable. The study does not suppose that there is any privileged route to the conquest of interrelational problems or any special methodological gimmickry that can either enhance or replace individual vision. Though the units of study are units of "empirical" subject matter, it sees no absolute distinction between what is called the "theoretical" and the "empirical," and it is as eager to encourage exploration of interrelations via theoretical integrations or realignments as it is to encourage attempts at charting relations among empirical variables approached in a systematically more neutral way.

The study, of course, supposes that any single study addressed to the problems at issue can make only modest progress and that the progress is to be measured more in terms of the habits of thinking it recommends to its readers than its particular findings. It does not pretend to address every field of psychology distinguished by current convention or even every important field. Though it has assembled the views of many creative and knowledgeable men, it has no intention of fusing them into some single "standard" view of the structure and associations of our science. On the contrary, it has sought to ensure against the emergence of an "official" map by arranging that most sectors of the terrain of study be inspected by a plurality of viewers. In the end, what matters to this study is that the individual reader enrich his *own* view of the science, in his own way. If the study provides materials which in any degree will enable this, its purpose will have been well accomplished.

COVERAGE, CONTRIBUTOR GROUP, AND WORKING ATMOSPHERE

In planning the study, we sought to ensure far-ranging coverage of subject matter and to encourage concrete and differentiated analysis, but to allow the specific representation of cross-field topics and analytic questions to be determined by the authors' predilections. The pattern of this study is thus very largely a pattern of its authors' sensibilities playing, each in its own mode, upon problems that interest them.

The units of subject matter available to the study for the initiation of its inquiries can, of course, be no more "rationally" bounded than the "fields" distinguished by current convention. The purpose, after all, is to explore, not prejudge, the structure of the science. Inclusion of a field implied no commitment as to its *actual* degree of coherence—whether in respect to the character of its empirical variables, its problems, its methods, its role in the systematic analysis of behavior or experience, or any other attribute. In establishing the general framework of coverage, it was felt best to select subject-matter areas of relatively broad scope (say, "learning," rather than "conditioning" or "verbal learning") or, in the case of cross-science relations, entire disciplines. These units were meant to set the framework for the inclusion of contributors; as will be seen, the role of contributors was not necessarily to consider the cross-field problems raised by the *entire* (crassly defined) area they represented, but rather to stress *specific* bridging problems in the line of their primary interests and research. In the choice of "intra-psychological" fields, it was felt wisest to concentrate on areas conventionally allocated to *fundamental* psychology but, because of the importance of stimulating more explicit interest in the relations between pure and applied psychology, to include as well at least two applied fields.

Against such a background, the "fields" ultimately arrived at for consideration in their relationships were (1) from within *psychology—*

sensory psychology, perception, physiological psychology, learning, motivation, personality, social psychology, psycholinguistics, clinical psychology, and human engineering; (2) from within *biological science*— aspects of physiology, neuroanatomy, and genetics; and (3) from within *social science*—aspects of sociology, anthropology, linguistics, economics, and political science. It need hardly be added that the study does not regard this list of fields as exhausting its domain; even for psychology per se, there are obviously so many incidences from which crosscutting and overlapping breakdowns can be derived that it is not possible to say what "exhaustiveness" could mean in such a connection.

The design of Study II called for individuals whose primary professional background was in some one of the "fields" indicated above to consider its relations to some one or combination of the others. In the terminology of the study, the field which the analyst represents, by virtue of professional affiliation, is the "field of primary reference"; the "field(s) of secondary reference" is the domain(s) whose relationship to his "own" field the analyst proposes to explore. The *specific* bounding, for purposes of the analysis, of *both* fields of reference is of course the option of the analyst, an option always influenced by his particular cross-field research history. Though each author was asked to place special emphasis on those "bridging problems" which had been central in his own research experience, he was encouraged also to reach out from this core and bound his field of concern as generally as he might wish.

A *plurality* of individuals of differing background, systematic predilection, or specialized cross-area interest, was invited to "represent" *each* field of primary reference. The hope was that—depending on the breadth and density of the given field—it might be represented by between two and five individuals. For most of the fields of primary reference, this hope was realized.

It should be emphasized that though a contributor was always invited to "represent" a given field of primary reference, his field(s) of secondary reference was never specified. Rather, he was asked to pursue the analysis of cross-field relations in whatever directions he might wish. Thus the pattern of specific cross-field relationships considered in the study was largely *author-determined*. Any attempt to compose the domain of study by some arbitrary combination and permutation of the fields of reference would have been close to meaningless. The chances of nontrivial knowledge about cross-field relations being won by an analyst who had not already established intimate interests in the relevant problems would be very slight. A major strength of the present study is precisely that it taps the knowledge and insight of authors in the *particular* contexts in which they are in fact most knowledgeable and insightful.

It will be noted also that the way in which the study's coverage was planned makes it possible for two (or more) authors to elect the same primary and secondary reference-field combination. Such overlap, when it occurs, is often more apparent than real, in that the meaning of "same" in such a context can be markedly qualified by the different perceptions that two analysts may have of their fields of reference. Be this as it may, provision for overlaps of this sort was considered another strength of the plan. The play of differing scientific sensibilities on the same substantive issues (be they *really* the same or only nominally so) can be highly illuminating. Moreover, patterns of convergence on given cross-field combinations and on given fields of secondary reference would to some extent be diagnostic of the distribution of interest in interstitial problems of the field at large; any clusterings of interest would mean clusterings of analysis at precisely those points which require maximum attention if a just picture of the status of the science is to be derived. In administering the study, it was standard policy to advise authors to plan their essays without regard to the possibility of overlaps with the topics of their colleagues.

A few words are now in order about the arduous process of converting these framework decisions into the *actual* coverage of the study. The initial step was to begin—with the help of the Project A panel and many consultants, each expert in some field of the study—a list of contributor candidates. A few months of intensive thought and interchange produced a list of imposing architecture. Like all such lists, it never did become fully stable: it required frequent adjustments to the exigencies of the study.

The more obvious criteria of election to the list were research distinction in the field of primary reference, significant evidence of scholarly and analytic ability, and established interest—preferably as realized in a long-range research program—in problems of a cross-field or cross-discipline nature. Among the more subtle criteria was a preference for men of especially self-determining cast.

In the background were a number of considerations of a more special sort. One was the hope that a number of men known to have original and stimulating ideas but not noted for their readiness to appear in the literature might be persuaded to participate. Others were addressed as much to the interests of the project as a whole as to those of Study II. Thus, because Study I had been populated by a high proportion of contributors in the "elder-statesman" category, it was hoped that the balance might be redressed by including a reasonable number of younger, if still mature, contributors in Study II. Another such consideration had much to do with the relative number of candidates sought to represent each area. This was the desire to represent more fully in the present study certain of the areas (e.g., physiological psychology) that had been only thinly sampled in Study I. Contrariwise, one of the fields especially widely covered in the first study (learning) was represented in the second by rather fewer contributors than might otherwise have been appropriate.

The numbers of contributors ultimately representing each of the study's fields of primary reference were conditioned by many factors, some planned and some outside our control. As already mentioned, it was envisaged at the outset that each field should be represented by between two and five contributors. Within these limits, efforts were made to represent subfields of fundamental psychology in a density roughly reflecting their extent and current importance. For each of the two applied fields (clinical psychology and human engineering), two contributors were to be sought. There were to be between two and three contributors for each of the biological and social sciences included as primary reference fields —this for a number of pragmatic reasons, such as the need to limit the study's size and the expected difficulty of enlisting nonpsychologist contributors.

Reference to the tables of contents will show that in a rough way these framework requirements were satisfied in the final distribution of contributors. The main disappointments were the failure to obtain plural representation of the three biological sciences included as fields of primary reference and of sociology. To some extent this is compensated for by the very large number of biologically oriented *psychologists* who consider relations with biological science, and the fairly large number of personality and social psychologists who entertain questions of relationship with sociology.

For areas having multiple representation, the constant effort was to achieve *diversified groups* of contributors—men who, by virtue of differences in systematic approach, research background, or scientific temperament, would be likely to see their problems in different ways. Obviously, for groups of the size involved and characteristics of the subtlety at issue, there could be no thought of some principle of diversification. If, however, inferences can be made from the essays to characteristics of their authors, it is fairly evident that this aspect of the planning was not frustrated.

So much for the *planning* of the representation. The final roster was not, of course, uninfluenced by the availability (and in a few cases the pertinacity) of authors. About as many people refused to participate as the number who ultimately did. This 50 per cent rate of refusals is, we think, fairly modest for a study of the present character, and was not out of line with expectation. In Study I, there had been a markedly lower rate. But in Study I the unit of analysis had been given systematic formulations and the men approached were in most instances their owners. Not only a vested interest in the objects of analysis but an expectation (not always borne out) that they need not go far afield in the preparation of their analysis, worked toward acceptance. In the present study, equally overcommitted people were being asked to take on a task which, though in the line of their interest, could not call on identifications of comparable power and which, moreover, was of a sort that often required extensive scholarly preparation. Despite these circumstances, relatively few of the Study II refusals came from the psychologist candidates. By far the largest number came from the "related" disciplines and, among these, most from the biologists.

These reality conditions of the present study are significant for understanding the character of the final domain but are instructive, too, as positive findings relative to the problems broached by the study. Thus, for instance, the almost standard pattern of the refusals from the biological scientists and, to a lesser extent, the social scientists, was to express enthusiasm for the aims of the study but to plead an almost total lack of knowledge concerning the area of secondary reference (psychology). If the editor is any judge of correspondence, he can report that these protestations were characteristically of the most sincere sort, even if it be supposed that their authors could sometimes have discovered supplementary grounds for refusing. When it is realized that each of these candidates was a distinguished investigator, known largely for work which had bridged over into psychology, and further, that the group as a whole (especially the biologists) represented a large proportion of those in their fields known at the time to be doing such interrelational work, a number of conclusions become fairly compelling. It becomes fairly evident that those committed to interdisciplinary work are not in general combining plural disciplines into single skulls (as the slogan of interdisciplinary training executives would have it) but tend to be crossing field boundaries rather adventitiously in the pursuit of problems originating in the home territory. One gets little impression of a concern with a broader environment of interrelationships which might condition the significance of the specific cross-field variables under study. Whether this state of affairs is regrettable is not here the issue. What *is* the issue is that we have here an important descriptive fact concerning the status of interdisciplinary thinking—one which can give pause to confidence in the imminence of sweeping interdisciplinary "integrations" and lend realism to interdisciplinary training schemes. But more appropriate to the immediate purpose, the reader approaching Study II may derive from the present finding some useful perspective. Questions of field and discipline relationships *have* been neglected, neglected even by many of those whose work is by way of erecting those relationships. These problems are *not* easy. Vision can and must be trained on them but will not readily come to focus.

The story of our working methods is the story of an *atmosphere* of work. For such tasks as are addressed by the study there are no secret weapons: there is only the hope of inviting the play of specialized, creative minds on the objects and issues which they most prize. The hope was to realize an atmosphere that invited self-determination, freshness, spontaneity, *and* intellectual craftsmanship.

As is already evident, a central awareness of the study was the desirability of a more differentiated attack on interrelationship issues than had been usual. To a large extent the design of the study guarantees this, in that the main basis for bounding topics is the authors' more or less specialized cross-field research interests. But it was hoped that a set toward differentiated questioning could be sharpened by working out a detailed breakdown of the *types* of analytic questions that can be asked about the relations between any two fields of knowledge. These "themes of analysis" were among the materials explaining the study that were sent to all authors before their work began. They were offered essentially as an illustrative check list of the *range* of questions that might be asked. It was made clear that the themes had no legislative intent, that in the analyses they could be responded to selectively or not at all.

The themes of analysis discriminate a large number of highly specified questions which fall into six categories: (1) "mapping," in terms of definitive variable-constellations and in other ways, the fields of primary and secondary reference; (2) realignments, resulting from the analyses of 1, of conventional "field" boundaries; (3) "bridging laws" (i.e., cross-area functional dependencies) and formal relationships; (4) interrelations of methods, both research and systematic; (5) knowledge overlaps, including transpositions *and* duplications of findings, as between the areas of primary and secondary reference; (6) collaborative, administrative, and educational mechanisms as these have affected or promise to affect the interrelations of the fields under analysis.

The problem addressed by such a breakdown is not, of course, the sort that has a unique solution. What can be claimed for the breakdown arrived at is that it separates issues which heretofore have often been considered in deceptively global form into constituent *particular* questions. It strives also to ask a sufficient range of questions to do some degree of justice to the many different things that can be meant by a "field" or "area" of a science. A field, after all, can be approached as a body of formulated knowledge, the totality of the inquiring action that has generated that knowledge, the methods—empirical and formal—that are definitive, or the institutional, ideological, and material arrangements that in some way may be characteristic. The field may be approached as a collection of lawful or lawlike functional relationships, as a characteristic family or constellation of *empirical* variables, as a group of *systematic* variables assigned some general common property or function in a theory, as the collectivity of all systematic variables discriminated by all theories addressed to a cluster of empirical problems believed in some sense cohesive, as a class of processes, phenomena, or empirical problems believed unified by a relatively cohesive set of empirical laws, as a class of processes having some relatively independent causal influence on organismic functioning, etc. In characterizing a field, or a relationship between fields as defined in any of these ways, one can raise questions of history, of present status, or of indicated trend for the future. One can raise *descriptive* questions, or *normative* ones concerning *desirable* future status or relationship.

The *nature* of the relations that may be asserted or explored as between any of the given units that result from the above multifarious criteria may itself be looked into from quite different incidences. One might, for instance, look into primarily *formal* relationships (as, e.g., independence, deducibility, subsumability, translatability, etc.)—a type of consideration, incidentally, which in too many earlier analyses tended to preempt other more useful lines of approach. Again, one can try to discern, or perhaps hypothesize, empirical, or for that matter, systematic, laws which bridge between variables in the one domain and the other. Or one can inquire into "methodic" relations (in several senses of the methodic) between any two areas, even when these are not *defined* against a methodic criterion. One can entertain questions about interrelations (as e.g., influence lines) between the institutional, ideological, or administrative factors which environ inquiry in the fields under analysis. And many other questions.

Not all such questions are equally significant but more than a few are quite significant. *None* are at all significant unless posed in at least fairly clear independence of the others. The themes of analysis are a selection from among such contexts of questioning as are implicit in the above illustrations. The items are formulated with some explicitness and often supplemented with rather full explanation. The result is a not unformidable document. It appears as an appendix to Volume 6 and is offered to the reader in the same spirit it was to the authors—as a device for encouraging differentiated thinking about questions of structure and relationship, if not in these particular terms, at least in some *particular* terms.

To ensure that the themes be considered with a certain high seriousness, they were submitted to authors as a kind of ideal discussion outline which—we were quick to point out—"no . . . analyst can hope fully to satisfy." The items were in fact developed and sequenced in such a way as to set the terms of something pretty close to an "ideal" analysis, given infinite time, intelligence, and indefatigability of soul. Since the relata of analysis were sizable fields of knowledge, it was not, of course, expected that any given one of the items was susceptible to full answer, let alone any marked number of them. It was emphasized in the introduction to the outline that the task defined was "in any literal sense, impossible," and that "the condition of psychological knowledge is such that only modest increments of insight into issues of the sort here envisaged are attainable." Other escape exits were lushly distributed throughout the themes of analysis, and even more so in the letter of invitation and ensuing correspondence with contributors. Moreover, unlike the practice in Study I, where the themes of analysis played a somewhat different role, no editorial response to Study II manuscripts was ever directed toward increasing, or even encouraging, adherence to the themes. That the escape exits were effective is fairly evident from the fact that the architecture of the outline is visible in precisely none of the essays.

The themes did, we think, play pretty much the role expected of them. At the most general level, the earnestness of their intent elicited earnestness in return. Again, the atmosphere of the themes certainly has encouraged *intensive* analysis—short of which few considerations of interrelationship issues can achieve much more than the circulation of stereotype. And finally, the evidence of the essays argues the probability that a wider range of questions, and more highly specified ones, have been asked than has characterized the *genre* of interrelational analyses in the past.

Did the themes have a "grooving effect"? The evidence says "No," while the range of the themes, and the variety of ways they comprehend of looking at the structure of the science, is such that they could hardly have constricted thinking.

But the themes should not detain us. What is important is not the questions men can raise but those they do raise, especially the questions that most recommend themselves to committed men at the frontiers of their fields. Whatever force this study has is gathered from the willingness of many such men searchingly to look *across* these frontiers at approximately the same time in history in directions set by their own curiosities. The emerging shape of a science is the emerging shape of what such men do and of what they see. If there has been anything happy about the study's conduct, this has been its disposition to hem in vision as little as possible, to depend on "mechanism" to a minimum, and to employ what mechanism it does for liberating ends.

The atmosphere of the study was the forty-nine atmospheres of the relationships, long-continued ones, with the individual authors. If any generalizations can be made about these, the main thing of note was the gallantry and forbearance of those on the productive side of the relationships. All gave the work their best effort and for most this meant exceedingly strenuous and long-continued effort. Many—however they approached their topic—found that the demands of such structural or interrelational problems as they were addressing were rather crueller than they had anticipated. Yet they pushed on without complaint. Virtually all were issue-centered, amiable, even appreciative, when editorial suggestions were made, no matter how obsessive the latter. The universal quantifier must, we fear, be dropped when it comes to the matter of promptness in meeting deadlines. A few men were model, a fair number finished within the secret timetable that most editors perforce sew in the lining of their Inverness, but not inconsiderable numbers worked agonizingly through their sixth, eighth, and even dozenth deadlines. This may sound like the kind of secret to which all editors are privy, but the present one doubts that extrapolation from normal editorial experience can give a sense of what can happen when there are forty-nine authors working on tasks so challenging as those posed by this study. Whatever the elements of anguish in these thoughts, it is by way of further praise of the authors that we mention them. For the rather considerable scatter in the receipt of manuscripts made it desirable to suggest that those received earlier be brought up to date. Of the many men thus penalized for their own virtue, almost all gave their uncomplaining cooperation.

At the editorial end of these forty-nine relationships, the main consistency was that such problems as the study was engaging could only be advanced by a pluralism of the widest excursion, by an utterly free play of the contributors' sensibilities within the quite general frame of the study's objectives. No goal or analytic direction that an author wished to pursue was ever discouraged. Whether the author wished to approach his topic via a theoretical or pretheoretical integration of the fields at issue, or primarily by empirical survey; whether he wished to stress one type of relationship question or many; whether he chose one field of secondary reference or several, or indeed, to train attention on the structure of the field of primary reference per se—all such matters were entirely his own option. Length of manuscript (short of flagrant indecency relative to the size of the volumes) was always his option, though we did, of course, uniformly express a preference for *detailed* analysis. In editing manuscripts, the editor's conception of his role was that of putting himself at the service of the particular objectives which the contributor had set. His suggestions were addressed to such ends as clarity, sound scholarship, consistency, occasionally style, and most generally, how best to strengthen or develop the author's argument.

A few *technical* injunctions were fairly consistently, though not inflexibly, asserted. Mention of these may give the reader some useful fore-knowledge about the character of the essays. One was that essays be written at a level which, though not necessarily nontechnical, would be clear to nonspecialized readers. Along with this went a constant concern that essays be written in a self-contained way and not lean too heavily on mere citations of the literature, especially literature not likely to be known to the nonspecialist. A related concern was that authors describe in at least a little detail empirical studies on which exposition or argument hinged in any important way. Finally, since almost all of the essays perform in part the function of a review article, authors were urged to prepare generous and careful bibliographies. As a result, whatever utility the study may have for handbook purposes—and it is a not inconsiderable one—has been maximized.

SOME ANTICIPATIONS

The value of the essays is in their detail—details of analysis, creative thinking, and scholarship, which are best left unblurred by synoptic survey or the manufacture of some synthetic pattern. Volume 7, the postscript volume of *Psychology: A Study of a Science,* will consider findings from various of the essays and even trends suggested by certain groupings of them, but with no disposition toward the manufacture of a "total pattern." Here we consider a miscellany of matters which may in some measure prepare the reader for navigating among the findings.

First, a few words about the grouping of the essays into the three volumes. The intention of the tripartite bounding is clear enough. Volume 4 is meant to embrace the essays of the biologists and those psychologists whose fields of primary reference are in most intimate contact with the biological sciences. Volume 5 demarcates those essays in which the primary fields of reference belong more strictly to "psychological psychology"; this does not imply that these areas are *unrelated* to biological science (or social science for that matter), either in principle or as seen by the authors of the essays. The final volume is of course meant to comprehend essays in which social psychology is taken as the primary reference field and those in which aspects of social science play this role. Here again, there is no implication that these fields are independent of the other groupings.

If there is an element of arbitrariness in the tripartite-volume breakdown, there is a greater one in the assignment of certain of the essays to given volumes. For instance, of the four essays in which perception is the field of primary reference, three appear in Volume 4; one (Postman's) in Volume 5. It is not at all clear that Postman's treatment of perception and learning is any further from biology than, say, Ittelson's presentation of perception and transactional psychology, but it was appropriate to put Postman's essay in Volume 5 because it forms a natural cluster with the essays in which learning is field of primary reference. Again, the essays in which personality is field of primary reference (especially Miller's, Sanford's, Child's) could have clustered about as well with the essays of Volume 6 as they do with those of Volume 5, where they are situated, but there were considerations of balancing the size of volumes. Nor, it may be added, is it an unrefreshing idea to interrupt the customary wedlock between personality and social psychology and assign one of the cowering partners to a volume which will come under the gaze of fundamental psychologists.

What is mainly to be emphasized *re* the "packaging" of the essays is that the unit of planning was the total study, not the individual volume. Indeed, a necessary consequence of the interrelational objectives is that the contents of each volume range freely (if with variable bias) over the entire breadth of psychology and related sciences. The fields of *secondary reference* were, it will be recalled, taken in any directions the authors wished to pursue. Thus, for instance, the geneticists David and Snyder (Volume 4) look toward personality, abnormal psychology, and individual differences, among other directions. The physiological psychologists Diamond and Chow (Volume 4) look largely toward learning. An essay by the anthropologist A. Irving Hallowell (Volume 6) is as firmly rooted in biological science as any of the papers in Volume 4. Another anthropologist, David French (Volume 6) looks toward perception and cognition. Donald T. Campbell (Volume 6), with social psychology as field of primary reference, pursues relationships with learning, perception, and certain developments in the neurological area. Psychology *as a whole* is inescapable in each of these volumes and the purity of the reader's specialism is nowhere without risk of violation.

The fact that fields of secondary reference were spontaneously chosen by the authors affords an instructive opportunity to gauge—from the distribution of choices—the directions in which bridging interests are going in the field at large. Though we do not argue that as the study goes, so goes the science, it is hardly likely that the choices of a group of authors so large, so influential, and so varied in field of primary affiliation would not, in some appreciable degree, be diagnostic of the general situation. In this connection, one of the most impressive general findings of the study is the convergence of bridging interests toward *perception*. Every author who took learning as field of primary reference (Guttman, Lawrence, Leeper, and Schoenfeld and Cumming in Volume 5) chose to consider relations with perception. One author, Postman (also in Volume 5), who was expected to take learning as his field of primary reference decided instead to put perception in its place and transpose learning to the secondary field. And the choice of perception as the main, or one of the main, fields of secondary reference by authors representing areas as diverse as neurophysiology, physiological psychology, sensory psychology, personality, human engineering, social psychology, anthropology, and linguistics will not of course escape the reader's notice. That the last several years have seen a quickening of interest in perception is evident from the general literature. What this study suggests is that perception is by way of becoming the "basic" field of psychological interest and the foundation field of its conceptualizations—indeed, that it has by now almost certainly supplanted learning in these respects.

An interesting by-product of the concentration of author interest on perception is that the reader can look forward to what amounts to a virtual subanthology on the topic of extending learning and behavior theories to this empirical domain. This is not only Postman's, Guttman's, Lawrence's, and Schoenfeld and Cumming's major theme, but it is conspicuously addressed also by Graham and Ratoosh, Ratliff, and Attneave (Volume 4), and Campbell and Osgood (Volume 6), and, in rather different spirit, by Zener and Gaffron, and Ittelson (Volume 4), and Leeper (Volume 5). Such a subanthology should have for the reader not only the drama of timeliness, but more substantial values. After all, agreement now seems general that among the things a psychologist cannot avoid coming to terms with are the problems and phenomena of perception. Moreover, no psychologist, especially if he be an American one, can avoid coming to terms with behaviorism. And the distinctive mark of the *present phase* of behaviorism—the "neo-neobehaviorism" that began to emerge in the early fifties—is in fact the concern with perceptual, and more generally, central process. It is well, then, that the particular intersection of theoretical and problematic interests at issue be viewed with utmost care and from many angles. It is well, also, that it be viewed both in celebrant mood (there is much to celebrate at the return of the repressed) *and* critically. Precisely such viewing is afforded by the study, though, because of the fortuities of representation, the volume of celebration exceeds that of the criticism. To compensate for this imbalance, may the editor suggest that such critical consideration of the rationale of behavioristic analyses of perception as exemplified, say, in the methodological section of the Zener-Gaffron paper, be given especial attention by the reader.

Turning now to the individual papers, the happiest generalization that can be made is that few can be made. The papers are widely varied in character but each in its own way realizes such qualities as we have seen to be definitive of the study's atmosphere. Some of them give primary emphasis to theoretical ideas intended to integrate or reveal the relatedness of discrete fields; others give the main concern to tracing cross-field relations among empirical variables. Some of the analyses are process-centered, some focus on the organization of extant clusters of knowledge, others are method-centered. Some papers accent emerging substantive and formal relationships as between fields at different levels of analysis; others focus on interstitial *problems* upon which a plurality of fields may bear in complementary fashion; still others concentrate on the structure of single large areas (e.g., personality) on the assumption that extrafield relations will be most naturally revealed when structure lines are drawn with sufficient fineness. Some of the papers approach their topics historically; others in terms of current status, or indeed, *sub species aeternitatis*. Some of the essays adopt the strategy of detailed analysis of "samples" of the literature in the areas under consideration; others are developed in a somewhat less Baconian fashion. In each, a man is speaking for himself, addressing his own problems in his own accents.

Though length and scope of the essays vary, even the shorter of them do not frustrate the hope for detailed and sustained analysis. That the essays raise far more differentiated structural and interrelational questions than has been customary in discussions of this sort is obvious. That such differentiated inquiry is important to our science and should be among its continuing responsibilities is made plain, if only from the complexities, the sometimes unsuspected moot alternatives, that emerge when *specific* questioning is pursued. Readers, say, of Volume 4, will find any of the textbook slogans concerning the "nature" or "role" of physiological psychology they may bring with them evaporating into a degree of triviality worse than emptiness before completing a few dozen pages. And, taking the study as a whole, similar claims might be made with respect to the time-worn textbook slogans concerning relations between perception and motivation, personality and perception, motivation and learning, social psychology and psychology, given social sciences and psychology, applied and pure psychology, etc.

Perhaps the major dimension of variation in authors' conceptions of their tasks had to do with whether they aimed primarily toward a theoretical integration of the fields comprising the relata of analysis, or a systematically more neutral survey of empirical structure or relations. This, it should be noted, is no simple continuum—especially if it be recognized that even the grouping of *empirical* variables local to specific studies into more general classes is a theory-like process. And, of course, there is no metric for the "degree of the theoretical," or decision rule which neatly separates "theory" and "pretheory." Whatever continuum such qualifications permit to exist is populated in virtually every segment by the essays of the present study.

Closest to that extreme which marks empirical survey as the method of preference are Lambert's paper on social psychology (Volume 6) and

Davis' on physiological psychology (Volume 4). Both of these men make an intensive effort to explore the structure and associations of their fields by reconstructing from characteristic samples of the relevant literature the chief empirical variable-classes that have set the terms of research. Comparable to such an approach are those parts of Rosner's essay on psychophysics and neurophysiology (Volume 4) in which he seeks to reconstruct the chief empirical and systematic variables characteristic of both fields of reference. Other articles, which focus primarily (but certainly not exclusively) on empirical interrelations, may be exemplified by David and Snyder's discussion of psychology and genetics, Diamond and Chow's of biological psychology (Volume 4); Berlyne's essay on exploratory behavior, Taylor's and Fitts' on human engineering (Volume 5); Sherif's essay on social psychology, French's and the Spindlers' essays on the relations between psychology and anthropology, Katona's on relations with economics (Volume 6).

By far the most typical approach is one which gives approximately equal weight to theoretical analysis and empirical survey. Good examples might be as follows: Volume 4—Rosner's paper (taken as a whole), Ratliff on joint relations of physics, physiology, and psychology for vision, Graham and Ratoosh on sensory psychology and perception, Livingston on psychology and neurophysiology, von Bonin on neuroanatomy and psychology, Zener and Gaffron on perception, Ittelson on perception and transactional psychology; Volume 5—Postman on perception and learning, Hilgard on motivation and learning, Leeper on learning, perception, and personality, Sanford on personality, Child on personality in relation to anthropology and sociology; Volume 6—Osgood on psycholinguistics, Inkeles on sociology and psychology, Hallowell on personality, culture, and society in behavioral evolution, Lane on political science and psychology, Simon on economics and psychology.

Finally, we have essays which in high (but varying) degree stress theoretical modes of analysis. Among the purest cases—though none are uncontaminated with the empirical—are Attneave's consideration of perception and related areas (Volume 4); Lawrence on learning and perception, Schoenfeld and Cumming on behavior and perception, and Miller on social aspects of motivation (Volume 5); Campbell on social attitudes and acquired behavioral dispositions, and Arrow on utility in economic behavior (Volume 6).

It is to be emphasized that both theoretical and (relatively speaking) "theoretically neutral" modes of analysis have their place in considering problems of field structure and relationships. "Theoretical integration" impresses one as the *mode par excellence*—especially if the analysis can disclose meaningful relations between fields, or parts thereof, which previously seemed discrete. But if it be the most dashing mode, it is not always feasible; still less often is it the mode of choice in the present state of the science. There are stages before theoretical integration (in any strong sense of "theory") is possible, at which analysis of cross-field relations at relatively empirical levels is a necessary condition to meaningful theoretical advance.

From the typing of the essays just offered, it should be clear that there are important continuities between Study I and Study II. In Study I, the unit of analysis was the individual theory ("systematic formulation," in our preferred phrase); in Study II, it is the research area(s). The body psychological being finite, these disparate cuts will overlap. Almost every essay of Study II makes reference—usually extensive reference—to theoretical materials, and some develop theoretical ideas in a focal way. Contrariwise, few of the analyses of Study I neglect considering the bearing of the systematic formulation at issue on a plurality of empirical domains, and thus on cross-field relations. Efficient use of the series requires that the reader keep in mind this complementarity of the two studies. With respect to *either* of the major types of question posed by the different studies, both taken together will give far fuller and better-balanced coverage than will the study of primary relevance per se.

In an earlier part of this introduction, it was indicated that though the conventionalized field distinctions are in many ways adventitious and arbitrary, certain of them derive historically from analyses which in some sense were considered ontologically significant. To put this in the most vulgarly direct terms, there was a time when perception or learning or motivation or emotion was unembarrassedly considered as in the first instance a real part-process (not, of course, an independent or self-subsistent one) within the process flux mediating real actions and even real experiences of a real organism in a real world. As the present century progressed, such uncouth ontologizing was displaced by the sophisticated and hygienic imagery of variables and functions, data languages and construct languages, along with the presumption that only fools could find the confines of the linguacentric predicament chafing. During this nominalist and conventionalist deflection in the recent history of our epistemology, it became almost a matter of course to ask questions not about subject matter, but about collectivities of sentences that the "literature" had deposited concerning subject matter. Or perhaps one *did* ask first-order questions, but the object of inquiry was so filmy and assumptional—so much a fiction based on an illegitimate inference—that one did not much care *what* questions.

Against this background, it is most refreshing to note in the present study a tendency to take *process,* and more generally, the *objects* of psychological knowledge seriously. In discussing field structure or interrelations, most of our authors are not merely revising or creating filing systems for indifferent units of knowledge, but are in fact looking beyond the bits and pieces of research that have emerged in the academic work-shop toward a psychological universe to which research must be adequate. That universe is once more acknowledged, and desire to render it intel-ligible seems burgeoning. Such changes are not evident in all essays in the same degree, but in some degree they are evident in all.

This new serious concern with process is perhaps most evident in Volume 4. By and large, the physiological psychologists represented in this study seem to have a compelling feeling that the brain (and to some extent the rest of the organism) is *there*. Our three biologists express this feeling perhaps even more uninhibitedly (some going so far as to specu-late about the relation between brain and mind, brain and consciousness, mind and body), but for biologists who always *were* "naïve," this is no departure. A similar concern for process, however, can be seen in many ways among the other contributors, the more strictly "psychological" psychologists. There is, for instance, virtually not a single empty-organism position expressed in the study: Learning theorists and even personality and social psychologists all not only acknowledge the organism in some general way, but often lean rather heavily on the recent advances in the neurological and neurophysiological disciplines. Again, the already noted interest in perception on the part of S-R and learning theorists seems an-other acknowledgement that a universe of actual problems exists.

Important among the developments here at issue is the tendency of not a few of the authors to approach their topics not first and foremost in terms of the exploration or realignment of extant bodies of knowledge, but in what might be characterized as "process-centered" terms. Thus, for instance, Zener and Gaffron (Volume 4) ask as their main question: What specifically is perception as a process phase in the economy of the organism—an organism which experiences in a significant sense, which acts, and which does both relative to a world and to itself? This is an ancient kind of question but one which we have too long been too "sophisticated" to re-raise. In raising it anew, the authors are led to cer-tain methodic suggestions, theoretical vistas, and empirical observations, all far from old. From a quite different perspective, Attneave (also Vol-ume 4) addresses perception in a process-centered way, in this case per-forming the remarkable feat of saying many things which seem sub-stantively apt or plausible about the real organism in terms largely of *information theory*. Other largely process-centered analyses are Ittelson's on perception and transactional psychology (Volume 4); Berlyne's on exploratory behavior, and Leeper's on learning-perception relations (Vol-ume 5); Campbell's on acquired behavioral dispositions, Hallowell's on personality, culture, and society, Lounsbury's on linguistics and psychol-ogy, Katona's on economics and psychology (Volume 6)—to mention but a sample.

The authors of Study II—as of Study I—are not merely recording history; they are extending history. Analysis of the shape and relational texture of knowledge as conceived by the study is not "mere" analysis. To see knowledge in new ways, to test the knowledge in a field against the objects of that field, to realign knowledge, is to *create* new knowledge. Those already acquainted in any degree with *Psychology: A Study of a Science* will know that one of its fondest aims has been to advance a conception of analysis which sees it as a joint analytico-creative task. This objective is well realized by the essays of Study II.

Few of the authors were left unchanged by the practice of such analysis: for the reader this means that he can expect something fresh in virtually every essay. In the course of their analyses, many of the authors make important theoretical and methodological contributions which had not before seen the light of day. Examples are to be seen in the papers by Rosner, Rosenblith and Vidale, Zener and Gaffron, Attneave (Volume 4); Guttman, Lawrence, Schoenfeld and Cumming, Leeper, Miller (Volume 5); Campbell, Hallowell, and Lane (Volume 6). In other cases, positions previously established are significantly extended or brought to bear on new ranges of subject matter. Conspicuous examples are the papers of Pfaffmann and of Graham and Ratoosh (Volume 4); Postman, Berlyne, Child, Rodnick (Volume 5); Sherif, Osgood, Inkeles, Katona, and Arrow (Volume 6). In still other cases, we get an essentially new way of viewing the content and organization of an interstitial area: e.g., the papers of Pribram and Davis (Volume 4); of Sanford and of Rotter (Volume 5); of Lambert, French, and Simon (Volume 6). Again, certain of the papers are unique in that they address interrelational topics which have never before been considered in any direct or extensive way: cases in point are Ratliff's consideration of physics, physiology (especially single-receptor physiology), and psychology relative to vision (Volume 4); the extended discussions in Volume 5 of the relations between human engineering and general psychology by Taylor and by Fitts; the evolutionary consideration of relations among personality, culture, and society in the mode of Hallowell, or the Spindlers' consideration of the specific problems of culture change in relation to psychology (Volume 6). These sources of creative novelty are not, of course, mutually exclusive: many, indeed most, of the papers present them in combination.

In these paragraphs we have been trying to anticipate certain of the qualities of the findings, yet protect the reader's freshness of vision by not constructing trends upon the findings. In minor violation of this restraint, may we raise an issue which the reader very probably already has in mind. What of psychology's current classification of "fields" (i.e., fields as defined at the level of generality of perception, learning, and the other "primary" reference areas of this study)? Does the study suggest some new and super-rational breakdown—a comfortable and tidy geography in which everything will find its place?

The study does not. Indeed, the study would tend to suggest that the perennial and poignant thirst of psychologists for a set of new-fangled field breakdowns is doomed to perennial and poignant frustration. The editor doubts that the findings of this study are a necessary condition to the verdict, but they are certainly confirmatory.

Field names are labels, variably applied, to what is seen by men as related clusters of inquiry. The flux of history, the variability of individual vision, and the unsystematic variety of senses in which a field itself can be defined, inevitably makes these labels highly ambiguous. Different men will—and *should*—continue to see fields differently relative to their own systematic beliefs and options.

Any new classification arrived at must be an organization dictated by the terms of some systematic view or theory. Until a "theory" sufficiently compelling to command general acceptance comes along, there can be no breakdown of fields any more serviceable than the present one. A theory of the requisite scope, analytic power, and adequacy to *warrant* any extensive realignment of fields is not exactly imminent and, indeed, may be unachievable in principle.

Whatever the degree of theoretical integration psychology ultimately achieves, it is well to recognize that certain of the fields currently demarcated cut into events from different incidences—incidences dictated by different universes of discourse. Different universes of discourse are not necessarily different "levels"; they *can* be just different—unsystematically so. This lugubrious circumstance is, we think, made evident, explicitly or implicitly, in many of the essays in these volumes. Given problematic ends in view—in life as in science—*are* often incommensurable; they require incommensurable concepts, methods, and will inevitably beget incommensurable answers. Much of what is comprehended, say, in social psychology, personality, or psychopathology, will probably not fall into the grain of any single conceptual language that might unite, say, aspects of sensory psychology, perception, and learning. Psychology will progress more rapidly toward whatever "rationality" of organization or conceptual integration may be possible, if such framework limits are clearly acknowledged and understood.

There are other (and not unrelated) expectations which, when carried into investigations of the shape and texture of knowledge, can work toward a trivial, if not illusory, outcome. An obvious one is the assumption that there are necessarily vast submerged riches in our attained backlog of research which, if only extracted by some felicitous culling, could lift us to a new level of knowledge. About such a hope we need perspective. There may indeed be in the history of our science hidden leads—even findings—of great value. But the history of our science also tells us that only a narrow and adventitiously chosen range of questions has been asked. This is not to our discredit. After all, we have had the courage to address a subject matter having the most awesome amplitude of any in the history of institutionalized knowledge-seeking.

The *realistic* likelihood is that the truly important advances in our science will come from new knowledge, based on new problematic sensitivities, and new ways of addressing questions. To this, a necessary condition is ceaselessly to look at past knowledge in a way at once faithful yet unconstrained, critical yet creative—by constant attention, that is, to some such questions of structure and relationship as have been raised in the present study. It is this consideration which defines the significance of the pursuits posed by Study II. The best use that the reader can make of the study is to approach it for such an end.

Recently the editor has had occasion to indulge his penchant for neologism by discriminating a syndrome called "ameaningful thinking." Ameaningful thought or inquiry "regards knowledge as the result of 'processing' rather than discovery; it presumes that knowledge is an almost automatic result of a gimmickry, an assembly line, a 'methodology'; it assumes that inquiring behavior is so rigidly and fully regulated by *rule,* that in its conception of inquiry it sometimes allows the rules totally to displace their human users. Presuming as it does that knowledge is 'generated' by processing, its conception of knowledge is fictionalistic, conventionalistic, 'a-ontological.' So strongly does it see knowledge under such aspects that it sometimes seems to suppose that the object of inquiry is an ungainly and annoying irrelevance, that knowledge can be created by fiat."

Ameaningful thinking is a specific yet highly complex syndrome, which requires far more subtle and extended description than can be given here. But psychologists will already have noted that such a trend is pervasive in the culture at large and, if they be heroically honest, that it is not unknown in the recent history of that subculture formed by "psychology." Perhaps the most direct and telling way to convey the special hope of a study like the present one is that it might serve, however modestly, *as a counterforce to ameaning in our science.* The tendency in past decades to raise questions concerning the shape of knowledge only intermittently and halfheartedly can be seen as related to an ameaningful habit of inquiry. For, in considering questions of structure and relationship, what are we doing other than setting local inquiry into a broader environment of meanings? And what *can* we be doing as inquirers if we do not at least try to do *that?*

SOME INTERRELATIONS BETWEEN PSYCHOLOGY AND GENETICS

PAUL R. DAVID   AND   LAURENCE H. SNYDER
Department of Zoology   *University of Hawaii*
The University of Oklahoma

The Scope of Genetics 1
Principles of Gene Action 5
   Introduction 5
   Variety of Gene Effects 7
   Gene Interaction 10
   Gene-and-environment Interaction 10
   Phenocopies 11
   Different Genes with Indistinguishable Effects 11
   Multiple Effects of Genes 12
   Major Genes and Polygenes 12
Interrelations of Genetics and Psychology 14
   Introduction 14
   Genetics and Differential Psychology 15
      Genetic variability and personality development 15
      Genetic variability and test intelligence 18
   Genetics and Abnormal Psychology 21
      Mental deficiency 21
      Mental disease 25
   Genetics and Comparative Psychology 29
Methodologic Interrelations 34
   A Metatheoretic Note 39
References 39

THE SCOPE OF GENETICS

Genetics is concerned with the distribution, development, and origin of individual differences. In its modern sense, the science dates from about 1900, when the Mendelian laws were rediscovered independently by at least three different investigators.

The subdivisions of genetics are difficult to delineate sharply, both because of their intimate interdependencies and because in content as well as in method they have frequently been subject to rather rapid flux. We can perhaps best give an idea of the scope of those subfields most pertinent to the present discussion by considering them within the framework of a very sketchy historical outline. More adequate treatment of particular aspects will be found in the references cited.

Although variations of all kinds and degrees in living organisms are properly the subject matter of genetics, not all categories of variability have consistently been given their proportionate shares of attention. Certain differences among individuals can be shown to depend upon materials transmitted to them at conception in the germ cells of their respective parents and to be uninfluenced by any subsequent circumstances compatible with the individual's survival. Individual differences that satisfy these criteria may be designated with little ambiguity as "hereditary." For some years after the rediscovery of Mendel's laws, geneticists were largely preoccupied with studying the patterns of distribution, among offspring from various types of matings, of "traits" or "characters" that were hereditary in this strict sense. With few exceptions, these were conspicuous variations in morphology or pigmentation.

The existence of *chromosomes* as ubiquitous structures in cell nuclei, and their constancy in number and in individual form in a given plant or animal species, had been discovered in the nineteenth century. By 1900 their behavior in the reproductive cycle had been studied in considerable detail. It soon became apparent that there was a striking parallelism between the patterns of transmission of hereditary differences and the distribution of the chromosomes in germ-cell formation and fertilization. This led to the early suggestion that the physical determinants of hereditary differences (the *genes* of later terminology) are located in or on the chromosomes. A consequence of the formulation of this hypothesis was a convergence of research in genetics with research in cytology, which is concerned with the intimate details of cell structure and function. The area of overlap was to develop into the field of *cytogenetics* which thus, historically at least, is at once a subfield of genetics and of cytology.

By 1916 the *chromosome theory of heredity,* that is, the theory that the genes are carried on, or are constituent parts of, the chromosomes, was securely established. It was shown to account equally well for the relatively simple regularities of hereditary transmission described in the laws of Mendel and for certain systematic exceptions to these laws which had been observed [190].

For a number of years after the consolidation of the chromosome theory, the bulk of research in cytogenetics dealt with rather specialized problems which need not concern us here. In the meantime, an increasing number of geneticists had begun to turn their attention toward the question of how genes produce their effects, and by the middle or late twenties the field of *developmental* (or *physiological*) *genetics* had evolved. The approach of developmental genetics was at first largely morphologic, with considerable dependence upon concepts and techniques derived from experimental embryology [65, 204, 210]. Since about 1940, however, biochemical approaches have become increasingly ascendent. This is traceable in part to the discovery that a bread mold, *Neurospora,* was exceptionally favorable material for both genetic and biochemical investigation and in part, of course, to the phenomenal developments during the past twenty years in biochemistry itself.

The penetration of biochemistry into genetics has become pervasive, and it is common to designate as *biochemical genetics* what is now a major subfield—an area of such rapid growth, we may add, that there is some prospect of its ultimately becoming coextensive with almost the whole of genetics [14, 71, 74, 83, 188, 205]. Investigations in biochemical genetics have dealt with such diverse phenomena as pathways of intermediary metabolism in bread molds and in man, the development of eye-color pigments in *Drosophila,* and abnormalities of the hemoglobin molecule associated with certain human anemias. Although biochemical genetics has contributed importantly to developmental genetics, the two terms are by no means synonymous. Many basic problems in the latter area require analysis on the morphologic level, even though biochemical studies may be simultaneously involved.

On the other hand, developmental genetics is not the only field to be invaded by biochemistry. Cytogenetics, which in an earlier day was largely concerned with the microscopically visible structure and behavior of chromosomes and other cell components, is now to a considerable degree occupied with biochemical problems. These relate to the molecular composition of chromosomes and genes and to the chemical processes involved both in the normal replication of genes and in their aberrant replication, or mutation [8, 19, 118]. Research in this most recent phase of cytogenetics, which is closely affiliated with research in the genetics of microorganisms and viruses, is thus finally attacking the problem of the *origin* of gene differences—the problem listed as the third concern of genetics in our definition at the opening of this chapter.

We have already noted that genetics, in its earlier years, was primarily a study of the *distribution* of individual differences, and that attention at that time was for the most part restricted to those individual differences which appeared to be unambiguously "hereditary." The distribution of these differences, moreover, was examined also in a restricted sense, for analysis was limited essentially to the question of how the variant characteristics were distributed *among the progeny of individual matings.* But, concurrently with the development of the subfields of modern genetics thus far reviewed, interest was turning also to the distribution of genes in *populations,* and since the early 1920s there has been a constantly expanding and important body of research in *population genetics.*

Population genetics undertakes to investigate the frequencies of various genes and genotypes in different population groups and to study the manner in which these frequencies may be affected by such processes as inbreeding, assortative mating, selection, and mutation.

The collection of large-scale data on the distribution of genetically determined variations in different populations began during World War I, when the Hirszfelds investigated the frequencies of the O, A, B, and AB blood groups in an aggregate of nearly ten thousand soldiers drawn from some dozen racial or national groups. The theoretical foundations and mathematical procedures requisite to analyzing the genetics of populations and of evolutionary processes have been developed in the ensuing years [112, 206, 211, 212]; elementary treatment of some of the major principles may be found in a number of sources [18, 187, 190].

To the degree that population genetics deals with systematic changes of gene frequencies in time, it is synonymous with *evolution genetics.* During the past two decades, numerous studies have been pursued on a variety of organisms, under both natural and experimental conditions, in which the analytic tools of population genetics have been applied to problems of evolution. In many of these investigations, there has been strong interpenetration between the subfields of population genetics and cytogenetics [42], as in other investigative areas cytogenetics and biochemical genetics have become intimately entangled.

In the foregoing attempt to characterize the major subfields of genetics, we have based our distinctions on the differences in the kinds of problems dealt with and on consequent differences in technique. Classification along a taxonomic axis is also possible, of course. Indeed, it is common to distinguish plant and animal genetics and successive subdivisions of each down to the particular genus (or species) that is the object of investigation—*Neurospora* genetics, maize genetics, *Drosophila* genetics, mouse genetics, human genetics, etc. This classification obviously cuts across the one we have presented above. In fact, a geneticist engaged in *Drosophila* genetics or in human genetics, for example, may be pursuing investigations in any or several of the subfields previously enumerated.

An appreciation of the actual or potential interrelations of various subfields of genetics with those of psychology can perhaps best be gained through consideration of certain general principles which have emerged from genetic research of the past twenty years, particularly in developmental, biochemical, and population genetics. At the same time, this should suggest some of the major problem areas where there are regions of overlap between genetics and psychology that may provide territory for interdisciplinary exploration.

Since the primary interests of the present authors have been in the genetics of the human species, our discussion of interrelations with psychology will concern mainly the implications of genetics for various areas of human psychology.

PRINCIPLES OF GENE ACTION

Introduction

An impressive body of research has established beyond equivocation that the fundamental principles of genetics, as they relate to mechanisms of hereditary transmission or to the action of hereditary factors in development, are in essence the same in all sexually reproducing organisms, whether they be men or rabbits, fungi or fish. Nevertheless, there are critical differences between the operation of these principles in the human species and their operation even in other animals. A reason for some of these differences—those concerning the action of genetic factors which may have relevance for behavior—should be immediately apparent: it rests upon the psychologic uniqueness of man, and especially upon the complexity of his psychosocial interactions. Equally important differences exist between the kinds of variations which until rather recently have received the major share of attention in studies on laboratory animals and those which may be most significant in the variability of *natural* populations. It may seem odd to refer to human populations, living under the highly artificial conditions of modern civilization as "natural." But in respect to genetic structure, human populations are in fact much more comparable to populations of field mice, foxes, or even fruit flies living in the wild than they are to herds of domestic cattle, poultry flocks, or laboratory stocks of mice or rats.

Although we shall of necessity lean rather heavily on observations of laboratory animals in the ensuing discussion of genetic principles, we shall try carefully to point out those particulars in which human materials require special treatment.

It is truistic that no two individuals—whether of the human species or any other—are completely identical either in physical appearance or in the details of their physiologic or psychologic activity. To the degree that individual differences have a hereditary basis, they have been found to be contingent in very nearly all instances upon the materials which compose the chromosomes. Following the discovery of genetic linkage early in this century, it became possible to determine the ultramicroscopic pattern of organization of these materials; and chromosome "mapping" was accomplished on an appreciable scale, first, and most spectacularly, in *Drosophila* and subsequently in numerous other forms, both plant and animal. This work demonstrated unequivocally that hereditary variations are referable to minutely localized regional differences within the chromosomes. These are *gene* differences.

Thus, the difference in *genotype* or genetic constitution between a color-blind man and a man with normal color vision is attributable to a gene difference—most likely involving an intramolecular alteration of a nucleic acid molecule—in a particular region or *locus* of their respective X chromosomes. The genotypic distinction between a hemophilic and a nonhemophilic individual lies in a difference between their respective X chromosomes at another locus. Differences in *phenotype* are those which can be observed either directly or indirectly. In the cases just cited, the phenotypic distinctions are in color vision and in the coagulability of the blood respectively.

We commonly speak of color blindness (in contrast to normal color vision) or of hemophilia (in contrast to the nonhemophilic condition) as the effect of a single-gene substitution or, more concisely, as the effect of a single gene. We shall use this terminology frequently in the ensuing discussion. It is well at this point to recall that in man, as in many other animal species, each body cell of the male contains only one X chromosome, whereas there are two X chromosomes in each somatic cell of the female. All other chromosomes (the so-called "autosomes") are present in matched or homologous pairs in the somatic cells of both sexes. The two chromosomes of a homologous pair are indistinguishable from each other under the microscope, and it has been shown that in each there is the same series of gene loci. Hence an autosomal gene—the gene for albinism, for example—may be present on only one member of the appropriate pair of homologous chromosomes. In this case, it is said to be in *heterozygous* (single-dose) condition. Or a gene for albinism may be present on each chromosome of the pair, in which case it is said to be in *homozygous* (double-dose) condition. We shall not generally distinguish between these two situations. Unless otherwise noted, the term *single-gene substitution* or *single gene* will mean a gene substitution at a single locus in whichever dosage, heterozygous or homozygous, is required to produce the gene's characteristic phenotypic effect.

We should warn at once that description of the classical genes of the genetics laboratory, which occupies a substantial part of standard textbooks, is only a beginning step in the analysis of heredity. As we have already noted, early studies in genetics dealt for the most part with individual differences that were unambiguously hereditary—hence with genes whose individual effects were clear-cut and relatively invariable. Consequently, the organism came to be looked upon, from the genetic

viewpoint, as a mosaic of "unit characters," with a one-to-one correspondence between gene and character. The inadequacy of this concept
soon became evident, however, through the discovery of numerous instances in which there were striking developmental interactions between
well-defined genes at different loci. It also became apparent that, while
the phenotypic expression of many genes is uniform over a wide range of
environmental conditions, there are many others whose manifestations
are affected, and often radically modified, by environmental variables.
We shall recur to this point below.

The modern concept of *genic balance* recognizes that, even with
environmental conditions constant, variability is a function of the genotype as a whole. The isolation of individual gene effects, while heuristically indispensable for the investigation of many important problems, involves an artificial disjunction of the gene from the total genotype. This
disjunction is valid and necessary at certain levels of analysis—compare,
for example, the disjunction of time and space, or of mass and velocity,
in classical mechanics—and it has been eminently useful in attacking basic
problems involving patterns of hereditary transmission and certain aspects
of developmental processes. We might suspect, however, that the atomistic
approach which it implies would prove methodologically inadequate at
other, more complex levels, and we shall see later some substantiation of
this suspicion. In the meanwhile, a brief consideration of the characteristics of "classical" genes as they have been discerned, primarily from
studies on laboratory materials, should serve two useful purposes: (1)
It will suggest why the isolation of individual gene effects has held so
prominent a place in the history of genetics; and (2) it will provide a
background for examining, in more modern perspective, the significance
of genes as factors in human psychologic variability.

Among the more important generalizations regarding genes and their
action which have been securely established over the years, those most
pertinent here are discussed in the ensuing paragraphs.

Variety of Gene Effects

*First, there is no structure or organ, and no physiologic process of an
organism, that cannot be altered, and radically altered, by a single-gene
substitution at one or another locus.*

In *Drosophila*, one single-gene substitution reduces the wings of the
fly to mere vestiges; another results in the development of two pairs of
wings instead of the characteristic single pair. These are genes which
alter the size, shape, or venation of the wings; others affect the size, shape,
or histologic structure of the eyes. A gene substitution at any of several
different loci prevents development of the eyes altogether. More than 40
different loci have been identified at which a single-gene substitution alters

the pigmentation of the eye, with effects ranging from various degrees of darkening or lightening to complete elimination of one or both of the pigments that are responsible for the brick-red eye color of the wild-type fly. Legs, bristles, sclerites, body color, and body size are but a few of the other features of the animal that may be conspicuously affected in a variety of ways by various single genes. Finally, in a large number of loci, a single-gene substitution may interfere so radically with the development of the animal that the effect is lethal, causing death in the egg, larval, or pupal stage [21].

Many of the genes just mentioned produce more than one discernible effect. One of the gene substitutions that reduces wing size, for example, also modifies the wing musculature, alters the angle of certain bristles, and affects the balancers, the shape of the spermathecae, the growth rate, fecundity, and length of life. Another gene simultaneously modifies the structure of legs, wings antennae, and bristles.

Mammals, of course, are far less conveniently dealt with in the genetics laboratory than *Drosophila,* and consequently their genetics has not been nearly so thoroughly studied. Nevertheless, enough is known to make it apparent that the variety and extent of single-gene effects are comparable to those observed in the fruit fly. In the house mouse, genetically the most-investigated mammal, the effects of more than a hundred different single-gene substitutions are known [68]. A considerable number of them affect pelage color, others affect the texture or growth of the hair; any one of at least three genes at different loci produces nearly complete hairlessness. Additional effects of single-gene substitutions in this animal include skeletal defects, eye abnormalities, short ears, several differentiable types of anemia, hydrocephalus, pituitary dwarfism, insulin-resistant hyperglycemia, complete absence of rods in the retina, and agenesis of the corpus callosum; any of several genes may produce severe disturbance of vestibular function. As in *Drosophila,* a single-gene substitution frequently has more than one observable effect. Thus, a gene which shortens the ears also predisposes the animal to spontaneous tail contractures; the gene for yellow pelage, besides affecting the development of hair pigment, produces marked obesity and diminishes the likelihood of spontaneous mammary carcinoma.

The identification of genic mechanisms in man is obviously a more difficult task than in laboratory animals. The geneticist is handicapped in dealing with the human species by its small family size and long generation span, and especially by its reluctance to submit to controlled matings. Beginning with the pioneer work of Weinberg and of Bernstein in the 1920s, however, statistical sophistication has to an appreciable degree compensated these handicaps, and critical genetic analysis of human materials has become possible within certain limits. [Orienting references will be found in 37, 115, 128, 165, 187, 196; for recent developments, see 4, 9, 10, *passim*.] But the statistical niceties required for the collection and interpretation of data on human genetics have been slow in obtaining full recognition. Hence, while the literature relating to human genetics is enormous, considerably exceeding in bulk that on the genetics of any other species, its reliability is roughly in inverse proportion to its mass, and it must be read with much critical caution. Even when we give appropriate attention to this caveat, however, we find evidence ranging from the presumptive to the secure that more than a hundred variations (essentially all pathologic) in the skin and its derivatives [34, 173], more than a hundred eye abnormalities [52, 191, 203], and a comparable number of skeletal anomalies in man [12, 49] can be attributed to single-gene substitutions. Other organs are somewhat less accessible to observation. Nevertheless, among conditions for which there is good evidence of single-gene determination, we may include a dozen or more blood dyscrasias, similar numbers of metabolic and endocrine disturbances, nervous disorders, aberrations in the muscular system, and neoplasms in a variety of organs [186, 192].

We must emphasize that evidence for single-gene determination in perhaps a majority of the pathologic conditions included in the preceding enumeration is no more than presumptive. But critical evidence is available for a substantial proportion of the conditions in each category, and there is little doubt that in the human species the effects of single-gene substitutions are at least as numerous, varied, and far-reaching as in the laboratory animals that have been studied.

Variations considered to be normal in man which can safely be attributed to single-gene differences are remarkably few. Those whose genetic mechanisms are most soundly established concern serologic characters; these are detectably affected by single-gene substitutions at a number of loci. They include antigens of the OAB series, the MNS and Rh series of antigens, and some others, as well as solubility differences in the A and B antigens (secretor versus nonsecretor) [144]. High taste thresholds for phenylthiourea appear to depend for the most part on a single-gene substitution [40, 185], as do differences in the haptoglobins of the blood serum [59, 184]. This modest list represents a substantial portion of our current knowledge of single-gene determination of *normal* human variations. If we include variations which might be regarded as very mildly pathologic, we can add premature pattern baldness and, of course, some types of color-vision defect. A few additional normal variations might be considered for our list, but judgment on their eligibility for inclusion must at present be suspended, because the data are as yet either very scanty or, though moderately numerous, not quite clear-cut. These include hyperextensibility of the distal phalanx of the thumb [64], pattern differences in the superficial veins of the anterior thorax [193], urinary excretion of methylmercaptan after eating asparagus, excretion of betani after eating beets [3], and elevated olfactory threshold for the odor of potassium cyanide [99].

Gene Interaction

As a second important principle of gene action, we will stress that *there is not necessarily, as was originally supposed, a one-to-one correspondence between the presence of a gene and the manifestation of an effect. The organism is not a mere mosaic of "unit characters."* Quite aside from environmental influences (which we shall consider presently), an animal's phenotype depends on developmental interactions involving the entire aggregate of genic materials, together with the materials of the extragenic protoplasm. Examples of striking interactional effects resulting from the combination of two or more identifiable genes at different loci can be found in any standard genetics text [179, 190, 194]. Interactions less conspicuous than those cited in the textbooks are certainly far commoner; and it is fairly safe to say that the effect of a gene substitution at any given locus is influenced by the nature of the genic material at virtually every other locus [65].

Gene-and-environment Interaction

A third basic principle is that *the phenotype of an organism is a function both of its genic constitution and of the environment in which the organism develops.* Different genes vary greatly in their responsiveness to various factors in the environment. The effects of some are expressed with invariable uniformity over the entire range of environmental conditions which permit the organism to survive at all. In man, the genes upon which the various blood-group antigens depend are in this category. In nearly every genetically studied laboratory mammal—as in man—the gene for albinism prevents melanin formation in the skin, hair, and iris, and no known environmental variable alters this manifestation.

Other genes are sensitive in varying degrees to environmental agents [82, 189]. The Himalayan gene, in rabbits reared at the usual room temperatures, prevents pigment formation except at the extremities, but if a newborn Himalayan rabbit is exposed briefly to moderate chilling (11°C or lower), the entire pelage develops pigmentation.

In some instances, manipulation of the environment can suppress altogether the effect which a gene produces under more usual conditions. Most domestic rabbits have colorless or "white" fat deposits. A single-gene substitution results in the deposition of conspicuously yellow fat, provided the animals are maintained on a conventional rabbit dietary. If, however, all xanthophyll pigments are kept out of their food, their fat deposits are also colorless, and there is no phenotypic distinction in color of fat between animals that are genotypically "yellow" and those that are genotypically "white."

Phenocopies

A fourth principle, closely related to the last, is that *in many and very probably in all cases, the effects characteristic of a particular gene can be simulated by environmental interference at an appropriate time during development in the absence of the gene in question.* In *Drosophila, phenocopies* of practically every known single-gene effect can be produced by properly timed heat shocks of varying intensity and duration [65]. X radiation *in utero* of mouse embryos at different developmental stages yields congenital anomalies of various kinds, several of which are known otherwise as effects of single-gene substitutions [97, 159]. Phenocopies have been produced in poultry by a number of methods, including notably the exposure of embryos to certain chemical agents [108]. Studies of the interacting effects of varied residual genotypes with different phenocopy-inducing compounds and with their chemical antagonists promise to add considerably to our knowledge of the developmental pathways through which certain genes produce their effects [109].

In the human species there is undoubtedly an appreciable number of pathologic abnormalities which are produced by single-gene substitutions in some families, but which occur elsewhere sporadically as phenocopies [189]. Among the best-substantiated instances are diabetes insipidus, microcephaly, "lobster claw," and congenital deafness.

Different Genes with Indistinguishable Effects

As a fifth principle relating to gene action, we must recognize that *superficially indistinguishable effects may result from quite different gene substitutions, that is, from gene substitutions at either of two or more different loci.* Among numerous examples of such "mimic" genes in mice are *Shaker 1 and Shaker 2.* Each of these produces the same syndrome of effects: deafness, choreic head movements, and "circling" behavior. But linkage tests have shown that their loci are on different chromosomes.

In man, mimic genes are not likely to be recognized as such unless they follow different patterns of hereditary transmission. In a single instance to date it has been possible to show by analysis of linkage data that either of two autosomal dominant genes, on different chromosomes, can produce what appears to be the same hematologic anomaly, ovalocytosis [122]. On the other hand, it is the rule rather than the exception to find more or less indistinguishable variants (differing commonly in age of onset and in severity) of a single "clinical entity" dependent on an autosomal dominant gene in some families, on an autosomal recessive in others, and in still others exhibiting a sex-linked pattern of inheritance. Examples include retinitis pigmentosa, peroneal atrophy, and the progressive muscular dystrophies [31, 123].

Multiple Effects of Genes

Finally, we should emphasize that *multiple effects of genes are highly characteristic*. We have already mentioned a few of the more striking examples of multiple or pleiotropic effects of single-gene substitutions in *Drosophila* and the mouse. Comparable illustrations can readily be found in a large number of hereditary syndromes in man. What we wish most to emphasize here, however, are the *viability* effects of gene differences. Virtually every single-gene substitution that it has been possible to study critically in laboratory animals or plants has been found to affect viability to some degree. Nearly all of those we have mentioned affect viability adversely, at least under standard laboratory conditions. And this is true of the overwhelming majority of single-gene substitutions which produce readily discernible effects. A few, however, improve the viability of the organisms possessing them, and in some instances the same gene substitution impairs viability in some environments and improves it in others [42, 69].

Major Genes and Polygenes

The effects of the single-gene substitutions we have been describing are so striking and so multifarious that one might plausibly expect them to account for most or all of the genetically determined variability found in human or other populations. We are coming more and more to realize, however, that the classical single-gene differences which are individually responsible for conspicuous effects do not provide the bulk of genetic variability in man or in any well-studied species of other animal. Gene differences originate as *mutations*, and the rate at which mutations occur is enormously accelerated by high-energy radiations, such as X rays. Many of the mutations observed in experimental animals, following treatment of a prior generation with X rays, produce conspicuous visible effects and have been shown to be identical to genes that have arisen spontaneously in natural populations and laboratory stocks. However, by far the largest number are those whose only readily discerned individual effects are very slight impairments or, perhaps less commonly, improvements in viability. Viability depends, of course, on morphologic or physiologic characteristics, or both, and there is at least a rough parallelism between degree of viability impairment produced by a gene and the conspicuousness of its visible effect. By and large, the more striking the phenotypic effect, the more drastic is the reduction in viability. Thus, the largest class of mutated genes produced by X radiation are those with individually imperceptible effects upon the phenotype. There is a substantial body of evidence indicating that "small mutations" of this kind also compose the largest category among mutations which occur spontaneously.

Genes with individually minute effects are commonly called *polygenes,* as distinguished from the single genes that produce conspicuous phenotypic discontinuities, which we shall designate as *major genes.* Major genes, as we have seen, can be individually identified (very readily in laboratory material and to an appreciable degree in man) by the discontinuities they produce, and they can be assigned to precise loci on one or another chromosome. Polygenes, on the other hand, appear to have quantitatively equivalent and cumulative effects, and cannot be individually identified and assigned to chromosomal loci. Secure evidence for their existence, however, is to be seen in the effectiveness of selective breeding for almost any continuously variable quantitative character in a genetically heterogeneous population of laboratory or domestic animals. It appears, moreover, that polygenes have the essential properties of classical genes, inasmuch as they exhibit segregation and crossing over [28, 120].

It has become evident, then, that in any animal species there must be an enormous reservoir of genetic variability based upon the existence of very large numbers of polygene differences with individually minute, but cumulatively appreciable, effects. We should expect also that by far the greater part of the phenotypic variability in natural populations would be attributable to polygenic differences rather than to major-gene effects. For, in general, as a consequence of the viability impairment associated with the effects of major genes, the frequencies of these genes should be kept quite low by natural selection. In fact, this seems usually to be the case: the only known single-gene effects with frequencies between 5 and 50 per cent in human populations are those which appear to have minimal effects on viability. For the most part, these involve variations that can be detected only by special techniques, such as abnormalities in color vision and the antigen differences that distinguish the various blood types. As we have remarked, there are hundreds of patent abnormalities in man that may safely be attributed to single-gene substitutions; but relatively few of these have a population incidence higher than about 1 in 10,000, and the vast majority are very much rarer even than this.

If we examine two unrelated persons from any human population, we may well find that they differ in one or more of the identifiable blood antigens, and perhaps in their ability to taste phenylthiourea. Few, if any, of the other differences between them are likely to be referable to known major genes. Yet the differences in physiognomy and habitus which commonly distinguish each individual from any other are determined to a substantial degree by differences in genotype. We knew this to be true because of the almost perfect physical resemblance between individuals known to have identical genotypes, namely, the respective members of monozygotic twin pairs.

It would seem reasonable to conclude that, within the nonpathologic range of human variability, the bulk of gene-determined differentiation —in respect to morphologic and physiologic characteristics at least—rests upon polygene, rather than major-gene, differences. This is very probably true also for genetic components in the etiology of a number of the commoner deviations from normal which are classed as pathologic—including hypertensive disease [139, 141]—as well as for genetic factors that may be involved in resistance and susceptibility to certain infectious diseases.

INTERRELATIONS OF GENETICS AND PSYCHOLOGY

Introduction

We turn now to consider how and in what degree genetic differentiation may be involved in the differentiation of mental processes and behavioral responses. We have earlier described genetics as claiming for its domain the study of all individual differences. In so far as psychologic differences may be the object of its study, genetics obviously comes into close interrelationship with the area of *differential psychology*, or may even be indistinguishable from it. *Social psychology*, defined as dealing with "the experience and behavior of individuals in relation to social stimulus situations" [178], in our view necessarily embraces consideration of the effects of social interactions on the differentiation of individuals with respect to status, role, and personality, and therefore overlaps the area of differential psychology. Hence genetics may impinge, at least peripherally, upon this subfield, as indeed it does also upon the *psychology of personality* when this is considered as an independent area. Additional points of contact are apparent with *abnormal psychology*—perhaps only by accident of historical development not conventionally considered a "branch" of differential psychology. How far the genetic principles and concepts we have thus far outlined are relevant to the interest areas just named within the field of psychology will necessarily depend on the degree to which genes affect psychologic functions.

For experimental animals the existence of polygenic and occasionally of major-gene differences affecting temperament and behavioral responses has been amply established. Tryon was able, by selective breeding, to establish lines of rats with low and high maze-running abilities, respectively [202]; Heron, in similar manner, obtained strains differentiated with respect to general activity level and motivation [78]; and

Hall successfully bred for increased and for reduced aggressiveness [73]. Consistent differences in susceptibility to audiogenic seizures have been demonstrated among various highly inbred (and therefore genetically differentiated) strains of mice by Hall, Ginsberg, Fuller, and others; and Scott and Fuller and their co-workers have found evidence for genetic differences relating to aggressiveness, trainability, and a number of other behavioral characteristics among several dog breeds [58, 61, 62]. The experimental work cited here obviously brings genetics into close interrelationship with *comparative psychology*. In addition, as we shall see when this interrelationship is discussed (page 29), the investigation of behavioral differences, in laboratory animals especially, by methods of physiological genetics brings genetics into intimate contact with the the area of *physiological psychology* also. Finally, there has been a modest but methodologically vital intrusion of genetics into portions of the sub-field of *experimental psychology*. The application, at a fairly sophisticated level, of principles derived from population genetics has become indispensable in the design and interpretation of certain types of experiment relating to animal behavior (see page 34).

The fields of psychology just specified as being closely related to genetics represent the breakdown within which the main interactions between the two sciences has historically emerged. Psychology, of course, can be subdivided in other ways; for example, into areas concerned with basic processes such as perception, motivation, learning and cognition, of which behavior and experience have traditionally been regarded as functions. Needless to say, consideration of genetic variability is important in all such areas. Indeed, however psychology is subdivided, it is clear that a science of the behavior and/or experience of organisms must find questions of genetics inescapable in all of its branches. We deem it best, however, to concentrate on three main areas within which relations between genetics and psychology have historically been compartmentalized: differential psychology, abnormal psychology, and comparative psychology. We shall then consider quite generally certain methodologic interrelations between the two sciences.

Genetics and Differential Psychology

Genetic variability and personality development.   We think it is quite likely that in the human species there is a genetic basis for differentiation in respect to organic drives analogous to those reflected in the behavioral differences noted in experimental and domestic animals. But it would be dangerous to equate "aggressiveness" or "shyness" in rats, for example, with the types of human response patterns that are similarly designated. There very probably are genotypic differences in the human species which produce neuroendocrine variations comparable to those which presumably distinguish "aggressive" and "shy" rats. But we think it is vital to recognize the striking qualitative differences in the significance of organic drives for animals whose interindividual relationships are on a physiologic or a biosocial level, and the implications of similar drives for behavior at the psychosocial level [13, 161, 162].

Several conspicuous and related characteristics of the human species set man apart, psychologically, from other animals. They include his extraordinary development of conceptual thinking and symbolic language, his capacity to transmit culture, and his unique social organization. There thus exists for man a whole array of complexly interacting variables not found in other species—variables which are significant as causal components in the development of human personality and social behavior.

There is, indeed, in the human species a number of major genes which produce extreme disturbances of mental development and of behavioral response [137]. Well-known examples are the genes for the infantile and juvenile forms of amaurotic idiocy, for phenylketonuric amentia, Huntington's chorea, Friedreich's ataxia, and several other serious neuropathologic disturbances. But the impairments of mental function which can safely be attributed to single-gene substitutions are individually quite rare. The incidence of phenylketonuria, for example, is in the neighborhood of 1 in 40,000; of juvenile amaurotic idiocy, around 1 in 10,000 or 20,000. Even in the aggregate, they are not sufficiently common to contribute importantly to the patterning of human behavior in general.

We can hardly doubt, moreover, that there is also a considerable amount of polygenic variability which has relevance, in one way or another, to individual differences in human behavior. But we must emphasize what seems to us to be the highly contingent character of this relevance. Thus we would expect that differences in skin pigmentation, in physique, in facial conformation, or in neuromuscular function, dependent on genotypic differences, could indirectly have significant effects upon psychosocial adjustment. The effects would be most clearly apparent in cases of extreme deviations—in one direction or the other—which might impair (or favor) social acceptability. The degree of social acceptance or rejection accorded to an individual may in turn influence the course of his personality development and thence the pattern of his social integration. It seems to us self-evident that even the *direction* of the influence on personality development (whether toward submission or toward agressiveness, for example), as well as its degree, must depend upon a multiplicity of still other factors. The character and intensity of an individual's biogenic needs (which are doubtless in part contingent upon genotype) may be involved, as well as the availability of satisfactions for them (which cannot be genetically determined). Almost certainly, his immediate social situation—the status of his family, for example, and his own status within the family—must be significantly implicated.

Polygenic variability may, of course, be assumed to influence the development of personality pattern through subtler differentiations than those suggested in the preceding paragraph—conceivably through primary effects on the minute structural or functional organization of the cerebral cortex, for example. (The extraordinary resemblance between the electroencephalographic records of most monozygotic twins, even when they have been separated since earliest infancy [88], provides evidence for the implication of polygenes in the determination of physiologic differences in cerebrocortical function.) But in all cases, the ultimate phenotypic distinctions which we recognize as differences in personality or psychosocial response are, developmentally, many steps removed from the primary effects of the differences in genotype. Intervening between genotype and phenotype is an extensive sequence of interactions of the developing individual with a variety of social and other environmental influences. If, anywhere along the line, the strength of one or another of these influences should exceed some threshold value (which itself must be a function both of genotype and of all preceding developmental history), this factor may become critical as a determinant of certain features of the final pattern. According to this concept, the genotypic constitution is but one of a large number of causal components whose dynamic interactions ultimately establish the pattern of the individual's psychosocial responses. Unless genotypic deviations from the norm are extreme—as in the case of the major-gene substitutions with the neuropathologic effects mentioned above—we should not expect them to be in any important degree *determinative* of psychosocial phenotype.

The essential plasticity of genotypic potentialities in relation to personality development and the establishment of social role is perhaps nowhere better illustrated than in the differentiation of behavior patterns associated with sex. Within the range of nonpathologic variability in the human species, few, if any, genotypic differences produce morphologic and physiologic differentiation more striking than that which distinguishes the sexes. Men and women in our society are also conspicuously differentiated, at least in a statistical sense, not only at the level of biologic behavior, but also by occupational roles and by certain characteristics of temperament or personality [199].

Numerous observations on the division of labor in different cultures, however, demonstrate that the social roles of the sexes, at least in respect to occupational activities, are not determined by sex genotype; quite often those activities which are socially stereotyped as wholly masculine in one society are performed exclusively by women in another [125].

There is good reason to believe that the development of sex differences in personality characteristics, as reflected in other areas of behavior, is also strongly influenced by the social context in which the individual develops. Foundation for this conclusion does not rest only on the often-cited, admittedly controversial, reports of Mead [121], but finds support in several other kinds of observations. It is common knowledge, for example, that a propensity toward ornamentation in dress is predominantly a feminine characteristic in our own society, while in many nonliterate cultures, it is the males who incline toward extravagant adornment. Likewise, in our culture, males consistently, and from a very early age, obtain higher scores than females on scales intended to measure aggression, dominance, and the like [200]. But there is also evidence that the sex difference in aggression scores at least in part may be contingent upon social interactions such as those imposed by the structure of the family. Thus, the results of one study indicate that difference in aggression ratings between boys and girls (at ages three and four) whose fathers had been absent from the home for a prolonged period was appreciably less than between those whose fathers had been regularly present [175, 176].

Even at the more immediately biologic levels of differentiation in human sexual response, genetic constitution with respect to sex does not appear to be decisively controlling. Again, there are numerous ethnologic observations which bear upon the social conditioning of homosexual versus heterosexual behavior, for example [15, 33]. But perhaps even more striking is the evidence found in the histories of pseudohermaphrodites. When gonadal sex and the sex assigned by the parents do not agree, the pseudohermaphrodite's sexual proclivities and coital behavior are, as often as not, those appropriate to the sex which has been prescribed by rearing, rather than those appropriate to the sex indicated by the gonadal tissues [13].

Genetic variability and test intelligence.   It is commonly asserted by psychologists and geneticists alike that variability in IQ is to some degree dependent upon both genotypic and environmental factors—and this, at the present time, is very nearly as definitive a statement as we can make.

We have earlier mentioned several major-gene substitutions whose effects include severe mental impairment (see p. 16). But no major genes have been identified as providing either a necessary or a sufficient basis for the development of intelligence quotients at the genius or near-genius level, and there is currently nothing to suggest that major genes are involved in determining individual differences within what is commonly regarded as the range of "normal" test intelligence [148].

On the other hand, as we concluded in our assessment of the role of genetic factors in the differentiation of personality patterns—and for similar reasons—we may plausibly infer the existence of a large reservoir of polygenic variability that must have at least potential relevance for individual differences in test-intelligence level [44].

It is characteristic of polygenes that their phenotypic expression is particularly susceptible to environmental modification [111]. Thus the constellation of polygenes possessed by any given individual may be conceived of as establishing (at conception) a *range* of developmental potentialities with respect to those characteristics which are reflected in intelligence-test score [2, 6]. How wide this range may be, there is at present no way of telling. Obviously, it has no lower boundary short of idiocy, for this can be produced by trauma and doubtless by near-complete sensory deprivation in individuals of all genotypes. On the other hand, we know little or nothing of the extent to which exposure to different environmental climates may stimulate the development of superior test intelligence or, more importantly perhaps, of superior behavioral adaptability in meeting problems outside a test situation. However, we do know—at least for many morphologic and physiologic characteristics —that there is no necessarily linear relationship between effective environmental variables and phenotypic expression when varied genotypes are involved. An environment which has a stimulating effect on the phenotypic expression of one genotype may even have a depressing effect on the expression of another.

There are, for example, several major-gene substitutions in *Drosophila* whose phenotypic effects include reduction in eye size through reduction in the number of ommatidial units in the eye. The degree to which eye size is affected by any one of these genes is a function of the environmental temperature during larval development, and it is a different function in each case. In particular for flies of the *infrabar* genotype, eye size increases with increasing temperature; for flies of the *Bar* genotype, increasing temperature decreases the size of the eye. Bar females reared at 15°C have eyes nearly twice as large as infrabars reared at the same temperature; but when both types are reared at 25°, the eyes of the infrabar females are almost three times as large as those of Bar and are, in fact, larger than the eyes of Bar females reared at 15°.

In the past thirty years numerous attempts have been made, on the basis of empirical data, to assess the proportional contributions of genotype and environment as codeterminants of test intelligence. Trenchant criticisms of these efforts have frequently been published [notably 5, 82, 114, 119, 209]; nevertheless, "balance sheets" of nature and nurture continue to appear [23, 24]. In view of this, it is perhaps necessary to reemphasize that any estimate of *heritability* (defined as that fraction of the total variance which can be attributed to genetic differences) *can at best be applicable only to the particular sample which provides the data.*

It cannot be properly interpreted as a general answer to the question of the relative importance of genetic and environmental determinants of test intelligence. The most readily seen reason for this, though not the most critically important one, lies in the dependence of the estimate of heritability on the respective ranges of genetic and environmental variation in the material studied. But, and more crucially—as Loevinger particularly has stressed [114]—the meaning of a heritability assessment, even for the sample on which it is based, comes into serious question because of the effects of genotype-environment *interactions* such as we have just described in the Bar and infrabar *Drosophila*.

To different sets of environmental conditions, one genotype may respond in one way and another quite differently or not at all. The six types of interaction that are possible, with just two genotypes and two environments considered and with the phenotypic responses ranked according to a single quantitative criterion, are shown in Table 1 [70]. The

TABLE 1. GENOTYPE-ENVIRONMENT INTERACTION*

Type of interaction	Rank of phenotype			
	1	2	3	4
I	G_1E_1	G_1E_2	G_2E_1	G_2E_2
II	G_1E_1	G_2E_1	G_1E_2	G_2E_2
III	G_1E_1	G_1E_2	G_2E_2	G_2E_1
IV	G_1E_1	G_2E_1	G_2E_2	G_1E_2
V	G_1E_1	G_2E_2	G_1E_2	G_2E_1
VI	G_1E_1	G_2E_2	G_2E_1	G_1E_2

* Possible types of genotype-environment interaction between two genotypes G_1 and G_2 and two environments E_1 and E_2. Phenotypes ranked by a single quantitative criterion.

Bar and infrabar responses to the two environmental temperatures, as described above, would represent a Type V interaction according to this schema. Interactions of this type and of the other five types are, of course, not restricted to major-gene effects. Examples involving polygene-contingent variations have been given [70]. Anastasi [6] provides plausible analogues in the area of human psychology, suggesting, for example, that genotypic predisposition to a mesomorphic physique might be a factor in juvenile delinquency under one set of environmental circumstances; under another, it might be contributory toward the attainment of a college presidency.

When interactions involving more than two kinds or levels of environment, or more than two genotypes, or both, must be considered, the number of interaction types increases, and at a rather astonishing rate. Thus, with three environments, three genotypes, and a single criterion for ranking, more than ten thousand types of interaction can be envisaged. It is hardly necessary to point out that the employment of several criterion scales (measures of Spearman's *g* and *s* factors, for example) in assessing the phenotype does not simplify the situation, but further adds to the variety and complexity of possible interactions. With three environments and three genotypes, as above, but with two criteria instead of one, the number of types of interaction is nearly four hundred million!

In those instances [111] in which valid estimates of heritability are possible (for certain aspects of physiologic performance, in domestic animals, for example), they are possible *only because controlled conditions permit isolation of the effects of a particular set of environmental factors.*

Genetics and Abnormal Psychology

In the foregoing sections concerned with interrelations between genetics and certain problem areas of psychology, we have had to content ourselves largely with suggesting how the psychologic problems in these areas appear when viewed in the light of prevalent concepts in genetics. In touching upon some aspects of abnormal psychology, however, we are able to discern at least a modest amount of actual interpenetration between psychologic and genetic disciplines.

Mental deficiency.   The distribution of test intelligence closely approximates a theoretical Gaussian (normal) curve over almost, but not quite, its entire range: the frequency of very low IQs is conspicuously in excess of the theoretical normal-curve value. This fact was apparently first noted in 1914 by Pearson and Jaederholme [134], who interpreted it as suggesting that the severest grades of mental deficiency, those commonly designated as "idiocy" and "imbecility," represent, on the whole, a discrete class of variants, pathologic in origin whether or not they are recognizable as pathologic by inspection. Subsequent study of this problem, on more fully representative samples than were available to Pearson and Jaederholme, has confirmed their findings [149] and has produced other evidence supporting their inferences [137, 148]. The distribution of the milder grades of mental deficiency appears to form part of the same distribution curve on which the frequencies of higher IQs lie; the frequency of variants with IQs below about 45 or 50, however, is around twenty times as great as would be predicted from the parameters of the curve which fits the rest of the distribution.

The conclusion that the variants of idiot and imbecile level, by and large, must be etiologically distinct from those of higher grade rests primarily on the results of investigating psychometric levels among sibs (and other relatives) of defectives in the two groups. The finding of major interest is that the average IQ of the sibs of idiots and imbeciles is *higher* than that of the sibs of morons and borderline defectives [136, 147]. Looked at in another way, there is a tendency toward bimodality in the distribution of IQs among the relatives of idiots and imbeciles. A comparable tendency among the relatives of the higher grades of defectives is not discernible—the variance of IQ within sibships which include defectives of IQ 50 or above is indistinguishable from the within-sibship variance in the 80 to 120 IQ range.

There are other respects, too, in which the two categories of defectives differ. Clinically recognizable impairments are very much commoner among idiots and imbeciles than among the less severely defective, and idiots and imbeciles are found with equivalent frequencies at all socioeconomic levels, while morons and borderline defectives occur with disproportionately high frequencies among the lower socioeconomic groups.

The subdivision of mental deficiency which embraces only defectives of idiot and imbecile grade is itself, of course, a very heterogeneous one. It includes several syndromes, some reasonably well defined, others rather uncertainly characterized, of which severe mental defect is a constant or almost-constant feature. Combined clinical and genetic investigation of a number of these syndromes has provided much information regarding their etiologic complexity.

Among the syndromes in question, some are clearly attributable to major-gene substitutions whose effects are regularly manifested under all ordinary environmental conditions. Those most securely established as being in this category include juvenile amaurotic idiocy [180] and phenylketonuria [87]. The evidence is only slightly less secure for infantile amaurotic idiocy (Tay-Sachs disease) [53, 183], for gargoylism (lipochondrodystrophy) which exists in two forms, one sex-linked, the other autosomal [53, 77], and for a number of rarer conditions. In each of these disorders, a single major-gene substitution is both a necessary and (under all ordinary circumstances) a sufficient condition for the development of mental defect.

In the etiology of microcephalic idiocy, on the other hand, it appears that the presence of a particular major gene in homozygous condition may be a sufficient condition for the development of the abnormality,

but it is certainly not a necessary one. The frequency of multiple occurrences in sibships, together with the incidence of parental consanguinity,
indicates that a single-gene substitution is responsible for a minor fraction
of all cases [17, 20, 103]. The great majority of cases is without discernible genetic basis. It has been suspected for some time, however, that
exposure of the embryo to X radiation during its early development can
induce microcephaly [126]. Observations on the survivors of Hiroshima
provide dramatic evidence that the microcephaly-inducing effects of
radiation are largely, if not altogether, independent of the embryo's
genotype: of 11 children born to mothers who, in the first twenty weeks
of pregnancy, were within 1,200 m of the blast's hypocenter, 7 were
microcephalic [142].

The great majority of cases of microcephaly appear to be without
specific genetic basis, and prenatal exposure to radiation can account
for only a small fraction of these. Therefore, we infer that there must
be other environmental agents which, acting at an appropriate embryonic
stage, are, like radiation, capable of inducing microcephaly largely without regard to the genotype of the embryo.

For endemic cretinism, there is no evidence that major genes are involved at all, and conditions of the prenatal environment are very likely
the exclusive etiologic determinants [45].

Mongoloid idiocy appears to be etiologically complex, and perhaps
heterogeneous as well. A dermatoglyphic feature (distal position of the
axial triradius) which is present in nearly 90 per cent of all mongoloid
idiots is found with a significantly higher frequency among their sibs and
mothers than in the general population. Moreover, those cases of mongoloid idiocy in which the mothers are related to each other appear to be
differentiated from other mongoloid idiots by having been born, on the
average, to somewhat younger mothers [138]. Such observations as these
have suggested that genotypic factors of the mother, if not of the affected
child as well, play some etiologic role. In 1959 it was discovered that
mongoloid idiots are characterized by the presence of an extra chromosome in their somatic cells [86, 110]; thus they *are* genotypically abnormal, in consequence of an abnormality in the process of germ-cell
maturation in a parent—presumably the mother. Nevertheless, it has
been difficult to establish, even from rather extensive data, that the risk
of mongoloid idiocy in the sib of a mongoloid is any greater than the
general-population risk for children born to mothers in the same age
group. As a maximum, the increase in risk can be little more than three-
fold [131, 138]. On the other hand, the effect of maternal age on the
liability to produce a mongoloid child is striking. In the general population, the risk increases sharply from about age thirty, and it is twenty-

five or more times as great for children born to mothers past forty-five as for those born to mothers in their twenties.[1]

From the preceding paragraphs we see that among those categories of severe mental defect that are nosologic entities, there is considerable diversity with respect to mechanisms of etiology. Some types may be of exclusively genetic determination; others may be genetically determined in a fraction of cases, while another fraction has a different etiologic basis; other types are primarily or exclusively of environmental origin; still others depend to a significant degree on both genetic and environmental factors.

Our list of more or less well-defined types of severe deficiency is, of course, by no means exhaustive. Even if it were, it would still leave out of account the very large class of low-grade defectives who are at present undifferentiable by clinical or laboratory signs. There is good reason to suspect, however, that among these the diversity of etiologies is comparable to that found among the recognized syndromes. It is worth remarking that cases of one of the best-defined nosologic entities, phenylketonuria, were of necessity classified among the undifferentiable amentias (the "residual" cases of Penrose and other British writers) before their common biochemical peculiarities were identified and their genetic homogeneity established.

For mental deficiency of moron and borderline level, the picture is quite different. A major-gene substitution—such as that responsible for phenylketonuria—which ordinarily results in idiocy or imbecility may occasionally produce a mild or questionable degree of mental defect. And there are a few conditions dependent on major genes with variable manifestation which sometimes involve high-grade mental deficiency; it is found, for example, in about 10 per cent of all cases of multiple neurofibromatosis [35]. But no major genes have as yet been identified which are regularly associated with mental deficiency of the higher grades. Indeed, it appears rather certain that major-gene substitutions cannot be responsible for any appreciable portion of mental deficiency in the moron and borderline range since, as we have already noted, the variance in IQ within sibships containing defectives in this range (more accurately, the within-sibships variance expressed as a fraction of the total variance

---

[1] *Note added in proof.* Observations published since 1959 have established that some cases of mongolism are associated with a chromosomal *translocation*— a fragment of the chromosome which is present in triplicate in the mongoloids cited above is attached to a chromosome of another pair. At the present writing (May 1961) it appears that, by and large, the mongoloids possessing the chromosomal translocation compose the group which Penrose [138] distinguished statistically as having equal likelihood of being produced at all maternal ages. For this group there is an appreciably increased—though as yet unmeasured—risk of mongolism occurring in a sib.

within and between sibships) is not distinguishably greater than that within the sibships of individuals whose IQs range from 80 to 120.

Thus, the question of how and to what extent genotypic variability may be etiologically involved in the higher grades of mental deficiency is in the same state of uncertainty as is the question of the role of genotypic differences as determinants of intelligence differences within the range currently regarded as normal. In fact, the two questions are quite probably for the most part the same. That is, it appears likely that such genotype-environment interactions as are responsible for the differentiation of morons and borderline defectives from individuals nearer the median in test intelligence are of the same character as those responsible for individual differences in test intelligence at higher levels.

Mental disease. Nearly all genetically oriented investigations of mental disorders have been concerned with the psychoses. Exceptions include relatively recent studies of neurotic behavior in twins [47, 48, 96, 182] and exploratory efforts to delineate categories of psychoneuroses by multivariate analysis and other methods [46, 145].

Among the psychoses, only one has been established as contingent upon a clearly identified major-gene substitution; this is the personality derangement which is characteristically associated with Huntington's chorea [132, 146]. Several other psychoses, or diagnostic complexes of psychotic disorders, which are conspicuous for their tendency to familial concentration have been studied genetically; of these, the schizophrenias have, of course, received the greatest attention.

Systematic investigation of the incidence of schizophrenia among sibs and other relatives of schizophrenic propositi, dating from the pioneer studies of Rudin, has consistently shown expectancy rates for schizophrenia in the cognate groups to be significantly in excess of the expectancy in the general population [116].

Age-corrected estimates of the expected incidence of schizophrenia among sibs of schizophrenics range from about 5 to 10 per cent if both parents are free from schizophrenia, and from 8 to 18 per cent if one parent is schizophrenic. For the children of schizophrenics with normal spouses, estimates range from 8 to 16 per cent, and for the children of two schizophrenics from 45 to 68 per cent. These rates are all greatly in excess of the incidence in the general population, which is generally taken to be less than 1 per cent. Expectancies estimated for categories of relatives other than those listed above, namely, half-sibs, grandchildren, nephews and nieces, and first cousins, are all above the general-population figure and decrease roughly in proportion to decreasing closeness of relationship.

The observed tendency of schizophrenia toward accumulation in family groups, in the absence of any *discerned* common factor in the environment, obviously suggests that genetic factors are etiologically significant. But it should be equally obvious that the cogency of familial-incidence data as evidence for the significant implication of genetic factors in the etiology of this or any other disease rests ultimately upon the degree of assurance that environmental influences cannot account for the observed accumulation [38, 196].

Studies of the frequency with which schizophrenia occurs among monozygotic and dizygotic co-twins, respectively, of schizophrenic propositi who are members of twin pairs have been undertaken by several investigators [93]. Investigations of this kind are commonly referred to as "concordance-discordance studies," because the data obtained for the two types of twins are often expressed in terms of the respective frequencies with which the two members of a pair are "concordant" for the condition under scrutiny.

By far the most extensive of the twin studies is that of Kallmann [90, 91], whose material involves nearly a thousand pairs of twins and includes information on several thousand of their close cognates also, Kallmann found schizophrenia in 69 per cent of the co-twins of monozygotic propositi; with his method of adjusting for age distribution, this corresponds to an expectancy rate of 86 per cent. The corresponding observed and age-corrected rates for co-twins of dizygotic propositi are 10 and 14 per cent. Slater, in another recent twin study [182], smaller, but more fully reported, than Kallmann's, using a more conservative age-adjustment procedure for the monozygotic twins, estimates their expectancy rate as 76 per cent; his figure for dizygotic co-twins is 14 per cent.

The findings of the two investigations just mentioned confirm the earlier twin studies in finding—whatever the precise estimates may be—a strikingly higher risk of schizophrenia among monozygotic than among dizygotic co-twins of propositi.

Because twin studies constitute a valuable and widely used research tool in human genetics, it is desirable to keep in mind their limitations as well as their possibilities. When the concordance frequency is markedly higher in monozygotic than in dizygotic twins, it is commonly felt that some or all of the higher concordance must be attributed to the genetic identity of the monozygotics. In general, this inference is a valid one if, but only if, the basic postulate of the concordance-discordance method can be shown to apply. The postulate is, of course, that *average intrapair differences in all environmental factors which could possibly have etiologic relevance are substantially the same for both types of twins.* This assumption is often open to grave question, and conspicuously so when psychologic responses are the subject of investigation; but in all cases, we should remember that its validity is something that needs to be substantiated, not taken for granted.

In fact, the valid inferences that can be drawn from studies restricted to a comparison of concordance rates in twin pairs alone appear to be quite limited in number, though not in importance. If a condition is exclusively determined by hereditary factors, we can assert that there must be 100 per cent concordance in monozygotic twin pairs. However, the converse is by no means equally true, that is, 100 per cent concordance in monozygotic pairs does not necessarily mean exclusively genetic causation. On the other hand, anything less than 100 per cent concordance among monozygotic pairs does permit us to *exclude* genetic factors as sole determinants. Finally, if there is *no difference* between concordance rates of monozygotic and dizygotic pairs, we are safe in ruling out genetic factors altogether. All other possible findings can tell us only that both genetic and environmental factors are, or may be, etiologically involved.

If twin-concordance studies are supplemented by simultaneous investigations of incidence data in sibs and other relatives, as has been done by Kallmann and some others, rather more can be learned. But the detection of significant genotype-environment interactions is not likely to be possible unless the material has been drawn from a representative range of environmental situations and can be classified in respect to what may be relevant ecologic variables.

Nevertheless, the inclusion of incidence data on sibs especially can add importantly to the value of a twin-concordance study, because comparison of incidences in the three groups (monozygotic twins, dizygotic twins, and sibs), in favorable cases, may indicate the general direction in which we should look for etiologically significant environmental factors. When monozygotic concordance is less than 100 per cent, an incidence among dizygotic co-twins appreciably higher than that found in the sibs suggests that the environmental factors of primary relevance are those for which *intrafamilial* variability is likely to be greater than variability *between* families; for example, prenatal influences associated with maternal age, exposure to an epidemic disease of relatively long cycle and narrow age range of susceptibility, birth rank in sibship.

On the other hand, an incidence among dizygotic co-twins indistinguishable from that found among sibs (with monozygotic concordance significantly higher than dizygotic) points to the implication of environmental factors of the sort which are likely to be relatively constant within an individual family, but which may vary considerably between families. Examples are nutrition, housing, occupational level, extent and character of social contacts, and so on.

The twin and family studies, then, are consistent with a conclusion that genetic factors are etiologically significant for the schizophrenias. They do not appear to demonstrate this unequivocally, but they do firmly establish that the determinants of the disease cannot be exclusively genetic. They further suggest—but with strong qualifications, because of some uncertainty as to the confidence limits of the incidence estimates —that environmental factors which do have an etiologic role are predominantly those for which variability between families is likely to be greater than intrafamilial variability.

The familial-incidence data do not appear at the present time to substantiate critically any hypothesis attributing predisposition for schizophrenia to a single major gene. Efforts to frame hypotheses of this kind would seem premature, if for no other reason than the considerable range of incidence figures reported by different investigators. Some of this variation is undoubtedly traceable to inevitable diagnostic uncertainties and to differences in diagnostic criteria which would lead one investigator to classify as "schizophrenic" certain cases which another might designate as "schizoid personalities" [16, 140]. But some of the disparities in incidence figures could also reflect real differences in the distribution of the schizophrenia-symptom complex in different ecologic situations. Indeed, this would seem to be the only reasonable explanation for the fact that Kallmann (who has given special attention to uniformity of diagnostic criteria) found the incidence of schizoidia among sibs of schizophrenic propositi to be three times as high (age-corrected expectancy, 31.5 per cent) in a large German sample [89] as in his extensive sample taken in the United States, where the comparable figure was 10.5 per cent [90].

Finally, in a paper reflecting uncommon perspicacity, Rosenthal [151] has called attention to clear evidence which has hitherto passed unnoticed for the etiologic heterogeneity of the schizophrenias. The evidence rests on an analysis of Slater's twin material [182], the only twin series of adequate size for which the data are reported in sufficient detail to permit this kind of reexamination. When the twin pairs are classified according to whether or not there is a family history of "probable schizophrenic illness," it is seen that the family history is positive for 60 per cent of the *concordant* pairs (13 out of 22), but for only 8 per cent of the *discordant* pairs (1 out of 13); the difference between the two groups is significant at well beyond the 0.01 level. The conclusion is inescapable that the schizophrenias of the concordant and discordant pairs, respectively, rest upon different etiologic bases, and that the significance of any genetic components in the etiology must be quite different in the two groups.

(It is conceivable that further differentiation of the schizophrenias might be accomplished by techniques which combine the use of discriminant functions with pedigree analysis, such as have recently been successfully exploited in the classification of the muscular dystrophies

[31, 123]; but sufficiently large bodies of data have not been reported in enough detail to make this possible at the present time.)

The conclusions pertinent to etiologic problems of the schizophrenias which we have cited may seem to some to be incommensurate with the extensive and conscientious labor that has been expended on genetic studies of a major psychosis. We believe, however, that they are of considerable importance, both intrinsically and as guide lines for future research.

Nor are these the only fruits of genetically oriented investigations. These studies have contributed valuable evidence that the preponderant majority of psychoses formerly classified as paranoia are in fact nosologically related to the schizophrenias [102, cited in 116]. They appear to have resolved most, if not all, suspicions that manic-depressive psychoses and schizophrenic states have any common predispositional background [91; 140, pp. 129, 132]. And they have provided strong grounds for inferring that many of the involutional psychoses, however different symptomatically from the schizophrenias, may share a common predispositional substrate with them [91].

Several familial-incidence and twin studies have been published dealing with manic-depressive psychoses [see references in 94, 197], and a few which concern involutional melancholia [92, 93, 198]. The data are much less numerous than those for the schizophrenias. A discussion of the specific findings would involve essentially the same interpretative principles as those we have applied to the schizophrenia materials.

Genetics and Comparative Psychology

We have mentioned earlier (page 14) some of the evidence that many differences in behavioral response among laboratory and domestic animals are contingent upon genotypic differences.

In a number of instances (chiefly, if not exclusively, in insects) a major gene has been identified as having a distinctive effect upon a particular aspect of behavior. In *Drosophila,* the *white* gene (named for its effect on eye color) affects speed of phototactic response [166]. In the same animal, the *yellow* gene (body color) reduces the rate and duration of the vibratory wing movements of the male which precede copulation and are apparently important in stimulating female receptiveness [11]. In the scarlet tiger moth, females heterozygous for a gene which, when homozygous, is responsible for the *bimacula* color variety, show a distinct preference for mating with homozygous (*bimacula*) males, rather than with males which are heterozygous (the *medionigra* color variety) like themselves; conversely, homozygous females show a clear preference for mating with heterozygous males [177].

In the honeybee, resistance to a bacterial disease of the larvae (American foul brood) in certain strains is achieved by the "hygienic" behavior of the workers, which uncap cells containing infected larvae and remove the larvae [155]. Recent work on the genetics of this activity suggests that the uncapping phase of the behavior may be dependent upon a single gene in homozygous condition and the removal phase upon another. Workers homozygous only for the first gene uncap the contaminated cells, but do not remove the larvae; those homozygous for the second gene (but not for the first) remove infected larvae, but only if the cells have previously been uncapped. Workers homozygous for both genes uncap the cells *and* remove the larvae [156]. (This remarkable situation is the only instance known to us in which an "instinctive" behavioral sequence appears to be dissectible into genetically controlled components.)

Other examples might be cited of single major genes in insects (and, with less critical evidence, in mammals) which affect behavior patterns within the nonpathologic range. Nevertheless, it seems fairly certain that by far the greater part of genotype-conditioned variability in the normal behavior pattern of any species is referable to polygenic variation rather than to major-gene differences. By this we mean that if a reasonable number of at least partially independent aspects of behavior are sampled in any genetically heterogeneous population, major-gene differences only exceptionally are found at the basis of behavioral differences. On the other hand, in nearly every such sampling as has been undertaken, the relevance of polygenic variability has been demonstrable [27, 58, 62].

The relative rarity of major-gene effects on normal behavior, we should add, need not be expected to be as pronounced in respect to interbreed differences among domesticated animals as in the case of individual differences in natural populations. In the former instance, artificial selection has made possible the preservation of major-gene mutations which would not have survived the rigors of natural selection. Indeed, the preliminary findings of Scott and his colleagues in behavioral-genetic studies of the basenji and cocker-spaniel breeds of dog are consistent with the *possibility* that as few as two major genes are responsible for interbreed differences in perhaps half of the aspects of behavior they have had under scrutiny [167]. These findings, however, are based only on observations of first-generation hybrids and the progeny of these hybrids backcrossed to the parent breeds; data on the offspring of matings between the backcross progeny and the parent breeds, which should be more definitive [160], have not been reported at the present writing.

Demonstration of the existence of polygenic variability affecting one or another kind of behavioral response has, in general, been accomplished in one of the following ways:

1. By selective breeding over a number of generations for opposite extremes in the manifestation of the response [73, 78, 158, 202].

2. By comparing different breeds of animals that have already become genetically differentiated as a result of prior selection [7, 55, 57, 170, 171].

3. By comparing strains of laboratory animals produced by many generations of close inbreeding. As a result of close inbreeding, even without selection, each strain comes to differ from the others in its particular array of polygenes, and the members of each strain tend to approach genotypic identity with one another [22, 26, 157, 195, 201].

4. More recently, by comparing populations which have been "synthesized" in such a way that all members of a given population possess a known number of identical chromosomes, and are therefore identical for whatever genes these chromosomes carry—a technique which at present is feasible only in *Drosophila* [79, 80].

Types of behavior for which, by the use of one or another of the procedures just listed, the relevance of polygenic influences has been established include (in addition to those indicated on page 14) phototactic [81] and geotactic [79, 80] response in *Drosophila;* geotactic response [36], emotionality [22, 73], and hoarding behavior [195] in rats; exploratory behavior in mice [117] and in rats [26]; avoidance conditioning [157] and emotionality [201] in mice; and a variety of behavioral responses in dogs [7, 55, 57, 170, 171].

The demonstration of either polygenic or major-gene differentiation of behavioral patterns should be regarded, we believe, as only the first step in the behavioral-genetic study of the patterns in question [56; 62; 163, p. 428]. This merely provides the material for attacking the more significant problem of analyzing the developmental mechanisms—the pathways between genotype and phenotype—through which the behavioral differences are produced. Here the investigation enters the area of developmental or physiological genetics (see page 3 above), and obviously may come into close interrelationship with physiological psychology.

Unfortunately, studies of behavioral patterns by methods of physiological genetics have been, to date, extremely few, so that evaluative generalizations concerning work of this kind cannot be made. Some account of two rather elaborate investigations (both still in progress) may, however, serve to indicate general directions of attack.

Krech reported in 1932 [106] that in certain test situations, laboratory rats fell into two behavioral categories: those predominantly responsive to clues provided by differences in light intensity ("visual" responders), and those preferentially responsive to clues involving positional relationships ("spatial" responders). Comparison of the frequencies with which visual and spatial responders were found respectively in rats of Tryon's maze-bright and maze-dull strains and in an unselected control group encouraged an inference that the difference between the two categories of response was to a significant degree dependent upon differences in genotype [107]. (The published data are clearly consistent with this inference; they do not appear to us, however, to establish it very securely.)

More recently, Krech and his collaborators investigated the cholinesterase activity of cerebral-cortical tissues from rats of the two response types and found that, in tissues of the visual and somesthetic areas, the activity of the enzyme was significantly higher for spatial than for visual responders [104, 105]. These observations prompted the following suggestions:

1. Differences in the rate of acetylcholine metabolism in the cortex may be genetically determined.

2. These differences in turn are responsible for the behavioral differentiation between spatial and visual responders.

Subsequent findings have revealed that the problem is appreciably more complex than was at first apparent. While they tend to confirm the first part of the proposed hypothesis, they indicate that the second part is scarcely tenable in any simple form:

1. There are striking changes in the cholinesterase activity of the cortical tissues with age. In particular, the behavioral differences between spatial and visual responders is evident *before* any difference in cholinesterase activity can be demonstrated [152].

2. In stocks of rats descended respectively from Tryon's maze-bright and maze-dull strains and from a cross (crosses?) between the two, cholinesterase activity at comparable ages appears to be quite different— suggesting genetic differentiation; but while it is higher for the spatial than for the visual responders in samples from each of the three stocks, the *visual* responders of the first stock (descendents of the maze-brights) show consistently greater cholinesterase activity than the *spatial* responders of the stock descended from the maze-dulls [152].

3. In fact, it has proved possible, by selective breeding for high and low levels of cholinesterase, to demonstrate genotypic control of the activity of this enzyme. But among animals of the strain successfully bred for *low* cholinesterase activity, *spatial* responses are commoner than in the high-cholinesterase strain [150].

It is obvious that the complex findings we have cited and some others [29, 30, 153] are hardly susceptible at the present time of any unequivocal and comprehensive interpretation. They do indicate rather strongly, however, that different genotypes may determine different *norms*, or ranges, of cholinesterase activity; and higher or lower activities of the enzyme within the range permitted by a given animal's genotype, as Fuller and Thompson have suggested [58], might as plausibly be a consequence as a cause of the animal's spatial or visual pattern of responsiveness.

A somewhat different line of attack is provided in the work of Ginsberg and his colleagues in their attempts to explore the metabolic pathways which may lie behind genetically differentiated sensitivity to audiogenic seizures in several highly inbred strains of mice [61, 62]. Their point of departure was the use of a variety of pharmacologic agents in screening tests designed to discover which, if any, would modify the seizure-response pattern under standardized conditions. They have found in this way a number of enzyme substrates and antagonists related to intracellular energy-transfer mechanisms which are effective, some in exacerbating, some in ameliorating, the seizures.

In particular, two of the seizure-sensitive strains respond favorably to the administration of monosodium glutamate, and the favorable effects of this agent are counteracted by substances known to be its metabolic antagonists, i.e., substances whose molecules are structurally similar to those of glutamate and which therefore presumably compete with glutamate for enzymes essential to its metabolic utilization. A point of major interest is that different strains may respond quite differently to certain of the pharmacologic agents tested. Thus diamox (a powerful inhibitor of carbonic anhydrase) alleviates seizures in all strains that have been studied, while glutamate is effective in only two, suggesting that the seizure sensitivity of the various genotypes is most probably traceable to *different* metabolic aberrations.

In mice of certain of the seizure-sensitive genotypes, there are consistent peculiarities in patterns of learning, especially under stress. These peculiarities have not been described in detail, but it appears that none of them would be regarded as pathologic. Nevertheless, they seem to derive from the same metabolic aberrations that are responsible for the seizures: both the learning peculiarities and the seizure sensitivity can be manipulated physiologically by the same agents and are responsive to them in the same directions. Thus the analytic study of seizure-susceptibility, a behavioral response conventionally regarded as pathologic, may reasonably be expected to contribute also to an understanding of behavioral differentiation within the normal range.

Biochemical studies of brain tissue from mice of the two seizure-sensitive strains that respond favorably to glutamate point to a defect in an enzyme system which is concerned with phospherylating reactions. It is well known that all energy release in tissues, including that which is involved in neuronal discharge, is dependent on the breakdown and resynthesis of adenosine triphosphate (ATP). The work of Abood and

Gerard [1] provides convincing evidence that the activity of an enzyme essential to ATP breakdown is markedly reduced in the brain tissues of one of the glutamate-responsive seizure-sensitive strains, and that the synthesis of ATP is also depressed. It is further observed that these metabolic abnormalities are demonstrable only from the time that the mice of this strain reach the seizure-susceptible age and that the abnormalities vanish when the susceptible age period has been passed. Since the animals of this strain can be convulsed only within the age range within which the enzymatic defects are in evidence, there seems little room to doubt a causal connection. The biochemical studies have been extended by Ginsberg and his collaborators [unpublished, cited in 62] to the other glutamate-responsive strain, with similar results.

The problem of completely elucidating the mechanisms through which the gene complexes of the several mouse strains produce the various patterns of seizure susceptibility and other associated behavioral characteristics is by no means solved. But we suspect that the systematic approach in the researches just described has significantly sharpened the focus for further investigation, and the methodologic model it provides, in its broadest outlines, should be applicable to a wide variety of problems.

METHODOLOGIC INTERRELATIONS

Methodologic interpenetration between genetics and psychology has perhaps been most evident in the area of animal-behavior studies, where the advantages of being able to manipulate the genotype, as well as to control experimental variables, are obvious. Genetics has provided psychologists with guide lines for the manipulation of genotypes; in turn, psychology has provided, for the growing number of geneticists who are interested in problems of behavior, invaluable refinements in the techniques of assaying behavioral differences.

We believe that certain principles which the study of population genetics has provided for the investigator of animal behavior have been of paramount importance. These principles relate primarily to the effects of inbreeding and to the theoretical and practical consequences of various programs of selective breeding.

The value of highly inbred lines (and of F_1 hybrids between such lines) for research which is aimed at evaluating the significance of genotypic variables, or in which it is desirable to reduce genotypic variability so that the effects of environmental variables are minimally obscured, is widely recognized. So also, presumably, is the fact that different inbred lines, even if similar in outward appearance, are almost certain to differ —and may differ widely—in physiologic and psychologic characteristics.

The strict breeding requirements necessary to guarantee an acceptable degree of genetic uniformity, the extent to which "sublines" of genetically homogeneous inbred strains may be genetically divergent, and the simplicity of techniques by which genetic homogeneity may be tested are possibly not so well known. Nor does it appear to be universally understood that no investigator can expect that designation of his animals as "Wistar albinos" or "Sprague-Hawley stock" can give any clue as to their degree of genetic uniformity.

There is, on the other hand, a clearly growing awareness that a measure of sophistication in genetics somewhat beyond a knowledge of Mendel's laws is desirable in the planning stages of many types of experiment. Genetic theory and experience, for example, can provide programs of selective breeding which will either diminish or preserve genetic variability in the selected strains according to the purposes for which they are used.

The principles of population genetics which are of major importance for research in animal psychology are, for the most part, presented in rather, sometimes highly, technical and abstract form in the genetics literature, and this has tended to limit their accessibility for nongeneticists. Hall [72] has done notable service to psychologist colleagues in calling attention to Russell's masterly compendium of caveats and constructive guidance which brings these principles down to earth [160]; Fuller and Thompson's chapter "Experimental methods in behavior genetics" [58] supplements Russell's essay in several respects. Ross, Ginsberg, and Denenberg [154] deal intelligibly with the particular problem of when and when not to use litter-mate controls.

In respect to human behavior, very possibly the major methodologic *rapprochement* that genetics can make with psychology is in the area of abnormal psychology, and it consists in a point of view. It suggests focusing on the *family*—and under some circumstances on a larger cognate group—rather than on the individual as the unit of study. We are quite aware that psychoanalytic and other theories in the field of psychopathology prescribe close scrutiny of interactions among members of the family group. But our point here is rather different; what it implies can perhaps best be indicated by specific illustration.

In the past decade a considerable body of research on schizophrenia has been initiated by the suspicion that vulnerability to the disease may rest upon a metabolic defect, and an appreciable number of biochemical studies of schizophrenic individuals has been reported. Several excellent critical reviews have appeared. The treacherous pitfalls to which this kind of research is subject are pointed out, and attention is called to the frequency with which the findings of one or more investigators could not be confirmed by others, or could be attributed to dietary eccentricities, emotional stress, etc. [95, especially 98]. In this instance, focusing attention on the family rather than the individual as a unit of study would mean simply that, if there is discovered in a schizophrenic subject any biochemical aberration or an anomalous drug response which is suspected of having causal relation to the disease, the same aberration should be searched for in all available immediate relatives of the subject—parents, sibs, children. If the anomaly is in fact either basic to, or an essential feature of, the disease rather than a secondary consequence, genetical experience indicates that there is at least a fair chance that the same abnormality will be present in lesser degree among the relatives with significantly greater frequency than in the population at large. This has been found to be the case for a variety of pathologic conditions in which a metabolic defect appears to be a significant feature, whether the frankly pathologic condition can with some certainty be attributed to a single major-gene substitution or whether its genetic mechanism is not fully clear. In the former category we may cite phenylketonuric amentia (phenylalanine level in blood significantly elevated in about 80 per cent of heterozygotes [101], phenylalanine tolerance reduced in a similar fraction [84]); galectosemia (reduced activity of the enzyme galactose-1-phosphate uridyl transferase in erythrocytes of most heterozygotes [100]); vitamin D resistant rickets (hypophosphatemia in nearly all who carry the gene [66, 85]); sensitivity, as manifested by acute hemolytic reactions to primaquine, naphthalene, broad-bean pollen, etc. (reduced activity of another enzyme, glucose-6-phosphate dehydrogenase, in erythrocytes of nearly all carriers of the gene [67]). The second category would include gout (elevated serum-uric acid level in nongouty cognates [75, 127]); diabetes mellitus (reduced glucose tolerance in relatives [references in 127]); and very probably pernicious anemia (achlorhydria in relatives [124, 127]).

Moreover, the significance of a familially distributed biochemical aberration among the cognates of one or several schizophrenics would not necessarily be contradicted by failure to find the same anomaly in all other instances. In fact, this would be expected if, as many suspect [151, 181], schizophrenic behavior patterns may be the end results of any of several different processes of pathogenesis. Again, genetical experience provides a number of parallels from which we may cite two here. Symptomatically indistinguishable cases of diabetes insipidus can be clearly classified into two categories: in one the symptoms respond to treatment with pitressin, in the other there is no response. Moreover, subtypes in each of these categories can be distinguished by differences in pattern of genetic transmission, besides which numerous cases are clearly secondary to traumata [25, 50, 135]. And, as we have already seen, there is persuasive evidence that there are different mechanisms of pathogenesis in several of the genetically differentiated strains of mice that are subject to superficially indistinguishable audiogenic seizures [61]. Many more instances could be mentioned.

Our earlier summary of the major conclusions that may be drawn from familial-incidence and twin studies of schizophrenia revealed that, however instructive the results of these studies have been, they are far short of being definitive. It appears, however, that other methodologic approaches have not been strikingly more successful. Several ably conceived and executed ecologic surveys have come no closer to providing definitive results [32, 174], and psychologically oriented anamnestic studies have been equally inconclusive [113, 130]. We think that much might be gained by a fusion of these methodologic approaches in a single program [32, pp. 496f.].

The familial-incidence data we have cited clearly show that the place to look for potential cases of schizophrenia is among the immediate relatives of schizophrenics [39, p. 19]. Specifically, they indicate that minimally 8 or 10 per cent of children who have one schizophrenic parent can ordinarily be expected to develop the disease, and apparently a much larger percentage becomes recognizably schizoid. Moreover, the findings of the combined twin-and-family investigations, as we have noted in an earlier section, strongly support an inference that environmental factors of a kind which vary from family to family are significant in the etiology of schizophrenia. The validity of this inference could be critically tested by a foster-child study, comparing the frequency of schizophrenia and schizoid states in those children of schizophrenics who have been adopted into foster homes in infancy with the frequencies in nonfostered children of schizophrenics and in the foster relatives [98, p. 1594].

We are fully aware of the difficulties involved in obtaining an appropriate sample for a study of the kind suggested. It would doubtless be necessary to comb several states to secure the material and, in the light of earlier foster-child investigations, it is obvious that there would be further difficulty in assuring methodologic rigor. But the effort might be well repaid, because decisive results *in either direction* would, we think, indicate rather clearly the most profitable pathways for further investigations or anamnestic studies of schizophrenics themselves.

If—in a sample large enough to provide reasonably narrow confidence limits for the estimate of expectancy—there should be no significant reduction in the expectancy of schizophrenia and/or schizoidia in the fostered children as compared with the unfostered, then serious, if not fatal, doubt would be cast on the inferences suggested by the twin-and-family data. A finding of this kind would suggest that further research would most sensibly be concentrated upon biochemical studies of schizophrenics and their immediate cognates, rather than upon ecologic investigations or anamnestic studies of schizophrenics themselves.

If, on the other hand, as we think is more plausibly to be expected, a significant reduction in the expectancy of schizophrenia and/or schizoidia is found among the fostered children, this would *not* argue against the value of continuing biochemical investigations. *But it would argue very strongly for the desirability of an intensive longitudinal study of fostered and unfostered children of schizophrenics,* both in relation to sociocultural variables and to variables in the psychosocial relations of the subjects to their familial and other associates [133]. Such a study would involve a convergence of methodologic approaches from sociology and epidemiology as well as psychology and genetics [32]. The difficulties inherent in an undertaking of this kind would clearly be formidable, but the problem it concerns is formidable also, and it does not seem likely that it will yield to piecemeal attacks.

In areas other than psychopathology, convergence of methodologic approaches from genetics and psychology can also be found. Co-twin control studies have probably been made more often by psychologists than by geneticists [60, 129]. Nevertheless, we feel that we can claim their methodology as belonging within the ambit of genetics, inasmuch as its rationale is based upon considerations of genetic theory. We think, moreover, that the peculiar advantages of the co-twin control method [143, pp. 297f.] have been by no means adequately exploited. There would certainly appear to be many problems in psychopharmacology for which this procedure would be useful [63]. And in therapy tests— whether of drugs or of psychotherapeutic measures—the use of co-twin controls is assuredly the method of choice for disorders which are common enough (schizophrenia, the psychoneuroses) to render its application feasible. Many of those who treat mental disease appear reluctant to resort to controlled comparisons of therapeutic procedures, and we can to a degree understand the basis for their reluctance; its appalling consequences, however, have been so trenchantly exposed [51!] that we can scarcely envisage its survival. The advantage of using monozygotic co-twins wherever practicable in controlled-therapy tests is readily apparent. In a series of ordinary, unrelated matched pairs of schizophrenic patients, for example—however close the mutual resemblance in reaction patterns may be between the members of a pair—we can never be sure that the disease in both members has the same predispositional basis. In a pair of monozygotic twins, on the other hand, we can be essentially certain of this, and reasonably certain of a common history of whatever experiences may have been of psychodynamic significance. In short, we can be sure that they both have the *same disease*.

A Metatheoretic Note

In concluding, we cannot resist a few words on a problem of meta-theory. Every science from time to time discovers that it has been embarrassed by its dependence on a terminology based on concepts which date from an earlier, and sometimes from a prescientific, period. Genetics, since its inception, has been shackled with the dichotomy of "heredity" and "environment"—both of which were concept names before genetics was born—and it shares these shackles with psychology. Numerous authors have attempted, in one way or another, to reduce the confusion engendered by the vague and ambiguous referents which the terms *heredity* and *environment* have in many contexts. Those who have made constructive contributions in this direction include psychologists from several subdisciplines [6, 76, 114, 164], psychogeneticists [54], geneticists [41, 70], and at least one biologist logician [207, 208], to cite only a few. Their consensus would seem to be that we have been asking the wrong questions when we have tried to decide *which* is responsible— heredity or environment—for such-and-such observed variability, or when we have inquired *how much* of the variability is attributable to hereditary factors and how much to environmental [6]. Instead, we should be inquiring *how,* that is, investigating the developmental mechanisms through which the variability arises.

The heuristic importance of this and other ideas suggested by the authors cited cannot be overemphasized. Nevertheless, it seems likely that a fundamental difficulty may persist, rooted in the lack of a conceptual framework adequate to embrace what we commonly call "interaction" except in terms of polar interacting forces or processes. We suspect that a more satisfactory resolution of the difficulty will not emerge without a conceptual revolution comparable to Einstein's resolving of the space-time and mass-energy dichotomies in physics. At present there appears to be no hint of the form this revolution will take, but laying the groundwork for it clearly invites the convergence of methodologic approaches from the widest variety of disciplines.

REFERENCES

1. Abood, L. G., & Gerard, R. W. A phosphorylation defect in the brains of mice susceptible to audiogenic seizure. In H. Waelsch (Ed.), *Biochemistry of the developing nervous system.* New York: Academic Press, 1955. Pp. 467–472.
2. Allen, G. Patterns of discovery in the genetics of mental deficiency. *Amer. J. ment. Defic.,* 1958. 62, 840–849.

3. Allison, A. C., & McWhirter, K. G. Two unifactorial characters for which man is polymorphic. *Nature*, 1956, **178**, 748–749.

4. *American Journal of human Genetics*. Baltimore, Md.: Williams & Wilkins, 1949, **1**, et seq.

5. Anastasi, A. *Differential psychology*. (3rd ed.) New York: Macmillan, 1958.

6. Anastasi, A. Heredity, environment, and the question "How?" *Psychol. Rev.*, 1958, **65**, 197–208.

7. Anastasi, A., Fuller, J. L., Scott, J. P., & Schmitt, J. R. A factor analysis of the performance of dogs on certain learning tests. *Zoologica*, 1955, **40**, 33–46.

8. Anfinsen, C. B. *The molecular basis of evolution*. New York: Wiley, 1959.

9. *Annals of eugenics*. London: Cambridge Univer. Press, 1934–35, **6**— 1953–54, **18**.

10. *Annals of human genetics* (formerly *Annals of eugenics*). London: Cambridge Univer. Press, 1954–55, **19**, et seq.

11. Bastock, M. A gene mutation which changes behavior pattern. *Evolution*, 1956, **10**, 421–439.

12. Bauer, K. H., & Bode, W. Erbpathologie der Stützgewebe beim Menschen. In G. Just (Ed.), *Handbuch der Erbbiologie des Menschen*. Vol. 3. Berlin: Springer, 1940. Pp. 105–334.

13. Beach, F. A. A review of physiological and psychological studies of sexual behavior in mammals. *Physiol. Rev.*, 1947, **27**, 240–307.

14. Beadle, G. W. Biochemical genetics. *Chem. Rev.*, 1945, **37**, 15–96.

15. Benedict, R. Sex in primitive society. *Amer. J. Orthopsychiat.*, 1939, **9**, 570–574.

16. Böök, J. A. A genetic and neuropsychiatric investigation of a North-Swedish population. Part I. Psychoses. *Acta genet.*, 1953, **4**, 1–100.

17. Böök, J. A., Schut, J. W., & Reed, S. C. A clinical and genetical study of microcephaly. *Amer. J. ment. Defic.*, 1953, **57**, 637–660.

18. Boyd, W. C. *Genetics and the races of man*. Boston: Little, Brown, 1950.

19. Brachet, J. *Biochemical cytology*. New York: Academic Press, 1957.

20. Brandon, M. W. G., Kirkman, B. H., & Williams, C. E. Microcephaly. *J. ment. Sci.*, 1959, **105**, 721–747.

21. Bridges, C. B., & Brehme, K. S. *The mutants of Drosophila melanogaster*. Washington: Carnegie Institute of Washington, 1944.

22. Broadhurst, P. L. Determinants of emotionality in the rat. III. Strain differences. *J. comp. physiol. Psychol.*, 1958, **51**, 55–59.

23. Burt, C. A note on the theory of intelligence. *Br. J. educ. Psychol.*, 1958, **28**, 281–288.

24. Burt, C., & Howard, M. The relative influence of heredity and environment. *Br. J. statist. Psychol.*, 1957, **10**, 99–104.

25. Cannon, J. F. Diabetes insipidus. Clinical and experimental studies with consideration of genetic relationships. *Arch. intern. Med.*, 1955, **96**, 215–272.

26. Carr, R. M., & Williams, C. D. Exploratory behavior of three strains of rats. *J. comp. physiol. Psychol.*, 1957, **50**, 621–623.

27. Caspari, E. Genetic basis of behavior. In A. Roe & G. G. Simpson (Eds.), *Behavior and evolution.* New Haven, Conn.: Yale Univer. Press, 1958. Pp. 103–127.

28. Cavalli, L. L. An analysis of linkage in quantitative inheritance. In E. C. R. Reeve & C. H. Waddington (Eds.), *Quantitative inheritance.* London: H. M. Stationery Office, 1952.

29. Chow, K. L., & John, E. R. Effects of intracerebral injection of anticholinesterase drugs on behavior in rats. *Science,* 1958, **128**, 781–782.

30. Chow, K. L., & John, E. R. Acetylcholine metabolism and behavior of rats. *Science*, 1959, **129**, 64.

31. Chung, C. S., & Morton, N. E. Discrimination of genetic entities in muscular dystrophy. *Amer. J. hum. Genet.*, 1959, **11**, 339–359.

32. Clausen, J. A. The sociology of mental illness. In R. K. Merton, L. Broom, & L. S. Cottrell, Jr. (Eds.), *Sociology today, problems and prospects.* New York: Basic Books, 1959. Pp. 485–508.

33. Cline, W. Notes on the people of Siwah and El Garah in the Libyan Desert. Menasha, Wis.: George Banta, 1936.

34. Cockayne, E. A. *Inherited abnormalities of the skin and its appendages.* London: Oxford Univer. Press, 1933.

35. Crowe, F. W., Schull, W. J., & Neel, J. V. *Multiple neurofibromatosis.* Springfield, Ill.: Charles C Thomas, 1956.

36. Crozier, W. J., & Pincus, G. Analysis of the geotropic orientation of young rats. X. *J. gen. Physiol.*, 1936, **20**, 111–144.

37. Dahlberg, G. Biometric evaluation of findings. In A. Sorsby (Ed.), *Clinical genetics.* St. Louis, Mo.: Mosby, 1953. Pp. 83–100.

38. David, P. R., & Snyder, L. H. Genetics and disease. *Proceedings Second National Cancer Conference.* New York: American Cancer Society, 1954. Pp. 1128–1138.

39. David, P. R., & Snyder, L. H. Principles of human genetics. In D. Hooker & C. C. Hare (Eds.), *Genetics and the inheritance of integrated neurological and psychiatric patterns.* Baltimore, Md.: Williams & Wilkins, 1954. Pp. 3–22.

40. Dencker, S. J., Hauge, M., & Kaij, L. An investigation of the PTC taste character in monochorionic twin pairs. *Acta genet.*, 1959, **9**, 236–244.

41. Dobzhansky, Th. Heredity, environment, and evolution. *Science,* 1950, **111**, 161–166.

42. Dobzhansky, Th. *Genetics and the origin of species.* (3rd ed.) New York: Columbia Univer. Press, 1951.

43. Dobzhansky, Th. *Evolution, genetics, and man.* New York: Wiley, 1955.

44. Dobzhansky, Th., & Wallace, B. The problem of adaptive differences in human populations. *Amer. J. hum. Genet.*, 1954, **6**, 199–207.

45. Eugster, J. Zur Erblichkeitsfrage des endemischen Kretinismus. Untersuchungen an 204 Kretinen und deren Blutsverwandten. I. Teil. *Arch. J. Klaus-Stiftung*, 1938, **13**, 383–494.
46. Eysenck, H. J. *The structure of human personality.* New York: Wiley, 1953.
47. Eysenck, H. J. The inheritance of neuroticism: a reply. *J. ment. Sci.*, 1959, **105**, 76–80.
48. Eysenck, H. J., & Prell, D. B. The inheritance of neuroticism: an experimental study. *J. ment. Sci.*, 1951, **97**, 441–465.
49. Falls, H. F. Skeletal system, including joints. In A. Sorsby (Ed.), *Clinical genetics.* St. Louis, Mo.: Mosby, 1953. Pp. 236–286.
50. Forssman, H. Two different mutations of the X-chromosome causing diabetes insipidus. *Amer. J. hum. Genet.*, 1955, **7**, 21–27.
51. Foulds, G. A. Clinical research in psychiatry. *J. ment. Sci.*, 1958, **104**, 259–265.
52. Franceschetti, A., & Klein, D. Les affections génétiques en ophtalmologie. In E. Velter & G. Renard (Eds.), *Ophtalmologie.* Vol. 26, fasc. 21400. Paris: Encyclopédie médico-chirurgicale, 1956. A 10–D 10.
53. Franceschetti, A., Klein, D., & Babel, J. Les manifestations oculaires des troubles primitifs du métabolisme des lipides. Étude clinique, génétique et anatomo-pathologique. *Arq. Neuro-Psiquiat.*, 1955, **13**, 69–160.
54. Fuller, J. L. *Nature and nurture, a modern synthesis.* New York: Doubleday, 1954.
55. Fuller, J. L. Hereditary differences in trainability of purebred dogs. *J. genet. Psychol.*, 1955, **87**, 229–238.
56. Fuller, J. L. Behavior genetics. *Annu. Rev. Psychol.*, 1960, **11**, 41–70.
57. Fuller, J. L., & Scott, J. P. Heredity and learning ability in infrahuman mammals. *Eugen. Quart.*, 1954, **1**, 28–43.
58. Fuller, J. L., & Thompson, W. R. *Behavior genetics.* New York: Wiley, 1960.
59. Galatius-Jensen, F. Further on the genetics of the haptoglobins. *Acta genet.*, 1958, **8**, 232–247.
60. Gedda, L. *Studio dei gemelli.* Roma: Ediz. Orizzonte Medico, 1951.
61. Ginsberg, B. E. Genetics and the physiology of the nervous system. In D. Hooker & C. C. Hare (Eds.), *Genetics and the inheritance of integrated neurological and psychiatric patterns.* Baltimore, Md.: Williams & Wilkins, 1954. Pp. 39–56.
62. Ginsberg, B. E. Genetics as a tool in the study of behavior. *Perspectives Biol. Med.*, 1958, **1**, 397–424.
63. Glass, B. The genetic aspects of adaptability. In D. Hooker & C. C. Hare (Eds.), *Genetics and the inheritance of integrated neurological and psychiatric patterns.* Baltimore, Md.: Williams & Wilkins, 1954. Pp. 367–377.
64. Glass, B., & Kistler, J. C. Distal hyperextensibility of the thumbs. *Acta genet.*, 1953, **4**, 192–206.

65. Goldschmidt, R. *Physiological genetics.* New York: McGraw-Hill, 1938.
66. Graham, J. B., McFalls, V. W., & Winters, R. W. Familial hypophosphatemia with vitamin D–resistant rickets. II. Three additional kindreds of the sex-linked dominant type with a genetic analysis of four such families. *Amer. J. hum. Genet.*, 1959, **11**, 311–332.
67. Gross, R. T., Hurwitz, R. E., & Marks, P. A. An hereditary enzymatic defect in erythrocyte metabolism: glucose-6-phosphate dehydrogenase deficiency. *J. clin. Invest.*, 1958, **37**, 1176–1184.
68. Grüneberg, H. *The genetics of the mouse.* (2nd ed.) The Hague: Martinus Nijhoff, 1952.
69. Haldane, J. B. S. *The causes of evolution.* New York: Harper, 1932.
70. Haldane, J. B. S. The interaction of nature and nurture. *Ann. Eugen.*, 1946, **13**, 197–205.
71. Haldane, J. B. S. *The biochemistry of genetics.* London: G. Allen, 1954.
72. Hall, C. S. The genetics of behavior. In S. S. Stephens (Ed.), *Handbook of experimental psychology.* New York: Wiley, 1951. Pp. 304–329.
73. Hall, C. S., & Klein, S. J. Individual differences in aggressiveness in rats. *J. comp. Psychol.*, 1942, **33**, 371–383.
74. Harris, H. *Human biochemical genetics.* London: Cambridge Univer. Press, 1959.
75. Hauge, M., & Harvald, B. Heredity in gout and hyperuricemia. *Acta med. scand.*, 1955, **152**, 247–257.
76. Hebb, D. O. Heredity and environment in mammalian behavior. *Br. J. animal Behav.*, 1953, **1**, 43–47.
77. Herndon, C. N. Genetics of the lipidoses. In D. Hooker & C. C. Hare (Eds.), *Genetics and the inheritance of integrated neurological and psychiatric patterns.* Baltimore, Md.: Williams & Wilkins, 1954, Pp. 239–258.
78. Heron, W. T. The inheritance of brightness and dullness in maze learning ability in the rat. *J. genet. Psychol.*, 1941, **59**, 41–49.
79. Hirsch, J. Recent developments in behavior genetics and differential psychology. *Diseases of the nervous system*, 1958, **19**, 17–24.
80. Hirsch, J. Studies in experimental behavior genetics: II. Individual differences in geotaxis as a function of chromosome variations in synthesized *Drosophila* populations. *J. comp. physiol. Psychol.*, 1959, **52**, 304–308.
81. Hirsch, J., & Boudreau, J. C. Studies in experimental behavior genetics: I. The heritability of phototaxis in a population of *Drosophila melanogaster. J. comp. physiol. Psychol.*, 1958, **51**, 647–651.
82. Hogben, L. *Nature and nurture.* New York: Norton, 1933.
83. Hsia, D. Y-Y. *Inborn errors of metabolism.* Chicago: Year Book Publishers, Inc., 1959.
84. Hsia, D. Y-Y., & Driscoll, K. W. Detection of the heterozygous carriers of phenylketonuria. *Lancet*, 1956, ii, 1337–1338.

85. Hsia, D. Y-Y., Kraus, M., & Samuels, J. Genetic studies on vitamin D resistant rickets (familial hypophosphatemia). *Amer. J. hum. Genet.*, 1959, **11**, 156–168.

86. Jacobs, P. A., Baikie, A. G., Court Brown, W. M., & Strong, J. A. The somatic chromosomes in mongolism. *Lancet*, 1959, i, 710.

87. Jervis, G. A. Phenylpyruvic oligophrenia (phenylketonuria). In D. Hooker & C. C. Hare (Eds.), *Genetics and the inheritance of integrated neurological and psychiatric patterns*. Baltimore, Md.: Williams & Wilkins, 1954. Pp. 259–282.

88. Juel-Nielsen, N., & Harvald, B. The electroencephalogram in uniovular twins brought up apart. *Acta genet.*, 1958, **8**, 57–64.

89. Kallmann, F. J. *The genetics of schizophrenia*. New York: Augustin, 1938.

90. Kallmann, F. J. The genetic theory of schizophrenia, an analysis of 691 schizophrenic twin index families. *Amer. J. Psychiat.*, 1946, **103**, 309–322.

91. Kallmann, F. J. The genetics of psychoses, an analysis of 1,232 twin index families. *Congrès international de psychiatrie*. Vol. 6. Paris: Hermann & Cie., 1950. Pp. 1–40.

92. Kallmann, F. J. Genetic aspects of mental disorders in later life. In O. J. Kaplan (Ed.), *Mental disorders in later life*. (2nd ed.) Stanford, Calif.: Stanford Univer. Press, 1953. Pp. 26–46.

93. Kallmann, F. J. *Heredity in health and mental disorder*. New York: Norton, 1953.

94. Kallmann, F. J. Genetic principles in manic-depressive psychoses. In P. H. Hoch & J. Zubin (Eds.), *Depression*. New York: Grune & Stratton, 1954. Pp. 1–24.

95. Kaplan, A. R. Biochemical studies in schizophrenia, a review. *Eugen. Quart.*, 1958, **5**, 86–94.

96. Karon, B. P., & Saunders, D. R. Some implications of the Eysenck-Prell study of "The inheritance of neuroticism": a critique. *J. ment. Sci.*, 1958, **104**, 350–358.

97. Kaven, A. Roentgenmodifikationen bei Mäusen. *Zeitschr. menschl. Vererb.-u. Konstitutionslehre*, 1938, **22**, 238–246.

98. Kety, S. S. Biochemical theories of schizophrenia. *Science*, 1959, **129**, 1528–1532; 1590–1596.

99. Kirk, R. L., & Stenhouse, N. S. Ability to smell solutions of potassium cyanide. *Nature*, 1953, **171**, 698–699.

100. Kirkman, H. N., & Bynum, E. Enzymic evidence of a galactosemic trait in parents of galactosemic children, *Ann. hum. Genet.*, 1959, **23**, 117–126.

101. Knox, W. E., & Messinger, E. C. The detection in the heterozygote of the recessive gene for phenylketonuria. *Amer. J. hum. Genet.*, 1958, **10**, 53–60.

102. Kolle, K. Über „paranoische" Psychopathen. Klinische und genealogische Untersuchungen. *Zeitschr. ges. Neurol. Psychiat.*, 1931, **136**, 97–127.

103. Komai, T., Kishimoto, K., & Ozaki, Y. Genetic study of microcephaly based on Japanese material. *Amer. J. hum. Genet.*, 1955, **7**, 51–65.

104. Krech, D., Rosenzweig, M. R., & Bennett, E. L. Dimensions of discrimination and levels of cholinesterase activity in the cerebral cortex of the rat. *J. comp. physiol. Psychol.*, 1956, **49**, 261–268.

105. Krech, D., Rosenzweig, M. R., Bennett, E. L., & Krueckel, B. Enzyme concentrations in the brain and adjustive behavior-patterns. *Science*, 1954, **120**, 994–996.

106. Krechevsky, I. The genesis of "hypotheses" in rats. *Univ. Calif. Publ. Psychol.*, 1932, **6**, 45–64.

107. Krechevsky, I. Hereditary nature of "hypotheses." *J. comp. physiol. Psychol.*, 1933, **16**, 99–116.

108. Landauer, W. Hereditary abnormalities and their chemically induced phenocopies, *Growth Sympos.*, 1948, **12**, 171–200.

109. Landauer, W. Phenocopies and genotype, with special reference to sporadically-occurring developmental variants. *Amer. Naturalist*, 1957, **91**, 79–90.

110. Lejeune, J., Gautier, M., & Turpin, R. Les chromosomes humains en culture de tissus. *Comptes rendus Acad. Sci.*, Paris, 1959, **248**, 602–603.

111. Lerner, I. M. *The genetic basis of selection.* New York: Wiley, 1958.

112. Li, C. C. *Population genetics.* Chicago: Univer. of Chicago Press, 1955.

113. Lidz, R. W., & Lidz, T. The family environment of schizophrenic patients. *Amer. J. Psychiat.*, 1949, **106**, 332–345.

114. Loevinger, J. On the proportional contributions of differences in nature and nurture to differences in intelligence. *Psychol. Bull.*, 1943, **40**, 725–756.

115. Ludwig, W., & Boost, C. Vergleichende Wertung der Methoden zur Analyse recessiver Erbgänge beim Menschen. *Zeitschr. f. menschl. Vererb.-u. Konstitutionslehre*, 1940, **24**, 577–619.

116. Luxenburger, H. Die Schizophrenie und ihr Erbkreis. In G. Just (Ed.), *Handbuch der Erbbiologie des Menschen.* Vol. 5. Berlin: Springer, 1939. Pp. 769–872.

117. McClearn, G. E. The genetics of mouse behavior in novel situations. *J. comp. physiol. Psychol.*, 1959, **52**, 62–67.

118. McElroy, W. D., & Glass, B. (Eds.) *The chemical basis of heredity.* Baltimore, Md.: Johns Hopkins Press, 1957.

119. Maddox, H. Nature-nurture balance sheets. *Br. J. educ. Psychol.*, 1957, **27**, 166–175.

120. Mather, K. *Biometrical genetics.* New York: Dover, 1949.

121. Mead, M. *Sex and temperament in three primitive societies.* New York: Morrow, 1935.

122. Morton, N. E. The detection and estimation of linkage between the genes for elliptocytosis and Rh blood type. *Amer. J. hum. Genet.*, 1956, **8**, 80–96.

123. Morton, N. E., & Chung, C. S. Formal genetics of muscular dystrophy. *Amer. J. hum. Genet.*, 1959, **11**, 360–379.

124. Mosbech, J. Heredity in pernicious anemia. *Op. ex Domo Biol. hered.* *human. Univ. Hafniensis*, 1953, **34**, 1–107.

125. Murdock, G. P. Comparative data on the division of labor by sex. *Soc. Forces*, 1937, **15**, 551–553.

126. Murphy, D. *Congenital malformations.* (2nd ed.) Philadelphia: Lippincott, 1947.

127. Neel, J. V. The clinical detection of the genetic carriers of inherited disease. *Medicine*, 1947, **26**, 115–153.

128. Neel, J. V., & Schull, W. J. *Human heredity.* Chicago: Univer. of Chicago Press, 1954.

129. Newman, H. H. *Multiple human births.* New York: Doubleday, 1940.

130. Oltman, J. E., McGarry, J. J., & Friedman, S. Parental deprivation and the "broken home" in dementia praecox and other mental disorders. *Amer. J. Psychiat.*, 1952, **108**, 685–693.

131. Øster, J. The causes of mongolism. *Danish med. Bull.*, 1956, **3**, 158–164.

132. Panse, F. *Die Erbchorea.* Leipzig: Thieme, 1942.

133. Pearson, J. S., & Kley, I. B. On the application of genetic expectancies as age-specific base rates in the study of human behavior disorders. *Psychol. Bull.*, 1957, **54**, 406–420.

134. Pearson, K., & Jaederholm, G. A. *Mendelism and mental defect: on the continuity of mental defect.* London: Cambridge Univer. Press, 1914.

135. Pender, C. B., & Fraser, C. Dominant inheritance of diabetes insipidus: a family study. *Pediatrics*, 1953, **11**, 246–254.

136. Penrose, L. S. Intelligence test scores of mentally defective patients and their relatives. *Br. J. Psychol.*, 1939, **30**, 1–18.

137. Penrose, L. S. *The biology of mental defect.* New York: Grune & Stratton, 1949.

138. Penrose, L. S. Observations on the aetiology of mongolism. *Lancet*, 1954, ii, 505–509.

139. Pickering, G. W. *High blood pressure.* London: Churchill, 1955.

140. Planansky, K. Heredity in schizophrenia. *J. nerv. ment. Dis.*, 1955, **122**, 121–142.

141. Platt, R. The nature of essential hypertension. *Lancet*, 1959, ii, 55–57.

142. Plummer, G. Anomalies occurring in children exposed *in utero* to the atomic bomb in Hiroshima. *Pediatrics*, 1952, **10**, 687–693.

143. Price, B. Primary biases in twin studies: a review of prenatal and natal difference-producing factors in monozygotic pairs. *Amer. J. hum. Genet.*, 1950, **2**, 293–352.

144. Race, R. R., & Sanger, R. *Blood groups in man.* (3rd ed.) Springfield, Ill.: Charles C Thomas, 1958.

145. Rao, C. R., & Slater, P. Multivariate analysis applied to differences between neurotic groups. *Br. J. Psychol., statist. Sect.*, 1949, **2**, 17–29.

146. Reed, T. E., & Chandler, J. H. Huntington's chorea in Michigan. 1. Demography and genetics. *Amer. J. hum. Genet.*, 1958, **10**, 201–225.

147. Roberts, J. A. F. Studies on a child population—V: the resemblance in intelligence between sibs. *Ann. Eugen.*, 1940, **10**, 293–312.
148. Roberts, J. A. F. The genetics of oligophrenia. *Congrès international de Psychiatrie*. Vol. 6. Paris: Hermann & Cie., 1950. Pp. 55–117.
149. Roberts, J. A. F., Norman, R. M., & Griffiths, R. Studies on a child population—IV: the form of the lower end of the frequency distribution of Stanford-Binet intelligence quotients, and the fall of low intelligence quotients with advancing age. *Ann. Eugen.*, 1937–38, **8**, 319–336.
150. Roderick, T. E. The genetics of variation of cholinesterase activity in the cerebral cortex of the rat with reference to possible physiological and morphological correlation. Unpublished doctoral dissertation, Univer. of California, 1959.
151. Rosenthal, D. Some factors associated with concordance and discordance with respect to schizophrenia in monozygotic twins. *J. nerv. ment. Dis.*, 1959, **129**, 1–10.
152. Rosenzweig, M. R., Krech, D., & Bennett, E. L. Brain enzymes and adaptive behavior. In Ciba Foundation symposium, *The neurological basis of behavior*. Boston: Little, Brown, 1958. Pp. 337–358.
153. Rosenzweig, M. R., Krech, D., & Bennett, E. L. Acetylcholine metabolism and behavior of rats. *Science*, 1959, **129**, 62–64.
154. Ross, S., Ginsberg, B. E., & Denenberg, V. H. The use of the split-litter technique in psychological research. *Psychol. Bull.*, 1957, **54**, 145–151.
155. Rothenbuhler, W. C. Genetics of a behavior difference in honey bees. (Abstract.) *Proceedings of the Tenth International Congress of Genetics*. Vol. 2. Toronto: Univer. of Toronto Press, 1958. P. 242.
156. Rothenbuhler, W. C. Personal communication, Aug. 29, 1960.
157. Royce, J. R., & Covington, M. Genetic differences in the avoidance conditioning of mice. *J. comp. physiol. Psychol.*, 1960, **53**, 197–200.
158. Rundquist, E. A. The inheritance of spontaneous activity in rats. *J. comp. physiol. Psychol.*, 1933, **16**, 415–438.
159. Russell, L. B., & Russell, W. L. An analysis of the changing radiation response of the developing mouse embryo. *J. cell. comp. Physiol.*, 1954, **43**, Suppl. 1, 103–150.
160. Russell, W. L. Inbred and hybrid animals and their value in research. In G. D. Snell (Ed.), *Biology of the laboratory mouse*. Philadelphia: McGraw-Hill–Blakiston, 1951. Pp. 325–348.
161. Schneirla, T. C. The "levels" concept in the study of social organization in animals. In J. H. Rohrer and M. Sherif (Eds.), *Social psychology at the crossroads*. New York: Harper, 1951. Pp. 83–120.
162. Schneirla, T. C. The concept of levels in the study of social phenomena. In M. Sherif & C. W. Sherif, *Groups in harmony and tension*. New York: Harper, 1953. Pp. 54–75.
163. Schneirla, T. C. Interrelationships of the "innate" and the "acquired" in instinctive behavior. In P.-P. Grassé (Ed.), *L'instinct dans le comportement des animaux et de l'homme*. Paris: Masson, 1956. Pp. 387–452.

48   PAUL R. DAVID AND LAURENCE H. SNYDER

164. Schneirla, T. C. The concept of development in comparative psychology. In D. B. Harris (Ed.), *The concept of development*. Minneapolis, Minn.: Univer. of Minnesota Press, 1957. Pp. 78–108.

165. Schulz, B. *Methodik der medizinischen Erbforschung*. Leipzig: Thieme, 1936.

166. Scott, J. P. Effects of single genes on the behavior of Drosophila. *Amer. Naturalist*, 1943, **77**, 184–190.

167. Scott, J. P. The effects of selection and domestication upon the behavior of the dog. *J. nat. Cancer Inst.*, 1954, **15**, 397–424.

168. Scott, J. P. The genetic and environmental differentiation of behavior. In D. B. Harris (Ed.), *The concept of development*. Minneapolis, Minn.: Univer. of Minnesota Press, 1957. Pp. 59–77.

169. Scott, J. P. *Animal behavior*. Chicago: Univer. of Chicago Press, 1958. Chap. VI.

170. Scott, J. P., & Charles, M. S. Some problems of heredity and social behavior. *J. gen. Psychol.*, 1953, **48**, 209–230.

171. Scott, J. P., & Charles, M. S. Genetic differences in the behavior of dogs: a case of magnification by thresholds and by habit formation. *J. genet. Psychol.*, 1954, **84**, 175–188.

172. Scott, J. P., & Fuller, J. L. Research on genetics and social behavior at the Roscoe B. Jackson Memorial Laboratory, 1946–1951: a progress report. *J. Hered.*, 1951, **42**, 191–197.

173. Scott, O. L. S. Diseases of the skin. In A. Sorsby (Ed.), *Clinical genetics*. St. Louis, Mo.: Mosby, 1953. Pp. 210–235.

174. Scott, W. A. Social psychological correlates of mental illness and mental health. *Psychol. Bull.*, 1958, **55**, 65–87.

175. Sears, P. S. Doll play aggression in normal young children: influence of sex, age, sibling status, and father's absence. *Psychol. Monogr.*, 1951, **65**, No. 6.

176. Sears, R. R., Pintler, M. H., & Sears, P. S. Effect of father separation on preschool children's doll play aggression. *Child Developm.*, 1946, **17**, 219–243.

177. Sheppard, P. M. Non-random mating in *Panaxia*. *Heredity*, 1952, **6**, 239–241.

178. Sherif, M., & Sherif, C. W. *An outline of social psychology*. (rev. ed.) New York: Harper, 1956.

179. Sinnott, E. W., Dunn, L. C., & Dobzhansky, Th. *Principles of genetics*. (5th ed.) New York: McGraw-Hill, 1958.

180. Sjögren, T. Die juvenile amaurotische Idiotie. *Hereditas*, 1931, **14**, 197–425.

181. Slater, E. Psychiatry. In A. Sorsby (Ed.), *Clinical genetics*. St. Louis, Mo.: Mosby, 1953. Pp. 332–349.

182. Slater, E., & Shields, J. *Psychotic and neurotic illnesses in twins*. Medical Research Council Special Report Series 278. London: H. M. Stationery Office, 1953.

183. Slome, D. The genetic basis of amaurotic family idiocy. *J. Genet.*, 1933, **27**, 363–376.

184. Smithies, O. Third allele at the serum β-globulin locus in humans. *Nature*, 1958, **181**, 1203–1204.

185. Snyder, L. H. The inheritance of taste deficiency in man. *Ohio J. Sci.*, 1932, **32**, 436–440.

186. Snyder, L. H. *Medical genetics.* Durham, N.C.: Duke Univer. Press, 1932.

187. Snyder, L. H. The principles of gene distribution in human populations. *Yale J. Biol. Med.*, 1947, **19**, 817–833.

188. Snyder, L. H. Fifty years of medical genetics. *Science*, 1959, **129**, 7–13.

189. Snyder, L. H., & David, P. R. Penetrance and expression. In A. Sorsby (Ed.), *Clinical genetics.* St. Louis, Mo.: Mosby, 1953. Pp. 9–26.

190. Snyder, L. H., & David, P. R. *Principles of heredity.* (5th ed.) Boston: Heath, 1957.

191. Sorsby, A. *Genetics in ophthalmology.* London: Butterworth, 1951.

192. Sorsby, A. (Ed.) *Clinical genetics.* St. Louis, Mo.: Mosby, 1953.

193. Spuhler, J. N. Some genetic variations in American Indians. In W. S. Laughlin (Ed.), *The physical anthropology of the American Indian.* New York: Viking Fund, 1951. Pp. 177–202.

194. Srb, A. M., & Owen, R. D. *General genetics.* San Francisco: Freeman, 1952.

195. Stamm, J. S. Genetics of hoarding: hoarding differences between homozygous strains of rats. *J. comp. physiol. Psychol.*, 1954, **47**, 157–161.

196. Steinberg, A. G. Methodology in human genetics. *Amer. J. hum. Genet.*, 1959, **34**, 315–334.

197. Stenstedt, Å. A study in manic-depressive psychosis. *Acta psychiat. neurol. scand.*, 1952, Suppl. 79, 1–111.

198. Stenstedt, Å. *Involutional melancholia.* Copenhagen: Munksgaard, 1959.

199. Terman, L. M., & Miles, C. C. *Sex and personality: studies in masculinity and femininity.* New York: McGraw-Hill, 1936.

200. Terman, L. M., & Tyler, L. E. Psychological sex differences. In L. Carmichael (Ed.), *Manual of child psychology.* (2nd ed.) New York: Wiley, 1954. Pp. 1064–1114.

201. Thompson, W. R. The inheritance of behavior: behavioral differences in fifteen mouse strains. *Canad. J. Psychol.*, 1953, **7**, 145–153.

202. Tryon, R. C. Genetic differences in maze-learning ability in rats. *Thirtieth Yearb., nat. Soc. Stud. Educ.*, 1940, Part 1. Pp. 111–119.

203. Waardenburg, P. J. Das menschliche Auge und seine Erbanlage. *Bibliogr. genet.*, 1932, **7**, 1–631.

204. Waddington, C. H. *Organizers and genes.* London: Cambridge Univer. Press, 1940.

205. Wagner, R. P., & Mitchell, H. K. *Genetics and metabolism.* New York: Wiley, 1955.

206. Warren, K. B. (Ed.) Population genetics: the nature and causes of genetic variability in populations. *Cold Spring Harbor Symposia quant. Biol.*, 1955, **20**, 1–346.

207. Woodger, J. H. *Biology and language*. London: Cambridge Univer. Press, 1952.
208. Woodger, J. H. What do we mean by "inborn"? *Br. J. Philos. Sci.*, 1953, **3**, 319–326.
209. Woolf, B. Environmental effects in quantitative inheritance. In E. C. R. Reeve & C. H. Waddington (Eds.), *Quantitative inheritance*. London: H. M. Stationery Office, 1952. Pp. 81–102.
210. Wright, S. The physiology of the gene. *Physiol. Rev.*, 1941, **21**, 487–527.
211. Wright, S. Evolution, organic. *Encyclopaedia britannica*. Vol. 8. Chicago: Benton, 1958. Pp. 915–929.
212. Wright, S. Genetics of populations. *Encyclopaedia britannica*. Vol. 10. Chicago: Benton, 1958. Pp. 111D–112.

HOW MAN LOOKS AT HIS OWN BRAIN: AN ADVENTURE SHARED BY PSYCHOLOGY AND NEUROPHYSIOLOGY

ROBERT B. LIVINGSTON
National Institutes of Health

Of all the wonders, none is more wonderful than man,
Who has learned the art of speech, of wind-swift thought,
And of living in neighborliness.

SOPHOCLES

Introduction 52
Neurophysiology in Historical Perspective 54
    The Western tradition 54
    The Russian tradition 58
    Boundaries of neurophysiology 61
A Few Rapidly Changing Neurophysiological Concepts Pertinent to Psychology 61
    The "all-or-nothing" principle 62
    The principle of specific point-to-point relations 64
    The doctrine of levels 65
    Central control of sensory signals 72
    The nervous system as a "reactor" 73
The Conceptual and Experimental Domains of Neurophysiology 75
    Circulation and Metabolism 76
    Comparative Neurophysiology 77
    Developmental Neurophysiology 78
    Biophysics and Physiology of the Neuron 80
    Physiology of the Neuroglia 82
    Techniques Applied to Brain Circuitry 83
    Ablations 83
    Electrical stimulation and recording 85
    Neurochemistry and neuropharmacology 85
How Do We Consider Mind and Brain? 89
References 96

51

INTRODUCTION

Both psychology and neurophysiology have to do with those things that mean the most in human life. Yet these disciplines have persisted for generations in isolation, one from the other; they have too often been applied independently to the same problems. Perhaps psychology and neurophysiology are separated because each is too highly specialized or holds too esoteric an attitude toward nature: perhaps we are all too readily enchanted by problems of limited scope. If this is true, it will do us good to detach ourselves from our work a while in order to view these fields in better perspective. We may thereby be inspired to widen our interests to embrace a larger portion of the total realm of life.

There exists a domain in science which properly belongs to both psychology and neurophysiology. Many questions in this area will seem less difficult when approached through an understanding of both fields; it is already evident that the conceptual force of the two disciplines is more powerful in combination. Because of recent discoveries, psychology and neurophysiology are now more than ever before able to benefit through the stimulation and discipline of a shared intellectual adventure. The understanding of psychology and neurophysiology has become urgent as well as important. As Paul MacLean [32] has remarked, "The towering question before the world concerns whether man can master his brain and behavior before he has blown himself to smithereens through his mastery of physics and engineering."

Despite differences in historical and technical development, psychology and neurophysiology are already growing nearer one another. In times past it was difficult to realize that scholars in such widely separated disciplines could be investigating responses shaped by the same organ. The few investigators who studied in both fields pursued their research as though they identified with only one. At present an increasing number of distinguished individuals and educational institutions deliberately combine the two disciplines, and a growing number of students realize the advantages of studying both. A real union will be established between psychology and neurophysiology when a large number of scientists are well grounded in both disciplines. How secure and useful a junction will be achieved remains to be seen: nonetheless, new areas for research have appeared, wherein students of behavior can manipulate the brain in addition to the environment and wherein students of the brain can make use of behavioral concepts and techniques. Many of the traditional identifications of the two fields are being lost. We should actively discard any remaining provincialism and sense of jurisdiction and rivalry between these disciplines. Whom are we against? Only ignorance in ourselves.

Despite recent progress, there are as yet relatively few resources around the world for basic research in psychology and neurophysiology. Problems that need solution are staggering. Understanding can be advanced only through our modification of present concepts. These in turn are subject to change only through resourceful experimental and theoretical pursuits. There is a continuing need for careful examination of our fundamental assumptions. The assumptions which we accept with least reflection are those common to our intellectual community; they may not even be recognized as assumptions. With few resources and staggering problems we must make especially effective use of the assets at our disposal. We must give maximum encouragement and intellectual stimulation to all the creative scientists who can be attracted to these fields.

Psychology and neurophysiology have separately addressed one of the oldest riddles—that of mind-body relations[1]: How can the physical world be represented through sensory mechanisms into an elaborate perceptual experience? Conversely, how do our presumably incorporeal ideas "hale along the sullen slaves" of our bodies, and through them move and shape the physical world? Stated in idealistic instead of materialistic terms, the issue can be inverted: Does matter as we know it exist only in sensation? Is the physical world to be taken only as regards its mental space-time constructs? Is consciousness to be found in matter? If so, in all matter to some degree, or only in particular kinds of matter?

The riddle of mind-body relations has lasted in our culture for so long that it has given rise to certain pervading assumptions which deeply penetrate our education, research, and general culture. Division of the world into categories of *mental* and *material* has led to a considerable remoteness between psychology and neurophysiology. Notwithstanding this, psychology and neurophysiology have each been contributing toward a solution of mind-body problems in relation to both their philosophical and practical aspects. It is exhilarating to realize that more progress along this research frontier has been made in the last two decades than in the previous two millennia.

It is hardly necessary to emphasize the intellectual and aesthetic satisfactions shared by psychology and neurophysiology. Apart from the urgency that presently surrounds our need to comprehend the mechanisms of individual and societal integration, all of the older reasons for pursuing this knowledge still exist in full force. Among the most compelling of these is the desire to understand ourselves. Man's search to discover the basis for his perceiving, thinking existence is one of the few human endeavors that can elevate the stature and hope of mankind.

[1] We are deliberately employing certain complex abstractions such as "mind" and "consciousness" as in common rather than scientific parlance. More explicit definitions are tedious and are not essential to the notions advanced here.

NEUROPHYSIOLOGY IN HISTORICAL PERSPECTIVE

The Western tradition. Among British, European, and American scientists, neurophysiology has traditionally been concerned with the function of physical entities—neurons and neuronal systems—without much regard for the psychological and metaphysical problems implied by a consideration of the *waking brain*. This has come about in a simple and direct way.

In the first half of the seventeenth century, René Descartes (1596–1650, Fig. 1*c*) provided attractive reasons for limiting psychological and metaphysical properties—which previously had been considered to be distributed throughout the ventricular system of the brain—to a location within the pineal gland. By conceiving the rest of the brain and the body as an automaton, Descartes opened the way for an examination of nervous and bodily functions as purely mechanical systems. Thus Descartes did for physiology what Aristotle earlier accomplished for anatomy. (Aristotle was the first to persuasively argue that dissections of the dead could not damage the soul [psyche] which had already departed.[2]) The ventricles of the brain and the "hollow," tubelike nerves were thought by Descartes to operate like hydraulic channels, utilizing cerebrospinal fluid to "animate" the body in a manner analogous to the activation by water of the wondrous mechanical fountains of that period.

In the beginning of the eighteenth century, the incomparable Isaac Newton (1642–1727, Fig. 1*d*) proposed that nerve transmission could be explained by conduction along the same "aether" he had utilized to account for the remote and instantaneous actions of the planets on one another. After ascribing many physical effects to his "aether," Newton adds

[Query 23]
Is not Vision performed chiefly by the Vibrations of this Medium, excited in the bottom of the Eye by the Rays of Light, and propagated through the solid, pellucid and uniform Capillamenta of the optic Nerves into the place of Sensation? . . .

[Query 24]
Is not Animal Motion performed by the Vibrations of this Medium, excited in the Brain by the power of the Will, and propagated from thence through the solid, pellucid and uniform Capillamenta of the Nerves into the Muscles, for contracting and dilating them? . . .[3]

[2] Viz. this poetic passage from Plato's *Timaeus:* "And, at last, when the bonds by which the triangles are united, no longer hold, and are parted by the strain of existence, they in turn loosen the bonds of the soul and she, obtaining a natural release, flies away with joy. For that which takes place according to nature is pleasant."
[3] From the second edition of Newton's *Opticks,* published in 1717.

Electricity was discovered by seventeenth and eighteenth century physicians and natural philosophers—Gilbert, Boyle, Newton, Franklin, and others. Galvani, in 1791, working with nerve-muscle and spinal frog preparations and employing dissimilar metals as a means of irritation (stimulation), discovered "animal electricity." A century later the idea was put forth that the mysterious "nerve force" *was* electricity. During this latter period, the intellectual disciples of Johannes Müller (1801–1858) conceived the goal of physiology to be an "explanation" of physiological phenomena according to the underlying physical and chemical mechanisms involved. There was then no imaginable method for detecting and measuring the physical and chemical events taking place inside the waking brain. At that time physiologists were confronted with a vast array of difficult problems, and especially with the need to confute vitalism. In reaction to this need, they leaned over backward to eschew psychological phenomena except in terms of strictly physiological (mechanistic) psychology.

At different times during the present century, physiologists have sought to explain nervous transmission on either exclusively electrical or chemical bases. Enjoying the great advances of microscopic neuroanatomy, biophysics, and biochemistry, and building upon the firmly established neuron doctrine, physiologists now generally assume that electrical (ionic) phenomena dominate in mechanisms that account for conduction of impulses along nerve fibers (axons). They believe further that transmission from one nerve cell to another (at the synapses) is accomplished predominantly through the action of specific neurochemical (facilitatory or inhibitory) transmitter substances. Popular conceptions, however, continue to make use of analogies outside of physiology to explain the functions of the brain as a whole: the waterworks of the seventeenth century have given place in modern times to electronic computers.

Thus we see that in the Western tradition neurophysiology has been essentially mechanistic in its devotion. In addition, most Western neurophysiologists have agreed with Sir Charles Scott Sherrington (1861–1952, Fig. 1*a*) that "thought, feeling and so on are not amenable to the energy (matter) concept. They lie outside it."

Mind, for anything perception can compass, goes therefore in our spatial world more ghostly than a ghost. Invisible, intangible, it is a thing not even of outline; it is not a "thing." It remains without sensual confirmation, and remains without it for ever. All that counts in life. Desire, zest, truth, love, knowledge, "values," and, seeking metaphor to eke out expression, hell's depth and heaven's utmost height. Naked mind. We live at a moment hitherto unmatched, for our planet has just evolved mind in us to the pitch that we can take in our local situation of this present as we walk her side.

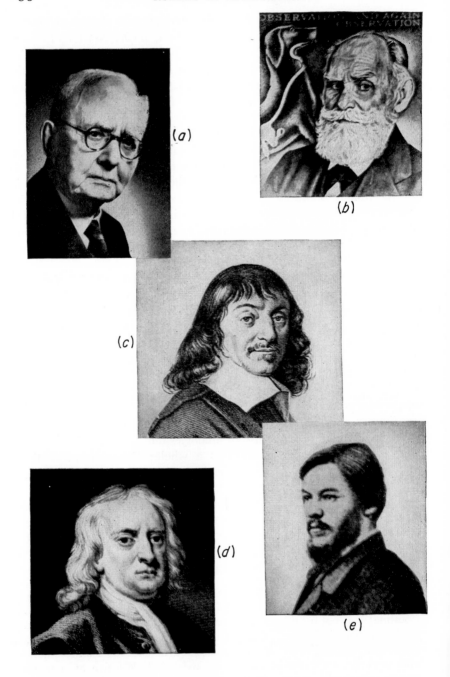

FIG. 1a. *Sir Charles Scott Sherrington.* By partitioning the nervous system, Sherrington was able systematically to develop much of our knowledge of the local mechanisms underlying reflexes. Descartes argued on logical grounds that there must be an inhibitory influence in brain mechanisms and that this would be an active principle. Sherrington was first to confirm this conception experimentally. FIG. 1b. *Ivan Petrovich Pavlov.* Sherrington in England and Thorndyke in America observed conditioning prior to Pavlov, but Pavlov deserves credit for intensive and systematic analysis and generalization of conditioning. According to Pavlov, conditioning accounts for almost all modification of behavior through experience. Pavlov's interest in the extrusion of purpose from biological concepts is exemplified by the repeated homage he paid to Descartes, Darwin and Sechenov. Pavlov began with studies on digestion, and only after a quarter of a century of distinguished accomplishment, for which he received the Nobel Prize, did he turn his attention to the nervous system. In this field of endeavor, he never lost sight of the importance of visceral mechanisms and of the intimate relations between somatic and visceral systems. [From the Collection of the National Library of Medicine] FIG. 1c. *René Descartes.* Descartes based his philosophy of universal doubt largely on observations which show that our senses are subject to error. However, he contended, largely on faith, that pure reason can recognize and comprehend truth. Descartes was very much interested in perception and recognized that amputees have phantom sensations of the missing limb. From this and other facts, he reasoned that distortions of perception may originate not only within the sense organs but along nerves arising from the periphery and within localized representative brain centers themselves. Descartes attempted imaginatively to articulate mechanical events within the brain to the mechanisms of reasoning and also to the soul. These passages are the best known but most artificial parts of his writings. He discarded the then prevalent methods of explaining phenomena by means of final causes and insisted upon a mechanical basis for all physical and biological phenomena. He believed that the whole could be understood entirely through an analysis of its parts. This was probably an essential and enabling gesture for much of the last three centuries of progress in experimental science. [From the Collection of the National Library of Medicine] FIG. 1d. *Sir Isaac Newton.* The seventeenth century opened with the struggle of Galileo for experimental science even though this brought him up against the Inquisition; it ended with Newton who was virtually worshipped for his scientific contributions. Newton struggled for many years over the problem of planetary motion. He finally resolved upon "aether" as a necessary carrier for the force of gravitation in order that the force of gravity could be instantaneously effected at a distance. He went on to reason that the same aether is the carrier for the supposedly instantaneous nerve impulse. [From the Collection of the National Library of Medicine] FIG. 1e. *Ivan Mikhailovich Sechenov.* Sechenov was a great idealist, and this is reflected in several aspects of his life: He participated in student demonstrations in 1848; later, he abandoned his honored post as a professor when his university refused admittance of a highly qualified Jew to its faculty. Sechenov's writings which bring psychology and physiology together as one discipline have greatly influenced Russian scientific and philosophic thought. Sechenov conceived that all higher brain functions are material in nature and reflex in character, stemming from sensations (including memory traces from previous sensations) and leading to muscular reactions.

Mind, yoked with life, how varied in its reaction! It will sit down and watch life acquiescent, or on the other hand take life and squeeze it like an orange.

And that other concept, energy; what of its yield? We saw that Time has winnowed its harvest too. How much remains? The perceptible world. All that the space-time continuum contains; a category which nothing which does not act on sense can enter and which all that does so act does enter. It sets us wondering whether what we sense can be just purely outcome of our mind.

Between these two, perceiving mind and the perceived world, is there then nothing in common? Together they make up the sum total for us; they are all we have. We called them disparate and incommensurable. Are they then absolutely apart? Can they in no wise be linked together? They have this in common—we have already recognized it—they are both of them parts of one mind. They are thus therefore distinguished, but are not sundered. Nature in evolving us makes them two parts of the knowledge of one mind and that one mind our own. We are the tie between them. Perhaps we exist for that [47, pp. 256–257].

The Russian tradition. Another way of looking at the nervous system took origin in Russia from the teaching and writing of Ivan Mikhailovich Sechenov (1829–1905, Fig. 1e). Sechenov, inspired by the potentialities of physiology but dissatisfied with the scholasticism and empiricism of Russian teaching in clinical medicine, went twice to Europe to study with Johannes Müller, Emil du Bois Reymond, Hermann von Helmholtz, Carl Ludwig, Claude Bernard, and others. In Bernard's laboratory he performed the renowned experiments in which he produced inhibition of reflexes in the frog by application of salt solutions and crystals to various parts of the brain stem and cut surfaces of the brain.

Sechenov drew upon these observations for generalizations which would account at once not only for the physiological, but also for the psychological properties of the nervous system. Whereas in the Western tradition no such sweeping generalizations were hazarded, Sechenov felt the need for a total accounting. He considered the mechanisms of afferent inflow, activity within the central nervous system, and efferent outflow to be entirely based upon physical and chemical laws. What took place centrally could be accounted for, by extension, from external observations. Learning, he thought, represents a balanced control of central inhibitory and excitatory mechanisms, the control being shaped according to expediency determined by pleasant and unpleasant experiences. Sechenov did not consider volition as being initiated through the actions of central components by themselves, but believed that volition is initiated and determined by activity left as a memory trace from previous sensory inflow. Thought is similarly conceived as laid down during experience in some material trace form. Sechenov's writings, and particularly his *Reflexes of the brain,* published in 1863, provide a basis for the principal philosophical and scientific assumptions of the Russian physiological tradition, and especially for those of Ivan Petrovich Pavlov (1849–1936) and his followers.

Another prominent Russian neurophysiologist who contributed importantly to extensions and variations of Sechenov's central ideas is Vasily Yakovlevich Danilevsky (1852–1934), who developed a special interest in the cortical representation of visceral functions. Russian neurophysiologists have since continued to place great emphasis upon the unity of control of both visceral and somatic mechanisms by the cortex. Although Caton in England had made the original discovery of the electroencephalogram (EEG) in 1874, Danilevsky in 1876 independently discovered that one could record electrical waves from the brains of animals. Further important contributions gave rise to the contemporary schools of physiological conception bearing the names of Nikolai Yevgenevich Wedensky (1852–1922) and Alexei Alexeivich Ukhtomsky (1875–1942), a pupil of Wedensky [see also 6].

Pavlov (Fig. 1*b*) specifically identified Descartes as the essential starting point for physiological investigations of the brain up to his own time. He credited Darwin with the characterization of a biological determinism to which he adhered. He took a materialistic, deterministic view of causality, believing that matter is primary and consciousness derives from the particular manner of organization and motion of matter within the brain. Nothing can be represented in consciousness which is not a reflection of some aspect of the physical world. Matter, according to Pavlov, is not regarded as separable from motion in time and space. Nevertheless, matter-in-motion can accommodate certain transformations which give rise to new qualities of matter-in-motion. Consciousness is the consequence of such transformed activity. Since alterations in the form of brain activity are supposed to be accompanied by corresponding alterations in behavior and consciousness, Pavlov believed that mental processes are amenable to objective analysis. The goal of neurophysiological research he conceived to be the discovery and elucidation of all of the processes and laws governing these phenomena.

An abiding conception in the Russian physiological tradition, about which more will be written later, is that the cerebral cortex rather exclusively dominates nervous integration. This cortical control is conceived to rule not only throughout the individual person but also between him and his environment. Thus a comprehension of laws governing cortical mechanisms becomes a matter basic to sociology (and politics) as well as to neurophysiology and psychology. The cortex, moreover, acts as a signaling system within the brain by attaching *significance* to other brain events taking place concurrently in relation to stimuli that would ordinarily evoke an inborn (unconditional) reflex. In man, a second signaling system relates to speech and language functions. This second signaling system enormously enhances the mechanisms of human discrimination and learning.

Each sensory pathway is visualized as an analyzer directed to a particular region of the cortical mantle. Physiological processes taking place during conditioning involve the development, under the control of the cortex, of temporary connections which join one or more analyzers to inborn reflex mechanisms and thereby enable the performance of a novel, *conditional* reflex. These mechanisms possess the teleological advantage of improving the interpretive and performance characteristics of an individual over his inborn capabilities. It is essentially this shaping of comportment by experience that occupies the Pavlovian neurophysiologist. Inborn reflex systems are thought to be located almost entirely within subcortical parts of the brain. They are subject to a certain degree of plastic reorganization according to the disposition of cortical mechanisms which are themselves responding in accordance with the expediencies of past and present experience.

Both inborn and conditional reflexes are thought to undergo a dynamic struggle for outward expression. Patterns of excitation and especially of inhibition determine the final outcome and are shifted in lawful ways by the continuing impact of fresh sensory inflow. Pavlov emphasized the "extraordinary dependence [of behavior] on the phenomena of the internal conditions of the organism as well as the phenomena of the outer world" [see also 6, 42, 43, 48].

It is clear that neurophysiology is practiced differently in the Western and Russian traditions. Materials, methods, assumptions, experimental design, and ways of reporting results are often conspicuously different. We can appreciate much that is worthy within each tradition, and yet, notwithstanding this, a wide gap in understanding persists. One of the most outstanding differences relates to the relative isolation, in the Western neurophysiological tradition, between vegetative and somatic nervous mechanisms. The Russian physiologists are almost monistic in their view of visceral-somatic relations. The earliest conditional reflexes were begun with somatic input–visceral output. Since then they have extended such studies to include somatic input–somatic output, visceral input–somatic output, and visceral input–visceral output. Our own traditional separation between visceral and somatic systems has affected our physiological experiments and the way we explain psychosomatic disorders and other medical problems. But, more than that, it has led to a philosophical isolation of these parts that tends to be reflected in our social and political philosophy, and especially in respect to how we communicate our ideals to others. Russia has, by contrast, been far more sensitive to the importance of visceral well-being and to the relations between the physiological and the social integration of man [6, 32].

During the postwar years, both neurophysiological traditions have flourished. In fact, Russian neurophysiology dominates all other biomedical research in that country, according to their seven-year plan. Only lately has there been enough exchange of persons and literature between Russia and the West to begin to relate one tradition to the other with respect to their separate conceptual advancements. Both traditions stand to benefit through serious scholarship devoted to constructive cross-comparison and cross-interpretation. Apart from an augmentation of straight translations and interpretive reviews now being made available[4] and examples of the Russian neurophysiological tradition going on in our own scientific community,[5] there is a need for further interpretive integration of the two traditions. Such was undertaken ten years ago in a brilliant monograph by Jerzy Konorski of Poland, *Conditioned reflexes and neuron organization* [23]. Another endeavor of this kind would be very useful now.

Boundaries of neurophysiology. Within physiology as an entirety, the study of the nervous system takes up an important central position. This is true not only because of the intrinsic interest of neurophysiological problems, but especially because the nervous system plays such a central role in controlling and interrelating all other physiological systems. Endocrinology, cardiovascular physiology, digestion, reproduction, and many other branches of physiology depend heavily upon neurophysiology. Outside of physiology, neurophysiology is overlapped at each of its boundaries by neuroanatomy, neurochemistry, neuropharmacology, and biophysics, as well as by psychology and sociology. The assembly of these seven disciplines, taken together, constitutes a coherent research entity of its own.

A FEW RAPIDLY CHANGING NEUROPHYSIOLOGICAL CONCEPTS PERTINENT TO PSYCHOLOGY

Nearly every concept relating to the function of the nervous system has been radically overhauled in the last ten or twenty years. Almost

[4] An example is the National Institutes of Health Soviet Translation Program which translates and arranges publication of nine contemporary Soviet medical journals (e.g., the *Sechenov Physiological Journal of the USSR*) and distributes these and other materials to approximately four hundred medical repository libraries. The program is coordinated with that of the National Library of Medicine, National Science Foundation, Atomic Energy Commission, and other public and private agencies.

[5] Viz., the research programs in the Pavlovian conceptual tradition by W. Horsley Gantt at The Johns Hopkins University Medical School and Howard S. Liddell at the Cornell University Animal Behavior Farm.

every great principle then firmly adhered to has now been shown to be incorrect or at least to require drastic qualification. Through a consideration of the timing of these conceptual changes, one can visualize the astonishing rate of accomplishment relating to neurophysiology. Examples are selected which may serve to emphasize how, through these revolutionary changes, neurophysiology has become substantially more cogent to psychology.

The "all-or-nothing" principle. It was formerly assumed that every neuron functioned along its entire length in an all-or-nothing fashion, i.e., if a stimulus were insufficient, nothing would happen; if a stimulus were just above threshold, a full-sized action potential would be generated. The action potential would not increase in amplitude with further increase in stimulus strength. It was, therefore, all or nothing. It is now recognized that graded responses, graded in accordance with the strength of a given stimulus, occur at both ends—the business ends—of each nerve cell, where it makes contact with other nerve cells [4]. Graded responses take place along the dendrites, cell body, and the final terminal branches of neurons. The all-or-nothing action potential is confined to the axon interconnecting the two graded response ends of the neuron.

The all-or-nothing principle was originally conceived on the basis of experiments upon the readily accessible axons which make up peripheral nerves. The principle, once established, was generalized to apply with equal validity to the rest of the cell by assuming neuron membranes were uniform throughout. The obvious faculty of the intact nervous system to yield graded responses was attributed to the function of assemblies of neurons—specifically to the narrow anatomical junction between neurons—the cleft lying between individual cellular surfaces. Experimental evidence indicates that, instead of simply the intercellular interface, the presynaptic terminals, dendritic branches, and the cell body itself—the entire synaptic region on both sides of the interface—provide graded, nonpropagated responses. Such evidence removes the phenomena responsible for graded responses in the intact nervous system from an intercellular "non-living" location to a large, metabolically active cellular region. This implies greater biological plasticity and control. It also probably represents an increase in our opportunities for experimental discovery of the underlying biological mechanisms of neuronal integration.

Graded responses recorded from aggregates of nerve cells are found to yield slow wavelike shifts in electrical potential. These findings reveal an experimental and conceptual linkage between impulses conducted along fibers and the slower brain-waves recorded by the electroencephalogram. EEG waves presumably represent the smoothed additive combination of nerve action potentials together with the graded response (synaptic) potentials taking place simultaneously within a large community of nerve cells.

It is now recognized that the all-or-nothing conducting axon is an interesting evolutionary device which entered upon the biological scene in the primitive nervous system of the jellyfish. This biological device provided for the delivery of impulses of all-or-nothing character as

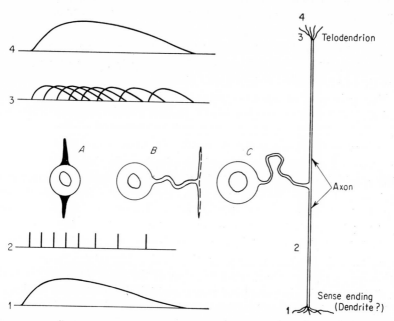

FIG. 2. *Graphic analysis of nerve activity. A, B* and *C* in the center of this figure represent sequential stages in the development of a bipolar cell such as a peripheral sensory nerve. *C,* 1, 2, 3, and 4 represent successive portions of the nerve, beginning with the sensory receiving terminals, the axon, and finally the arborizations associated with the nerve's termination in spinal centers. On the left are represented the duration of local response associated with points 1, 2, 3, and 4 of the same nerve. The farthest branches of the receptive endings show a prolonged graded depolarization. The conducting axon 2 has "translated" the graded response into a succession of individual all-or-nothing nerve impulses, a virtual "coding" of the graded response into a pattern of nerve impulses beginning at a rapid rate and later slowing in correspondence with the reduced amplitude of the graded response. At the first branching of the nerve terminals 3, the same series of nerve impulses leads to graded responses which, at 4, representing the response at the nerve terminals, are summed into a smoothed curve analogous in duration and contour to that of the initial depolarization. [4, p. 388]

stabilized coded messages reliable over the long distances required by the increasingly larger nervous systems of higher animals. The all-or-nothing character of these impulses serves to safeguard against distortion or loss of the signal en route. Within the branching terminals of each neuron as it ends upon the receptive surfaces of succeeding neurons the all-or-nothing action potential is once more converted into a graded response.

The receptive surfaces of the next-order neurons must synthesize conflicting as well as consonant data from a number of sources (varying from one or a few to perhaps tens of thousands) and code them into new patterns of action potentials which will then be distributed to the next furthest constellation of synaptic stations. The individual dendrites, cell bodies, and nerve terminals act as if they were miniature biological analogue computers, synthesizing and transducing continually renewing patterns of neuronal activity. Plasticity in the central nervous system is apparently achieved by this means. Reliability is apparently provided through a redundancy of signals and circuits.

The principle of specific point-to-point relations. George Ellett Coghill (1872–1941), along with C. Judson Herrick (1868–1960) and others, argued on anatomical grounds for a diffusion of nerve impulses into a meshwork known as the *neuropil* [16]. Most neurophysiologists, on the other hand, have emphasized localized projections and point-to-point specificity of relations within the brain. Recently, the studies of Morison and Forbes, Bremer, Magoun, Jasper, and others have demonstrated the importance of diffuse or nonspecific projection systems [1, 19, 34]. Rather specific point-to-point relations obtain between some of the phylogenetically most recent and anatomically most clearly circumscribed nuclear masses of the brain. However, these specific pathways represent only a small fraction of the total. In addition, there are diffusely projecting neuronal systems which distribute their excitatory or inhibitory influences in widespread fashion. These projections are characteristic of the phylogenetically older parts of the neuraxis, e.g., the central gray substance and its surrounding spinal and brain stem reticular formation, and the older neuronal matrix of the forebrain, within which phylogenetically newer and more circumscribed nuclei are embedded.

Again, with the advantage of hindsight, it is easy to justify the more limited level of earlier understanding. Because of technical limitations which no longer obtain, animals were usually examined either while under the influence of centrally acting anesthetic agents or after the more cephalic portions of their neuraxes had been destroyed. Both anesthetic agents and truncating operative procedures predominantly affect the diffusely projecting systems and especially those in the brain stem reticular formation [11, 22]. In anesthetized animals, the diffusely projecting systems are relatively unresponsive; by way of contrast, the phylogenetically newer systems which have point-to-point relations tend to be more reliable and stereotyped when the animal is under a central anesthetic. In their classical study which provides the first description of cortical evoked responses to sensory stimulation, Marshall, Woolsey, and Bard used "anesthesia of sufficient depth to reduce the Berger waves to minimal frequency and size." They stated:

. . . During periods of twenty-four hours the potentials obtained in response to tactile stimulation do not progressively undergo significant reduction or changes in character. . . . This study, based on receptor stimulation and correlated electrical response, has disclosed a cortical representation of tactile sensibility which is definitely stable. We conclude that whatever functional variations may characterize the total cortical response to a tactile stimulus they are based on a highly stable anatomical substratum which is functionally demonstrable [35, pp. 389–390].

This same effect occurs when the brain stem reticular formation is destroyed: the rest of the diffusely projecting systems tend to be less active and the phylogenetically newer parts of the nervous system become more reliable and stereotyped [11, 15, 33, 34]. Recent studies involving animals without central anesthesia and without surgical interference with the diffusely projecting systems indicate that sensory evoked responses are far more widespread in distribution and far less reproducible from one stimulus to the next than in anesthetized animals. In fact, (1) sensory evoked responses can be recorded beyond the limits of the classical sensory pathways; (2) they involve midline structures and both hemispheres rather than being practically exclusively contralateral in projection; (3) they vary in amplitude not simply with respect to the parameters of the stimulus, but also in accordance with the previous experience of the waking animal with similar stimuli; and (4) they appear to vary with the animal's behavioral "set" [12, 15, 29, 34]. Thus responses within the brain are found to be modifiable in a variety of ways, in accordance with the particular environmental setting, and according to what the animal has been given reason to anticipate.

The doctrine of levels.   John Hughlings Jackson (1835–1911) was largely responsible for establishing the doctrine of "levels of function" throughout the neuraxis. He conceived the nervous system to be composed of three hierarchical levels:

(*1*) The lowest or first level is roughly and incompletely defined as consisting of cord, medulla, and pons, and more completely, and yet still roughly, as being that sensori-motor division of the central nervous system, to and from which pass nerves (all cranial and all spinal nerves) for every part of the body. This level, speaking of its motor elements, represents simplest movements of all parts of the body by a series of lowest motor centres (lowest motor centre being a proper name for a centre of the lowest level) from those in the aqueduct of Sylvius for simplest movements of the ocular muscles to those of the sacral cord for simplest movements of the muscles of the perineum. This universally representing level is cerebro-cerebellar; it is at once the lowest level of the cerebral system and of the cerebellar system. . . . (2) The middle or second level (its motor province) of the cerebral system is composed of centres of the Rolandic region (so-called "motor region" of the cerebral cortex), and, possibly, of the ganglia of the corpus striatum also. It represents complex movements of all parts of the body from eyes to perineum (re-represents). (*3*) The highest or third level (its motor

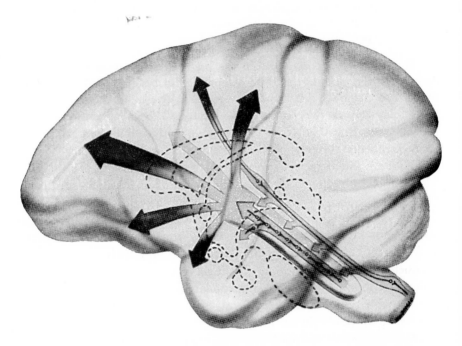

Fig. 3. *Relationship between classical sensory pathways and reticular activating system.* This is a side view of the monkey brain showing in phantom outline the classical ascending sensory pathway (the medial lemniscus) which has synaptic relays in the bulb and the thalamus and projects to the postcentral gyrus, the somaesthetic receiving area of the cortex. As this bundle of neurons traverses the brain stem, it gives off multiple collaterals to the diffusely projecting reticular formation. The ascending pathways in the reticular formation are depicted as a multisynaptic chain which projects upward through the thalamus finally projecting to the entire cortical mantle. It is by means of this association among sensory transactional mechanisms that sensory arousal accomplishes a generalized activation of the entire brain.

province) of the cerebral system is made up of centres of the praefrontal lobes (highest motor centres, motor division of the "organ of mind"). It represents most complex movements of all parts of the body from eyes to perineum (re-re-represents). The highest centres (sensory and motor divisions of the highest level)—the "organ of mind," or anatomical substrata of consciousness—are the acme of the evolution; they have the same kind of constitution as lower centres; they are sensori-motor as certainly as the lumbar enlargement is. . . .

The separation of the frontal lobe into middle motor centres ("motor region"), making up the motor province of the middle level, and the highest motor centres (praefrontal lobe) making up the motor province of the highest level, is, of course, hypothetical; there is no obvious morphological separation. I do not suppose that the evolutionary distinction is so abrupt or so decided as that beween the middle and lowest levels. . . . Distinguishing the psychical from the physical, I would say that psychical states are not functions of any centre, but are simply concomitant with functioning of the most complex, etc., sensori-motor nervous arrangements—those of the highest level ("organ of mind") of which level the praefrontal lobe is the motor division [18, pp. 413–414].

Each level contains certain functional centers linking it with corresponding functional centers of less flexible capacity at each lower level. Lower levels have a certain degree of autonomy but are provided with greater plasticity and are actually manipulated by the successive higher levels. When a lower level is "released" from higher-level influence, its actions may be diminished, as in spinal shock following spinal transection, or excessively overactive as in decerebrate rigidity following transection of the midbrain. The actions of the lowest level by itself are relatively stereotyped and imperious.

Jackson reasoned that the highest level is most susceptible to deleterious effects. When illness, injury, or drugs damage the nervous system, a descending disability strikes successively the highest to lower functional levels. Thus the nervous system undergoes a kind of "dissolution," as he called it, from above downward. It was conceived that alcohol and anesthetic agents would have their initial and most powerful influence upon "the praefrontal cortical centres." As dosage is increased, successively lower levels of the neuraxis would be affected until finally vital mechanisms ceased operation and death would ensue. Jackson's doctrine of levels dominated Western neurophysiological concepts regarding the effects of transection of the neuraxis. Since the nervous system is like a sausage in that it can be most easily sliced crosswise, the simplest experimental and neurosurgical practices tend to reinforce conceptions of an increasing number of successive *horizontal* levels acting up and down upon one another.

More recently, mainly as a result of studies by Bremer, Magoun, Jasper, Moruzzi, and others, certain longitudinal components of the nervous system have been recognized as possessing an importance complementary to that of Jackson's hierarchical levels [1, 19, 30, 33, 34, 39]. What is found experimentally is that certain vast regions of the central core of the neuraxis are neither sensory nor motor in character, but may be in mutual interdependence with both sensory and motor systems. Moreover, patterns of convergence and divergence within these central regions are not altogether fixed in character but may change with time. Using waking animals with implanted electrodes, observers have found that some of these relatively plastic systems can be altered in accordance with deliberate environmental manipulations. The most dynamically plastic and modifiable parts, taken together, have been called the "transactional components" of the brain [30].

The longitudinal or vertical organization of the neuraxis is seen as containing three major compartments—sensory, transactional, and motor. Incoming sensory signals streaming upward influence successive groups of neurons which are more or less directly associated with both sensory and motor functions. Sensory impulses also contribute, all along the neuraxis, to neurons that cannot be identified as being either sensory or motor, e.g., to neurons of the spinal and brain stem reticular formation and diffusely projecting forebrain systems, limbic lobe, association areas of the cortex, and cerebellum. These important sectors participate in complex transactions going on between their own intrinsic ("spontaneous") activities and activities taking place along both the sensory and motor compartments. Such transactions may be initiated by incoming sensory signals, but they are demonstrably affected in accordance with previous experience [12, 28, 29]. Such transactions find their only outward expression through behavior. But in their intracentral trajectories they have served to unify the organism into a functionally integrated whole.

This increasing emphasis upon the organization of vertical systems running lengthwise through the neuraxis puts a new light upon ablation experiments which traditionally cut across the neuraxis. By means of stereotactic instruments, it is now possible to destroy relatively discrete pathways in the neuraxis and to show that consciousness, emotional experience, and motivation are not exclusively dependent upon classical sensory and motor projection systems, nor upon the neocortical mantle itself. Instead they seem to be more dependent upon projection systems belonging to the phylogenetically older, transactional parts of the brain stem and limbic systems [34]. Stimulation and ablation of neocortex, and disruption of the classical sensory and motor projections seem to interfere with subjective experiences in rather objective, depersonalized, detached ways. Similar interventions into the reticular formation and limbic system, and other phylogenetically older parts seem to affect the individual's internal state more intimately by interfering with his attention, by awakening him from sleep or obtunding his consciousness, and by inducing pervasive motivational and affective reactions.

It has long been recognized that when a part of the central nervous

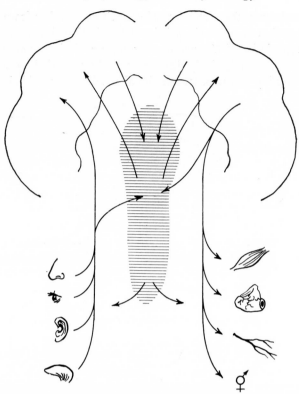

Fig. 4. *A plan of the neuraxis.* Note in the lower left a nose, eye, ear, and tongue which represent the origins of nerve impulses generated by olfactory, visual, auditory, and taste stimuli and, more generally, all sensory input to the nervous system. Ascending pathways from the sensory receptors project to the sensory receiving areas of the cortex and by way of collateral pathways into the diffusely projecting systems of the brain stem and thalamus. Relays from the diffusely projecting systems are projected in a widespread way to the cortical mantle of both hemispheres. Paired descending arrows represent downward projections from those cortical fields which can modulate the brain stem and thalamic diffusely projecting systems; the lowermost descending pair of arrows depicts the influence of descending systems upon sensory and motor transmission systems. At right a long descending arrow representing motor pathways projects from the cortex to skeletal muscle, smooth muscle of the gut and blood vessels, and to the hypothalamic pituitary axis which governs endocrine function. These pathways provide collaterals to the diffusely projecting systems. The major sensory and motor pathways are relatively insensitive to anesthetic agents, whereas the shaded zones of diffusely projecting systems are markedly susceptible to anesthetic agents. The central mechanisms for arousal and for both sensory and motor "tone" are dependent upon these diffusely projecting systems. (See also Fig. 8 for greater detail in the organization of these same projections.)

system is cut away, the distortion of capacities resulting from ablation is less an expression of *what the missing part did* than it is an expression of *what the remainder of the nervous system can do in the absence of that part.* Something qualitatively different may be provided by certain small changes in highly complex transactional mechanisms. This is apparently

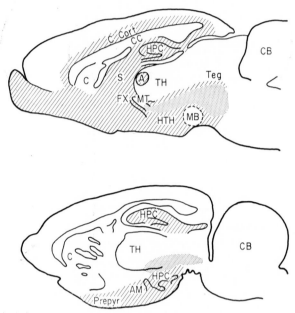

Fig. 5. *Central mechanisms of "reward" and "punishment."* Two saggital sections of the rat brain are depicted; the upper one is mid-saggital, the lower more lateral. The crosshatched areas indicate zones throughout the brain stem, thalamus, and limbic system (including olfactory tract and bulb) from which positive reenforcement ("central reward") can be obtained by direct stimulation. The stippled areas in the brain stem localize regions of negative reenforcement ("central punishment") evoked by central stimulation. Electrodes placed in the area of positive reenforcement yield self-stimulation. Electrodes placed in the negative reenforcement regions yield behavior directed to the avoidance of such central excitation. Comparable responses have been identified although not so thoroughly mapped in other species, including cat, monkey, and man. [From Olds, J. Self-stimulation of the brain. *Science*, 1958, **127**:315–324.]

true of the nervous system of man. The idea of *inter-actions,* as between linear cause-effect sequences, is inadequate. Instead, what occurs may be better described by the term *transactions.*[5] The concept of transactions

[5] Classical physics has addressed itself very successfully to two domains of structural complexity: one concerns the interactions of one- to three- and, sometimes, four-body systems, which is principally the domain of statics and mechanics; the other deals with extremely large numbers of bodies which are homogeneous in

taking place within a vertically as well as horizontally organized nervous system tends to denegate the notion of self-contained centers and levels summing with one another. Two-part analyses give way to attempts at interpreting transactions of a vastly increased functional potentiality resulting from the simultaneous involvement of many mutually interdependent relations.

Sensory signals invade *ongoing activity,* which is capable of distorting these signals to favor or work against their further penetration of the central nervous system, all in accordance with concurrent and antecedent events taking place simultaneously in many regions of the nervous system. Sensory signals, as they penetrate the phylogenetically older parts of the brain stem and forebrain, appear to become endowed with differential values and motivational import. This is understandable inasmuch as direct stimulation of these phylogenetically old brain regions affects behavior as though that behavior had been associated with externally applied punishment or reward [38, 40].

The patterns of this sensory trajectory, and hence the kinds of values and feelings generated, seem to be affected by neuronal "channeling," the mechanisms of which are not at all understood, but in which learning clearly plays an essential role. Out of such dynamic transactions come motor performances which seem to have purpose and which have in turn an influence upon future behavior through their direct impact back upon the sensory and internal transactional systems, now with additional signals relating to "success" or "failure" of the completed behavior.

We do not visualize it [the transactional component] as an amorphous mass of undifferentiated nerve cells through which impulses pass in a haphazard fashion. It is conceivable that in the very young infant the cells making up this functional unit might be unorganized in the same sense that the embryonic blood vessels are first represented by a vast syncytium of capil-

---

character. Here the physicist can say little or nothing about the transit of any individual body, but can derive probabilities of events arising within such a system. This is mainly the contribution of probability theory and quantum mechanics. In between these two areas lies a domain of physics which has been largely neglected and which is tremendously more complex. In this third category belong most systems relating to the biological and social sciences. Here multiple, mutually interdependent bodies relate to each other simultaneously in complex space-time patterns. Such complex systems presently defy satisfactory prediction. They cannot be accounted for on the basis of interaction as among a few parts or on the basis of probability because they involve a very large number of nonhomogeneous elements. Peter Drucker has suggested that an attempt should be made to develop a "calculus of potential" to describe such complex systems. If such be possible, it will undoubtedly have the same stimulating effect on the biological and social sciences as did the calculus of probability on classical physics.

laries and only later does a selective channeling take place to enlarge a few of them to form arteries and veins. This simile suggests something of the way in which, on the basis of experience, reiterated patterns of sensory impulses might become channeled so that the motor response was appropriate to the stimulus [30, p. 494].

Central control of sensory signals. For more than fifty years, anatomists have recognized that certain bundles of descending nerve fibers enter the classical sensory nuclei from above. Furthermore, neurons project from the central nervous system outward to the retina, cochlea, vestibular apparatus, and olfactory bulb. Many sensory receptors elsewhere in the body are known to receive an efferent nerve supply, but this was previously thought to be entirely vegetative or trophic in function.

Recent studies have shown that both peripheral sensory endings and special sense organs can be modulated with respect to their generation of afferent impulses, as a result of activity taking place within the transactional components of the central nervous system. Moreover, at each successive sensory relay station, all the way up to and including the cortex itself, incoming sensory volleys are subjected to a similar modulating influence. The anatomical pathways by which such centrifugal control is exerted are not yet completely worked out. Yet physiologically it is known that these centrifugal sensory control mechanisms involve an active process. In the waking state, the sensory pathways seem ordinarily to be under a moderate, fluctuating inhibitory influence. The loss of this influence during anesthesia accounts for the classical sensory pathway responses becoming larger in amplitude and more stereotyped in character.

Behavioral studies combined with these neurophysiological revelations indicate that activity taking place along sensory paths can be modified appreciably according to an animal's environmental experience and according to its overtly evident direction of attention. The losses and distortions of central signals brought about by this mechanism lead to the conclusion that some teleological mechanism[7] is at work: this appears to reduce the degree of involvement of the neuraxis with those signals having relatively less significance to the animal. The central nervous system is thus able to shut out or to modulate patterns generated by a given stimulus long before those patterns ever reach the cerebral cortex. These

[7] By teleological mechanism we mean the original Aristotelian notion of design and purpose in natural phenomena and not the later religious connotation of design and purpose introduced by an external intelligence. We are accustomed to talking about *homeostasis* with suitable calm, even though this is nothing other than a *teleological* mechanism. There is no question in our mind but that the structural complexity associated with biological phenomena is sufficient *sui generis* to account for the relative autonomy of individual organisms. Organisms possess self-initiating, self-adjusting growth, action, and reaction mechanisms that go a long way toward permitting them to realize biological purposes and goals built into their organization.

findings imply that at least some of the central distortion of perception, long recognized by psychologists but assigned by them to a presumed cortical location, may in fact occur all along the sensory pathways, even as far downstream as the external sense organs themselves [28, 29].

The nervous system as a "reactor." In giving consideration to the chains of activity that take place within the central nervous system in

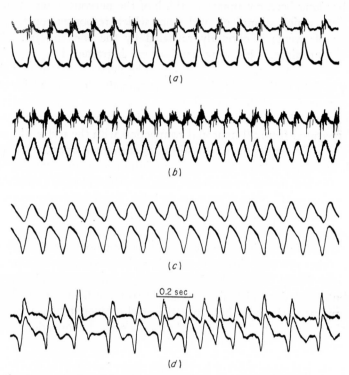

(a)

(b)

(c)

(d)

Fig. 6. *Synchrony produced by electrotonic (non-synaptic) influences in the spinal cord.* When strychnine is given, the entire motor column all along the spinal cord is thrown into a synchronous, highly abnormal rhythmic discharge. (a) top tracing: efferent discharges of a ventral (motor) root; lower tracing: tetanus waves recorded from the motor nucleus at the same spinal level. (b) same experiment, acceleration of the tetanus rhythm by adding nicotine. (c) another preparation: synchronized rhythm of cervical, upper trace, and lumbar tetanus waves. The identity of phasing of discharge patterns at the two widely separated levels of the spinal cord argues against synchronization by conduction along the connecting fibers. (d) another preparation: persistence of the tetanus synchronization of two adjacent segments of the spinal cord anatomically separated by a complete transection of the cord. Since the two segments have no anatomical connection with each other, the synchrony of discharge must be controlled by electrotonic field forces. In all records, time is indicated in one-fifth second intervals [From Bremer, F. *Some problems in neurophysiology.* University of London, The Athlone Press, 1953, ix + 79, p. 17].

response to a given introduced variable, one's conceptual thinking is limited by language. Language built up by subject-verb-predicate sequences is best suited to explain linear cause and effect relations. When multifactorial, transactional systems are in operation, however, as they are in most neurophysiological and psychological problems, language imposes a serious limitation to adequate description.

It has long been customary to think of the nervous system as a mechanism into which stimuli go and from which responses come, and that the flow of events is correctly revealed by the conventional stimulus-response paradigm. This view has become ingrained into experimental designs as well as conceptual thinking. The nervous system was thought to be put into action only through the introduction of outside stimuli. However, well-established experimental facts reveal that aggregations of neurons throughout the brain are themselves spontaneously active, even when separated from all neuronal connection with the rest of the nervous system [7]. Evidently, then, no stimulus can enter upon a *tabula rasa*. All of the sense organs themselves maintain a steady state of activity even in the absence of recognizable stimuli. Afferent influx contributes to the "spontaneous" central nervous activity. Each neuronal constellation in the brain shows some activity even during sleep, hibernation, or deep anesthesia.

A second fact of importance is that neurons are functionally related to each other not only through synaptic articulations, but also by electrotonic field forces. Not only do intricate microanatomical connections contribute, but dynamic microscopic electrotonic field forces, rising and falling momentarily, also influence the level of excitability among neighboring neurons, even though no strictly anatomical connections may exist between them.[8]

[8] The classical experiments of Lashley and Sperry involving the insertion of conductors and dielectrics into the brain were directed at testing the existence of postulated field forces of a much larger scale. The interventions of these investigators would probably not greatly interfere with the microscopical dimensions of electrotonic field forces which have been demonstrated neurophysiologically. There is no experimental contradiction here that we are aware of; the two sets of facts relate to quite different cerebral dimensions. [Lashley, K. S. Studies of cerebral function in learning. XIII. Apparent absence of transcortical association in maze learning. *J. comp. Neurol.*, 1944, **80**, 257–281; Lashley, K. S., Chow, K. L., & Semmes, Josephine. An examination of the electrical field theory of cerebral integration. *Psychol. Rev.*, 1951, **58**, 123–136; Sperry, R. W. Cerebral regulation of motor coordination in monkeys following multiple transection of sensorimotor cortex. *J. Neurophysiol.*, 1947, **10**, 275–294; Sperry, R. W., Miner, Nancy, & Myers, R. E. Visual pattern perception following subpial slicing and tantalum wire implantations in visual cortex. *J. comp. physiol. Psychol.*, 1955, **48**, 50–58; Sperry, R. W., & Miner, Nancy. Pattern perception following insertion of mica plates into visual cortex. *J. comp. physiol. Psychol.*, 1955, **48**, 463–469.]

Further pertinent consideration relates to the number of nerve cells which make up the central nervous system. There are approximately 1.7 million afferent neurons entering the central neuraxis. Of these, nearly two-thirds are accounted for by the optic nerves. There are only a quarter of a million neurons which leave the central nervous system to serve all muscles and glands. These are the only effector units we possess for the composition of all of our visceral and somatic performances. Entirely contained within the central nervous system there are some ten billion neurons! Thus there are roughly five thousand internal neurons for each neuron that enters or leaves the central neuraxis.

These elementary anatomical and physiological facts imply that information entering the central nervous system comes into relations with the direct or indirect influence of a very, very large population of spontaneously active central neurons. If attention is directed exclusively to an investigation of the stimulus and the response alone, this leaves entirely aside all that might be learned through an analysis of activities taking place within the very large central aggregation of neurons. These facts illustrate that the nervous system seems to be built for action as well as reaction. Although stimuli introduced into the nervous system will modify its output, central neuronal events are important with respect to (1) the degree to which any incoming signal is able to invade and activate the central transactional pool of neurons, and (2) the degree to which such activation will be released into subsequent motor performance.

The experimental device relied upon in most psychological experiments has been to make certain that the subject gives some degree of attention to a given signal. Most behavioral experiments depend in the first instance on this contingency. Recently, for the first time, it has been possible to define some of the neuronal mechanisms affected during the act of attention [34]. Securing attention involves almost as radical an intervention in terms of qualitative and quantitative change in neuronal activity as does anesthesia—although of a nearly opposite kind. As a consequence, neurophysiologists view the nervous system as being far more complex, subtle, and plastic in terms of internal control mechanisms than they had any reason to assume heretofore. Moreover, certain fundamental aspects of behavior which were previously considered unassailable in regard to their explanation in terms of brain mechanisms can now be brought under experimental control.

THE CONCEPTUAL AND EXPERIMENTAL DOMAINS OF NEUROPHYSIOLOGY

Attempts to divide neurophysiology into separate domains must be recognized at the outset as entirely artificial. But the unfortunate fact is that neurophysiology, like psychology, is so large that any one individual is likely to become immersed within a relatively small part of the subject. Thus it is that the experimental domain engaged in by one individual tends to involve only a limited portion of the whole of neurophysiology. Many individuals read and discourse across these boundaries, and a few have done significant work in more than one field, but in general each domain has its own more or less specialized equipment, separate avenues of communication, and often isolated intellectual resources.

Circulation and Metabolism

First and foremost, the brain is living tissue, quite exacting in terms of its metabolic needs. Although its weight is only about 2 per cent of that of the whole body, it utilizes at rest about 20 per cent of the total oxygen consumed. The brain's oxygen consumption is not much modified by mental or neurological disorders, unless the cerebrovascular bed is directly affected. During sleep there is no diminution in cerebral blood flow; in fact, the blood flow may be moderately increased as a result of a relatively higher carbon dioxide tension in the blood, which is due to a reduced excitability of the bulbar mechanisms regulating breathing. Interestingly enough, anxiety is one of the few conditions which significantly increases cerebral blood flow and cerebral oxygen consumption [21].

Modern knowledge of cerebral blood flow and metabolism largely rests upon the work of Kety and his associates, who first established experimental methods for the accurate measurement of cerebral blood flow, cerebrovascular resistance, oxygen consumption, and the like in unanesthetized human subjects. Recently, using radioactive gas uptake in cats, they have shown that during alterations in functional activity of the nervous system, blood flow specific to local regions of the brain may be appreciably altered [50]. Thus there are demonstrated differences in the local blood-flow patterns as between waking and anesthetized states, and between an unanesthetized animal presented with flashing bright light and the same animal receiving no such visual stimulation. Evidently, there is a considerable partitioning of local blood flow according to local functional needs, although the total cerebral blood flow often does not reflect these changes. Considerable partitioning may be accomplished according to the amount of local metabolic activity and, hence, local CO_2 production, without having to involve localized nervous reflexes.

The brain is housed within a hard, bony box, supported by fibrous meningeal coverings and partitions, and buoyed by cerebrospinal fluid which reduces the inertial weight of the brain as affected by gravitation and other acceleratory forces. As a result of this support and protection, the feebly rigid brain is enabled to withstand stresses inflicted on the head in the course of everyday living. The cerebrospinal fluid bath protects the nervous system not only against physical damage but against chemical perturbations as well. The brain lies in a special fluid compartment defended by the blood-brain barrier. This functional barrier is not yet well defined anatomically, but it separates the blood stream from the interstitial fluid and cerebrospinal fluid surrounding nerve cells, thus isolating them in certain important biochemical respects and tending to ensure a more competent homeostasis for the nervous system than exists for other organs of the body [26].

Comparative Neurophysiology

One thread running through all domains of neurophysiology concerns comparative studies. For most experimental neurophysiological pursuits, the brain of man is not available. For many purposes, the usual laboratory animals—cats, dogs, and monkeys—are suitable. Many nutritional, metabolic, and neuroendocrinological problems associated with the nervous system have been carried out on rats and rabbits. The invertebrate squid is useful because it contains the largest single axon that can be readily isolated. This axon may be as large as 0.3 to 0.6 mm in diameter, permitting the insertion of considerable experimental equipment into the interior of the fiber. The horseshoe crab is studied because its uninverted light-receptor system is relatively more accessible. The crayfish has interesting stretch receptors and an accessible efferent fiber which modulates the level of excitability of the stretch receptor itself. The lobster has a cardiac ganglion of nine neurons which are mutually interdependent and which can be studied individually in relation to each other. The chameleon has completely independent eye movements but yet the brain stem organization of its eye-motor nuclei and their anatomical relations conform to the usual vertebrate scheme. The list of animals which can serve a useful purpose in neurophysiological investigations, in addition to the usual cats, dogs, and monkeys, is almost unlimited. As Herrick recognized, there is hardly an experiment that nature has not prepared for us.

Much of what we know about the functional properties of sensory receptors, central neurons, and motor effectors has been achieved by means of relatively exotic animal preparations. This is not as risky as would first appear: evolution is conservative. Mechanisms which have evolved for communication from one cell to another have been preserved through countless eons and still form the fundamental bases for communication within the human brain. As Bishop pointed out, ganglionic masses have gotten larger, axons have been stretched to greater length, but the fundamental neuronal mechanisms seem to be the same.

. . . . One need not expect an exact correlation between the stage of development of a particular function and the evolutionary scale of the animal exhibiting that stage. The lowly medusa, not to neglect the plant Nitella, has lived and died throughout only a relatively longer temporal expanse than has man, during which it has enjoyed and suffered the same or equivalent vicissitudes as has the self-anointed Lord of Creation; we have all been around a long time [4, p. 394].

It is true that the rudimentary beginnings of a cortical mantle make their first appearance in reptiles and birds, and that an increase in total surface area represented by cortex is one of the main distinctions of successively higher forms. Although an emphasis used to be laid on the obvious expansion through phylogeny of the frontal lobes (*viz.*, the highest-level functions attributed to this location by Jackson), measurements indicate that the temporal lobes have grown to an even greater relative degree. Although it has been assumed that the corticospinal (pyramidal) tract represents the epitome of evolutionary development, a careful count has shown that another tract, the fornix, which is associated with phylogenetically older limbic regions of the brain, has increased to a relatively greater extent than the corticospinal tract. In going from monkey to man, the fornix increases by a factor of 5, whereas the corticospinal tract increases by only a factor of 2. Obviously many exciting hints will be exposed through increased efforts in comparative neuroanatomy and comparative neurophysiology. Yet it would be a mistake to assume from these facts that successively higher functions are entirely attributable to a succession of anatomical accretions acting in some way apart from the whole.

Developmental Neurophysiology

One of the most admirable careers in science and, incidentally, one which has perhaps had more impact on psychology than on neurophysiology is that of George Ellett Coghill, referred to above. Although he was not the first, he was one of the most conscientious and imaginative of those who attempted to correlate structural development with the maturation of behavior. Coghill showed that the common salamander embryo begins to wriggle and to show swimming activities before its sensory neurons have established their connections with muscles and body wall. Motor nerves precede sensory neurons in developing a capacity to transmit impulses. The sensory and very probably also the intercolated interneuronal elements of the reflex arc are late in becoming functional [16]. This implies that the nervous system is built for action and that responses to sensory stimulation are secondary, at least developmentally. Coghill showed, furthermore, that the first actions of a developing salamander are mass actions. Individuation of particular responses appears only gradually. Although Coghill looked for the initiation of elementary reflexes which could be built up into more comprehensive integrations, he found that individuation develops out of already integrated total responses. This principle of gradual individuation of responses has been shown to hold for the developing human foetus as well as for other animals [17]. From their first appearance, mass actions are coherently organized expressions of the total organism. Throughout ontogeny they represent the integrated action background upon which individuated reflex systems are superimposed.

Many superb experiments of Weiss and Sperry and others indicate that there are potent organizing principles at work during development and regeneration of the nervous system [54, 51]. Peripheral tissues seem capable not only of stimulating, but also of providing specific identification for their own particular innervation. Muscle cells developing in a limb bud constitute a necessary stimulus to the maturation of motor nerve cells in the spinal cord, which then proceed to innervate the muscles. Thereafter, the nerves serving specific muscles seem to have a unique specification, an endowment from their particular peripheral association. Retinal ganglion cells which send fibers back to the central nervous system, and which will regenerate in certain lower vertebrate forms if the optic nerves are cut, are apparently similarly endowed with specificity according to their point of origin in the retina. If the optic nerve is cut and the eye rotated or transposed from one side to the other, regeneration is followed by behavior that is disoriented in a specific way, indicating that ganglion cells from the upper part of the retina, even after transposal and regeneration, still contribute that specific "local sign" along with impulses contributing to vision.

Altogether, the pattern of peripheral and central organization of innervation is intricate in the extreme for both specific and diffusely projecting systems. It is estimated that of 10,000 genes in the human germ cell, more than half are devoted to organizing factors, governing the embryonic development of the nervous system. The hypothesis of neurobiotaxis, which contends that neural aggregates migrate in the direction of their principal source of activation, can account for only a small fraction of the anatomical relations found in the nervous system. Barron separated cortex from thalamus prior to the infolding of the Rolandic fissure and found that the fissure goes on to develop without either the structural attachments or the functional influences of thalamocortical relationships [2].

It is now well known that certain untoward pathological conditions in the mother, particularly during the first precious weeks of pregnancy, when the nervous system of the embryo is most rapidly developing, may critically interfere with later neurological and psychological performance of the offspring [37]. Much more needs to be learned about hereditary and environmental factors, including maternal environmental factors, that may ordain among the complex processes of neurophysiological and psychological becoming.

Biophysics and Physiology of the Neuron

Painstaking research of recent years has shown that various portions of the membranous surfaces of a single nerve cell behave differently. The most active sites along the axon, where all-or-nothing conduction takes place, occur at points of stricture of the myelin sheath, the nodes of Ranvier. When a nerve is stimulated, these nodes become the functional locus of action-current responses. Electrical stimuli just sufficient to activate a node elicit from it an action current which is in general much stronger than the applied current. Each activated node is by itself capable of activating the next two or three nodes. When any given node is stimulated, the next two or three nodes are activated, although the intervening internodal segments remain relatively quiescent. Thus, repeating the process of restimulation by successive action currents, all the nodes of the fiber are successively excited, one after the other. Even if two successive nodes are inexcitable, the impulse can jump to a third and still be effective. These processes of saltatory conduction ensure improved reliability as well as increased velocity of signal transmission along axons [52].

The electrical field forces generated during the propagation of a nerve impulse along a given fiber can influence conduction along adjacent fibers: thus there is some slight "cross talk" among normal fibers and this apparently is exaggerated in regions of partial nerve injury and interference with central tracts.

The nerve impulse conducted along axons is associated with ionic movements across the active nodes. When the nerve impulse arrives at the region of synaptic junction with the next-order neuron, however, a different process takes place. An impulse reaching the terminal arborizations of the first fiber slows down and yields a graded rather than an all-or-nothing response. This apparently releases a chemical transmitter substance into the synaptic cleft between the neurons. The transmitter substance may be either excitatory, tending to depolarize the postsynaptic nerve membrane, or inhibitory, tending to stabilize the membrane against whatever perturbations may be affecting it. Thus the next-order neuron can be subjected to conflicting signals which tend simultaneously to excite and inhibit it. A resultant synthesis of all of the local graded responses taking place along its dendritic and cell-body surfaces is ultimately expressed in the form of all-or-nothing action currents generated in the point of origin of the axon of that cell. Each nerve cell acts as a biological computer which can synthesize a tremendous amount of conflicting information and deliver an unambiguous output. The computer's output is in the form of discrete nerve impulses delivered to its axon and destined directly, and by way of collaterals, to influence nearby and remote neuronal stations throughout the nervous system.

An important derivative of these neurophysiological facts is that only a part of the individual nerve cell's activities are all or nothing. A number of currently popular models of brain function depend upon a primary assumption that nerve cells can express only "on" or "off," "yes" or "no" signals. However, the complex processes of analysis and synthesis (which after all seem to be the principal business of the nervous system) take place within the presynaptic and postsynaptic regions of the nerve cell, and an all-or-nothing impulse is only a more reliable system for coding and transmitting impulses among cells which are too remote from each other to do their graded-response business directly. The all-or-nothing axon seems to be a device for the reliable transport of graded responses! A large proportion of the neuron population of the brain does not have axons of any appreciable length. Nobody knows how such short axon cells function. Perhaps they participate importantly in sustaining the tides of excitability and inexcitability throughout the ganglionic centers of the brain.

Sensory nerve endings act as mechanical and chemical transducers which respond to changes in local state by generating electrical currents which activate the initial parts of the afferent fiber. This in turn generates a single or repetitive discharge of impulses along the fiber. The sensory ending is in many respects like a cell body in that it codes a graded stimulus into discontinuous all-or-nothing nerve impulses. The interval between impulses is ordered by the level of graded excitability (or inexcitability) of the sensory ending and the refractory period of the axon stemming from it. A similar pacemaking phenomenon appears to obtain at the point of origin of axons where they arise from cell bodies and also in certain specialized cells, such as those of the pacemaker of the heart.

Specificity of sensory nerves appears to depend upon differences in susceptibility to certain chemical and physical perturbations; upon the number and distribution of endings serving a single afferent axon; upon the sheathing of the endings within the parent tissue (whether an identifiable specialized end-organ sheathing is present or not); and upon both the location of the parent tissue and the destiny of the afferent fiber projecting centrally.

The concept of four primary sensory modalities is oversimplified. Recording activity in single fibers isolated from various skin nerves in the cat, Tasaki and his associates were able to classify various afferent fibers according to whether or not they will respond to a variety of arbitrarily differentiated stimuli applied to the field of distribution of the individual fibers. In this way they were able to determine the physiologi‑ cal properties of single sensory units. They classified these into touch, pressure, large- and small-diameter nociceptive, cold, wide-receptive, hair, subcutaneous, scratch, and unmyelinated afferent fibers.

(a) A touch fibre of the cat is 8–14 μ in diameter and innervates gener-ally one, sometimes two, touch spots which adapt quickly. (b) A pressure fibre is 3–5 μ in diameter, its receptive field is spot-like and adaptation is slow. (c) Nociceptive fibres vary between 3 and 11 μ, the receptive fields range from 2 to 9 (sometimes 50) mm^2, and the impulse discharge is gener-ally phasic. (d) Cold fibres are 1.5–3 μ in diameter, their receptive field is punctiform, and their endings are insensitive to mechanical stimuli. (e) A wide-receptive fibre is 2–5 μ, and it has a receptive field ranging from 1500 to 4000 mm^2 which is sensitive to all kinds of mechanical stimuli. (f) An afferent fibre associated with hair is 6–12 μ in diameter; it innervates a large number of hairs over an area ranging from 100 to 500 mm^2. (g) There are afferent fibres which arise in the subcutaneous tissue of the cat. (h) There are fibres connected with endings which respond to scratching of the skin but not to pressing. (i) Unmyelinated fibres subserve perception of heat and mechanical stimuli [36, pp. 149–150].

Motor-nerve endings are likewise fascinating. They also act as trans-ducers, changing nerve impulses into the secretory and contractile per-formances by the glands and skeletal, cardiac, and smooth muscles. This is probably accomplished, like synaptic transmission, by the elaboration and release on the part of the terminal nerve fibers of special chemical substances which exert their effects upon the contractile or secretory elements.

Physiology of the Neuroglia

A whole domain of cellular physiology which has hardly engaged attention is that relating to neuroglia. Although it has generally been supposed that the neuroglia serve only a supportive function, recent evi-dence suggests that they may play a far more dynamic and subtle role in brain physiology. For example, electron microscopy reveals that astrocytes have protoplasmic extensions which surround most of the enormous endothelial surface of the entire cerebral capillary bed. Is it possible that astrocytes play some regulatory role in relation to the blood-brain barrier? This possibility is given suggestive impetus in that irradiation injury to the brain is associated with death of astrocytes and edema formation in the regions most strongly affected.

Oligodendrocytes have been shown to be sensitive to hypoxia and they appear to have an important function in myelin formation. Some oligodendrocytes have been shown to receive terminal axonal endings of nerve fibers resembling synaptic endings. May these carry out certain functions that are elicited by nerve impulses? Oligodendrocytes show slow contractile motions in tissue culture. Astrocytes in tissue culture also show a slow direct-current potential shift in response to stimulation, and this is associated with a slow mechanical contraction which lasts several minutes. Similar electrical responses (presumably from glia) have been recorded from mammalian cortex [53]. Microglia provide at least some of the scavenging macrophages for the central nervous system. All of these findings suggest that neuroglia, far from having only a structural role, may participate actively in the developmental, nutritive, restorative, and also the electrical processes of the nervous system [55]. Altogether, this evidence indicates that the nervous system should be considered as operating neurons and glia in intimate and interdependent relations. Galambos goes further to raise the question whether glia may not "organize and program neuron activity" in relation to higher mental processes [13].

Techniques Applied to Brain Circuitry

Ablations. A vast domain of neurophysiology concerns the search for the functional organization of the nervous system. The oldest and one of the most popular techniques is to remove parts of the brain or spinal cord and to determine from physiological, neurological, and behavioral analysis what defects are exhibited. Ferrier pioneered in studies of this kind and performed cortical ablations in various regions, such as the frontal and temporal lobes. He was among the first to observe that brain damage could lead to psychological and personality changes [10]. He used monkeys, dogs, foxes, and other animals, and in a very short time was able to establish several insightful generalizations with respect to cortical ablation applied to various regions. Then Goltz succeeded in removing all of the cortex in one or both hemispheres of dogs and described the limited behavioral capacities of such animals [45]. Later it was found possible to analyze posture and locomotion on the basis of residual functions in animals with transections at various levels of the neuraxis. The spinal animal, for example, is incapable of standing or bearing weight but retains some reflexes which are considered to be related to locomotion and the maintenance of posture. The classical decerebration studies of Sherrington and his followers reveal animals with hyperactive stretch reflexes, especially in the antigravity muscles, so that an animal is capable of supporting its own weight if its legs are placed. The head and the tail are likewise erected against the force of gravity. The classical transection for this preparation is in the midbrain between the superior and inferior colliculi. Because the so-called "higher centers" of the brain can be removed in this case without sacrificing the most essential respiratory and cardiovascular functions, the decerebrate preparation has been a popular physiological technique for the study of brain stem and spinal mechanisms in the absence of anesthesia. It was accepted that an animal with a transection at this level must be incapable of perception. A large proportion of Sherrington's classical studies in *The integrative action of the nervous system* [46] are based upon decerebrate animals. Still higher transections, leaving the ventral half of the diencephalon available to endocrine, visceral, postural, and locomotive mechanisms, yield animals that can reflexly stand, walk, and, if properly held, make a peculiar springing jump. Bard has shown that such "diencephalic" females can go into heat, will assume appropriate posture for coitus, will breed, and bear normal young. The male, however, apparently needs cortex for his part in the act [3].

It is readily appreciated how studies of this kind reinforced the Jacksonian doctrine of levels of function in the nervous system. The idea of "dissolution of function" could now be demonstrated experimentally in the decorticate, hypothalamic, decerebrate, and spinal animal. Locomotor, cardiovascular, respiratory, temperature-control, neuroendocrine, and other complex somatic and visceral mechanisms were analyzed according to their hierarchical representations. Ablation and transection studies led to a functional separation and isolation of parts. Sometimes the smaller part might be of the greater interest in the study. For example, patches of cortex have been cut around and undercut without disrupting local circulation so that a study can be made of cortical functions in the absence of connections with surrounding cortex and subcortical structures; brain slices, the isolated retina, and perhaps even tissue culture—all involving techniques by which living nerve cells are removed from the body and kept alive *in vitro*—belong to this same category. Only fairly recently, with the introduction of stereotactic means for electrolytic destruction of localized regions deep within the brain, has it been possible to examine the effects of relatively discrete ablations of subcortical loci, leaving some ascending and descending pathways intact.

Often biochemical, pharmacological, behavioral, and anatomical studies have been the primary objective of given investigators. Indeed, much of what we know in each of these disciplines stems from examination of animals with transections or ablations of the peripheral or central nervous system. Although it is not possible to embody all disciplines in each study, and the use of certain techniques may mean that an investigator will discard that part of the biological system of greatest interest to other disciplines, there is nonetheless a case to be made for a combined-discipline approach. Often the information most critically lacking in the analysis of the effects of a given transection or ablation are anatomical, or behavioral, or physiological, etc. Not too many people can crowd around a given animal, nor can very many be effectively involved in a given experimental series. Nevertheless, a more comprehensive grasp of the bases and limitations of performance of certain neural mechanisms, and more satisfying controls, can be obtained when a fuller combination of skills is brought to bear on the same experimental materials. For example, how much of the physiological or behavioral disability in a given experimental series might be due to correctable endocrine or biochemical impairment? Is the basis or perhaps part of the expression of this impairment due to an alteration in appetitive mechanisms? Altered appetitive mechanisms might be investigated by behavioral techniques, but not without an initial recognition of their pertinence to a given experimental context. How much of the anatomical consequences of a transection or ablation are obscured by the utilization of a single anatomical technique, say, one that reveals only myelinated fibers? How much of the observed behavioral deficit in certain cases is due to unwitnessed spontaneous-seizure activity?

Electrical stimulation and recording. Although the electrical excitability of nerve and muscle have been known for two hundred years, direct stimulation of the brain was not accomplished until less than a century ago. Improvements in operative procedures, the introduction of stereotactic devices for accurate placement of electrodes, developments in electronic instrumentation, and aseptic implantation of electrodes for chronic studies—all of these have made it possible to study the effects of localized stimulation and to record simultaneously from a number of localized points in waking, behaving organisms, including man. Recordings can be made of single units, populations of neurons and of complex interactions and patterns occurring in both controlled and relatively free behavioral situations, and in situations where central neuronal events become internal cues to continuing behavior. By much the same means, it is also possible to introduce minute amounts of specific chemical agents and to examine their effects.

Neurochemistry and neuropharmacology. At first, the chemistry of the brain had to be examined in terms of what constituents are present and what are the principal metabolic pathways. Evidence now accumulating suggests that there is a good deal of regional specificity within various systems of the brain, and the neurochemist is having to brush up on his neuroanatomy. Functional organizations based on anatomical and physiological findings are now showing up with neurochemical and neuropharmacological specificity [31, 34]. The neuropharmacologist used to chase about among the branches of the peripheral autonomic ganglia, but now does everything that a neurophysiologist does, with the addition of exotic chemical interventions [22]. A few neuropharmacolo-gists are likewise inextricably involved in behavior, and a few behavioral scientists are as much committed the other way. Think of the astonishing relief we should enjoy from the impediments that so discouraged our intellectual grandfathers! There probably has not occurred so sweeping a revolution of opportunity in any other branch of science.

Part of the results of the application of these various techniques appears in the form of an improved understanding of the circuitry and functional organization of the brain. The organization of even small sectors, paths, and individual nuclei is astonishingly complex. Thus a given patch of the retina responds not only in accordance with the quality and intensity of light directed locally, but also in integrated zones of inhibition and reinforcement which shift according to the character and intensity of light applied to other neighboring and even distant retinal fields [24]. Similarly, adjacent regions of a sensory or motor nucleus or cortical field, and even the homotopic cortical field in the contralateral cerebral hemisphere, can interfere with the activity of response in a given part [8, 9, 41]. Furthermore, the same retina, nucleus, or cortex will respond differently in accordance with the level of activity of the brain stem reticular formation and other parts of the diffusely projecting systems [12, 14, 15, 20, 25, 39, 41]. Individual pathways of the nervous system are continually being affected by what is taking place in closely related parts and within the transactional systems of the brain, including the reticular activating system, the limbic system, and associative regions of the cortex.

Briefly, this sensory control mechanism appears to provide the perceptual processes with an active organizing principle, including an element of pur-pose, which tends to select and modify sensory messages within the earliest stages of their trajectory. If overt behavior may be assumed to provide a cogent index for the interpretation of *telos*, then this sensory control mech-anism is designed to diminish the engagement of higher centers with those signals that have the least significance to the individual. . . .

As the experience is repeated many times, there develops a significant economy in terms of the extent of brain involvement. Perhaps recognizable signals can eventually be reduced to a quite small number of impulses, repre-senting minuscule abstractions of reality. Perhaps recognizable identity can be established even before the sensory evoked impulses have time to ascend all the way to the cortex. . . . Clearly the cortex is not the first step in sensory integration. During wakefulness sensory integration is taking place continously and dynamically, beginning with the farthest afferent outposts. This involves an erosion of information that originally started into the nervous system and an intrusion of influences which are based upon the animal's previous experience as well as its momentary disposal of attention. This implies that there is a reduction and distortion of sensory evoked signals from the actual nature of the stimulating world. Perhaps "value" is likewise inserted into the complex at these early stages of sensory integration. Certainly significance to the organism appears to be a guiding principle with respect to the operation of sensory control mechanisms, hence a survival of incoming impulses in the unanesthetized brain would appear to be *prima facie* evidence of their significance. . . .

Something of a parallel sort appears to take place within motor circuits as one proceeds from the execution of a complex novel movement to that same movement when it is established as an ingrained motor habit. There is evidently an analogous economization and automatization of neuronal activity in relation to the habituated act as finally executed [29, pp. 757–758].

A number of structures in the brain stem, midline thalamus, and limbic system appear to be involved in positive and negative primary reinforcement [38, 40]. Many of these same parts of the brain are modulated by incoming "sensory" signals and many of them participate in the integration of outgoing "motor" responses. Perhaps it is by virtue of activation, *pari passu*, of these phylogenetically older parts of the nervous system that "value" may be attached to various other concurrent brain activities.

What values may be placed upon signals invading some of these parts may be inferred from MacLean's analysis of localization within the limbic system of two important life principles: *preservation of self* and *preservation of the species* [31]. The frontotemporal region of the limbic system seems to be fundamentally involved in the experiencing and expression of emotions relating to obtaining and assimilating food, appreciating and reacting to pain, etc. The septal, hippocampal, and cingulate regions seem to be related to the feeling states and expressions necessary to grooming, copulation, and reproduction.

Experimental evidence favors a lessening of our conceptual isolation of sensory from motor and other central mechanisms. The nervous system appears to be made up less of independent linear pathways than of mutually interdependent loop circuits which stitch together the various parts of the brain into a functional whole. Along ascending as well as descending projections, the brainstem reticular formation and the cerebral and cerebellar systems linked closely with it seem to modulate impulse traffic in a continuous action that modifies the composition of perceptive as well as projective neural patterns [29, p. 759].

In the last five to ten years, scientists have learned many crucial features concerning the bases of consciousness and emotion, mechanisms of appetite, and ways in which experience forms and distorts perception. They have identified internal reward and punishment systems, and alto-

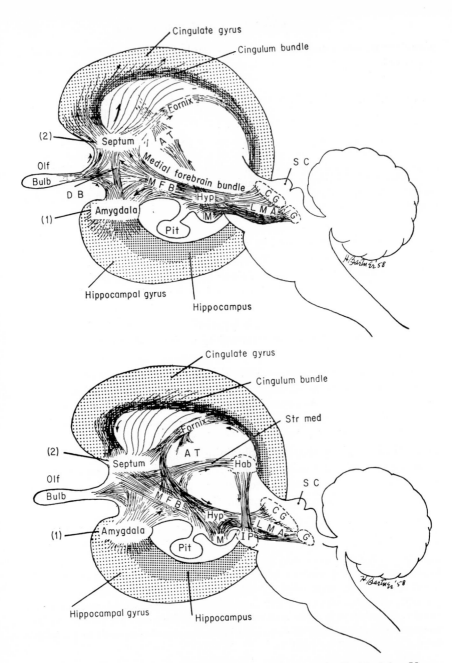

F<small>IG</small>. 7. *Ascending and descending pathways relating to the limbic lobe.* Upper figure: Ascending projections from the olfactory bulb and brain stem to the limbic lobe. The limbic lobe can be seen as a ring surrounding the upper end of the brain stem. Ascending projections from the brain stem are seen to accompany the medial

88

gether, have come a great way toward understanding the unity of mind and brain.

HOW DO WE CONSIDER MIND AND BRAIN?

Mankind has asked questions about himself since the beginning of reflective thinking. But it remained for the Greeks to bring up the idea of "mind" for the first time. It was around 400 B.C. that this concept first came into existence [49]. No suggestion of what we conceive to be mind or mental, nor of the idea of the separateness of mind from matter, is found in earlier writings throughout Egypt, Babylonia, and Greece. In fact, this concept is singularly unique to Western civilization. Although Plato did not invent the idea of mind, it is largely from his writings and influence that we have inherited the fundamental assumption that the world possesses two inevitably disparate and incommensurable aspects relating on the one hand to mind, and on the other hand to matter.

Throughout the writings of both Plato and Aristotle, the peculiar attributes of living things are accounted for by a very broad conception

---

forebrain bundle and to project largely to the amygdala (1) and septum (2) located at the cephalic ends of the ring of the limbic lobe. Incoming impulses from the olfactory bulb similarly project mainly to these two regions. The amygdala is intimately related to the hippocampal gyrus and hippocampus. The septum is intimately related to the cingulate gyrus and the bundle of the cingulum. The septum and amygdala are connected together by the diagonal band (DB). During its ascending trajectory, the medial forebrain bundle contributes to the hypothalamus and particularly the mammillary body (M) which, in turn, projects to the anterior thalamic nucleus (AT) and, thereby, to the cingulate gyrus. The lower figure illustrates outflow from the limbic lobe projecting back into the brain stem by way of the bundle of the cingulum and fornix into the septum, median forebrain bundle and mammillary body, as well as the anterior thalamic nucleus. The amygdala also projects to this downward flow, principally to the medial forebrain bundle and hypothalamus, but also along with the septum to the stria medularis, to the habellular complex (HAB) and, finally, in a ventrally descending projection through the brain stem to the interpeduncular nuclei (IP). On the ventral surface of the brain stem, this latter contributes upwards to the mammillary body (M) and also directly into the brain stem itself. The limbic system taken as a whole apparently has to do with primary reward mechanisms and with the experiencing and expressing emotion. Dr. MacLean has shown that the amygdala region (1) of the limbic ring has to do predominantly with those emotional and behavioral reactions associated with preservation of the individual, for example, the seeking and fighting for food and the visceral process of the alimentation. The septum (2), at the other end of the limbic ring, has to do predominantly with the emotional and behavioral activities relating to the preservation of the species, for example, the seeking and defending a mate, grooming, and sexual activity [30, p. 615].

of universal pneuma or world soul. This, in its loftiest form, accounts for a part of what we identify by the term *mental life*. Cruder aspects of the soul—responsible for vegetative life, growth, and reproduction—inhabit all living creatures, including plants. Animals are endowed with an additional, qualitatively higher-order aspect of soul which "animates" them, i.e., which gives them the capacity for movement. Man alone possesses a third, highest form of soul, the rational soul, which is devoted entirely to mental processes.

Traditionally, as biomedical scientists, we think we know something about mind and something about matter, and that these are incommensurably different from each other. First of all, it should be recognized that this schema is based upon an assumption we have inherited from Plato. Second, the old definition of matter is now known to be operationally incomplete: it fails to include the mental processes inevitably involved in any conception of matter. As the great theoretical physicist Max Born wrote recently—

Matter as given by our senses appears as a secondary phenomenon, created by the interaction of our sense organs with processes whose nature can be discovered only indirectly, through theoretical interpretations of experimentally observed relationships; in other words, through a mental effort. To designate the result of this operation by the old word "matter" seems to me wrong [5, p. 319].

It follows that until the basis and limitations of these mental processes are completely understood, any definition of matter must be correspondingly limited and tentative. Altogether this may seem hard to accept. Yet the alternatives, over which so many philosophers have struggled, are not particularly alluring. Let us consider them briefly. Some believe that thoughts, ideas, wishes, and other mental phenomena are essentially epiphenomena, that they grow out of or run parallel to certain particular material events. Others consider that such mental events are essentially incorporeal, perhaps occupying only "virtual space." Still others consider mind as a property of matter, believing that there may be a certain amount of "mindness" extended in some degree throughout all forms of matter. You may have your choice. In each case, it is still the old word "matter" that is being considered. Bertrand Russell on the other hand holds—

. . . that whatever we know without inference is mental, and that the physical world is only known as regards certain abstract features of its space-time structure—features which, because of their abstractness, do not suffice to show whether the physical world is or is not different in intrinsic character from the world of mind [44, p. 224].

This view dismisses the prior assumption and gives encouragement to further scientific study of the whole mind-brain issue. We believe that the assumption of Plato, even though it has a great hold on our imaginations, is unnecessary, and that it is disadvantageously distracting in relation to our quest for further knowledge about the nervous system. Its admission as an original premise seems to us to be unhelpful to our everyday performance in the hospital, classroom, and research laboratory. We feel that dualism is undesirable also because it fosters professional, intellectual, and conceptual isolation among scientists who are trying to understand the whole of existence.

When people say, in common parlance, that they can know or recognize matter independently of mind, they are really confessing a further assumption which is unnecessary and may indeed be entirely wrong. What they really mean is that they consider percepts to depend upon some other more reliable internal processes than thoughts, memories, or wishes. The latter, admittedly mental functions, are supposedly less reliable, less consistent, and perhaps less substantial (in the literal sense of the word) than are perceptions. The fact is, we do not know enough yet to make such a comparative evaluation.

We do know, however, that perception is definitely a mental act. We also know that in vast ways perception is subject to error in the sense first described by Descartes. It was upon this insight that Descartes based his whole philosophy of universal doubt. We know further that sensory messages upon which perception must depend are themselves subject also to direct interference through the actions of the central nervous system. A central nervous control is exerted even out to the peripheral sense organs, and acts throughout the entire trajectory of the ascending sensory pathways. This control, which was unknown until only a few years ago, appears to be exercised in accordance with internal value systems which themselves are affected by previous as well as concurrent appetites and purposes. Thus the modulation of incoming sensory impulses seems to be based upon expectation, relative significance to self, and so forth.

Value systems are incorporated in central nervous mechanisms of reward and punishment, emotional experience and expression, and are accessible to the presumably more objective and depersonalized systems of neocortex [29, 31]. This complex set of value systems is built into the chassis, so to speak, and cannot be divorced from either the ascending signals coming in from the outside world, or from the outgoing sensory-control impulses which can modulate these incoming messages. Evidently the nervous system is continually exercising and refining its control over sensory pathways, just as it has long been known to do in relation to motor performance. Presumably the brain can shape our

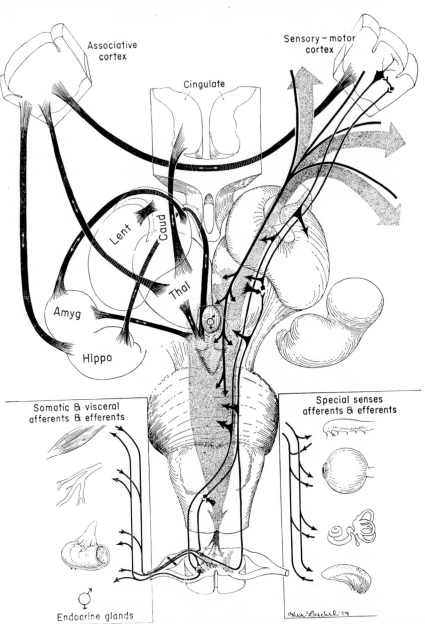

Associative cortex

Sensory—motor cortex

Cingulate

Lent

Caud

Thal

Amyg

Hippo

Somatic & visceral
afferents & efferents

Special senses
afferents & efferents

Endocrine glands

FIG. 8. *Summarizing diagram of brain mechanisms relating to behavior.* A composite diagram of the nervous system dependent upon concepts developed in figures 3, 5, and 7, particularly, and in the text. The cortex is removed except for patches of "associative cortex" on the left, "sensory-motor cortex" on the right, and "cingulate cortex" belonging to the limbic lobe in the center. The left-hand part of the diagram illustrates in diagrammatic form the two-way communications

perceptions more or less as it shapes our comportment: in both cases, teleological mechanisms are at work.

At the very least, then, perception is a mental act; and the data upon which this mental act depends are themselves affected according to the cumulative patterns of previous mental acts, acting together with mental acts relating to purposes. The psychologist, from an external view of behavior, has long known this to be true, and has been trying to communicate the idea to other scientists. But many scientists, not being directly involved in examining the processes of perception, have continued to preserve a distinction between what they have assumed can be directly, clearly, and unequivocally apprehended through the senses and what might thereafter be subject to mental operations. This now can be thrown out on other than psychological grounds.

Neurophysiology and psychology are not alone in being affected by erroneous prior assumptions. For example, similar difficulties existed in classical physics during the last century when that discipline was considered to be concerned only with "inanimate matter." Many physicists wondered then whether concepts of force, energy, and so on, had to do with "physically real" problems, or whether they were merely a kind of logical instrument, needed only for the time being. In the course of much theoretical and experimental work, such primitive definitions gave way before more subtle conceptions which incorporated both matter and energy and now flirt with a further incorporation of field forces. Thus, formerly isolated aspects of physics, some of which appeared to lie com-

---

among various major components of the forebrain. In the lower portion of the figure and in the right-hand side are depicted the major sensory and motor pathways and their associated collateral projections into and out of the diffusely projecting systems in the brain stem, thalamus, and spinal cord. The shaded area in the center of the figure, illustrating the diffusely projecting systems, depicts how these project downward upon spinal, sensory, and motor centers and upward through the internal capsule to distribute diffusely throughout the forebrain. This same system receives projections from certain areas of the cortex. Both afferent and efferent projections are seen to relate to somatic and visceral components, including skeletal muscle, smooth muscle of blood vessels and gut, and the neuroendocrine system. Similarly both afferent and efferent projections go to sense organs in the special senses, skin, and body wall receptors. The classical relay of ascending sensory pathways is seen to be subject to influence (arrows arising from the diffusely projecting system) at the spinal, bulbar, and thalamic levels. Similarly, the descending long motor (pyramidal) tract, which on its descending trajectory projects collaterals to the basal ganglia (lent and caud) and diffusely projecting systems, is seen to be subject to modulation at both cortical and spinal levels. An attempt to portray the relations among several components of the brain will be better understood if the several components are recognized as being related to each other by way of continuous mutually interdependent processes. The final complex functional performance is considered to be a *transaction* as contrasted with the more simple linear cause-and-effect relations of *interactional* systems.

pletely outside the proper province of that discipline, have come to be viewed much more holistically. Yet, even in physics, there still exist great bogs of ambiguities in atomic theory, cosmology, and other areas. The one universally respected conviction is that we must be tentative, willing to tolerate ambiguities, and prepared to participate in quite revolutionary non–common-sense ways of conceiving of nature. The major advances in physics have been associated with a greater unification in theory. We do not pretend that brain and mind will follow a similar history, but only that the speed of progress in any discipline and the dimensions of contribution by individual scientists are dependent in large part upon the tentativeness with which their fundamental assumptions are manipulated.

Now, taking the common-sense view of the separateness of mind and matter, a view which seems to pervade most of our culture, does that operate to our disadvantage—as patients, physicians, professors, or experimentalists? Does it retard our advancement toward a more complete understanding of life? If we saw that it were disadvantageous, would we abandon it?

First, let us be explicit. We are not attempting to make an exclusive abstraction from experience, either of brain or of mind. We are acknowledging, however, that it is only by conceptual artifice and cultural habit that we consider these separately. In effect, the expression "mind-brain" or "brain-mind" is more adequate than either "mind" or "brain" alone. A further practical handicap of Plato's assumption, in addition to its interference with our conceptual advancement, lies in the professional antagonisms it cultivates. The extreme views are readily characterized:

> Those who believe too zealously in matter are confident that biological phenomena can be "explained" entirely on the basis of laws of physics and chemistry. Mind is an illusion. Since mind is the most anthropomorphic thing in man, it should be dispensed with. "Teleology, also," they say, "should have no place, excepting, of course, for homeostasis and a few other selected forms of purposive biology." It comes as a shock to these persons to learn that modern physics is becoming more anthropomorphic, even to admitting mind.
>
> Those who believe too zealously in mind, on the other hand, can show that matter is inferred. They mistakenly conclude from this that matter is therefore an illusion. Think of the impact of this conceptual isolation on a patient with a disorder of his "brain-mind." This will inevitably interfere with his recognition of illness, finding professional help, participating in the therapeutic regimen, seeking rehabilitation, and explaining his disorders to himself and to society. My own experience leads me to believe that there is no intellectual satisfaction to be derived from considering either of these "opposites" to be an illusion [27, pp. 10–11].

Ideas, not things, rule mankind. When we use some concept for purposes of guidance in our daily lives, we must avoid confusing the concept with experience and believing that the one is a sufficient explanation of the other. Where can we divide the nervous system to hedge off the limits of mind? Until we know enough to be able to answer that question, how can we be satisfied with practically complete isolation in training, research, and practice between those who examine and treat the mind and those who examine and treat the brain? We cannot immediately dispense with such isolation as exists, but how long should we be satisfied with this as an adequate intellectual frame of reference? Of course, until it was possible to determine some of the brain mechanisms responsible for certain mental processes, such isolation was perhaps inevitable, even though it were acknowledged that both professional lines of activity ultimately relate to the same organ system. But already there are several brain mechanisms known to be responsible for mental processes. Many of these have been discovered through the efforts of neurophysiologists and psychologists, often teamed up with one another.

To our enormous advantage, a cluster of recent technical advancements has made possible the examination of the living, waking, behaving organism in terms of internal brain-mind mechanisms. There is presently flowering a tremendous renaissance of all of the sciences relating to the nervous system. All that is being discovered in neuroanatomy, neurochemistry, neuropharmacology, neurophysiology, psychology, and sociology has suddenly become far more meaningful to each of the other disciplines. Rapid expansion and increase of conceptual penetration into these complementary fields has taken place at a time when the world—more than ever before—needs desperately to understand and to be able to deal with the basic realities of human capabilities and limitations.

Some of the great questions raised by the Greeks have now proven approachable through experimentation. By means of resourceful theoretical and experimental approaches, scientists are beginning to derive principles that will define the ranges of invariance and of indeterminacy in the operation of the brain-mind.

No one has yet been bold enough to outline what is unknown in the fields of neurophysiology and psychology. Although such a sketch would provide great challenges to research, it would also be dimensionally overwhelming. The fraction of known to unknown in these disciplines is vanishingly small; we are fundamentally and immeasurably ignorant. Problems that resist solution may be insoluble, yet, if you will believe the history of science, it is more likely that the means of solution being attempted are inadequate. We need to turn aside from some of our established conceptions to seek out new ones which can lead to a more fundamental level of understanding.

From this brief description, we hope it is evident that much is being learned through basic research on the brain-mind and behavior. Findings from such research are important in relation to our better grasp of the bases and limitations of all human concepts. Outside experience is not the whole of experience. In relation to brain-mind mechanisms, it would be desirable to be able to understand and to predict the full scope of internal reality. Because of the structural complexity of an individual brain-mind and the lack of uniformity in any given detail from one brain-mind to another, and because of thermal and Heisenberg indeterminacies, even great insight into the detail of mechanisms cannot account for and predict the full scope of internal reality. The best for which we can hope is an ability to grasp and to predict, within certain limits of variance, the limits, potentialities and controls acting upon internal reality.

Does man have freedom to manipulate the channels between his feelings and ideas? Can he choose his purposes? We believe that recent neurophysiological and psychological research now support the surest hopes in this regard that have ever been put before mankind. Reason and feeling are not at war from their natures; they are fused elements which we separate only through reflection. The most important issue before mankind relates to the vigor with which he will seek to understand his own brain-mind and behavior and how he will use this knowledge.

REFERENCES

1. Adrian, E. D., Bremer, F., & Jasper, H. H. (Eds.) *Brain mechanisms and consciousness: a symposium organized by the Council for International Organizations of Medical Sciences.* Oxford: Blackwell, 1954.

2. Barron, D. H. An experimental analysis of some factors involved in the development of the fissure pattern of the cerebral cortex. *J. exp. Zool.,* 1950, **113,** 553–581.

3. Beach, F. A. Neural and chemical regulation of behavior. In H. F. Harlow & C. N. Woolsey (Eds.), *Biological and biochemical bases of behavior.* Madison, Wis.: Univer. of Wis. Press, 1958. Pp. 263–284.

4. Bishop, G. H. Natural history of the nerve impulse. *Physiol. Rev.,* 1956, **36,** 376–399.

5. Born, M. The concept of reality in physics. *Bull. atom. Scientists,* 1958, **14,** 313–321.

6. Brazier, M. A. B. (Ed.) *The central nervous system and behavior. Transactions of the First Conference.* New York: Josiah Macy, Jr. Foundation, 1959.

7. Bremer, F. *Some problems in neurophysiology.* London: Univer. of London, 1953.

8. Chang, H. T. Cortical response to activity of callosal neurons. *J. Neurophysiol.,* 1953, **16,** 117–131.

9. Chang, H. T. Interaction of evoked cortical potentials. *J. Neurophysiol.*, 1953, **16**, 133–144.
10. Ferrier, D. *The functions of the brain.* London: Smith, Elder, 1876.
11. French, J. D., Verzeano, M., & Magoun, H. W. A neural basis for the anesthetic state. *Arch. Neurol. Psychiat.*, Chicago, 1953, **69**, 519–529.
12. Galambos, R., Sheatz, G., & Vernier, V. G. Electrophysiological correlates of a conditioned response in cats. *Science*, 1956, **123**, 376–377.
13. Galambos, R. A glia-neural theory of brain function. *Proc. Nat. Acad. Sci.*, 1961, **47**, 129–136.
14. Granit, R. Centrifugal and antidromic effects on ganglion cells of retina. *J. Neurophysiol.*, 1955, **18**, 388–411.
15. Hernández-Peón, R., Scherrer, H., & Velasco, M. Central influences on afferent conduction in the somatic and visual pathways. *Acta Neurol. Latino-Americana*, 1956, **2**, 8–22.
16. Herrick, C. J. *George Ellett Coghill, naturalist and philosopher.* Chicago: Univer. of Chicago Press, 1949.
17. Hooker, D. *The prenatal origin of behavior.* Lawrence, Kan.: Univer. of Kan. Press, 1952.
18. Jackson, J. H. *Selected writings of John Hughlings Jackson.* Vol. 1. J. Taylor (Ed.) New York: Basic Books, 1958. 2 vols.
19. Jasper, H. H., et al. (Eds.) *Henry Ford Hospital, international symposium, reticular formation of the brain.* Boston: Little, Brown, 1958.
20. Jung, R. Co-ordination of specific and non-specific afferent impulses at single neurons of the visual cortex. In H. H. Jasper et al. (Eds.), *Henry Ford Hospital, international symposium, reticular formation of the brain.* Boston: Little, Brown, 1958. Pp. 423–434.
21. Kety, S. S. Considerations of the effects of pharmacological agents on the overall circulation and metabolism of the brain. In H. A. Abramson (Ed.), *Neuropharmacology.* Transactions of the First Conference. New York: Josiah Macy, Jr. Foundation, 1955.
22. Killam, E. K., Killam, K. F., & Shaw, T. The effects of psychotherapeutic compounds on central afferent and limbic pathways. *Ann. N.Y. Acad. Sci.*, 1957, **66**, 784–805.
23. Konorski, J. *Conditioned reflexes and neuron organization.* London: Cambridge Univer. Press, 1948.
24. Kuffler, S. W. Discharge patterns and functional organization of mammalian retina. *J. Neurophysiol.*, 1953, **16**, 37–68.
25. Lilly, J. C. Correlations between neurophysiological activity in the cortex and short-term behavior in the monkey. In H. F. Harlow & C. N. Woolsey (Eds.), *Biological and biochemical bases of behavior.* Madison, Wis.: Univer. of Wis. Press, 1958. Pp. 83–100.
26. Livingston, R. B. Cerebrospinal fluid. In T. C. Ruch and J. F. Fulton (Eds.), *Medical physiology and biophysics.* Philadelphia: Saunders, 1960. Pp. 889–902.
27. Livingston, R. B. *Annual report, basic research program.* Washington: National Inst. Mental Health, National Inst. of Neurological Diseases and Blindness, 1958. (Processed)

28. Livingston, R. B. Central control of afferent activity. In H. H. Jasper et al. (Eds.), *Henry Ford Hospital, international symposium, reticular formation of the brain.* Boston: Little, Brown, 1958. Pp. 177–185.

29. Livingston, R. B. Central control of sensory receptors and sensory transmission systems. In *Handbook of neurophysiology.* Baltimore, Md.: Williams & Wilkins, for American Physiological Society, 1959. 3 vols. Vol. 1, pp. 741–760.

30. Livingston, W. K., Haugen, F. P., & Brookhart, J. M. The vertical organization of function in the central nervous system. *Neurology,* 1954, 4, 485–496.

31. MacLean, P. D. Contrasting functions of limbic and neocortical systems of the brain and their relevance to psychophysiological aspects of medicine. *Amer. J. Med.,* 1958, 25, 611–626.

32. MacLean, P. D. Personal communication. 1958. [See also 6, pp. 418–419].

33. Magoun, H. W. Caudal and cephalic influences of the brain stem reticular formation. *Physiol. Rev.,* 1950, 30, 459–474.

34. Magoun, H. W. *The waking brain.* Springfield, Ill.: Charles C Thomas, 1958.

35. Marshall, W. H., Woolsey, C. N., & Bard, P. Observations on cortical somatic sensory mechanisms of cat and monkey. *Science,* 1937, 85, 388–390.

36. Maruhashi, J., Mizuguchi, K., & Tasaki, I. Action currents in single afferent nerve fibers elicited by stimulation of the skin of the toad and the cat. *J. Physiol.,* 1952, 117, 129–151.

37. Masland, R. L., Sarason, S. B., & Gladwin, T. *Mental subnormality: biological, psychological, and cultural factors.* New York: Basic Books, 1958.

38. Miller, N. E. Experiments on motivation: studies combining psychological, physiological, and pharmacological techniques. *Science,* 1957, 126, 1271–1278.

39. Moruzzi, G., & Magoun, H. W. Brain stem reticular formation and activation of the EEG. *EEG Clin. Neurophysiol.,* 1949, 1, 445–473.

40. Olds, J. A preliminary mapping of electrical reinforcing effects in the rat brain. *J. comp. physiol. Psychol.,* 1956, 49, 281–285.

41. Purpura, D. P. Organization of excitatory and inhibitory synaptic electrogenesis in the cerebral cortex. In H. H. Jasper et al. (Eds.), *Henry Ford Hospital, international symposium, reticular formation of the brain.* Boston: Little, Brown, 1958. Pp. 435–457.

42. Razran, G. Soviet psychology since 1950. *Science,* 1957, 126, 1100–1107.

43. Razran, G. Soviet psychology and psychophysiology. *Science,* 1958, 128, 1187–1194.

44. Russell, B. *Human knowledge: its scope and limits.* New York: Simon & Schuster, 1948.

45. Schäfer, E. A. The cerebral cortex. In E. A. Schäfer (Ed.), *Textbook of physiology.* Vol. 2. Edinburgh: Young J. Pentland, 1898–1900. Pp. 697–782.

46. Sherrington, C. S. *The integrative action of the nervous system.* (2nd ed.) New Haven: Yale Univer. Press, 1947. (First ed., Scribner's, 1906.)

47. Sherrington, C. S. *Man on his nature: the Gifford lectures, Edinburgh, 1937–1938.* (2nd ed.) London: Cambridge Univer. Press, 1951.

48. Simon, B. (Ed.) *Psychology in the Soviet Union* (papers by Ananiev, Bogioavlensky, Boiko, Elkonin, Galperin, Leontiev, et al.), translated by J. and M. Ellis, J. McLeish, et al. Stanford, Calif.: Stanford Univer. Press, 1957.

49. Snell, B. *The discovery of the mind.* Translated by T. G. Rosenmeyer Cambridge: Harvard Univer. Press, 1953.

50. Sokoloff, L. Local blood flow in neural tissue. In W. F. Windle (Ed.), *New Research techniques of neuroanatomy.* Springfield, Ill.: Charles C Thomas, 1957. Pp. 51–61.

51. Sperry, R. W. Mechanisms of neural maturation. In S. S. Stevens (Ed.), *Handbook of experimental psychology.* New York: Wiley, 1951. Pp. 236–280.

52. Tasaki, I. *Nervous transmission.* Springfield, Ill.: Charles C Thomas, 1953.

53. Tasaki, I., & Chang, J. J. Electric response of glia cells in cat brain. *Science,* 1958, **128,** 1209–1210.

54. Weiss, P. (Ed.) *Genetic neurology, problems of the development, growth, and regeneration of the nervous system and of its functions.* Chicago: Univer. of Chicago Press, 1950.

55. Windle, W. F. *Biology of neuroglia.* Springfield, Ill.: Charles C Thomas, 1958.

BRAIN AND MIND

GERHARDT VON BONIN
College of Medicine
University of Illinois

Introduction 100
Nerve Cells 100
Character and Brain 102
Consciousness 102
Brain and Mind 103
Architecture of the Cortex 104
Sensory Input 106
Optic Sensations 107
Sensorium Commune 110
Motor Output 110
Speech 113
Attention 113
Emotions 113
Free Will 114
Summary 115
References 115

INTRODUCTION

Brain and mind mean for many people brain anatomy and mind. It is, of course, true that the anatomical arrangement imposes certain enduring restrictions upon the ways in which the brain can work, but that leaves the way in which it actually works still largely undefined. Similarly, the mind is mainly known by its functions, but it, too, has certain restrictions imposed upon it by such things as character. In any event, it is probably correct to say that in the case of the brain, we think first of anatomy; in the case of the mind, we think first of its functions. But in either case, it is important not to lose sight of the other side.

NERVE CELLS

We shall start with a short account of the workings of nerve cells [14]. Many of the data concerning nerve cells are actually derived from peripheral nerves, frequently sensory nerves. These receive their impulses

100

from organs which are exposed to long-lasting stimulations—long as compared with the duration of nervous impulses. Moreover, these stimuli are of very different strengths at different times. Also, in the central nervous system nerve cells are always found in great masses, so that the behavior of a single cell is not a true indicator of what happens in the brain when a stimulus goes through. With these things in mind, let us review briefly some of the main characteristics of nerve cells.

Modern electron-microscopic work [52] has made it clear that there is a membrane around a nerve cell. What this membrane consists of is not so clear. It is seen as a thin line in the image, sometimes double, somewhat darker than the plasma inside the cell. Some of the Nissl bodies appear to lie immediately adjacent to the membrane, but that is certainly not the rule. Nissl bodies and mitochondria can easily be made out. Their detailed structure, although of great interest, does not concern us here.

There is the "all-or-nothing" law, which seems to govern the workings of nerve cells. At a given moment, the cell will either fire or not, but if it fires, it will do so with all the power it is at that moment capable of putting out. Strength of a stimulus is therefore not transmittable by graded impulses from a cell; the only way a cell can indicate the strength of a stimulus is by the rate of firing. The stronger the stimulus, the faster the firing of a given cell.

That the impulse is generated by the breakdown of the membrane is now pretty generally admitted. The breakdown leads to a depolarization which must occur within a fairly large region of the cell in order to lead to a propagated impulse. How large is "fairly large" is a moot point, and we do not know whether it is of the same absolute size in all cells or whether it is a certain percentage of the surface of the cell. A single impulse lasts at best about 1 msec. After firing, the nerve cell remains incapable of firing again for a few milliseconds, while it recovers and builds up the membrane again. The time of recovery varies in different nerve cells; it may be as short as 1 or 2 msec—the cerebellar units are supposed to be able to fire 500 times per second—or may be 15 msec or longer.

That a nerve cell will not respond to one stimulus alone, but only when a "conditioning" stimulus has preceded the actual stimulus, is well known [36, 37, 38, 39, 40]. It is generally stated that the whole of a synaptic field must get excited before the stimulus can break through.

The dendrites conduct with much lower velocity than the axon, or even the cell body, so that what takes milliseconds on a cell body may take hundredths or even tenths of seconds on a dendrite. Thus the time within which stimuli on a dendrite may sum up may be as much as 15 msec [56].

These characteristics are, of course, mainly important for the first neuron, where the rate of firing depends on the strength of the stimulus applied to the end organ. This can be detected easily enough in the peripheral nerve, and has been measured hundreds of times. Once the impulse is in the central nervous system, the rate of firing is determined partly by the rate in the peripheral organ, partly by interactions between the neurons making up the second-order nucleus.

A point to keep in mind is that practically never do we find the firing of just one nerve cell as the initial condition for an impulse. For example, in the eye, an adequate stimulus consists of five to eight quanta transmitted to about five different rods [21]. In the muscle, a proprioceptive stimulus activates a large number (about fifty) of muscle spindles simultaneously. Taste buds are generally found in large groups, and so on. Since the individual thresholds within each group of end organs vary somewhat, this is usually a way of answering to the intensity of a stimulus: the more cells become involved, the more intense a stimulus will have been. Whether stimuli from various cells will reenforce each other at the next station (nucleus) or whether, on the contrary, they will narrow down to fewer channels depends on circumstances which are still shrouded in mystery.

In addition to these impulses, there are inhibitory impulses in the nervous system, about which we will not concern ourselves here.

CHARACTER AND BRAIN

What we mean by character probably comes nearest to the enduring pattern in the realm of the mind. We mean that the person is forgetful, neat, has an even or easily aroused temper, for example. These attributes appear to be inborn and to stay with the individual for the duration of life. In most important cases, we are absolutely unable to point to anything in the brain with which it might be correlated. In the case of musical gifts, people have pointed to a large development of the gyrus of Heschl (on the supratemporal plane) as an anatomical counterpart, but even here the evidence is not very convincing [1, 26].

CONSCIOUSNESS

Most of our psychology concerns conscious processes [31]. Can we make any intelligent remarks about consciousness? We are fairly sure that it does not reside in the cortex, for we (or a disease) can take parts of the cortex away without our becoming aware of it, a state for which Babinski [2] coined the term *anosognosia*, meaning not being aware of one's disease. But clinical experience as well as animal experimentation have shown that consciousness appears to be connected somehow with the midbrain and the brain stem. Operations near the quadrigeminal bodies lead almost invariably to a loss of consciousness. Consciousness may be restored after manipulations in that region are over, or it may never come back—the patient may become a vegetable [15]. This latter state of affairs, with good care of the patient, may last for years. Experimentally, it was shown in dogs that pressure on the brain stem can abolish consciousness, but not manipulations of the cortex.

This has recently been put on a much more understandable basis by Magoun and his co-workers [42], who practically discovered the reticular substance in the brain stem and showed its connections up and down the central nervous system. In particular, they showed the importance of this substance for the arousal reaction and for a proper functioning of the cortex.

The observations by Penfield [46], who was able to bring to recall in some persons—the number really does not matter—concrete incidents in their former life, does not really belong to the phenomena with which we are here concerned. These stimulations of the temporal lobe only change the contents of consciousness—not consciousness itself.

Introspective observations in themselves may not be very convincing, yet it may be pertinent to remark that the idea of the little man sitting somewhere in the brain and watching what goes on is easiest to explain on the assumption that *consciousness* does not reside in the cortex—only the *contents of consciousness*.

Another important aspect of the problem is that the processes underlying consciousness must go on fairly slowly as events are measured in neurophysiology. For consciousness involves planning ahead, and it involves a continuity which can only come from remembering what has gone before and realizing that what has been planned is what is executed now. Whether that is the way the reticular substance works we do not know, but it would be interesting to find out, and probably could be done with modern electrophysiological apparatus. Some cortical events, of course, would have to go equally slowly [54].

BRAIN AND MIND

In a sense, there is really no intelligent question that one can ask about the relation of the two sciences of physiology and of psychology. The simile of the two viewpoints when observing the circle may still be valid. For a person outside the circle, it looks convex; for a person inside, it looks concave. That the two views are of the same thing simply has to be taken for granted. We cannot accept the causal theory [50]. We simply have to admit that conscious processes and mental processes do not mean the same thing. Our viewpoint is better expressed by Bohr [6], who invoked the principle of complimentarity. Just as we need both the wave picture and corpuscular theory to explain the behavior of the electron, so we need both the physiological and psychological picture to explain the working of the brain. If we investigate the brain with the hope of finding the working of the mind, we have to apply all sorts of physical and chemical apparatus which disturb the process under investigation, until it has been disturbed so profoundly that the original process is lost sight of. "By the time you know everything about the atoms, the creature will be dead" [8]. More than a hundred years ago, Wordsworth said, "We murder to dissect." That somehow there must be a connection between the mind and the brain is clear, but what it is remains a mystery. Looking at sections is perhaps the least promising way to find out. The physiologist and the physiological psychologist appear to be in a much better position to advance our understanding.

It might be said, but again that leads to no more than generalities, that the mind models reality [13]. To put it into slightly different words, the formal laws of the activity of the mind must be the same as the formal basis of nervous activity.

ARCHITECTURE OF THE CORTEX

A few words should be said about the way in which the cells in the cortex, and in those parts of the brain which have to do with the cortex, are arranged [3, 37, 57].

The cortex is a thin (2 to 4 mm thick) sheet of gray matter containing cells and fibers, many of which are myelinated, as well as blood vessels and glia elements. The arrangement probably becomes clearest if we start with the fibers.

There are, as one would expect, incoming, outgoing, and intrinsic fibers in the cortex. Many of them are arranged in radii or bundles, each containing from 20 to 40 fibers, generally fairly thick, going from the upper third of the cortex down to the medullary center. They are at distances of 200 to 300 μ from each other. Then there are incoming fibers. Those which come from the thalamus take an oblique course through the lower part of the cortex, to end mostly in about the middle, in layer IV or IIIC. Finally, there are horizontal stripes. Three are generally recognized. The two lower ones in layers V and IV, respectively, are known as the inner and outer stripe of Baillarger; the top one, situated in layer IIIA, is known as the stripe of Kaes-Bechterew. In many parts of the cortex, it is very faint and hard to see. There are also horizontal fibers in the first layer, and, like all other fibers, they are of varying degrees of density. This variability has been made the basis of an extensive subdivision of the cortex into more than one hundred fields. It is doubtful that we can make any functional interpretation of this, and there is little point in going into detail here.

Finally, there is the ground-feltwork of fibers which appear to fill the cortex fairly densely and which run in all directions. They appear to make synaptic relations between the cells of the cortex. How dense this network is and whether it has the same density in all parts of the cortex are questions which at the moment cannot be answered with certainty. Bok's claim [7] that it is equally dense throughout the cortex remains to be confirmed.

The cells of the cerebral cortex are arranged in six or seven layers, depending on the way in which they are counted. We know very little about the reasons for this arrangement. Of course, what matters most is how the cells in the cortex are transmitting impulses from one to the other. That depends on several things—in the first place, on the number of contacts which can possibly be made or, in other words, on the density of the fibers and on the ratios of dendrites to axons. This has been worked out in fair detail by Bok [7] in Leiden and Amsterdam, and by Sholl [53] in London. We shall briefly review their work.

That the number and size of nerve cells per unit of volume determines how much space there is between the cells for their processes goes without saying. The packing density of the cells is therefore our first consideration. This is given by the gray/cell coefficient which was found to vary in man between 4 and 9 per cent. That leaves the vast majority of the cortex free for dendrites and axons. According to Bok [7], the processes—it becomes very difficult, if not impossible, to differentiate between dendrites and axons—occupy only about 200 μ in a cube of 1,000μ^3, and much of the rest of the space is filled by vacuoles of about 2.6 μ diameter. Around each vacuole there are on the average 10 fibers which meet in knots by twos. These vacuoles may be an artifact. Schultz and others [52], in their electron-microscopic work, did not find them but found very little "free" space.

The first layer nearest the surface is the molecular layer, so called because it is almost completely devoid of nerve cells which, when growing out toward the cortex during embryogenesis, mostly stop at the second layer and only very occasionally go beyond it. The second layer is filled quite densely with small cells. It is narrow, about 10 per cent of the thickness of the whole cortex. Then comes the broad third layer, which is filled only loosely with cells which become larger the deeper we go. It comprises about 30 per cent of the whole thickness. Then follows a layer of small cells which are again arranged rather densely. This layer varies very much from field to field. It is in some parts, as in the visual area, as broad as 15 to 20 per cent of the whole cortex, while elsewhere it is so attenuated as to be hardly recognizable at all. In the parieto-occipital region, the fourth layer appears to be divided into an upper small-celled, and into a lower, somewhat larger-celled part. The fifth layer, more sparsely populated, contains rather large cells in some fields. In the area gigantopyramidalis the giant cells of Betz are situated. Again, the sixth layer contains somewhat smaller cells, a little more densely arranged, and in many parts of the cortex goes gradually over into the white matter beneath the cortex.

Bok [7] stated that the cell size followed simple rules: in the upper part of the cortex the cell size increases in proportion to the depth; in the lower part, in proportion to the square of the depth, and the two pupula-tions overlap in the fourth layer. Bok also states that the length of the dendrites stand in definite relation to the size of the nerve cells. This was disputed by Sholl [53].

SENSORY INPUT

All impulses coming to the cortex reach first the thalamus, but before they get there, they go through one or more filters in the lower parts of the central nervous system. Let us go briefly over them.

The optic impulses have a first filter in the bipolar, a second one in the ganglion cells of the retina. From there, they go to the lateral genic-ulate body in the thalamus, and then to the striate area in the cortex.

Acoustic impulses go to the spiral ganglion and then to the cochlear nuclei in the brain stem. From there they go to the superior olive, then to the inferior colliculi in the midbrain and from there to the medial geniculate body, and finally to the gyrus of Heschl on the supratemporal plane of the cortex. This is a simplified account, of course; there are more way stations, but the exact mode of transmission is actually not quite clear.

Touch goes to the sensory ganglia just next to the spinal cord, then into the posterior funiculi—medial one for the leg, lateral one for the arm—to the nuclei of the posterior funiculi in the medulla oblongata, to the ventroposterior nuclei of the thalamus, and then to the postcentral convolution of the cortex.

Pain and temperature go to the spinal ganglia, then to the posterior horn in the cord, then in the lateroanterior funiculi to the thalamus, where they also end in the ventroposterior nuclei [48a]. Some of them appear to go to the anterior quadrigeminal bodies of the midbrain. From the ventroposterior nuclei they go to the postcentral convolution of the cortex. Some touch also goes this way. Deep sensibility goes either of the last two ways and ends also in the postcentral convolution.

Taste goes into the ganglia near the brain stem (of the VIIth, IXth, and Xth nerves) then into the nucleus and tractus solitarius, and from there to the thalamus (it is not quite clear where they end), and then, most likely, to the infraparietal plane, just next to the postcentral convolution.

Smell, finally, goes to the glomeruli of the olfactory bulb where contact is made with the mitral cells, which, in their turn, conduct the impulses to the prepyriform area of the brain. This is on the medial and the inner side of the temporal lobe; from there somehow they must reach the neocortex, but exactly how and where is still a mystery.

This rapid survey, sketchy though it is, shows at least that all incoming impulses have gone through several nuclei or "filters" before they reach the cortex. What these filters do is still largely conjectural, but it is clear at any rate that only a fraction of what comes in at the sense organs can be transmitted to the cortex. That appears to be true in almost all cases; it may not hold true for the acoustic system.

We know a little more in the case of the eye. There are something like 100 million receptors, and only about 1 million ganglion cells in the retina. There may not even be more than about 500,000 fibers in the optic radiation from the lateral geniculate body to the striate area. In principle the same thing appears to hold true for the somesthetic system, and certainly for the olfactory system, where there are millions of receptors and only about four thousand glomeruli. But this narrowing down of information may be more than compensated for by the ability to perceive forms and what is known technically as *Gestalten*.

But the cortex receives not only sensory impulses; it also receives unspecific impulses from the reticular substance of the brain stem which appear to arouse it to proper activity. This reticular substance, the importance of which was only realized during the last ten years or so, occupies a comparatively large space in the brain stem and consists of cells and myelinated fibers. It has been studied in great detail by Olszewski and Baxter [44], Brodal [8a], Scheibel [51a], and others. It can be subdivided into numerous nuclei.

OPTIC SENSATIONS

Although we fully realize that the brain is, first of all, an apparatus for steering the motions of the body, we shall follow the time-honored order of describing first the sensory and then the motor system. Among the sensory systems we shall single out the optic system, since we know somewhat more about it than about the other systems.

Recall that there are roughly 100 million rods and cones in the retina, and only about 1 million fibers from the retina to the lateral geniculate body, and there may be only half a million fibers from there to the striate area in the cortex, the end station of the visual radiation. The metric of the striate area differs profoundly from that of the outside world. Just consider how a circle will look on the striate area. It consists of two half circles, each lying in one hemisphere. Moreover, they are not semicircular, but rather distorted. The *corpus callosum* may provide a connection between the two halves, but no clear evidence as to the presence of callosal fibers between the two striate areas exists. Also, when the *corpus callosum* is cut, no serious deterioration in the appearance of the circle occurs. All this is hard to reconcile with a strict isomorphic representation of an object in the brain. Moreover, we constantly move our eyes by a few degrees, so that the image of the circle should also move, since it does not fall on the same cones (or rods) in the retina. But that is, as everybody knows, not the case. This *Konstanz der Sehdinge* has also never been explained.

If, on the other hand, we fix in a dark room a solitary light, this light will soon begin to move, sometimes to quite a large extent, although it stays on the same, or roughly the same, point of the striate area. Also, when we see objects at various distances, their images will fall on different parts of the striate area, yet the size of the object appears to remain essentially unaltered. Under unusual conditions this does not hold, e.g., on photographs of unusual objects, taken at an unusual magnification. But these are comparatively rare exceptions. By and large, the *Konstanz der Sehdinge* is a fact, but it is quite inexplicable to the neuroanatomist.

One might make here the interjection that the optic impulses do not go to the striate area exclusively, but to some other part of the brain (midbrain) as well. But numerous experiences have shown that, after destruction of the striate area, the patient is unable to see any shapes, only light. There are practically no cases of total destruction of the striate area, but partial destructions are not uncommon in war wounds and lead to partial blindness [25]. Experiments with monkeys show that no vision of form is retained after destruction of the striate area [27], but the animals continue to respond to light.

Incoming impulses can impinge in the striate area on a variety of neurons. Some are not affected by incoming impulses at all. There are "on" neurons, "off" neurons, and "on-and-off" neurons. These observations were made by Jung and others [4, 22, 23, 24] on the cat. Among 76 neurons, they found five different types: those which did not respond to light; those which responded with an "on" effect; those which were inhibited by light and by the "off" light; those which showed an "off" effect; and those which showed both an "on" and an "off" effect. In their investigations, there were about 25 per cent *B* neurons, 5 per cent *D* neurons, 20 per cent *E* neurons, and 3 per cent *C* neurons. The *A* neurons comprised about half of all the neurons encountered. The investigators point out that all this makes for a very steady activity of the cortex, in spite of great differences in the intensity of light that enters the eye. But the processes which go on in the striate area after a light stimulus has struck the eye are more complicated than we thought formerly.

Objects within a wide range are judged to be of about the same absolute size, regardless of whether they appear small because they are far away or large because they are close. It is clear that the intervening space, when it is filled with other objects, plays a role in this phenomenon. "Texture" of this space is of importance in judging the distance, as Gibson pointed out [17, 18].

The former experiences of objects, such as circles and triangles, are of importance, and this has been confirmed by von Senden [60] in his analysis of cases born blind and operated on in later life, thus finally regaining vision. While some of von Senden's cases are of no more than anecdotal value, particularly the older ones, others are well documented and should be taken seriously. In any event, the conclusion just stated appears to be true. Von Senden's conclusions have recently been confirmed by Riesen, who reared two chimpanzees in total darkness for sixteen months. When he brought them out, it took these animals a long time to learn to use their vision in an appropriate manner [49].

In the human cases, even the recognition of simple forms, such as a triangle or a square, was at first impossible; it only came subsequently, and in some older or less intelligent persons never. This fact should be emphasized because it shows that recognition, even in a comparatively simple sensory act, involves just that—re-cognition. In other words, recognition cannot take place without sensory traces with which the sensed object can be compared.

In all sensory systems there are fibers which run from the center to the periphery. These have been shown for the eye, the ear, and the nose. Their functional significance is obscure, but it is generally assumed that they in some way attune the peripheral organ to the sensory stimuli which hit the organ. It may be a change of threshold, thus ensuring a more even transmission of intensities to the brain than would otherwise be the case.

This may be linked up with what Kluver [27] pointed out some years ago, namely that the cortex is mainly concerned with keeping the external milieu as constant as possible. To return once more to the visual system, we see indeed that the intensities of visual stimuli vary enormously, but that the subjective intensities vary over a much narrower range.

Whether the area surrounding the striate area, the so-called "parastriate area," has to do exclusively with vision is a disputed point. The parastriate area is much smaller in animals than in man, so that its importance may well be missed in animal experimentation. But, both in the rat and in the monkey, Lashley [32] found that retention of habits based on vision is only abolished when the striate area itself is destroyed, not when the surrounding tissue has been removed. On the other hand, stimulation of the parastriate area in patients gave rise to the perception of movements, while that of the striate area proper gave rise to steady figures [15]. In other words, the question cannot be considered settled.

What comes out of this survey is that even quite simple facts of perception cannot be explained anatomically or physiologically in a straightforward manner. It always appears easy at first to set up a correspondence between neural events and sensation, but if we try to work this out in detail, we land in more problems than facts and we finally have to admit that we can say very little.

SENSORIUM COMMUNE

The problem of the sensorium commune goes back to Aristotle, as everyone knows. Beyond saying that it is in the cortex, we probably cannot go. For in all higher activities the cortex appears to work as a whole. That the various parts may be involved with different intensity or in different patterns is probably true. The parietal lobe is probably the first part to be involved, situated as it is between the optic, the acoustic, and the somesthetic fields, but activity stretches to the frontal lobe and to the limbic region in a manner which we do not fully understand.

Von Weizsäcker [61] and many others have emphasized that considering the two sides, sensory and motor, divorced from each other—in a sort of vacuum, as it were—is artificial and leads to a lack of understanding. They are actually intimately connected, and any sensory deficit will lead to a motor impairment and vice versa.

MOTOR OUTPUT

The main business of the brain has always been to do something rather than to contemplate serenely [55]. Memory plays a paramount role in sensation and perception; in action, forecasting plays a similarly important role, which is frequently only imperfectly realized. Moreover, it is well known that with training, movements are performed with greater ease and probably actually with less expenditure of energy. This can only mean that the coordination of muscular activity has been improved. There is little doubt that we can learn to innervate our muscles properly, and also that this process is completely involuntary.

The next problem is: How does the brain steer the motor mechanisms, e.g., the muscles? For obviously something is first in the mind and then becomes an overt movement of some sort or other. Again, we must confess to our ignorance as to the exact way in which that happens. We know that always there is first an intention to do something, and then the actual execution follows. This was called by Liepmann [35] the *Bewegungsentwurf* and has, in some form or other, survived till now. Where it is formed is a question that cannot be answered so easily. Liepmann's apraxia can be provoked by lesions in the parietal as well as in the frontal lobe, so we have probably to assume that the *Bewegungsentwurf* can be equally far strewn over the cortex. From these large areas, the impulses funnel down to those cortical areas from which the fibers to the deeper parts of the brain and spinal cord originate.

These fibers are grouped traditionally into pyramidal and extrapyramidal fibers. This distinction has of late been very much attacked [10, 43] and perhaps cannot be upheld. The arrangement of the extrapyramidal centers has recently been explained by Bucy in a number of diagrams to which the reader may be referred [10]. All the extrapyramidal nuclei evidently funnel directly or indirectly into the reticular substance, and from there reach the spinal cord over a chain of short neurons, while the pyramidal fibers go directly from the cortex to the spinal cord. We do not know anything about the timing of these impulses. What we do know is that they all seem to arrive in good time to influence the muscles.

The prevailing ideas about the pyramidal system are extremely naïve. Coghill [11] pointed out some years ago that the first function of the pyramidal system was to suppress the mass action which is the original mode of the working of the animal body. In a newt, for example, the whole body moves upon an impulse impinging upon any part of its surface. In man, only a very restricted group of muscles will respond to any stimulus. The young baby, when it wants to lift up its head or move its legs, will still move numerous muscles which have nothing to do with the movement in question. When the pyramidal tracts have developed, only small groups of muscles will become involved. The spasticity after a lesion of the pyramidal tract, the positive Babinski, are probably signs of primitive inhibitory function of the tract.

That the spinal cord alone is capable of a certain amount of coordination has been shown time and again. Goltz [19] was probably the first to show that a spinal dog, when pinched at one hind foot or the tail, will make alternate movements with his hind legs. To some extent, this was confirmed later in man by von Monakow [59], who observed that patients with transverse lesions of the cord will, on peripheral stimulation, flex a leg and then, after a fairly long time (up to a minute), stretch it out again and flex the other leg and extend it again. Further repetitions of these movements have not been observed in man.

What the cortex does can better be circumscribed by such phrases as "The cortex wants to have the limb in such and such a position," rather than "The cortex wants the contraction of such and such muscles." The work of Gellhorn [16], who showed that cortical simulation had different effects according to the proprioceptive inflow, points in the same direction.

With this in mind, we can perhaps say that the main purpose of the pyramidal tract is to send down to the cord a more or less general idea of what should happen, leaving the details to the apparatus that is in the cord itself. They send down, in other words, a command of the goal to be achieved, leaving the details of how to achieve it to the internuncials and the anterior horn cells. But this general information is not sufficient to assure a smooth execution of movements. We also need an extra-pyramidal apparatus. Schaltenbrand and Hufschmidt [51] have likened the activity of these centers to that of a brake and a spring, the pyramidal tract proper exercising the function of a motor. It does not do to spin this out too finely, but as a first approximation, so to speak, it is useful.

Cortex and spinal cord are coupled only loosely in the cat: four to five impulses have to come down the pyramidal tract before the final common pathway becomes activated. In the monkey it takes fewer impulses; according to Bernhard and others [5], it may even occur immediately. Moreover, the time is variable even in the same animal; with exercise it becomes shorter, so that it may go down from five to, say, two impulses in a matter of minutes.

The cortex is essentially a forecasting mechanism, forecasting primitively only for a short space of time, but gradually in phylogenesis lengthening that span until in man the problem of infinity has become almost threateningly persistent.

If this scheme is to work, we must have a system by which the higher center is informed of what has gone on in the lower one. The ideas of *Rückmeldung* were developed by von Holst [58]. According to him, the higher center is informed of what has happened as the result of the impulses that went down to the lower center. Part of the apparatus of the muscle spindles is undoubtedly involved, but the fibers in the pyramidal system which run from the spinal cord up to the brain may also play a role here [9], as well as in numerous other systems. It cannot be our object to go into details here, but it has seemed appropriate to touch briefly on these ideas.

SPEECH

A few words should be said about speech, which occupies a unique place in the achievements of the human brain, for after all, it is only man who can use articulate speech to communicate and to impart information. Neurologically there are several peculiarities in the speech apparatus. While practically all other muscles of the body are steered by proprioception, the muscles of speech get their control from the spoken sounds—hence the congenitally deaf cannot speak properly, if at all. They are deaf-mute. In the second place, the uttering of intelligible speech demands a working together of larynx, pharynx, mouth, and lips, which can only be learned in the course of several years. Once established, it is fairly rigid; for example, it is extremely difficult to speak a foreign language without accent, since every language has its own peculiarities of pronunciation. This correlation of all the muscles cannot yet be explained neurologically.

The next question is whether we can point to certain areas in the brain which might be particularly involved in these activities. It used to be thought that Broca's and Wernicke's areas in the left frontal and the temporal lobes, respectively, were mainly involved. However, recent observations have cast serious doubts on this theory. It now appears as though aphasia can be produced by various lesions almost anywhere in the cortex [12], and it also was shown that Broca's area, at least, can sometimes be extirpated without causing aphasia [48].

ATTENTION

One of the questions that may involve either motor performance or sensory input is that of the focusing of attention. Everybody knows that most people—Caesar was supposed to have been an exception—are able to concentrate on only one or, perhaps for a short time, two things at a time. They can listen to the ticking of the clock or they can concentrate on reading or writing, but they cannot do both at the same time—at least, not perfectly. It is true that Lashley stated during a conference in 1954 that he received sensory messages both from his right great toe and from Dr. Jasper simultaneously [34], but sooner or later one of the messages might have gotten dominance. Since Lashley does not say any more, it is possible that his great toe got the upper hand, so to speak!

EMOTIONS

The fact that emotions have been located to some extent in the brain should be mentioned briefly. In 1937, Papez [45] was the first to develop a theory that large parts of what used to be considered olfactory brain really had to do with the emotional life of the individual. As somehow regulating the emotional life of the individual, he considered the cornu ammonis, the mamillary body, the anterior nucleus of the thalamus, and the medial aspect of the cerebral cortex, in particular its anterior part, area 24. This is certainly one of the circuits which may be involved. It should be noticed that it involves in the mamillary bodies a para-sympathetic center. There probably is an orthosympathetic route, going from the septal region to the anterior part of the hypothalamus via the medial forebrain bundle, although less well worked out. Of course, we know very little in detail about the working of either system. It should be further mentioned that both nucleus amygdalae and the nucleus caudatus appear somehow to be connected with it, and that it has been said by the Montreal group that the former is facilitating, the latter inhibitory. But these things are still largely in the speculative stage. The Lange-James theory of emotion, with its primacy of the bodily states, is, in any event, no longer tenable.

FREE WILL

The problem of free will is extremely complicated. While it is funda-mental to our civilization to assume that a man can do certain things or can abstain from doing them and that he is, therefore, responsible for his actions (our whole jurisprudence is built on this assumption), it is not at all sure how free he really is. Every man is born into the mental climate of his time, and it is generally possible to say how a certain person will act under certain circumstances, at least within certain limits.

Heisenberg's principle of indeterminacy has often been called in to explain the so-called "freedom of the will." Here, too, the indeterminacy is only relative. There may well be doubt whether, in nervous trans-mission, any processes are involved which are on the subatomic level. But that slight variations in the threshold of nerve cells do occur—varia-tions which may make the difference between firing and not firing—can be admitted. If we realize that this happens in thousands or millions of cells, it is conceivable that impulses may be shunted on to different paths according to the exact state in which the cells are at the time when an impulse arrives there. In this somewhat loose sense, indeterminacy may be admitted, although this has little in common with the indeterminacy as formulated by Heisenberg. Thus, within limits, we are probably free but not completely lawless. Certain values are given us, and to these standards we have to adhere.

This brings us to the question of values. Köhler [28, 29, 30] has tried to tie up the question of values with the facts of closure which had been determined by the gestalt school of psychology, of which he is now the leader. By *closure* is meant the tendency to augment figures which are defective to the status of whole figures, e.g., a circle out of which a segment of, say, 30° has been omitted will be seen, especially when tachistoscopically presented, as a whole circle. It is a far cry from here to the idea of value, but it cannot be denied that in both cases we have to do with something that *ought* to be rather than with something that *is*. In that sense, Köhler's rather ingenious explanation stands.

SUMMARY

In summary, while the idea that the life of the mind and the life of the brain are correlated seems eminently reasonable and true, we cannot yet work it out in detail. We do not know exactly what the cortex does, how consciousness or, for that matter, the metric of the outside world arises, or how we move our bodies.

At the moment, we cannot do much more than point to the difficulties inherent in the questions we have raised. It might be said at the very end what perhaps should have been said in the beginning: To equate cortical events with conscious events is certainly quite unjustified. Many processes go on in the cortex of which we are not conscious. It should not be forgotten that the cortex develops properly only in the mammals, that the lower forms must guide their lives in some other way. It is most likely that the reticular substance is the oldest coordinating mechanism, and therefore probably the oldest seat of consciousness. How much the quadrigeminal bodies contribute is simply not known, but it seems clear that only by the working together of all these parts can the life of the human mind come about. To understand that completely will require many more years of study and research.

This article could only be a summary. It is hoped that the reader will be stimulated to look further into the literature and get a broader and deeper picture of this fascinating problem.

REFERENCES

1. Auerbach, S. Zur Lokalisation des musikalischen Talentes im Gehirn und am Schädel. Beiträge 1–3. *Arch. f. Anat. u. Physiol.*, 1906, 197–230; 1908, 31–38; 1911, 1–10.
2. Babinski, J. Contribution à l'étude des troubles mentaux dans l'hémiplegie cérébrale. *Rev. Neurol.*, 1914, **22**, 845–848.
3. Bailey, P., & von Bonin, G. *The isocortex of man.* Urbana, Ill.: Univer. of Ill. Press, 1951.

4. Baumgartner, B. Reaktionen einzelner Neurone im optischen Kortex der Katze nach Lichtblitzen. *Pflüger's Arch.*, 1955, **261**, 457–469.

5. Bernhard, C. G., Bohm, E., & Peterson, I. New investigations on the pyramidal system of Macaca mulatta. *Experientia*, 1953, 9, 111–112.

6. Bohr, N. *Atomic theory and the description of nature.* New York: Macmillan, 1934.

7. Bok, S. T. *Histonomy of the cerebral cortex.* Amsterdam: Elsevier, 1959.

8. Born, M. *Physics in my generation.* London: Pergamon Press, 1956.

8a. Brodal, A. *The reticular formation of the brain stem.* Edinburgh: Oliver and Boyd, 1957.

9. Brodal, A., & Kaada, B. P. Exteroceptive and proprioceptive ascending impulses in pyramidal tract of cat. *J. Neurophysiol.*, 1955, **16**, 567–586.

10. Bucy, P. C. The basal ganglia and muscular skeletal activity. In G. Schaltenbrand & P. Bailey (Eds.), *Introduction to stereotaxis.* Stuttgart: G. Thieme, 1959. Pp. 334–353.

11. Coghill, G. E. Flexion spasms and mass reflexes. *J. comp. Neurol.*, 1943, **79**, 463–486.

12. Conrad, K. New problems of aphasia. *Brain*, 1954, **77**, 491–509.

13. Craik, V. J. W. *The nature of explanation.* London: Cambridge Univer. Press, 1943.

14. Eccles, J. C. *The physiology of nerve cells.* Baltimore, Md.: Johns Hopkins Press, 1957.

15. Foerster, O. Sensible Felder und Bahnen. In O. Bumke & O. Foerster (Eds.), *Handbuch d. Neurol.* Vol. 6. Berlin: Springer, 1933.

16. Gellhorn, E., & Bosma, J. F. Muscle tone and the organization of the motor cortex. *Brain*, 1947, **70**, 262–273.

17. Gibson, J. J. *The perception of the visual world.* Boston: Houghton Mifflin, 1950.

18. Gibson, J. J. Perception as a function of stimulation. In S. Koch (Ed.), *Psychology: a study of a science.* Vol. 1. New York: McGraw-Hill, 1959.

19. Goltz, F. C. *Über die Verrichtungen des Grosshirns.* Bonn: G. Strauss, 1881.

20. Hayek, F. A. *The sensory order.* London: Routledge, 1952.

21. Hecht, S. Energy and vision. *Amer. Scient.*, 1944, **32**, 159–177.

22. Jung, R., Baumgartner, R. v., & Baumgartner, G. B. Mikroableitungen von einzelnen Nervenzellen im optischen Kortex der Katze. *Arch. f. Psychiat. u. Nervenkrkh.*, 1952, **189**, 521–539.

23. Jung, R., & Baumgartner, G. B. Hemmungsmechanismen und bremsende Stabilisierung an einzelnen Neuronen des optischen Kortex. *Pflügers Arch.*, 1955, **261**, 434–456.

24. Jung, R., Creutzfeld, O., & Grusser, O. J. The microphysiology of cortical neurones. *German med. Mon.*, 1952, 3, 269–276.

25. Kleist, K. Gehirnpathologie. In *Handbuch d. Aerztl. Kriegserfahrungen.* Vol. 4. Leipzig: Barth, 1933. Pp. 343–1408.

26. Klose, R. Das Gehirn eines Wunderkindes. *Monatsschr. f. Psychiat. u. Neurol.*, 1920, **46**, 63–102.

27. Kluver, H. Functional significance of the geniculo-striate system. *Biol. Symp.*, 1942, **7**, 253–300.
28. Köhler, W. *The place of value in a world of facts.* New York: Liveright, 1938.
29. Köhler, W. Relational determination in perception. In L. A. Jeffress (Ed.), *Cerebral mechanisms in behavior.* New York: Wiley, 1951.
30. Köhler, W., & Wallach, H. Figural after-effects. *Proc. Amer. Phil. Soc.*, 1944, **88**, 269–357.
31. Kuhlenbeck, H. *Brain and consciousness.* New York: Karger, 1957.
32. Lashley, K. S. The mechanism of vision XVI: the functioning of small remnants of the visual cortex. *J. comp. Neurol.*, 1939, **70**, 45–67.
33. Lashley, K. S. The problem of cerebral organization in vision. *Biol. Symp.*, 1942, **7**, 301–322.
34. Lashley, K. S. Dynamic processes in perception. In J. F. Delafresnay (Ed.), *Brain mechanisms and consciousness.* Oxford: Blackwell, 1954.
35. Liepmann, H. *Drei Aufsätze aus dem Apraxiegebiet.* Berlin: Karger, 1908.
36. Lorente de No, R. Analysis of the activity of the chain of internuncial neurons. *J. Neurophysiol.*, 1938, **1**, 207–244.
37. Lorente de No, R. Architectonics and structure of the cerebral cortex. In J. F. Fulton (Ed.), *Physiology of the nervous system.* London: Oxford Univer. Press, 1938. Pp. 291–370.
38. Lorente de No, R. Limits of variation of the synaptic delay of moto-neurons. *J. Neurophysiol.*, 1938, **1**, 185–194.
39. Lorente de No, R. Synaptic stimulation of moto-neurons as a local process. *J. Neurophysiol.*, 1938, **1**, 195–206.
40. Lorente de No, R. Transmission of impulses through cranial nuclei. *J. Neurophysiol.*, 1939, **2**, 402–464.
41. Lorente de No, R. Action potentials of the moto-neurons of the hypo-glossus nucleus. *J. cell. comp. Physiol.*, 1947, **29**, 207–287.
42. Magoun, H. W., & Rhines, K. *Spasticity.* Springfield, Ill.: Charles C Thomas, 1947.
43. Meyers, R. The extrapyramidal system. *Neurology*, 1953, **3**, 627–655.
44. Olszewski, J., & Baxter, D. *Cytoarchitecture of the human brainstem.* Basle: Karger, 1954.
45. Papez, J. W. A proposed mechanism of emotion. *Arch. Neurol. Psychiat.*, 1937, **38**, 725–743.
46. Penfield, W. Some observations on the functional organization of the human brain. *Proc. Amer. Phil. Soc.*, 1954, **98**, 293–297.
47. Penfield, W. Consciousness and centrencephalic organization. *Ier Congrès International Science Neurologique*, Bruxelles. London: Per-gamon, 1957. Pp. 7–18.
48. Penfield, W., & Roberts, L. *Speech and brain mechanism.* Princeton, N.J.: Princeton Univer. Press, 1959.
48a.Poggio, A. F., and Mountcastle, V. B. A study of the functional con-tributions of the lemniscal and spinothalamic systems to somatic sen-sibility. *Bull. Johns Hopkins Hosp.* 1960, **106**, 266–316.

49. Riesen, A. H. The development of visual perception in man and chimpanzee. *Science*, 1947, **106**, 209–210.

50. Rohracher, H. *Die Arbeitsweise des Gehirns und die psychischen Vorgänge*. München: J. A. Barth, 1953.

51. Schaltenbrand, G., & Hufschmidt, H. J. The role of the extrapyramidal system in the organization of motility. In G. Schaltenbrand & P. Bailey (Eds.), *Introduction to stereotaxis*. Stuttgart: G. Thieme, 1959. Pp. 354–371.

51a. Scheibel, M. A., and Scheibel, A. B. Structural substrates for integrative patterns in the brain stem reticular core. In *Reticular formation of the brain*. Boston: Little, Brown, 1958, pp. 31–55.

52. Schultz, R. L., Maynard, E. M., & Pease, D. C. Electron microscopy of neurons and neuroglia of cerebral cortex and corpus callosum. *Amer. J. Anat.*, 1957, **100**, 369–407.

53. Sholl, D. A. *The organization of cerebral cortex*. London: Methuen, 1956.

54. Smith, H. W. *From fish to philosopher*. Ciba Edition, 1959.

55. Sperry, R. W. Neurology and the mind-brain problem. *Amer. Scient.*, 1952, **40**, 291–312.

56. Tasaki, I., Polly, E. H., & Orrego, F. Action potentials from individual elements in cat geniculate and striate cortex. *J. Neurophysiol.*, 1954, **17**, 454–474.

57. von Bonin, G. *Essay on the cerebral cortex*. Springfield, Ill.: Charles C Thomas, 1950.

58. von Holst, E. Zentralnervensystem und Peripherie in ihrem gegenseitigen Verhältnis. *Klin. Wschr.*, 1951, **29**, 97–105.

59. von Monakow, C. *Die Lokalisation im Grosshirn*. Wiesbaden: J. F. Bergmann, 1914.

60. von Senden, M. *Raum- und Gestaltsauffassung bei operierten Blindgeborenen vor und nach der Operation*. Leipzig: J. A. Barth, 1932.

61. von Weizsäcker, V. *Der Gestaltkreis*. 3. Aufl. Stuttgart: G. Thieme, 1947.

INTERRELATIONS OF PSYCHOLOGY AND THE NEUROLOGICAL DISCIPLINES

KARL H. PRIBRAM

Department of Psychiatry
Stanford University School of Medicine

With the advancement of practical and scientific knowledge through the centuries the primitive demonolatries have been generally (although by no means universally) abandoned in the domain of inorganic nature. The primitive spiritistic tradition lingers, however, under various disguises in many reputable scientific circles, and in the vast domain of human affairs probably the majority of men today believe as one of their most cherished articles of faith that the human personality comprises a physical body which is "natural" and a spirit which is unnatural and in some inscrutable way may control the movements of the natural body.

If it is true that human nature is a blend of the natural and the unnatural, then natural science is baffled—and the basic problem of psychobiology is scientifically insoluble and must be turned over to the metaphysicians. This is the opinion of many philosophers and a considerable number of biologists. Some of the latter try to evade the issue by exclusion of everything "mentalistic" from their science. That, of course, is a feckless subterfuge, for this opinion, like every other, was conceived mentally and has no existence apart from this mental act. It does no good to declare that consciousness is a negligible epiphenomenon in the face of the fact that the most significant things people do are consciously motivated and consciously directed. One does not solve a problem by leaving out the troublesome factors. . . .

Defeatism is an unhealthy scientific attitude; it is, in fact, radically unscientific, for science has a legitimate interest in everything of which we have veridical experience. We have ample scientific evidence that a man's mental processes—his thoughts and emotions—are tied in with his physical behavior in lawfully ordered ways. If we do not know just how this is done, the thing to do is to try to find out by skillfully designed experiments. The answer will never be found if the plain facts of common experience are ignored and the mental factors of behavior are left out of consideration [c. JUDSON HERRICK, *The Evolution of Human Nature*, pp. 234–236].

Introduction 120
The Mind-Brain Relationship 121
What Is Neuropsychology 121
Neural Variables Critical to Behavior 123

On the Neurology of Intention and Will: An Example of Neurobehavioral
    Analysis 124
    The Initiation of Intentions 125
        Experiment 1: the effect of food deprivation 126
        Experiment 2: the effect of amygdalectomy 126
        Interpretation of experiments 1 and 2 128
        Experiment 3: transposition 129
        Experiment 4: sequential discrimination 131
        Interpretation of experiments 3 and 4 132
    The Execution of Intentions 137
        Experiment 5 138
        Interpretation of experiment 5 138
Interrelations Among Methods 141
    Fact and Fantasy 141
    Data-gathering Methods 143
    Bridging Laws and Methods of Systematizing 146
    A Psychological, Subjective Behaviorism 149
Where the Neuropsychologist? 153
References. 155

INTRODUCTION

The task assigned me is to discuss the interrelationships between psychology and the neurological sciences. This task has been largely in the hands of philosophers of science—yet every thoughtful neurologist and many psychologists are concerned, at one time or another, with the traditional mind-brain problem. I believe that the moment is at hand for intensive inquiry into the problem, inquiry that will prove fruitful not only to philosophers but to empirical and experimental scientists and clinicians as well.

The thesis to be presented runs something like this: The widest gap today in the scientific universe of discourse, and indeed of all human discourse, is that between the humanistically oriented social disciplines on the one hand and the physical and biological sciences on the other. The bridge across the gap is held by a handful of individuals of various backgrounds whose investigations and observations are directed to the clarification of the relation between the brain and mental processes. The efforts of these individuals are contributing a body of knowledge—a body of knowledge which is appropriately named "neuropsychology." This body of knowledge can serve human endeavor much as does that of biochemistry. Today's discontinuity in the universe of discourse parallels that which existed a century ago between the physiological and physical sciences. The slogan "vitalism" characterized the issue in the nineteenth century; today "mentalism" has taken this place. A common framework for the physical and physiological sciences resulted from *experiments*—experiments such as the synthesis of urea. I believe that a framework common to the physiological and behavioral sciences is emerging from experiments—especially neurobehavioral experiments.

Neurobehavioral data are already sufficient to allow first attempts at lawful systematization. Systematic presentation of data that unite the now disparate and often discordant views of man's universe can be one of the major achievements of the second half of the twentieth century. Such an achievement can make the further step to socially practical consequences only to the extent that the presentation becomes part of the educational process. Toward this end, the suggestion is offered that neuropsychiatry, which now is practically devoid of training in any basic discipline related to its body of knowledge, make an effort to nourish the lusty neuropsychological infant.

THE MIND-BRAIN RELATIONSHIP

What Is Neuropsychology?

The empirical evidence upon which translations between psychological and neurological concepts can be based are the results of neurobehavioral experiments and observations. The systematization of such evidence constitutes the science of *neuropsychology*. By definition, neuropsychology is a reductive discipline. As such, it partakes of the characteristics of its nonreductive siblings, psychology and neurology. The three sciences differ in that the dependent variables used to gather relevant data represent the interaction of different systems of independent variables. Though all three sciences have in common a reference to *environment*—systems of independent variables that can be completely specified by the techniques of the physical sciences[1]—psychological and neurological sciences differ in the systems of variables specified by biological techniques: in the psychological sciences these systems refer to the whole organism, in the neurological sciences to only part of that organism. Neuropsychology, if it is to be effectively reductive, must relate all three systems of variables: environmental, organismic, *and* neural. When structural concepts are under consideration, these distinctions appear self-evident. However, when function is in question, the temptation arises to confound two of these three classes of independent variables. The neurologist is prone to disregard the distinction between organism and environment—psycholo-

---

[1] Social environment is excluded here for purposes of simplification. See the section *Bridging Laws and Methods of Systematizing* for an analysis of this aspect of the problem.

gizing of neural processes follows and activity in the brain-stem reticular formation becomes identified with consciousness. On the other hand, the psychologist is prone to disregard the distinction between organism and its parts—neurologizing of the psychological process is a common consequence, and drive becomes synonymous with hypothalamic function.

Three corollaries follow from these basic statements. One is a general proposition regarding the limitations of reductive disciplines. The properties of a system are not given simply by summing the properties of the component subsystems. An understanding of the wetness of water or the fact that it floats when frozen is not derived solely from an understanding of the properties of its constituents, hydrogen and oxygen. The property, coalition, cannot be understood in terms of study of the behavior of the monadic or dyadic components of the group in which the coalition forms. The neural processes uncovered by neuropsychological analysis are thus expected, at best, to have properties that critically determine those of the behavioral system—*never are the neural and the behavioral processes identical.*

Second, according to these basic statements, clinical neurology (and neurosurgery) are neuropsychological as well as neurological disciplines, since many useful concepts are derived from the neurological examination—an examination of the behavior of the patient under specified environmental conditions. Direct examination of the nervous system (e.g., by X rays) is, of course, recognized as such in the clinic, but the behavioral aspects of the neurological examination and the resulting *psychological* concepts (e.g., the visual field) are seldom recognized for what they are. The kinship between clinical neurology and experimental neuropsychology is not a superficial one and the current lack of communication between the two endeavors must be remedied.

Third, there is a danger that the neurologist and neurosurgeon—and the experimental neuropsychologist associated with the clinic—make the error of early introspectionists in psychology. The propositional verbal reports of introspections of patients whose brains have lesions or are being excited in the surgery are insufficient in themselves to provide more than the initial fragments of data for a scientific neuropsychology. Concepts derived from these fragments must be validated by the use of other nonlinguistic behavioral techniques lest ambiguity result. Statements about consciousness, sensations, and the like are sufficiently vague to allow multiple interpretations. Precision is attained when the situations in which verbal reports are obtained are varied, and several nonpropositional verbal or other behavioral dependent variables, preferably measurable ones, are used. Unless this is accomplished, identical data can be variously construed: e.g., electrical stimulation of the temporal isocortex of unanesthetized man results in verbal reports of experiences not unlike those which can be spontaneously recalled. On this basis, the interpretation has been made at one time that the temporal isocortex serves memory—at another time, that perceptions are located there. Obviously, either the data or the concepts or both are imprecise. And these deficiencies can readily be remedied (see the section *On the Neurology of Intention and Will*).

Neural Variables Critical to Behavior

This approach to the relation between psychology and neurology places emphasis on a laboratory analysis of problems that are often initially posed introspectively. Such a problem-oriented neuropsychological science need not be technique-bound and is free to search through all sorts of phenomena. After all, scientific endeavor so often begins with childlike wonders, such as the observation that one can "attend" an object other than that upon which the gaze is fixed. This wonder and the many like it are not different in kind from those concerned with the fall of an apple or the whistle of the steaming kettle. But the empirical solution to the problem differs—in the case of the falling apple or the whistling kettle, the relations are between physical objects in the environment of the observer; in the case of attention, between the observer and his environment. To overcome the difficulties posed by this difference, the first step to empirical solution of the psychological problems must be that the observer observes other observers whose reports can be collated with his own observations—the behaviorist's approach. Just as a precise specification of the variables that determine falling and whistling is possible, so also a precise specification of the variables that determine attending is possible. But only some of these variables turn out to be critical, i.e., in any system of interacting variables, only the properties of some determine the *essential* characteristics of the system as a whole. The molecular properties of water, when heated, and the dimensional properties of the opening in the tea kettle critically determine the whistle; the particular type of heating element, the shape of the kettle, and the wetness of water are irrelevant, though heat, kettle, and water are necessary constituents of the system. In like manner, though much of the organism and certain aspects of environment are necessary constituents of the systems of variables that describe attending, only some of them can be considered critical. For complex mental processes—attending, judgment, attitude, and thought—critical organismic variables appear to be located in the brain: the behavior from which these complex processes are inferred remains essentially unimpaired after a man has suffered a fairly high cervical transection of his spinal axis—an observation which has led to the notion that the head is not hollow [11]. And this notion is supported by evidence that such behaviors are deranged when the brain is injured or artificially irritated. Experiments can therefore be performed to add precision to the notion. For example, exactly what are the neural mechanisms that make it possible to fix the gaze on one object and yet respond reliably to another? Though the answer to this particular question is not yet available, answers to similar questions can be obtained. An example of such an answer follows.

ON THE NEUROLOGY OF INTENTION AND WILL: AN EXAMPLE OF NEUROBEHAVIORAL ANALYSIS

The concept of will has a peculiar place in neuropsychology today. On the one hand, experimentalists of the behaviorist tradition usually dismiss the issues subsumed as recalcitrant to direct observation. On the other, to neurologists, the terms *voluntary movement* and *willed action* are part of the everyday language used uncritically in the clinic and in the surgical amphitheater. The gap between these realms of endeavor and their universes of discourse seems indeed great. Yet *rapprochement* might be more easily achieved than appears at first glance. Properties of the "operant" of the behaviorist have been compared and identified by some with those of voluntary behavior of man [20]. A large body of evidence about intent has been gathered by those interested in clinical and social problems in psychology [24]. And the neurological data that are relevant to these issues are by no means sparse [32, 8]. Experiments undertaken to help bridge the gap are feasible.

The case for will is to be presented somewhat as follows: Certain basal forebrain structures have been shown to control relatively simple appetitive behavior, e.g., eating. The question is asked whether these structures are concerned exclusively with the regulation of such drives or whether their concern extends to other appetitive-like behavior sequences.

Experiments are described which show the effects of lesions of these forebrain systems to be due to interference with an active build-up of an adaptive neural process used by the organism to identify the invariant and recurrent properties of his environment.

Next is pursued the proposal that the organism's own behavior and its consequences become a part of the total stimulus situation which the organism internalizes. The neural nature of this internalization process is examined and its relation to error sensitivity is discussed. The suggestion is made that thus *intentions*—the identification and prediction of the consequences of actions—are initiated.

Finally, another experiment is presented to show that, once they are initiated, intentions often guide behavior somewhat independently of the immediate outcome of any particular action. Adequate or erroneous performances, even though identified, must be able to modify the existing neural representation in order to gain active control over behavior. This fact is clearly brought out by the experiment which demonstrates that several alternative, though predictable, response patterns serve equally well to reduce error. The most forward part of the frontal cortex of primates is shown to be concerned with this type of choice among the alternative performances. This choice depends not on situational variables per se and therefore not on those aspects of the model built up within the brain that deal with identifications of the properties of the environment. Rather, the choice is guided by some other neural process that determines the distribution of responses. And it is argued that it is these intentional determinants of choice that make plausible the concept of will.

The Initiation of Intentions

Operant behavior is tested in a situation in which a simple response pattern is used as an indicator of an organism's actions in that situation [10]. The apparatus used in this series of experiments is similar to the one-armed bandit familiar to those who inhabit gambling institutions. And the "willful" behavior of the monkeys, apparently guided only remotely by the outcomes of their actions, is also familiar to those who have watched any but the most "skillful" gamblers in action.

At least three sets of measures were found usefully related to the events that determine this operant behavior. One of these is the number of reinforcements obtained per unit time. Another is the rate at which the response takes place. Finally, the distribution of responses across any time unit can be specified. Perhaps the simplest of the situations in which this measurement can be applied is the so-called "fixed-interval situation." In this, an organism is permitted to make a response and, at some predetermined and equal time interval regulated by a clock, he is given a signal that the response is appropriate (a reward). In such a situation, the organism tends to group his responses in the period just prior to the occurrence of the reward. As a rule, a gradually increasing number of responses is made—the increase reaching its maximum immediately prior to the occasion for reward. When responses are recorded cumulatively over time, a smooth "scallop" describes the behavior of the organism in this situation. The three measures of the behavior already noted can be taken: (1) the number of reinforcements obtained during a training session; (2) the total number of responses per unit time (the rate of response); and (3) the shape of the response curve (the scallop), which can be determined either by recording the time between responses or by graphing the per cent of the total number of responses made during successive portions of the interval. Experiments were undertaken to find out whether these measures could be independently affected and, if they could, to note which changes in the environment and in the organism were related to each.

Experiment 1: the effect of food deprivation [35].   In this experiment, 12 rhesus monkeys were trained to press a lever in a situation in which a ½-gram food pellet appeared in a tray every 2 min, provided the lever was pressed at least once at or after 2 min had elapsed since the last pellet was obtained. Each training session lasted 2 hr and the monkeys were fed a sufficient amount of laboratory chow immediately after each session to maintain them at approximately 80 per cent of the weight which they had attained after a 3-week period of ad libitum feeding. Daily weighing assured this 80 per cent figure. All animals were tested every other day (except Sunday) for two hours until a stable level of performance was obtained. The occurrence of responses and pellets obtained was recorded in two fashions: (1) on a moving paper tape in which an ink writer stepped perpendicular to the time axis whenever the lever was pressed, and a large, very brief excursion in the direction opposite to the step indicated the delivery of the pellet; (2) on counters so arranged as to accumulate the number of responses made during each of six equal subdivisions of all of the total 2-min intervals of a testing session. In this manner, a performance graph could be constructed for each of the testing sessions or for any multiple number of such sessions to demonstrate the distribution of responses across any number of 2-min intervals. Averages of the responses of groups of animals could be established, and the variations between performances of an animal or between individual animals could be taken into account.

The aim of this experiment was to find out whether the rate or the distribution of responses was the sensitive index of changes that result from manipulations of food deprivation. The experiment consisted of the following procedure. Ten 2-hr sessions were given. Then each animal was subjected to a 72-hr fast and retested for one session, after which the prefast schedule was immediately resumed—again for ten sessions. The entire procedure was repeated once again; this time the monkeys were fasted for 118 hr before the test session.

The results are shown in Fig. 1. As can be seen clearly, the effects of food deprivation are upon the rate of response and not upon the number of reinforcements obtained nor upon the distribution of responses across the interval. Note the minimal variation between sessions and between animals. Rate, *not* response distribution, is altered when monkeys are starved from 3 to 5 days.

Experiment 2: the effect of amygdalectomy [43].   The aim of this experiment was to discover some of the neural mechanisms that regulate these alterations of the rate of response that are determined by food de-

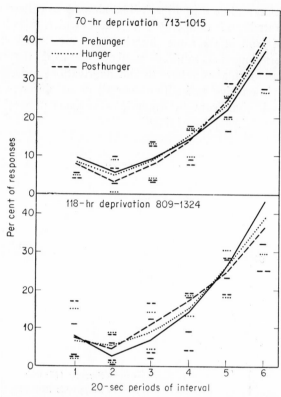

Fig. 1. Graph showing the effect of food deprivation on monkeys' rate of lever-pressing response to food (a small pellet of laboratory chow) which became available every two minutes. The change in total rate is indicated by numbers under the deprivation label. The lack of change in the distribution of responses is shown by the curves. Each curve represents the average of the responses of 10 monkeys; each point represents the average rate during a period of the interval over ten hours of testing. Variance is indicated by the short horizontal bars.

privation. From the results of earlier experiments [50], it appeared likely that bilateral removal of the amygdaloid complex in the basal forebrain would affect the rate-deprivation interaction.

The experimental procedure was essentially the same as that used in Experiment 1, except that two groups of four monkeys each were used. One served as an unoperated control group; the monkeys in the other had been given a one-stage bilateral amygdalectomy some 6 months prior to testing.

The results are plotted in Fig. 2. The changes are those in performance of operated and unoperated monkeys which follow prolonged deprivation of food in the same situations as were described in Experiment 1. When amygdalectomized monkeys are used, they are far less responsive than normal monkeys to the deprivation, although they are by no means insensitive to it. The over-all group difference averaging across sessions is significant by analysis of variants at well beyond the 0.05 level (F = 7.25 for 1 and 6 dF).

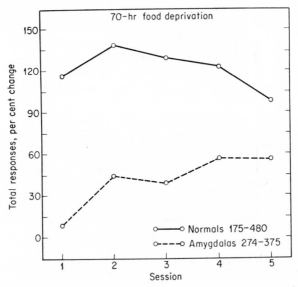

Fig. 2. Mean percentage changes in total responses of test sessions which followed prolonged deprivation of food. The values in the legend refer to the range of total responses for the three preceding control sessions on which the percentage changes are based.

Interpretation of experiments 1 and 2. How is this effect of amygdalectomy to be interpreted? Amygdalectomized animals tend to eat more in an ad libitum feeding situation [37, 43]. This would point to an increased food drive in these animals. Yet they also show decreased responsiveness to prolonged deprivation. This consistently lower level of performance with prolonged deprivation could be interpreted to show that under these conditions amygdalectomized monkeys have a lower than normal drive for food. Perhaps a single process could be conceived to be so impaired that the organism knows neither when he is hungry nor when he is sated. Or separate appetitive "start" and satiety "stop" processes could be involved and reciprocally affected by the brain lesion.

There is an alternative way to interpret the more persistent pattern of responding by the amygdalectomized monkeys. Rather than postulate an impairment specific to food hunger and satiety, the more sustained response (whether of not eating or of eating) may be symptomatic of a general disturbance in habituation processes that extends to classes of stimuli other than food. Thus, amygdalectomized animals are reported to be generally more responsive as well as persistent in their response to objects in their environment—the so-called "hypermetamorphotic reaction" (of Wernicke) described by Klüver and Bucy. The operated monkeys also show much less of a locomotor-reaction decrement with repeated tests in a novel situation [51]. These findings suggest that general habituation factors are presumably involved in so far as satiation arises from repeated exteroceptive sensory consequences of food, in addition to postingestional consequences. Amygdaloid hyperphagia would, therefore, be interpreted in terms of some form of general defect in satiation or habituation not specific to food consumption.[2]

Experiment 3: transposition [44]. In this experiment, the notion of a generalized defect in habituation was tested by examining the performance of amygdalectomized monkeys in a transposition situation. The tests were run in a modified Wisconsin General Testing Apparatus. Eight rhesus monkeys were used—four had had bilateral ablations of the amygdaloid region approximately a year prior to this experiment; four served as unoperated control subjects. The Wisconsin General Testing Apparatus was fitted with a specially designed board, 18¼ in. high and 24 in. long, that sloped toward the animal at an angle of 80° to the horizontal plane. The board contained two 4¹⁄₁₆-in. square cutouts, spaced 3¾ in. apart and 6 in. above the base, which accommodated a pair of stimulus panels measuring 4 by 4 in. Each stimulus panel was mounted on a frame hinged at the top to the board. Thus the panels could be swung open, allowing access to a small food cup located behind each one. The hinges were designed in such a way that the panels could be easily interchanged. Interposed between the board and the test cage was a movable one-way screen which shielded the board from the animal between trials. A distance of 6 in. separated the panels from the front of the test cage. Two 40-watt fluorescent fixtures mounted above and to the side of the test cage provided the illumination.

The stimuli consisted of three different shades of gray, each painted on a separate panel. The grays were prepared by appropriate mixture of a flat black and a flat white paint so as to appear spaced equally apart. When matched to the Munsell Neutral Value Scale, the following values were obtained: dark gray, N 3.5; medium gray, N 5.0; light gray, N 7.5. The board itself was finished in a flat black to provide a uniform

---

[2] For further evidence see Schwartzbaum [43].

contrasting background for the stimuli. Both the stimuli and the board were sprayed lightly with a transparent fixative to minimize fingerprints and other stains. Several panels were prepared with each of the grays so that a given panel was never used throughout a test session.

Three days of preliminary training were required to accustom the animals to operate the panels and to retrieve a food reward. In this training the Ss received 30 trials a day with two black panels. Either response was rewarded except when persistent position biases developed. In this event, the opposite response was rewarded selectively until the position habit was broken. The reward used throughout the experiment consisted of half a peanut.

The formal testing began with a simultaneous form of gray discrimination. A dark-gray stimulus was paired with a medium-gray stimulus, with the medium gray as the positive stimulus, i.e., associated with the reward, for all animals. Thirty trials a day were given, using a non-correction technique in which the positions of the stimuli were varied in a balanced order in accordance with a Gellerman procedure. The trials were spaced approximately 25 sec. apart. Training continued to a criterion of at least 90 per cent correct responses on each of 2 consecutive days.

The transposition tests followed the attainment of the criterion on the initial discrimination. The previously positive medium gray was now paired with a light-gray stimulus, and both were made positive. These conditions maximize the contribution of the prior training in the transposition performance. Six tests of transposition were carried out daily for two consecutive days during a continuation of the original discrimination procedure. Thus a total of 12 such observations was obtained. The transposition stimuli appeared in counterbalanced position on every fifth trial of these sessions. This meant that on 24 of the 30 trials the dark-gray and medium-gray stimuli were presented. On 6 of the trials the medium-gray and light-gray stimuli appeared.

The results show that the amygdalectomized monkeys tended to learn the brightness discrimination slightly more slowly than did the normal monkeys, but the differences were small and are not significant statistically. They required an average of 172 trials (range of 150 to 240) and 60 errors (range of 51 to 76) to reach criterion, exclusive of criterion performance. The normal animals averaged 112 trials (range of 90 to 150) and 48 errors (range of 34 to 69). A t test of these mean differences yields values of 2.25 and 1.60 for the two measures respectively, which for 6 df do not reach the 0.05 level. Indeed, the differences obtained are exaggerated by the fact that, of all the animals, two in the lesion group missed by 1 error, attaining criterion in 120 instead of 150 trials.

The transposition tests, on the other hand, strongly differentiated the two groups. As shown in Table 1, the normal animals markedly transposed their responses to the light gray. The over-all median for the group was 11 transposed responses out of a possible 12, with little variability among animals. In contrast, the amygdalectomized animals did not typically transpose. Their median number of transposed responses was 5.5. Three animals in the group approximated closely the chance level of performance, with perhaps a slight preference for the previously positive medium-gray stimulus. The fourth animal, which took longest to learn the original discrimination, exhibited a normal pattern of transposition.

TABLE 1. NUMBER OF TRANSPOSED RESPONSES MADE ON TRANSPOSITION TESTS

	Normals		Amygdalectomized	
	Number of subject 439 441 443 447	Median	Number of subject 397 405 438 442	Median
Day 1	6 5 6 6		2 5 2 4	
Day 2	5 5 5 6		3 6 2 2	
Total	11 10 11 12	11.0	5 11 4 6	5.5

Experiment 4: sequential discrimination [44]. In order to define better the characteristics of the impaired transposition behavior, an additional test was performed. A sequential form of brightness discrimination was presented in which the medium gray was paired randomly on different trials with either the dark gray or the light gray—in either event, the medium gray remained as the positive stimulus. If the amygdalectomized animals had indeed shown a stronger response tendency toward the previously positive stimulus of the transposition pair, then they would be expected to do relatively well on this sequential discrimination. If, on the other hand, their transposition performance had simply reflected the transient effects of a novel stimulus, then there would be little reason to expect any group differences on a test that involved frequent repetitions of the experimental condition. But in neither case would deleterious effects of the lesion be anticipated. The results obtained, however, tend to rule out both these possibilities.

The same set of Ss that completed the transposition experiment was tested on the sequential-brightness discrimination. They were given 30 trials a day, using a noncorrection technique. Each pair of stimuli appeared in a randomized order on half the trials within a session. The criterion of learning was set at 90 per cent correct responses on each of 2 consecutive days. The sequential discrimination was separated from the last transposition test by 2 additional days of training with the original pair of stimuli. All animals performed at criterion level on both of these sessions.

The results are summarized in Table 2. The number of trials required by each group to meet criterion on the sequential discrimination demonstrates clearly a deficit in the performance of the amygdalectomized animals, although they were by no means unable to learn the problem. They required about five times as many trials to reach criterion as did the normal animals ($p = 0.028$ by a two-tailed Mann-Whitney U Test). But the rapidity with which the normal animals mastered the problems must also be noted.

A comparison of the performance on the sequential discrimination with that on the original discrimination, expressed as a percentage change in the number of trials to criterion (Table 2), provides a check

TABLE 2. PERFORMANCE ON SEQUENTIAL BRIGHTNESS DISCRIMINATION

	Normals					Amygdalectomized				
	Number of subject 439 441 443 447				Mean	Number of subject 397 405 438 442				Mean
Trials to criterion*....	60	30	30	30	38	150	330	210	120	202
Per cent change from initial discrimination	−60	−67	−67	−75	−67	0	38	40	−20	14

* Excludes criterion trials.

for any initial group differences. Examination of the data shows that the groups still differed markedly on this measure of performance in the sequential discrimination ($p = 0.028$). The normal animals mastered the sequential discrimination in about two-thirds fewer trials than they took to learn the original discrimination. The animals with lesions required about the same number of trials as before.

It can be seen from Table 3 that the difficulty which the amygdalectomized animals encountered on the sequential-brightness discrimination related almost exclusively to the presentations of the transposition pair of stimuli. About 95 per cent of their total errors occurred with the transposition stimuli. This accounts for virtually all of the differences in performance between the groups on the sequential discrimination. Animal AM-405 showed this same form of impairment on the first 150 trials; then its performance pattern broke down into a more generally distributed deficit.

Interpretation of experiments 3 and 4. The transposition findings are consistent with the supposition that the effects of amygdalectomy transcend situations specific to the obtaining and consumption of food.

Amygdalectomy thus may be conceived to produce some generalized defect in satiation or habituation. And additional evidence for this view comes from an entirely different source—the results of electrophysiological experiments. Stimulations of and recordings made from the basal forebrain structures such as the amygdaloid and hippocampal regions are interpreted, e.g., by Grastyan [13], to indicate that these structures normally function to prevent repeated diversions of attention and to make it possible for conditioning to occur.

The story goes something like this: An organism's exposure to a relatively intense novel environmental stimulus is accomplished by generalized desychronization in the electrical activity recorded from both

TABLE 3. DISTRIBUTION OF ERRORS ON SEQUENTIAL BRIGHTNESS DISCRIMINATION

	Normals		Amygdalectomized	
	Number of subject 439 441 443 447	Median	Number of subject 397 405 438 442	Median
Total errors*.......	15 10 4 11	10.5	43 131 49 32 60†	46.0
Per cent total errors with transposition stimuli..........	87 100 100 91	95.5	95 76 94 100 90†	94.5

* Excludes criterion trials.
† Based on first 150 trials.

isocortex and the basal forebrain (e.g., hippocampus). This startle reaction or orienting reflex is accompanied by behavioral arrest of movement except for head and eye (and perhaps body) orientation toward the stimulating event. This initial state may give way to behavioral fight or flight. Of particular interest here, however, are those occasions where the original stimulus remains or is repeated and the organism becomes familiar with the events. In these instances, desynchronization of the isocortically recorded electrical activity continues, but hypersynchronous slow waves are now obtained from the basal forebrain. When such hypersynchrony is experimentally induced in these structures, on-going problem-solving behavior is interfered with [26] in much the same fashion as when these structures are surgically removed [15, 40]. As already noted, animals with such lesions are hyperreactive to novel stimulation. The assumption is therefore made that the slow activity in the basal forebrain reflects the cessation of its usual gating action on the central effects of novel stimuli. (This gating action is conceived to take place via the brain-stem reticular formation.)

This second stage is called the "orienting reaction"—to distinguish it from the orienting reflex—and is characterized by heightened behavioral orientation and attention to *all* aspects of the environment. With repetition of the situation, however, another stage sets in—the organism is said to "habituate." This stage is again characterized by both isocortical and basal forebrain electrical desynchronization—though the isocortical manifestation is now no longer generalized but relatively restricted, in the experimental situation, to the cortex subserving the sensory mode through which the environmental stimulus has been presented.

Even more impressive evidence for the time course of the neural activity involved in this process has been demonstrated by E. Roy John and the Killams [18], who employed electrical tracers in the form of visual-stimulus frequencies to which the brain's electrical activity becomes locked. Their tracer frequencies are found generally in recordings made from electrodes implanted in allo- and isocortical formulations during the initial stages of the problem-solving behavior of cats. As the experiment proceeds, these tracer frequencies become more limited in distribution until, during error-free performance, they are recorded only from the isocortical systems (geniculostriate) concerned with vision.

Furthermore, when such a problem-solving situation is used, W. Ross Adey [1, 2, 3] has shown, by a beautiful series of experiments, that basal forebrain electrical activity (recorded from the hippocampus) is also characteristically different in the initial startle stage of the experiment and the final conditioned stage. As habituation proceeds, a shift is recorded in electrical phase of the activity of the several layers of the hippocampal cortex. In the initial stage, the electrical activity of the layers that are connected with the brain-stem core (including the reticular formation) precedes that recorded from the layers more immediately connected to the isocortex; in the final stage, the phase relationship is reversed. In this final stage in the problem-solving situation, the behavior of the habituated organism is appropriate to the task, i.e., performance is approximately errorless. When occasional errors do occur, they are accompanied by the recrudescence of slow activity in the electrical record made from the basal forebrain!

But what is this "habituation" [45] that thus becomes so all-important? Is it merely the fatiguing-out of the neural mechanism of attention? The indications from the animal experiments already reviewed are to the contrary. Sokolov [46], in another exquisitely designed and performed series of experiments, has further demonstrated that habituation in man results to the extent that a neural representation of the stimulus is built up in the nervous system. When the input (e.g., a tone) matches this representation, no characteristic behavioral, autonomic effector, or electroencephalographic (EEG) responses can be recorded; when the input departs from prior inputs (e.g., diminution of the intensity of the tone, or making the tone shorter or longer), it reevokes the orienting responses (behavioral, autonomic effector, and EEG). This reevocation is limited to the specific occasions on, and durations over, which current input is disparate from prior inputs!

Taken together, the electrophysiological and neuropsychological evidence points to a series of specifiable stages that can be summarized as follows:

1. When exposed to a novel event, an organism takes this in—and this stage is accompanied by desynchronization of the electrical activity of both the isocortical and basal allocortical formations of the endbrain. The only behavioral concomitants of this stage are "reflex" orientation movements that focus the stimulating event. Lacey [21] has noted that this stage corresponds pretty much to "primary attention" as this was defined in introspective psychology.

2. Should this novel event recur repeatedly, remain unchanged, or change relatively slowly, another process supervenes. This is characterized by continued desynchronization in the electrical activity recorded from the isocortex, but a change in the activity recorded from allocortical structures (especially of Ammon's formation). From this neural location, slow waves (i.e., hypersynchrony) can now be recorded. Behaviorally, searching characterizes the activity of the organism. This is the orienting reaction—the organism follows the stimulating event, searches when changes occur and especially once habituation is under way. In many respects, this is similar to the secondary attention described by the introspectionists.

3. After repeated exposure to the unchanging or recurrent event, habituation has resulted. The desynchronous electrical activity recorded from isocortex has become restricted to relevant input channels and slow activity has disappeared from allocortical structures. Here, electrical phase has shifted from precedence of brain-stem input to precedence of input from isocortex. And any noted change in the situation is immediately and specifically accompanied by recrudescence of the electrical activities in both the iso- and allocortex characteristic of stage 2 (the orienting stage).

During stage 3, the actions of the organism directed toward the stimulating event may be included in the habituation process. This obtains in conditioning and other problem-solving situations. So, orienting responses reemerge when the organism's actions result in changes from the recurrent regularities that characterize the total stimulus event— e.g., when the oft-obtained reinforcing food stimulus fails to appear, or when the for-the-most-part-eliminated shock stimulus fails to be avoided.

In other words, the organism now has a mechanism for sensing error or incongruity![3] The rudiment necessary to intentional behavior is laid down.

Note that sensitivity to incongruity thus depends on maintenance of a modifiable neural representational process built up during habituation. Resection of the amygdaloid region of the forebrain could produce the reported behavior in the transposition experiments if, during the habituation that accompanied learning of the discrimination, an overly rigid representational process had been laid down. Something like a sharpening of the generalization gradient would be evident: i.e., the organism's behavior would remain invariant over a more restricted range of input events—he would be *more* sensitive to incongruity. So conceived, the normally functioning amygdaloid region is deemed necessary to the continued modification of neural representations—in the absence of the amygdaloid region, representation would become fixed, and these fixed representations would narrowly proscribe limits beyond which the organism would respond as if the situation were novel. This interpretation of the data is in essential agreement with an interpretation of the effects of amygdalectomy made earlier, but at that time restricted to behavior controlled by hypothalamic mechanisms [38]. The suggestion was forwarded then that amygdalectomy removes normal regulation on homeostatic processes—that, as a result of the surgery, the homeostat can get stuck either in a hyper- or hypo- position, depending on the current state of the organism, its experiential history, as well as the environmental situation. A considerable amount of evidence has accumulated to lend support to this suggestion [7]. However, the results of the experiments reported here emphasize that the effect is not restricted to feeding or other situations usually thought to involve the organism's control of its internal environment. If this analysis proves viable, the amygdaloid region and its neighbors contain neural mechanisms that operate to control the organism's behavior with respect to his external environment as well.

Specific aspects of this mechanism can be further tested in the laboratory. The effect of amygdalectomy on measures of the orienting response (autonomic effector, EEG, and behavioral) can readily be determined. The effect of such lesions, and those of other basal forebrain structures, on an organism's sensitivity to error and other forms of incongruity in various situations can be explored and the element common to this increased sensitivity can be traced. And so on.

Intent is thus initiated. The mechanism to identify environmental regularity is set up in the organism by virtue of a neural representation of

[3] The prediction can be made from this formulation that only when a reinforcing event occurs at a perceptibly different level or in a perceptibly different pattern from average prior occurrences will it guide subsequent behavior.

the prior recurrences of these invariances. Whenever this representation includes regularities in the organism's own behavior and the outcome of that behavior, identification of the outcomes of actions can become possible—i.e., intentions can be initiated. Flexibility with respect to the representational process that initiates these intentions appears related to the functions of basal forebrain structures.

The Execution of Intentions

So much for the initiation of intentions. Now for their execution. A quotation serves as an appropriate introduction to the relationship between the initiants of intention and their execution, between the behavioral operant and willed action. In his chapter on Lewinian theory Hilgard states that—

. . . this is not unlike Skinner's later notion of the role of the discriminative stimulus in operant behavior: the stimulus does not elicit the behavior, but it does set the occasion for it. The sequence of events from perception [attention] to satiation [habituation] is as follows. The perception of an object or event may give rise to a psychological tension or it may communicate with a state of tension already existing, in such a way that this tension system thereupon assumes control over motor behavior. The aroused "valences" act as environmental forces steering subsequent behavior. This behavior then leads to satiation or to the resolution of tension so that a state of equilibrium is approached [14, p. 212].

As a result of the recently reported experiments already summarized, a somewhat more neuropsychological statement can be made to describe this sequence. When an organism observes a novel event, an orienting response occurs. This initiates or modifies (Lewin says "gives rise to or communicates with") a representational process in the brain of the organism (Lewin terms this "psychological tension"). In a task situation, this representation comes to include the organism's own behavior and its outcome ("assumes control over motor behavior," according to Lewin). Any deviation from recurrent behavioral regularities and invariant outcomes signals error. (Lewin speaks of "aroused valences that steer subsequent behavior.") The resultant modification of the behavior with respect to the representational process leads to habituation ("satiation," "the resolution of tension," in Lewin's words).

Some further notion as to what occurs as the representational process assumes control over behavior can be obtained from additional neurobehavioral analysis of the fixed-interval operant. As already noted, performance in this situation is reflected not only in the over-all rate of reward and response, but also in the distributions of responses across the interval between reinforcing events. Obviously, neither the over-all rate of response nor the scallop is a measure of the *accuracy* with which the behavior meets the contingency of the situation—only rate of reward measures this. Other descriptive notions must be employed to cover differences in response rate and distribution. For instance, a conservative approach would characteristically lead to a lower over-all rate of response, whereas a rapid banging-away-at-the-bar might be more fun. Both would be equally effective, as measured by the total number of rewards obtained during the experimental session. When changes in food deprivation alter the response rate, accuracy of response to the situation is not affected. Habituation takes place, i.e., the neural representational process is altered except in animals that have had amygdalectomy. One could describe the events as follows: Food deprivation disposes the animal to behave less conservatively; this shows up, in the experimental as well as in other situations, in heightened generalized reactivity. But note that the distribution of responses across the interval remains unaltered and the animals invariably get their due. Though amygdalectomy helped with the analysis of habituation, some other neural mechanism must be sought if the relation between the representational process and the regulation of response *distribution* is to be understood. Study of the scallop should give clues about the manner in which the representational process steers the organism's actions. The scallop is, in a way, an externalization in behavior of the mechanism by which the organism's neural representation of the situation and his actions in that situation are connected—*viz* an externalization of his intentions with respect to the situation.

Experiment 5 [35]. The procedure of this experiment was identical to that in Experiments 1 and 2, except that the monkeys were always fed regularly every 24 hr. Twelve monkeys were used—three received bilateral frontal eugranular cortex removals; three others were given control lesions that consisted of bilateral resection of the inferior portion of the temporal isocortex; the remaining six monkeys served as unoperated controls.

The results shown in Fig. 3 reveal no differences between the over-all rates of response between groups as a result of the experimental procedures. On the other hand, the frontal lesion selectively alters one aspect of the behavior—the scallop. That is, the crescendo-like distribution of responses across the interval is flattened in this group of monkeys, whereas no such effect is obtained in the two control groups. This effect of frontal ablation on fixed-interval behavior is thus considerably different from the effects of starvation and of amygdalectomy.

Interpretation of experiment 5. In view of the fact that the frontally lesioned animals invariably and selectively press the lever when the reinforcing occasion demands, the change in their behavior cannot be attributed to a loss in their ability to make temporal discriminations—they continue to identify the occasion when reward is to appear. The neural representation of the problem situation seems adequate. So to what can the alteration in behavior be ascribed?

Those who have used operant conditioning techniques have emphasized that very different patterns of responding are elicited in the operant situation by different schedules of the occasions for reinforcement. But this is not all. Equally important is the observation that a variety of manipulations, especially manipulations of the organism by means of drugs and brain stimulations and ablations, result in *different* response patterns in the *same* situation. To take this into account, the operant, just as the gambling situation, can best be looked at as a task or a game. The rules that describe the situation are programed as schedules of discriminative and reinforcing stimuli. But nothing happens unless the organism works at the task or plays the game. He thus must acquire sufficient know-how in the situation to meet the schedules and to *make* the events happen with some recurrent regularity. He must actively develop a strategy to guide his behavior and, as already noted, a variety of strategies can be used to meet the rules of the situation. Thus one must infer not only that a neural representation of the rules of the situation is set up in the organism, but that, as habituation to the task

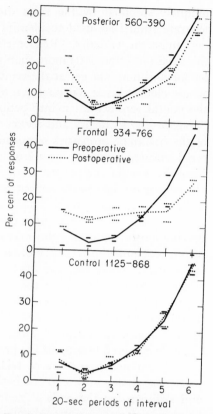

FIG. 3. Graph showing the change in distribution on monkeys' response rate following frontal intrinsic-sector ablation (three monkeys). Note that the distribution of rate over the interval is not affected in the controls (four monkeys) and after posterior intrinsic-sector ablations (three monkeys). Also note that the total rate of response did not increase; rather, rate was somewhat decreased, probably due to the ad-libitum feeding period which all groups were given prior to operation—approximately two weeks before postoperative testing. (Compare with Fig. 2 and see legend to that figure.)

or game occurs, processes for guiding behavior with respect to the representation become available to the organism. In short, a variety of successful performances is possible; they have properties that can be described and measured; and further, the several varieties are not uniquely specified by the rules that describe the situation. A process separate from that used to identify the rules must therefore operate to determine the varieties. "Response chaining" has been suggested to fill this need but offers little more than a descriptive label of the observed behavior and does not get at the regularities in the differences between response chains. What is necessary is a description of the processes that map the neural representation into action. These processes have been called "plans"—the strategies and tactics that connect a neural representation of the invariant properties of a situation with action [28]. Whereas the error-sensing, congruity-incongruity processes determine the organism's identifications of the properties of his environment, plans determine his choice among alternative actions appropriate to these identifications.

The results of Experiment 5 can thus be readily interpreted. Bilateral ablation of the frontal eugranular cortex alters the crescendo distribution of responses. However, it leaves intact both the over-all rate of response and the accuracy of responding with respect to the occasions for reward. Therefore, the effects of the lesion cannot be attributed either to an impairment in the build-up of the neural representational process nor to an impairment of its modifiability. The effect must then be on those other processes that connect the neural representation with action—plans. A wealth of other neuropsychological data can now be properly gathered to support the propriety of this interpretation.

Clinical neurologists have taken for granted that removals of the precentral motor cortex affect both willed and skilled actions [8]. Will and skill can, on the basis of neuropsychological evidence and analysis, be given separate operational definitions. Intention and volition will refer to processes whose properties are largely determined by plans. Skills, on the other hand, refer to processes whose properties are much more intimately meshed into identifications of the environmental situation and especially to the outcomes of action. In the case of skills, the regularities in behavior sequences are sensitive to patterns and schedules of environmental contingencies. This is essentially the same as the classical view of operant conditioning. In the case of will, however, behavioral regularities cannot be ascribed to the rules, but are attributed to the development by the organism of a variety of intentions or strategies to meet the rules. The results of Experiment 5 suggest that interference with intention, or will thus defined, is a function of the anterior frontal eugranular and not of the precentral agranular isocortex. The results of other experiments have also shown that, in spite of resulting clumsiness, the sequence of actions used in opening a latch box is not impaired by precentral-motor-cortex ablations whereas these sequences are disrupted by anterior frontal lesions [16, 17, 39]. The prediction can therefore be ventured and tested that anterior frontal lesions would, and precentral lesions would not, affect the scallop—the distribution of responses in the fixed-interval situation. And such a result would strengthen the body of evidence—obtained from introspection, from ordinary social communication about the problem, and from social and clinical observation and experimentation—that will and skill can be usefully distinguished.

The contribution of neurobehavioral experiments can thus be placed in proper perspective. Such experiments—as in the examples shown—are often useful in defining issues in the behavioral sciences. The data obtained bridge the gap between the realms of discourse used in social and psychological—yes, even philosophical and humanistic—communications and those used in the biological and physical sciences. And in addition, a great deal of understanding is obtained about how the brain functions to regulate behavior.

The novelty of recently attained understanding generates enthusiasm, and therefore some overstatements and overgeneralizations occasionally are made. (In spite of caution, these may have crept into the preceding pages, for it is a new and provocative story that is told.) And whenever such errors in judgment result, the scientific process (of error sensing) counters the excesses—and scientists, through disillusionment, hard work, and *critical* analysis, restore balance between their neural representations and the state of their art. The following sections deal with these equally important but somewhat less substantive problems of the relation between psychology and neurological disciplines.

INTERRELATIONS AMONG METHODS

Fact and Fantasy

One of the major deterrents to precision in interdisciplinary investigations is confusion between data and theory. Both fact (from the Latin *factum,* to make) and theory are scientific constructions based on the observation and manipulation of variables. Facts can be distinguished as being either theoretically neutral or systematic. The distinction is, however, as can be seen from the pursuit of the example detailed in the section *On the Neurology of Intention and Will,* a complicated one. In the early phases of a science, experimentally produced relations—data—are readily communicable as such. However, as the data-gathering process proceeds, a short-cut terminology begins to dominate communication: *neuron, reflex, inhibition, synapse, PTO cortex, association areas, limbic systems* on the neurological side; *SD, cue, reinforcement, fixed-interval schedule, stimulus, expectation, action, utility, outcome* on the behavioral side. To the group conversant in the terminology—usually the group that has created it—each word or phrase denotes a specific body of knowledge; there is often very little theory involved. But when the base of communication is broadened, differences in the connotative meaning of the phrases arise, since the communicants are not all equally conversant with the data denoted by the phrases. As long as the terminology is denotative, i.e., short-cut for data, the difficulties in communication are surmountable. Explication using longer descriptions, pictorial and graphic material, and direct demonstration can be resorted to. When, however, in addition to the short-cut jargon of the laboratory, intervening constructs are postulated and these postulations or hypotheses are referred to by short-cut phrases (e.g., "habit strength," "drive," "excitatory potential") that become intermingled with those denoting data, communication, though not impossible, becomes cumbersome. Paradoxically, this lack of true communication is often glossed over by a communicative effort that appears to succeed—the translation of the phrases that refer to one system of hypotheses into the phraseology that refers to another such system (e.g., Hullian into Freudian). Such translations, many times removed from data, provide a feeling of satisfaction much as does autistic thinking; unfortunately, little of enduring value is accomplished by either.

Thus, one distinction between theoretically neutral and systematic variables can be made. Whenever laboratory argot refers to data (the relation between independent and dependent variables) one might say that language is theoretically neutral; when intervening variables, and especially systems of such variables are referred to, then the language is certainly not theoretically neutral. But this is not the whole story. *All* words have connotative as well as denotative meanings. Most words are chosen by the scientist, intentionally or not, because of the body of knowledge a phrase connotes, as well as for the appropriateness to the data to be denoted. Operational definitions overcome this difficulty as long as the communicative base is restricted. Such definitions fail to convey meaning when the defining operations are far beyond the acquaintance of the communicants. In these instances, and they are the ones of interest in a discussion of the interrelationships between sciences, *the phrases used denotatively in one science become constructs to the investigator in another science.* The behaviorist can either accept or reject the neurologically derived concept of a "hypothalamus" or a "neuron"; the neurologist can either accept or reject the behaviorally constructed conception of "reinforcement," or "expectation." Neither the psychologist nor the neurologist can modify, on the basis of data, the total conception put forth by his colleague. I believe, therefore, that these conceptions are not, per se, theoretically neutral; neutrality is restricted to the occasions when those who use the concepts are intimately acquainted with the data the conceptions denote.

A final step, by way of a relating experiment, is necessary before the facts of one science become more than hypothetical constructs for other sciences. Once this is accomplished, phrases, though they denote systematic variables, again become theoretically apparently neutral to the communicants involved. "Willed action" or "voluntary movement," already discussed, and "visual field" are cases in point. The concept— visual field—originates introspectively (as it is differentiated from one's visual world) [12], but is in the main derived from behavioral data. The visual field is that extent of the environment to which an organism can respond with one eye without moving that eye. The phrase "visual field" stands for the systematization of (1) extent of environment as independently specified by physical techniques, e.g., measuring arc; (2) fixation of vision—having an organism look at one point but attend to the surround of that point; (3) make a verbal or instrumental discriminative response that is to represent seeing, i.e., looking and attending; and (4) in the final analysis, the phenomena subsumed under "I see." Further, the clinician uses details of the specification of the critical organismic variables that determine the visual field to good purpose. For example, a bitemporal hemianopia suggests a chiasmatic lesion. One hardly stops to ponder the theoretical neutrality or lack thereof of the psychological term *vision* or the physical term *field*. There are sufficient data denoted by phrases such as "arc," "lens," "eye," "optic nerve," "chiasm," "optic tract," "geniculostriate system," to make the term *visual field* theoretically neutral, and, to all intents and purposes, fact. This neutrality is shaken, however, when new groups of investigators gather new data and choose to apply this supposedly neutral term to denote their data. Thus, recent discoveries regarding the effects of extrageniculostriate cerebral lesions on the discriminations from which visual fields are inferred have led to confusions [5, 30]. These confusions will not be resolved until new limits are accepted—limits that specify which operations usefully define the concept of visual field.

Data-gathering Methods

The interrelations between psychology and the neurological sciences can be conceived in another fashion. Interrelationships of method are again basic to the development of any reductive discipline. But methods are of two sorts: (1) data gathering, and (2) systematic. So we are back to earlier discussions. In order to be of immediate relevance, data must be so gathered that both neurological and behavioral concepts can be constructed from them. In other words, neural and behavioral variables (as well as environmental, of course) determine the data.

When methods are used to study only the behavior of the total organism in its environment, the resulting data have only an indirect bearing on neuropsychological formulation—judicious guesses perhaps dignified as hypothetical constructs. Such guesses provide considerable satisfaction to large numbers of behavioral scientists. Of course, when neurobehavioral data become sufficient (as in the determination of the visual field) precise inferences regarding the neural variables can be made from the behavioral data and these can, in turn, lead to further empirical neurological explorations. As already noted, clinical neurology and neurosurgery utilize this method to good advantage. But neurobehavioral data are rarely available in such quantity to the behavioral scientist—thus the necessity for neurobehavioral experiment.

The neurological clinician and scientist usually faces a somewhat different problem. Neurobehavioral data are available to him, but they are imprecise. Both the neural and the behavioral variables have, as a rule, been only grossly specified. Lesions are in the "front" or in the "back" parts of the brain; consciousness is perhaps "altered"; intelligence is "impaired." Refinements are proceeding in several clinics and their laboratories. Progress is in part dependent on increasing the precision of introspectively specified concepts by improving the instrumental tasks used in the neuropsychological analyses—recent advances in this regard have been rapid [25, 29, 31, 47, 49].

Some examples may serve to highlight a few of these empirical problems associated with interdisciplinary research. The assessment, control, and manipulation of neural variables in neurobehavioral experiments often lead to heated discussion. Proponents of electrical stimulation decry the limitations of lesion and ablation techniques, and vice versa. The specific value of the neural-ablation technique is that a relatively stable preparation results. Such stability with respect to the neural variables allows, *par excellence,* the exploration of the experiential and immediate environmental variables that also determine behavior. Stimulation, electrical and chemical, of nervous tissue provides a different asset—relative reversibility of the process. This reversibility allows repeated controls to check the reliability of the phenomenon observed. However, each laboratory and clinical procedure is restrictive in one way or another—laws and concepts are attained *only* from judicious combinations of the available procedures. For the behavioral as for the physical sciences, experiments in which obvious limitations are imposed often provide the key to understanding. The laws of mechanics were possible only after experiments were accomplished in which the behavior of a sphere or an inclined plane could be observed—watching birds in flight could initiate the problem, not solve it. Neuropsychological laws are more likely to result from experiments in which the behavior of brain-lesioned monkeys is observed in an operant conditioning or a discrete trial-discrimination apparatus than from watching people with normal brains behave in unstructured situations.

Since neural function in behavior is the prime interest of the neuro-psychologist, the body of data must include the results of an extensive exploration of relevant environmental variables. In the past, failure to realize this has led to so-called "inconsistencies of neurobehavioral fact." As recently as a decade ago, the notion was prevalent that neurobehavioral data, both animal and human, were destined to be totally unreliable. Results of experiments and observations were difficult to replicate. The history of frontal lobotomy and the now-famous story of the amygdalectomized Baltimore cats [4] versus the Washington cats [42]

DAVE 1
Dominant, self-assured, feared

ZEKE 2
Aggressive, attacker

RIVA 3
Aggressive, active

Hierarchy before any operation

HERBY 4
Placid, unaggressive

LARRY 8
Submissive, cowering, frequently attacked

SHORTY 7

ARNIE 6
Noisy, eager

Submissive to others, aggressive towards Larry

BENNY 5
Alert, active food getter

Fig. 4. Dominance hierarchy of a colony of eight preadolescent male rhesus monkeys before any surgical intervention.

are cases in point. Amygdalectomy resulted in rage in one situation, in taming in the other; in hyposexuality in the hands of the Hopkins investigators, in hypersexuality when the Walter Reed group studied their animals. The cat controversy—as most of the others—has yielded to greater precision in method. The recently reported Hollywood cats [9] show that when adequate control of *both* the environmental and the organismic variables is accomplished and a sufficient behavioral repertoire is explored, discrepancies all but vanish: The behavior of amygdalectomized cats is that of normal cats in home territory; after surgery cats can no longer make the distinction between home and foreign territories.

Another example of the clarification of the diversity of the effects of brain operations on social behavior is illustrated in Figs. 4, 5, 6, and

7 [33]. As can be seen, the effects of amygdalectomy are as much a consequence of the immediately postoperative dominance situation as they are the consequence of locus of the lesion.

Such are some examples of the special ambiguities that brain ablation and clinical neurological lesion studies encounter unless precautions are undertaken to ensure precision. These special problems have been dealt with at length in an earlier paper [33]. It is sufficient to note here

ZEKE 1
Dominant, aggressive

RIVA 2
Daring, competes
with Zeke

HERBY 3

Hierarchy after Dave's operation

BENNY 4

LARRY 7
Dominates and
attacks Dave

SHORTY 6

DAVE 8 (1)
Completely sub-
missive, fearful

ARNIE 5

FIG. 5. Same as Fig. 4 after bilateral amygdalectomy had been performed on Dave. Note his drop to the bottom of the hierarchy.

that *properly* used, satisfying precision can be attained today from these much maligned surgically and pathologically produced data from which stem practically all of our knowledge about the relations between brain and behavior.

Bridging Laws and Methods of Systematizing

But methods are not all observational and experimental. Analysis and treatment of data are as important as data gathering. Neurologists especially have been prone to consider precision in data analysis to be unnecessarily statistical or a matter of semantics. After all, does it really matter whether we say "afferent" or "sensory"; "efferent" or "motor"?

Afferent and efferent refer to neural data; motor and sensory refer to behavioral data. The terms began to lose their distinction as a result of the overgeneralization of the law of Bell and Magendie. The result—considerable confusion and, in addition, suppression of findings such as direct afferents reaching the precentral motor cortex; eye movements obtained from stimulation of the occipital visual area [27, 34].

Of equal importance is the resistance of some psychologists to an attempt at rigorous formulation of psychological concepts. Protests that one is defining the problem out of existence are voiced when an attempt

RIVA 1
Dominant, not
threatened by others

HERBY 2

BENNY 3

ARNIE 4

Hierarchy after Zeke's operation

ZEKE 7 (1)
Submissive to others,
intermittently aggres-
sive toward Dave

LARRY 6

SHORTY 5

DAVE 8
Cringer, avoids
interaction

FIG. 6. Same as Figs. 4 and 5, except that both Dave and Zeke have received bilateral amygdalectomies.

is made to give operational definitions of concepts such as those of will, intention, reinforcement, anxiety, or stimulus, even when the difficulty of the problem becomes apparent only after such attempts at definition [22, 23, 36, 48]. In a similar manner, there is often heard an outcry against the use of precise models—physical or mathematical. The accusation runs that analogical thinking is fuzzy thinking, but this is not necessarily so. According to the view taken here, all behaviorally derived concepts are in the final analysis (or the initial one, or both) analogically compared with introspectively derived concepts. The properties of the one are in some ways similar and in some ways different from those of the other. The more precise the conceptual tools, the more precise can be the comparison. But comparison it is, whether or not it is precise. The visual process can be specified in terms of images or in terms of transformations on environmental events. In one case, the model is apt to be a camera; in the other, systems of electromechanical devices or mathematical equations. Models are practically always used (implicitly

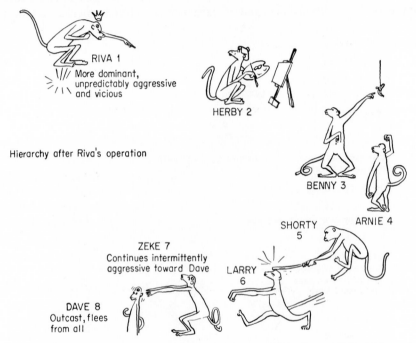

RIVA 1
More dominant,
unpredictably aggressive
and vicious

HERBY 2

Hierarchy after Riva's operation

BENNY 3

SHORTY
5

ARNIE 4

ZEKE 7
Continues intermittently
aggressive toward Dave

LARRY
6

DAVE 8
Outcast, flees
from all

FIG. 7. Final social hierarchy after Dave, Zeke, and Riva have all had bilateral amygdalectomies. Minimal differences in extent and locus of the resections do not correlate with differences in the behavioral results. Herby's nonaggressive "personality" in the second position of the hierarchy accounts for the disparate effects of similar lesions.

or explicitly) to subsume any fairly extensive body of data; at different stages of the science, different levels of precision in models are possible and useful in generating testable hypotheses. In some areas, neuropsychology is ready for precise models, e.g., vision [12], reinforcement [36]; in other areas somewhat less rigorously formulated models are more useful, e.g., intention, affect.

But one caution must be voiced. Models are not laws, though ideally they are based on the determination of lawful relationships between variables. When models are constructed from systematizations of hypothetical constructs or intervening variables, they are apt to lose power, since almost any set of phenomena seemingly can be explained if a sufficient number of hypotheses are admitted. This was the error of the early mathematical biophysicists, and of the Hullians, and currently it may be the flaw in the arguments of the statistical-learning theorists. Truly useful models make analogies between sets of lawful empirical relationships, not between the hypotheses derived from such relationships. Such models are hard to come by, since a great deal of empirical work must precede them.

And, of course, though some kind of systematization of data is necessary, not all systematization need be formally theoretical. Aside from supporting data, spans of communal interest in problems shared by those working on either side of the neuropsychological chasm may suffice. The complexity of the systems studied in the behavioral sciences (of which neuropsychology is one) makes possible the collection of a vast amount of data, which, if irrelevant to any kind of systematization, is lost because information transmission becomes too costly. But the systematization can be of two sorts: relevance to a practical problem (e.g., psychosurgery) or to a theoretical formulation (e.g., information-measurement theory). These two approaches to systematization are not as mutually exclusive as some of the proponents of one as against the other will have us think. (Psychosurgery alters information processing by patients; models of information processing are used by computer engineers.) Only the scientist's temperament raises the issue of incompatibility. My own preference is that proposed by Shaw in his *Don Juan:* when bored with heavenly theory, the problems of the flesh are refreshing; when, in turn, these pall, a return to the upper reaches of abstraction is welcome.

A Psychological, Subjective Behaviorism

This flexible, though precise, approach to the mind-brain issue has implications that transcend neuropsychology per se [28]. Once a truly monistic (yet paradoxically pluralistic) approach to *simultaneous* interdisciplinary study at *several* levels is attained, some old problems can be seen in a new light—experiments can be designed and patients can be approached in ways up to now plagued by confusion. Briefly, the approach here taken can be summarized as follows: All scientific inquiry begins with introspection. A first step toward precision is made when these introspections can be verbalized or in some other way communicated to others. The philosophy of science is concerned with such consensual validations [41]. The job of psychologists is to give precision to one aspect of the scientific universe of discourse. Briefly, the proposal accepted begins much as does that of classical behaviorism. Any concepts derived from behavioral data irrespective of their terminological cloak are considered to be psychological concepts. Such concepts are of two sorts: those derived from propositional statements about introspections, and those derived from instrumental behavior or from the nonpropositional aspects of verbal statements. The extreme behaviorists have, as a rule, been made uncomfortable if the psychological concepts derived from these disparate sources of behavioral observation are treated as identical. And there is good reason for the discomfort, since at least two levels of discourse are involved. Yet psychology is of a piece. How is a unitary body of knowledge to be attained? The position taken here is that concepts derived from instrumental and like behavior are to be juxtaposed to those derived from statements about introspections. Then similarities and differences are to be ascertained. Two extremes must be avoided in this process. When the behaviorally derived concepts, because of a lack of empirical evidence, are indistinguishable from those derived from introspection, confusion results. When the two classes of concepts are so distinct that no relation between them is recognizable, the behaviorally derived concept is apt to be trivial.

This problem of collating concepts derived from observed data with those introspectively derived is logically the obverse in the psychological and the physical sciences. An apparent handicap to the solution of the problem for psychology is that psychological concepts do not have the attribute of projection. Whereas a table appears to be "out there," my perception of it appears to be "in here." But this very attribute has been blamed for the difficulties encountered in the philosophy of the physical world. So perhaps psychological philosophy has the easier task at that.

According to this view, the philosopher and the psychologist have the common task of relating observational and experimental data to phenomenological data. The philosopher of science, aided by the burgeoning developments in linguistics, is especially concerned with the verbal analysis of language as this describes phenomenal interrelations. The behavioral psychologist on the other hand, is especially interested in instrumental and other nonverbal behavior and in the nonlinguistic uses of verbal behavior. As already noted, concepts that result from observations of behavior are likely to be trivial unless they are initially close to those derived from introspection. Even the most rigorous behavioristic psychology must not be completely sundered from the phenomena which originally gave birth to psychological inquiry. However, when the behaviorally derived concepts are not distinguishable from the phenomenological, an objective psychology is thwarted.

Thus the distinction must be gradually attained. Some introspectively conceived phenomenon must be tentatively externalized by the suggestion that an observed behavioral process is representative of the phenomenon. For instance, the discomfort which one recurrently feels and which leads to eating behavior is labeled as "hunger." When its characteristics are more clearly specified, "appetite" may be the more appropriate label. The eating characteristics of other organisms may be observed and these also found to be cyclical. The cycles can be accentuated by manipulations of the accessibility of food and the specific characteristics examined by the manipulations of the accessibility of different types of edible objects.

This externalization of the introspectively derived concept can then be approached in a variety of ways. Deprivation variables, neural variables, endocrine variables, situational variables, and somatic variables can be studied as these affect the eating process. And gradually lawful relationships between the consuming of food and some of these variables can be noted. Furthermore, obstacles can be placed in the path of consuming behavior. And again, the interaction of the various classes of variables with each other can be lawfully described. During this series of experiments some of these lawful relationships may be identified with hunger. For instance, it may be suggested that the number of hours of deprivation correlates specifically with the state of the organism which is introspectively defined as hunger. But when this identification is made, it very quickly becomes inadequate. For, introspectively, the hunger mechanism is cyclic and hours of deprivation do not correlate linearly with what is felt.

Experiments are again undertaken to demonstrate this added dimension of the phenomenon. On the other hand, the laboratory may show, as it actually has, that there is not a one-to-one correlation between how much an organism will eat when food is easily accessible and how much work that organism will do to overcome an obstacle in order to eat. This kind of observation can then be referred back to introspection and differences can be distinguished between hunger and appetite, between zest for food and zest for search, and between search and a tendency to complete actions once they are initiated. Each of these in turn is only vaguely specified by the introspection. Some of the distinctions may be erroneous; others incorrectly drawn. Again, externalization into the laboratory can sharpen the distinctions.

Gradually a more and more precise description and empirical analysis of the behavioral process can be attained and a scientific, multilevel understanding of the conception under scrutiny follows this ever-widening and deepening spiral of definition and empirical evidence. In this stepwise process, the reductive empirical and experimental analysis of the mind-brain problem has an important place.

What are the limitations of this approach? The most significant limitation is that introspectively derived concepts and those derived from instrumental behavior are never expected to match completely. This may lead to considerable dissatisfaction on the part of those who need to have their world neat and tidy. But the discordance between what people say and what they do and what people do and what animals do, is one of the facts of life of the behavioral sciences. This discordance cannot be explained away by verbal magic. Nor is the classical dualistic frame more than a giving-up. For aside from the paucity of empirically precise data soundly systematized, the most important deterrent to fruitful inquiry into the relation between psychology and neurology has been philosophic dualism. Such dualism has taken two especially pernicious forms, extreme psychophysical parallelism and pseudomonism. Many eminent philosophers, neurologists, and neurophysiologists, and some psychologists, have settled into a comfortable journey along the parallel rails of the physical and the psychical. Rails that are wishfully believed to extend to some future infinity called "correspondence." Pseudomonists on the other hand, whether they be extreme materialists or extreme phenomenologists fail to face the issue squarely. By volubly denying the alternatives, pseudomonists in fact accept them by default. Neurological concepts are founded in neural data, psychological concepts in behavioral data. Words by themselves cannot transform the one into the other. Experimental and observational evidence is needed before useful translations between the results of systematizations of neural and of behavioral data are accomplished.

If either of these dualistic approaches is accepted, the bridge between the behavioral sciences and humanities on the one hand, and the physical and biological sciences on the other, can never be constructed. As a result, both worlds will be impoverished because of lack of communication between them. Recognition that the problem, though difficult, can be approached and solutions approximated, though never completely attained, should give rise to a new way of scientific inquiry. If the methods of early classical physics as we see them from this distance are slavishly followed, then *rapprochement* between science and man's humanistic endeavors can never be attained. The proposal set forth in a recent publication [28] is that the scientist has often followed and should explicitly follow a path hitherto reserved for the artist: i.e., enactment and reenactment of his internalized representation of the world. Analysis and systematization have an important part in enactment but they are not the whole story. Explication by the judicious use of highly perfected technical analogy is admitted. Already this has occurred in the efforts of the physical and mathematical model builders. When these analogies are specifically labeled for what they are and a continuous check between model and systematically analyzed data is made, the process—far from being pernicious—is the only hope for a unified universe of discourse among all of man's endeavors. This approach includes systematizations with respect to models, with respect to theories, with respect to urgent problems such as those provided by the clinic. The horizons hitherto reserved for the poet and the humanist become the frontier of behavioral science. And at the core of these endeavors lie such multilevel reductive disciplines as neuropsychology. Without giving up precision, a wider range of problems is thus admitted to the scientific enterprise. This approach, dubbed psychological or subjective behaviorism, reaffirms that a recently neglected subject matter for a scientific and experimental psychology is after all appropriate—the study of man by man.

WHERE THE NEUROPSYCHOLOGIST?

Unless the reductive scientist is especially wary, his problem-oriented discipline can become dangerously superficial. The hard work of methodological mastery is doubly his. Techniques must be acquired wherever the problems lead him—and, as is already evident, the problems lead him far. The tools of data gathering are not always easy to acquire. To obtain data relevant to a particular problem from operant equipment is at times a frustrating task. To have an animal die for lack of surgical judgment or tender postoperative care after that animal has been subjected to many months of rigorous behavioral testing can be a devastating experience. Or, having accomplished successfully the data-gathering process, the statistical, mathematical, and logical tools may not be at hand to make maximum use of the findings. Where are the neurologists who today are sufficiently acquainted with linguistics or with statistical behavioristics to interpret within a broader scientific frame the uniquely available opportunities to study language disturbances? Where is the psychologist who knows enough about the brain to discuss the mechanisms of the *creation* of information—information which he so glibly communicates and so noisily discriminates? Certainly competent neuropsychologists are not to be found in abundance. The reasons for this are several, not the least of which is the lag in institutional acceptance of new areas of scientific development.

Efforts are being made by many institutions to provide a place for neuropsychologists to work and teach. Departments of psychology at universities are showing a new interest in physiological psychology. Departments of anatomy and of physiology more and more frequently find their neuroanatomists and neurophysiologists engaged in neurobehavioral work. Departments of pharmacology and the pharmaceutical houses are increasingly staffed by scientists of this new discipline. But in the spot where he is most needed, the neuropsychologist is as yet practically unknown. Departments of psychiatry in medical schools and psychiatric institutes are slow to recognize the advantages that the new discipline offers. The historical fact that psychiatry stems from faculties of medicine, while psychology stems from faculties of philosophy has estranged the medical discipline from its basic sciences. One might expect clinical psychology to provide the necessary impetus toward the development of a *rapprochement*. But that this has not happened is fact; just as it is fact that pathology has had only a limited effect in providing such *rapprochement* in medicine and surgery. Neuropsychology is concerned with medical physiology and chemistry; neuropsychology is a behavioral science. The neuropsychologist is at home as much with the effects of altering the chemical structure of an antihistamine to produce chlorpromazine as he is with the concept of role. He is as much at home with the organization of the ventrobasal nuclear complex of the mammalian thalamus as he is with the process of consensual validation. Does today's psychiatric training have comparable reach? How else is the trainee to cope with the new developments in his field which come from the social, the intrapersonal, and the neurochemical directions? The impressive advances in the caliber of medical training during the past half century have been associated with the interest generated in the basic sciences concerned with the medical disciplines. Psychiatry is sure to profit from the example [6]. Now that the most ardent psychoanalysts are beginning to remember that Freud first formulated his conceptions from neurobehavioral as well as from strictly behavioral evidence [19], now that the organicists have been sufficiently exposed to the importance of experiential and other socioenvironmental factors so as not to ignore them completely, perhaps neuropsychiatry is ready to welcome and give adequate berth to one of its most essential basic disciplines—neuropsychology.

But irrespective of where he finds himself—and the locations may be many—the neuropsychologist has an interesting task ahead. And his is perhaps the most important in this latter half of the twentieth century: to help establish the dignity of man as a scientific as well as a political tenet.

In our own culture the cleavage of the "spiritual" from the "natural," which is a survival from the most ancient mythologies, has fostered popular ideologies of religious fanaticism, class rivalries, and political antagonisms that are biologically unfit and even suicidal because they result in social disintegration. Our ultimate survival is endangered as long as ideological fantasies that are incompatible with things as they are control individual and national patterns of behavior. We must somehow manage to heal this artificial dismemberment of the human personality before we can hope for a permanent cure of the present disorder [C. JUDSON HERRICK. *The evolution of human nature*, pp. 416–420].

REFERENCES

1. Adey, W. R. Studies of hippocampal mechanisms in learning. In UNESCO symposium *Brain Mechanisms and Learning*. London: Blackwells, 1961.
2. Adey, W. R. Studies of wave activity in the hippocampal system in approach learning, and use of correlation analysis of the wave process. In E. N. Sokolov (Ed.), *Cybernetics and brain mechanisms*. Moscow: 1960.
3. Adey, W. R., Dunlop, C. W., & Hendrix, C. E. Hippocampal slow-waves: distribution and phase relations in the course of approach learning. *AMA Arch. Neurol.,* in press.
4. Bard, P., & Mountcastle, V. B. Some forebrain mechanisms involved in expression of rage with special reference to suppression of angry behavior. *Res. Publ. Ass. nerv. ment. Dis.,* 1948, **27**, 362–404.
5. Battersby, W. S. Neuropsychology of higher processes: cerebral damage and visual perception. *Progr. clin. Psychol.,* 1956, **2**, 303–325.
6. Braceland, F. J. Psychiatry and the science of man. *Amer. J. Psychiat.,* 1957, **114**, 1–9.
7. Brennan, W. The effects of orbito-insulo-temporal lesions on metabolism. Unpublished doctoral dissertation. Yale Univer. School of Medicine, 1955.
8. Bucy, P. C. *The precentral motor cortex.* Chicago: Univer. of Ill. Press, 1944.
9. Clemente, C. D., Green, J. D., & deGroot, J. Studies on behavior following rhinencephalic lesions in adult cats. *Anat. Rec. Amer. Ass. Anat.,* 1957, **127**, 279.
10. Ferster, C. B., & Skinner, B. F. *Schedules of reinforcement.* New York: Appleton-Century-Crofts, 1957.
11. Gerard, R. W. Physiology and psychiatry. *Amer. J. Psychiat.,* 1949, **106**, 161–173.
12. Gibson, J. J. Perception as a function of stimulation. In S. Koch (Ed.), *Psychology: a study of a science.* Vol. 1. *Sensory, perceptual, and physiological formulations.* New York: McGraw-Hill, 1959. Pp. 456–501.
13. Grastyan, E. In M. A. B. Brazier (Ed.), *The central nervous system and behavior.* Transactions of the Second Conference. New York: Josiah Macy, Jr. Foundation, 1959.
14. Hilgard, E. R. *Theories of learning.* New York: Appleton-Century-Crofts, 1948.
15. Hunt, H. F., & Diamond, I. T. Some effects of hippocampal lesions on conditioned avoidance behavior in the cat. In *Proceedings of the 15th International Congress of Psychology,* Brussels, 1957. Amsterdam: North Holland Publishing Co., 1959.
16. Jacobsen, C. F. Studies of cerebral function on primates. *Comp. psychol. Monogr.,* 1936, **13**, 3–60.
17. Jacobsen, C. F., & Haslerud, G. M. A note on the effect of motor and premotor areas lesions on delayed response in monkeys. *Comp. Psychol. Monogr.,* 1936, **13**, 66–68.

18. John, E. R., & Killam, K. F. Electrophysiological correlates of avoidance conditioning in the cat. *J. Pharmacol. exp. Ther.*, 1959, **125**, 252–274.

19. Jones, E. *The life and work of Sigmund Freud.* Vol. 1. *The formative years and the great discoveries.* New York: Basic Books, 1953. Pp. 365–404.

20. Keller, F. S., & Schoenfeld, W. N. *Principles of psychology.* New York: Appleton-Century-Crofts, 1950.

21. Lacey, J. I. In M. A. B. Brazier (Ed.), *The central nervous system and behavior.* Transactions of the Second Conference. New York: Josiah Macy, Jr. Foundation, 1959.

22. Lacey, J. I., & Smith, R. L. Conditioning and generalization of unscious anxiety. *Science,* 1954, **120**, 1045–1052.

23. Lacey, J. I., Smith, R. L., & Green, A. Use of conditioned autonomic responses in the study of anxiety. *Psychosom. Med.,* 1955, **17**, 208–217.

24. Lewin, K. *Principles of topological psychology.* New York: McGraw-Hill, 1936.

25. Lindsley, D. B. Physiological psychology. *Annu. Rev. Psychol.,* 1956, **7**, 323–348.

26. MacLean, P. D., Flanigan, S., Flynn, J. P., Kim, C., & Stevens, Janice R. Hippocampal function: tentative correlations of conditioning, EEG, drug and radioautographic studies. *Yale J. Biol. Med.,* 1955–56, **28**, 380–395.

27. Malis, L. I., Pribram, K. H., & Kruger, L. Action potentials in "motor" cortex evoked by peripheral nerve stimulation. *J. Neurophysiol.,* 1953, **16**, 161–167.

28. Miller, G. A., Galanter, E., & Pribram, K. H. *Plans and the structure of behavior.* New York: Holt, 1960.

29. Milner, Brenda. Intellectual function of the temporal lobes. *Psychol. Bull.,* 1954, **51**, 42–62.

30. Pasik, P., Pasik, T., Battersby, W. S., & Bender, M. B. Visual and tactual discriminations by Macaques with serial temporal and parietal lesions. *J. comp. physiol. Psychol.,* 1958, **51**, 427–436.

31. Patton, R. A. Physiological psychology. *Annu. Rev. Psychol.,* 1954, **5**, 247–262.

32. Penfield, W. Bilateral frontal gyrectomy and postoperative intelligence. *Res. Publ. Ass. nerv. ment. Dis.,* 1948, **27**, 519–564.

33. Pribram, K. H. Toward a science of neuropsychology: method and data. In *Current trends in psychology and the behavioral sciences.* Pittsburgh, Pa.: Univer. of Pittsburgh Press, 1954. Pp. 115–142.

34. Pribram, K. H. Neocortical function in behavior. In *Biological and biochemical bases of behavior,* Madison, Wis.: Univer. of Wis. Press, 1958. Pp. 151–172.

35. Pribram, K. H. The intrinsic systems of the forebrain: an alternative to the concept of cortical association areas. In *Handbook of physiology: neuropsychology II.* Washington: The American Physiological Society, 1960. Chap. LIV, pp. 1323–1344.

36. Pribram, K. H. A review of theory in physiological psychology. *Annu. Rev. Psychol.*, 1960, **11**, 1–40.

37. Pribram, K. H., & Bagshaw, M. Further analysis of the temporal lobe syndrome utilizing fronto-temporal ablations. *J. comp. Neurol.*, 1953, **99**, 347–375.

38. Pribram, K. H., & Kruger, L. Functions of the "olfactory" brain. *Ann. N. Y. Acad. Sci.*, 1954, **58**, 109–138.

39. Pribram, K. H., Kruger, L., Robinson, F., & Berman, A. J. The effects of precentral lesions on the behavior of monkeys. *Yale J. Biol. Med.*, 1955, 6, 28, 428–443.

40. Pribram, K. H., & Weiskrantz, L. A comparison of the effects of medial and lateral cerebral resection on conditioned avoidance behavior of monkeys. *J. comp. physiol. Psychol.*, 1957, **50**, 74–80.

41. Reichenbach, H. *The rise of scientific philosophy.* Berkeley and Los Angeles: Univer. of Calif. Press, 1951.

42. Schreiner, L., & Kling, A. Behavioral changes following rhinencephalic injury in cat. *J. Neurophysiol.*, 1953, **16**, 643–659.

43. Schwartzbaum, J. S. Relation of amygdaloid complex to deprivation and reward determinants of food motivated behavior in monkey. Unpublished doctoral dissertation, Stanford Univer., 1958.

44. Schwartzbaum, J. S., & Pribram, K. H. The effects of amygdalectomy in monkeys on transposition of response along a brightness continuum. Paper read at Eastern Psychol. Ass., Atlantic City, N.J., April, 1959.

45. Sharpless, S. & Jasper, H. Habituation of the arousal reaction. *Brain,* 1956, **79**, 655–680.

46. Sokolov, E. N. In M. A. B. Brazier (Ed.), *The central nervous system and behavior.* Transactions of the Third Conference. New York: Josiah Macy, Jr. Foundation, 1960.

47. Stellar, E. L. Physiological psychology. *Annu. Rev. Psychol.*, 1957, **8**, 415–436.

48. Stevens, S. S. Mathematics, measurement and psychophysics. In S. S. Stevens (Ed.), *Handbook of experimental psychology.* New York: Wiley, 1951. Pp. 31–32.

49. Teuber, H. L. Physiological psychology. *Annu. Rev. Psychol.*, 1955, 6, 267–296.

50. Weiskrantz, L. Behavioral changes associated with ablation of the amygdaloid complex. Unpublished doctoral dissertation, Harvard Univer., 1953.

51. Wilson, W., Schwartzbaum, J. S., & Morrissette, J. R. The effects of amygdalectomy on locomotor activity in monkeys. *J. comp. physiol. Psychol.*, in press.

BIOLOGICAL PSYCHOLOGY

I. T. DIAMOND   AND   K. L. CHOW
Department of Psychology   *Department of Physiology*
Duke University   *University of Chicago*

Introduction 159
Part I. The Place of Learning in Comparative Psychology 161
  The Study of Behavior as a Species Character 161
  The Study of Individual Differences and the Problem of Hereditary and
    Environmental Variation 166
  Learned and unlearned behavior 167
  The phenotype as an expression of the genotype and environment . . 168
  The Genetics of Behavior 170
  Summary 173
  The Comparative Method for Determining Physiological Mechanisms. . 174
  The evolution of the nervous system and behavior 177
Part II. The Evolution of Cortex and Thalamus 178
  The Origin of Cortex 178
  The Diencephalon 179
  The Organization of the Mammalian Thalamus 180
  The intralaminar and midline nuclei 182
  The anterior nuclei and *n. medialis dorsalis* 184
  Fiber Size and the Development of Sensory Systems 185
  The dorsal- and lateral-column systems 186
  Further Analysis of the Difference between Extrinsic and Intrinsic Nuclei . 188
  Essential and sustaining projections to the cortex 194
  Summary 194
Part III. Sensation and Learning: the Problem of Sensory and Association
    Cortex 195
  The Classical View of Sensation and Perception 195
  Electrophysiology and the Concept of Sensory Quality 197
  The gestalt view of sensory quality 197
  Revisions in the meaning of sensation 197
  Clinical Evidence for and against the Theory of Memory Loss 199
  Experimental Studies of Sensation and Perception 200
  Ablation studies of the auditory cortex in carnivores 202
  The Pavlovian View of Association Cortex 206

Lashley's Study of Learning 207
  The relationship between the deficit and the lesion 207
  The Loss of Learned Visual Discrimination Following Ablation of the
    Temporal Lobe in Monkeys 210
  Conclusion 215
Part IV. The EEG and Learning 216
  Introduction 216
  EEG Changes during Learning 217
  Conditioning the EEG 220
  Conditioning by Means of Direct Stimulation of the Central Nervous System 221
  Disruption of Learning by Electrical Stimulation of the Brain 222
  Conclusion 223
Part V. Biological Psychology and Learning Psychology 224
  The Hierarchy of the Biological Sciences 225
    The difference method 227
  The Behaviorists' Organization of Science 227
    Sherrington's methods 228
    Conclusion 229
Summary 229
Abbreviations in Figures and in Text 231
References 231

INTRODUCTION

Biological psychology can be classified according to the various biological methods employed in the study of behavior. The investigation of behavioral differences corresponding to species or gene differences is commonly called "comparative psychology." The study of the behavioral effects of ablation or stimulation of the nervous system is commonly called "physiological psychology." Our purpose is to consider the issues in biological inquiry that concern learning.[1] The various biological methods determine the division of our discussion into four parts.

Part I begins with an illustration of how behavior can replace morphology in studies of evolution, taxonomy, and genetics. The questions of heredity and environment, and instinct and learning, are shown to be important issues in studies of this type. The discussion then turns to the relation between the phylogeny of behavior and the phylogeny of the nervous system. The study of this relation is aimed at uncovering neural mechanisms of behavior.

[1] This inquiry was supported by grants from the National Science Foundation (G-7020), the Duke University Regional Center for the Study of Aging (NIH M-2109 and H-3582), the National Institute of Health (B-801), and the Wallace C. and Clara Abbott Fund of the University of Chicago.
  We are very grateful to Dr. Hans-Lukas Teuber, whose penetrating criticism of this manuscript led to its final revision.

The capacity to learn is often said to be the greatest achievement of evolution. Since the development of neocortex is the outstanding structural change correlated with the evolution of highly organized adaptive behavior, Part II is devoted to a discussion of current views of the evolution of cortex.

Part III treats the method of ablation. The discussion is couched in terms of the distinction between sensory and association cortex. The functional significance of this anatomical separation has been associated with the psychological distinction between sensation and memory.

The recent discoveries of striking parallels between behavioral conditioning and changes in the EEG have excited the interests of neurophysiologists and learning psychologists. In a relatively short time an extensive literature has accumulated. We shall review this field in Part IV.

Following the four main parts is a summary section. In this final part the relations between biological psychology and learning psychology will be considered.

The four sections are not equivalent in the treatment of subject-matter content. In Part I content is introduced only to provide some substance to the discussion of method. The methodological issue suggested by the phrase "heredity and environment" was selected as the central theme because of the connection between this problem and the problem of unlearned and learned behavior. The choice of the topic of innate versus learned behavior led us to a consideration of the meaning of inheritance, both before and after Mendel. To illustrate changes in the meaning of the words "innate behavior," some older works, such as those of Darwin, as well as some recent papers were selected. This range in the dates of the papers cited in no way reflects an effort to survey the history of the field from Darwin's time to the present.

In Part II, subject-matter content serves a double purpose. As in Part I, the content is used to define biological psychology in terms of various biological methods and problems. Part II also has the more specific purpose of bringing together recent evidence—some not yet published—on the organization of the thalamus.

Part III has a central issue, the relation between sensory and association cortex. As in the case of Part I, the choice was determined by the bearing this issue has on the biology of learning. When it came to selecting illustrative material, we relied on our own experimental studies to a much greater extent than would be justified in any kind of review article.

The fourth section was not part of our original plan and was added because of the growing number of studies relating the EEG and learning. Selection of material was in part determined by our desire to illustrate the variety of types of study. A description of one or a few articles of each type might best serve the interest of someone who wishes to get an idea of this new field.

The final section is an attempt to bring together and summarize the methodological arguments made in the four subject-matter parts. The various points concerning method are all related to general topics such as the place of biological psychology in the sciences. In Part V we hope to make explicit our view of the organization of the biological sciences.

PART I. THE PLACE OF LEARNING IN COMPARATIVE PSYCHOLOGY

The Study of Behavior as a Species Character

The starting place of many of the problems and methods of comparative psychology is Darwin's inquiry into the origin of species. In Chapter 8 of the *Origin of species,* Darwin applies the theory of evolution to behavior [37]. How can the mechanisms of variation, inheritance, and selection established in earlier chapters account for behavioral differences and similarities between species? Darwin must show that traits of behavior can be passed unchanged from one generation to the next generation; that there are slight variations even among offspring of the same parents which in turn can be inherited; and, finally, that variations in behavior have different survival values.

That behavior is inherited seemed to Darwin the only explanation for the identical behavior patterns of widely distributed species. He cites many examples of behavior patterns which are as characteristic of a group as any morphological trait. The male hornbill, for instance, imprisons the female in a hole in a tree, leaving only a small opening through which he feeds the young and mother. If a trait is characteristic of a species, the presumption is that it has played a role in evolution, and only *inherited* variations can be selected, that is, only inherited traits play a role in evolution.

To establish further that behavior is inherited, Darwin contrasts instinct with habit. This distinction is not drawn in terms of rigidity or the presence of purpose. Habit and instinct are indeed similar in so many respects that if a habit were to require less and less practice over many generations, it would become inseparable from instinct. In the following passage Darwin suggests that the role of practice in the development of a trait may vary. "If Mozart, instead of playing the pianoforte at three years old with wonderfully little practice, had played a tune with no practice at all, he might truly be said to have done so instinctively" [37, p. 185]. Thus, another way of establishing that a behavioral trait is instinctive is to observe the trait in the very young. The very young, it is assumed, have had little or no opportunity for practice.

In order to illustrate instinctive behavior, Darwin described in some detail the behavior of cuckoos. The European cuckoo lays one egg at a time at intervals of two or three days. The egg, which is remarkably small for the size of the cuckoo, is placed in the nests of other birds smaller than the cuckoo. When the eggs are hatched, the young cuckoo ejects his smaller foster brothers from the nest. Darwin speculates that the first step in the evolution of this behavioral pattern might be a general restlessness. If a generalized heightened activity were adaptive and could be transmitted from one generation to the next, then the behavior might gradually become directed and more specific. "I can see no more difficulty in this, than in the unhatched young of other birds acquiring the instinct to break through their own shells;—or than in young snakes acquiring in their upper jaws, as Owen has remarked, a transitory sharp tooth for cutting through the tough eggshell" [37, p. 192].

In order to demonstrate the presence of variations, Darwin points to the Australian species of cuckoo whose eggs vary in size and are laid two or three at a time. If fewer and smaller eggs had greater survival value, there is no difficulty in conceiving an evolution in the direction of the European varieties. A similar degree of variation can be found in behavior. The American cuckoo either builds a nest of its own or seizes one belonging to another species. It either lays eggs in the nest thus appropriated or builds another nest on top of the stolen one. Usually it hatches its own eggs and rears the young, but occasionally the young are reared by foster parents. Darwin supposes that the ancient progenitor of the European cuckoo exhibited the variation in behavior shown by the present American strain. If the tendency to lay eggs in foreign nests is inherited and has selective advantage, the stage is set for the transition to the present-day European bird.

Two important features in Darwin's approach have special implication for psychology. Behavior was treated by Darwin as a trait just like a morphological character. According to Darwin, an animal has behavior just as an animal has long legs or white marks. This point of view invited the use of behavior for taxonomic study. Another area of study opened by Darwin concerned the perception of stimuli that direct adaptive behavior. For example, cuckoos show a preference for nests containing eggs similar in color to their own. But any question concerning the role played by color, shape, and size in determining the bird's choice can only be answered experimentally.

The perceptual problem in instinctive behavior was emphasized by MacDougall's distinction between cognitive and conative dispositions [101]. The heuristic value of this separation was developed in an example. Solitary wasps prey on only one kind of species. One species of wasp selects caterpillars, another selects grasshoppers, and a third selects spiders. The choice of prey cannot be learned in the ordinary sense, since the wasp is fully adult when hatched and immediately proceeds to seek its food. Further, each species of wasp handles the prey in a characteristic manner. Therefore, there is a characteristic perceptual pattern, a motor pattern, and a linkage between the two innately determined for each species. Each of these may further be modified by experience.

The comparative study of behavior received a setback with the appearance of the influential writings of J. B. Watson. Watson argued that behavioral traits were not inherited and that structure only was inherited [163]. This statement may simply mean that behavior depends on structure. If this was Watson's meaning, his point appears to be trivial. By the same token, only genes are inherited, since all morphological traits depend on genes. An alternative interpretation is that there are no structural inherited differences which determine behavior. If this was Watson's meaning, his point can hardly be correct. In either case, the effect of the argument was to draw the attention of psychologists away from the comparative study of behavior. The view of behavior as something the organism "has got" was considered unsophisticated by Watson's followers. It was left largely to zoology to continue the Darwinian tradition.

Emerson's [45] study of the nests of termites can be used as an illustration of the interest of zoologists in the phylogeny of behavior. Emerson showed that each species of termite constructed the nest wall in a characteristic manner. Every nest contains a system of interior chambers which make contact with the outside by means of a funnel leading to a surface pore. These funnels were found to be simply or complexly constructed. A comparison of a series of nests revealed obvious homologies between the funnels made by different species. This investigation of termite nests is especially interesting in that behavioral differences were revealed by extraorganic structure. Nests can be compared in the same way that organic structures are compared, yet obviously the nest is the result of behavior.

Lorenz has been a spokesman for the approach to innate behavior initiated by Darwin [99]. The study of the behavior of a series of closely related genera of cichlids illustrates the methods and aims of comparative ethology. According to Lorenz, certain movements of the head, body, and fins, associated normally with the start of swimming, are homologous. In all the groups studied, the movements are signs to the young, but different meanings have developed. In its most primitive form, the movement determines the direction in which the young swim. This original meaning, Lorenz argued, diverged along two lines. In one species it became a warning stimulus to the young, while in other species it became a sign for the young to return to their nest hole for the night.

In addition to their taxonomic studies, Lorenz and Tinbergen initiated an experimental investigation of the perceptual cues that elicit instinctive acts. In common-sense terms we say that a bird selects a mate or escapes from a predator—the stimuli for these acts being the mate or the predator. Tinbergen [154] showed, however, that sensory stimuli necessary to release innate responses constitute only a part of the total environment which normally would be present at the time of the response. The escape reaction of many birds from passing birds of prey was found to be a response to a special feature of shape. The nature of the adequate stimulus was demonstrated by the use of cardboard models. Any dummy which had a short neck released the escape reaction, regardless of the shape of its wings or its size.

The use of artificial stimuli which vary along a number of dimensions must be considered as a major contribution in the psychological analysis of instinctive acts, and is similar to Klüver's use of equivalent stimuli in the study of learned behavior mechanisms in monkeys [76]. A characteristic experiment is the one showing that red belly serves as the stimulus for fighting in the stickleback. In the spring, the male stickleback selects a territory, defends it against other males, and builds a nest. It is during this season that the color of the animal's throat and belly becomes a brilliant red. The striking correlation between the change in color and the appearance of nesting behavior and the absence of any obvious physiological purpose served by the color both suggest that color change may be a sign for other members of the species. Models were prepared with red or with neutral bellies and were brought into the territory of a male. The models with red on the ventral side were vigorously attacked. Tinbergen concluded that the red belly is a social releaser.

It has often been pointed out that some common experience may be responsible for all the members of a species showing the identical pattern of behavior. MacDougall gives the example of baby lambs who may first follow any large moving object. Later, the "following" response is elicited only by other sheep. Common experience in this case is the basis for the specificity of the stimulus which can elicit the following response. To take account of the possibility that learning is responsible for behavior characteristic of a species, Tinbergen carried the experimental analysis of perceptual releasers one step further. In the study described above, a male stickleback was reared in isolation and was tested with models before it had ever seen another stickleback. The animal reared in isolation reacted to the models in the same way as an animal reared in the society of other fish. The conclusion drawn from this observation is that the response to red belly does not depend on common experience.

Recently Lehrman has questioned the heuristic value of the term *innate* and the distinction between instinct and learning [96, 97]. Lehrman points out that any trait, even one common to all members of a species, depends for its development on related structures and on features normally present in the environment. To illustrate the plasticity of structure, Lehrman cited studies of Washburn on the development of the bones of the skull. In these studies of development, it was demonstrated that the shape of the skull, which is a taxonomic character in rodents, depends on the presence of attached muscles.

Lehrman questioned whether the rearing of animals in isolation is a suitable method for ruling out the role of experiential factors. The building of nests and the retrieving of the young occurs in all normal rats, even when they have been reared in isolation. It is innate according to the criterion formulated first by Darwin and adopted by the school of comparative ethology. Nevertheless, when rats were prevented from birth from manipulating or carrying objects, they did not build normal nests. According to Lehrman, this shows that some learning was necessary for the development of the trait, even though practice of the specific act itself was not required. Lehrman's point is that the isolation procedure can prevent practice of the act under investigation, but it cannot rule out experience in general. The stickleback reared in isolation might have seen his own reflection. This experience, according to Lehrman, would have some bearing on the significance of the models.

Lehrman's criticism, as well as his own experimental work on ring doves, points to the importance of the study of development. When we say, for example, that blue petals are inherited as a Mendelian recessive, nothing is said concerning steps involved in the development of the blue petals. Certainly blue pigments are not present in the zygote. The egg is not a miniature version of the adult, and the genes do not make traits simply by unfolding. This is the central point of Lehrman's argument. Lehrman is calling for a study of the role of environmental factors in the development of inherited behavioral traits. We view this as an additional kind of investigation without taking away any of the significance of the term *innate*. Our meaning will be clear when the discussion turns to inheritance and development.

In the following section, we will describe the growth of Mendelian genetics and the subsequent study of gene action or physiological genetics. For the present, suffice it to say that in the first type of study a genetic difference is established by breeding methods. For example, the difference between blue and purple flowers is genetic if a certain phenotypic ratio is obtained in the F_2 generation following a cross of blue and purple strains. A further question is: How does the gene produce the trait? It may be found that, with soil of a certain pH, the flowers will be blue regardless of genotype. The role of the environment becomes a part of the inquiry into development. Lehrman shows the need for an area of investigation which may be related to comparative ethology as physiological genetics is related to classical genetics.

We conclude that the methodological contribution of comparative ethology is to reaffirm the Darwinian view of behavior as something the organism "has got." What an achievement this is can be appreciated by returning to Lehrman's example of the development of skulls. While the growth of the skull is responsive to impinging forces, a skull is not simply a response to environmental stimuli.

The Study of Individual Differences and the Problem of Hereditary and Environmental Variation

We have attempted to show the important position in the Darwinian tradition occupied by the concept of inheritance. Of the various mechanisms postulated by the theory of evolution, inheritance is the one that has undergone the greatest transformation since Darwin. The view of the mechanism of inheritance has changed, but the role of inheritance in evolution remains important. Only the variations, behavioral or otherwise, that are transmitted in the germ plasm can have bearing on the course of evolution.

The converse is equally valid. Any taxonomic character, one that has played a part in the divergence of a population, must be innate. Clearly there are some innate characters which are not shared by all members of a class. The question we raise now is: How can the inheritance of individual differences be studied? Without the criterion of "species constant," the only method left for determining inherited variation in Darwin's day was to minimize environmental variation. Differences in practice must be included under environmental variation. Even a man with a slight build can develop large muscles with proper training. Differences in the reaction to practice must be considered as inherited variation. Some men must exercise daily to achieve the same development that others attain with little effort. If the trait appears in newborns, the required control of the environment may already be achieved, at least to the degree that direct practice has been eliminated as a factor. Where this criterion is inappropriate, a trait may be chosen which is not readily affected by differences in environment. Thus Galton [50] selected height to determine the laws relating the appearance of parents and offspring. Presumably height is less affected by practice or habit than is weight or muscular development. Such studies suffer from the lack of certainty that environmental variation is ruled out. Variations in nutrition, for example, may produce variations in height.

The uncertainty of obtaining adequate environmental control has led some writers to belittle the problem of the relative importance of hereditary and environmental variation. It is often said that phenotype is the result of heredity interacting with environment, and that neither factor can be eliminated without destroying the product. This misses the point because the classical problem concerns the relative role of hereditary and environmental *variation*—not heredity and environment. It is actually possible to reduce one of these factors—hereditary variation—to zero by breeding methods. Breeding methods will be considered in a later section. There are still many behavioral problems that can be studied only by exercising some control over environmental variation.

Learned and unlearned behavior. Since the modification of behavior produced by experience is called "learning," individual differences in what is learned can be assigned to environmental variation. The effort of the introspectionists to rule out the effects of learning on mental content may be considered an attempt to minimize environmental variation. At least the difficulties encountered were comparable to those faced by Galton and other pre-Mendelian geneticists. The trained introspectionist attempted to view the world as it would appear to a person without any past experience. This effort may be prejudiced by a sophisticated concept of the relation between simple sensation and the dimensions of the stimulus.

A more direct approach to unlearned sensation is provided by restricting experience from birth and testing the subject at some more mature stage in development. Hebb [64] has pointed out that these conditions are met in part by human patients who have had a congenital cataract removed in adulthood. However, the degree to which the diseased lens restricted vision varied from case to case, so the results are difficult to interpret. In general, it is clear that months of training were required for patients to recognize simple geometrical figures, letters, or numbers, and some never attained this level of form vision. On the other hand, a few days after the operation patients could discriminate between colors. This is consonant with the classical view that sensations of quality and intensity are unlearned, while perceptions of form and meaning require learning. The absence of a lens and the persistence of symptoms such as spontaneous nystagmus after the operation must be considered as a further qualification to any final conclusion.

To permit the exercise of greater control over conditions of deprivation, Riesen [128] has brought this area of inquiry into the experimental laboratory. He has restricted the visual experience in chimpanzees, monkeys, and cats. Two newborn chimpanzees that were raised in the dark showed marked deficiencies in perception when they were returned to the unrestricted environment. The animals were unable to recognize objects after months of experience. Postmortem examination revealed structural changes in the retinas of some of these animals [33]. In order to prevent the effect of light deprivation in the retina, Riesen gave his animals periods of unpatterned light. For example, one chimpanzee was placed daily in a plexiglass dome which admitted only homogeneous light. At all other times the animal was kept in the dark. After such a deprivation period, animals can regain normal visual functions, but only after months of experience.

Riesen points out the similarities in methods employed in studies of visual deprivation and those used in studies where motor function was limited. In both cases, the goal is to determine the role of maturation. In the experiment by Carmichael [20], tadpoles were raised under anesthesia to prevent practice of swimming movements. Such experiments have shown that behavior that might have been the result of practice was instead the result of maturation. Darwin's distinction between instinct and habit may be recalled. If tadpoles had failed to show skillful swimming in the absence of practice, swimming would be a habit.

These considerations can be applied to Watson's [163] attempt to determine innate emotional behavior. He described infants crying in response to a loud noise and showing pleasure in response to stroking the skin. Watson concluded that adult emotional behavior developed from these simple innate stimulus-response connections by conditioning. In the process of conditioning, new stimuli replace old ones in eliciting the response. Watson's reasoning is premised on the view that innate behavior is limited to those patterns present shortly after birth. The studies of sensory or motor deprivation have just the opposite premise.

In all of these studies, from Galton to Riesen, there is an attempt to arrive at that which is native by imposing some control over the environment. In the following paragraphs, the methods of controlled breeding will be described. The control of breeding provided a new way of approaching the heredity-environment question.

The phenotype as an expression of the genotype and environment. An entirely different approach to the study of genetic and environmental variation was introduced by Johannsen in 1903 [74].[2] Rather than attempting to ensure a uniform environment, he used the method of pure lines. A pure line consists of the progeny of a single plant, and therefore all members of a pure line have the same genotype. Individual differences within the pure line must be entirely the result of environmental variation. Johannsen showed that within a pure line there was no correlation between the weights of parents and their offspring. In

[2] The reference is to an English translation of Johannsen's paper *Concerning heredity in populations and in pure lines.* This translation by H. Gall can be found in a syllabus of readings edited by H. Gall and the staff of Natural Sciences 3, the University of Chicago. Many of the genetics papers we have cited are reprinted in this syllabus entitled *Population genetics and physiological genetics and their relations to problems of evolution and development,* University of Chicago Press, 1955.

other words, differences in weight resulting from differences in environment were not transmitted from parent to offspring. On the other hand, when a large number of individuals belonging to many different lines were treated as one population and classified according to weight, then the average weight of the offspring of heavier parents was found to be greater than the population mean. Similarly, the average weight of the offspring of lighter parents was found to be less than the population mean. The mean weight of the offspring of a given parental class lies between the weight of the parents and the mean of the entire population. The finding of correlation between parents and offspring in a population suggests that Galton's law of regression depends on taking phenotype alone as the basis for classifying a genetically mixed population. Apparently the law of regression is the result of confounding genetic and environmental variation.

Mendel's discoveries also depended on the control of breeding. These discoveries ultimately led to a new meaning for the terms *innate* and *inherited*. The difference between yellow and green seed coat is genetic when a certain phenotypic ratio is obtained in the F_2 generation bred from the hybrid. The definition of "innate" contains no reference to the role of environmental variation. At the same time, from a practical standpoint, a genetic difference can be established only if some limit is placed on environmental variation. If differences in the environment produced variations that bridged genetic classes, the F_2 ratio would be meaningless. Once a mutant has been located, the finding that its expression depends on the environment is a useful step in the analysis of gene action. For example, a mutation may occur in *E. coli*, which prevents this organism from synthesizing pantothenic acid [69]. This substance must be supplied from the environment. However, when the temperature was lowered from 35 to 25°C, the mutant did not require the pantothenic acid. The mutant apparently synthesizes an altered enzyme which is inactivated at 35°.

A study by Ephrussi [46] shows how the role of the environment can be examined after a genotypic difference is established. He reported that normal yeast, grown for several generations in the absence of oxygen, develops the same enzyme deficiency that is found in a mutant strain. In contrast to the genetic deficiency, the one produced by the environment is reversible. With a supply of oxygen, the genetically normal strain once again synthesizes the cytochrome required to oxidize glucose. Ephrussi concluded that environmental oxygen can determine whether precursors to the essential cytochrome will differentiate in the normal fashion.

In general, physiological genetics has explored the relation of heredity and environment. In this study, the term *heredity* has the meaning given to it by the Mendelian theory. Results have shown that gene action depends on environmental conditions. An environmental difference may have the same effect on phenotype as a gene difference. Presumably it is also possible for a gene to duplicate an environmental effect.

Waddington [160] pictured development as proceeding along channels or canals established by the genotype. A particular environmental influence may serve as a trigger, a last step necessary for the appearance of the trait. Thus an organism with high tendency to develop calluses might require just the slightest rubbing to produce the callous. Conceivably a gene might replace the environmental stimulus, and the callous would appear at birth before rubbing could occur.

Recently there has been considerable interest in those behavioral patterns which require but little experience to establish. The learning period must occur during a specific stage of the animal's life in order to be effective. MacDougall's example of the lamb's following response may serve in this context. The newborn lamb has the tendency to follow any large moving object. At a critical period, the stimulus for following may be restricted to the one moving object present. A number of experiments have been designed to test the duration and the variability of the critical period [67]. Baby birds only a few hours old were exposed to a moving model bird. The time between hatching and the training period was varied for different groups. Later the birds were tested to determine the effectiveness of the training. In the test period, the baby birds were confronted with two models. One was identical to the model used in training, while the other was a replica of the mother. If the baby birds preferred the training model, it was concluded that the training period had been effective. Whether or not the training period produces learning was found to depend on the age of the birds at the time of training. This phenomenon is called "imprinting" to emphasize its stability as compared with other learning situations. One might speculate that if further stability had adaptive value, eventually baby birds would not require training to follow a specific stimulus. The relation between a given stimulus and the following response would then be genetically determined. At this point, the pattern of behavior would resemble a social releasing mechanism in the terms of the ethologists.

Waddington speculated that in the development of a callous a gene obviated the need for rubbing. We have imagined that in the development of the significance of certain stimuli, genes could obviate the need for experience.

The Genetics of Behavior

The genetics of behavior usually denotes the study of innate behavioral differences by the method of controlled breeding [59]. Many interesting questions of inheritance cannot be approached by inbreeding and crossing. To study the inheritance of intelligence in man, one must fall back on the statistical methods of Galton and Pearson. Controlled breeding is, of course, not possible when man is the object of investigation. Further, the pedigree method is not suitable for analyzing a continuously distributed character. Burt [18] has recently reviewed these ideas in a paper on the inheritance of mental ability. One way of approaching the problem is to determine the variability in intelligence while holding either environment or heredity as constant as possible. Children reared in institutions provide the best instance of uniform environment, while identical twins provide the only instance of uniform heredity. The wide variation in intelligence found among inmates of orphanages led Burt to conclude that innate factors play the major role in intelligence.

A second approach to the inheritance of intelligence is statistical. The data consist of correlations in intelligence between various degrees of kinship. Intelligence is estimated in the usual ways, by group tests, teacher's judgments, and the like. Two ways of treating the data were described by Burt. In the first technique, expected correlations are deduced from hypothetical variances. These hypothetical values are arrived at by making certain assumptions, particularly that intelligence is transmitted by a large number of independent Mendelian factors. A further assumption concerns the extent to which breeding is random. The theoretical correlations are then compared with the empirical values. A good agreement between empirical and expected values is a sign that inherited variation accounts for a large part of the total variance. Another way of treating the data is to deduce from the observed correlations the respective contributions of genetic and environmental variance. The detailed mathematical reasoning is clearly outside the scope of this paper. Our purpose is to show that Galton's approach to inheritance is not entirely obsolete. For some problems of inheritance, phenotypic correlations remain the chief source of data. Incidentally, from studies of his own, Burt concluded that the variance assigned to genetic factors contributed the greater part of the total variance in intelligence.

It has often been noted that the traits found to segregate in classical Mendelian studies were not physiologically important. Traits like color, however, did provide starting points for biochemical study. Beale [9] showed that the presence or absence of a single hydroxyl group in a pigment (anthocyanin) is associated with a single mutant. Studies of this type led to the insight that the gene acts primarily through its role in the formation of cytoplasmic enzymes. Later, techniques were developed which permitted the selection of important phenotypic differences such as the ability to synthesize vitamins. The point we wish to make is that the inheritance of audiogenic seizures, for example, has been investigated not because audiogenic seizures are psychologically important, but because this kind of study can lead to an understanding of how a gene can produce a behavioral trait. Ginsburg [54] has investigated the neurochemical mechanisms associated with these seizures. The tendency toward seizure incidence has been changed in a number of genotypes by the administration of various substrates and enzyme antagonists related to the Krebs cycle. The various mutants must then have their effect on behavior by changing enzymatic patterns in the nervous system. There must be a number of different kinds of deficiencies or different ways in which a metabolic deficiency is produced, because a given chemical in one strain will alleviate the symptom, and in another strain the same chemical will fail to change the incidence of seizures. Thus two strains out of many respond favorably to administration of glutamate. Further studies suggest that in both of these strains the deficiency involves enzymes required for high-energy phosphorylation. The region of the brain affected, however, is not the same for the two groups.

There are a few instances in the genetics of behavior in which a trait was selected for its psychological importance. Tryon [156, 157], for example, attempted to study the inheritance of learning ability in rats. The study began with a heterogeneous population of rats. Each animal was given a score measuring its facility in maze learning. "The breeding schedule consisted in mating together the brightest rats within each of the brightest litters, the dullest within each of the dullest" [156, p. 112]. Selection on the basis of number of errors required in learning the maze continued for a number of generations. In every generation, matings were restricted to members of the same litter in order to develop homozygous strains. Eventually two populations were produced with little overlap in their learning ability.

There is no expectation, of course, that the two populations differ in one or a few loci. It is more likely that they differ in a large number of factors. The multiple-factor hypothesis can be tested. If the maze-bright animals were homozygous "plus" at many loci, while the maze-dull rats were homozygous "minus" at the same loci, the genotype for all offspring resulting in a cross of bright and dull would be identical. In the F_2 generation produced by mating members of the F_1, all possible genotypes could be recovered. The prediction of a much greater variability in F_2 over F_1 was not, however, realized by the data. Hall [59] pointed out that the bright and dull strains each probably consisted of a number of different sublines. The F_1 generation then would consist of several genotypes instead of one. Even if the number of genotypes in F_1 is greater than one, it should be small compared to the number of recombinations (3^n where n is the number of factors) unless, of course, the parents of the F_1 were not homozygous. While the genetics of maze-bright and maze-dull strains has not been entirely solved, it is possible to raise the question of the physiological difference between the two groups of rats. Such investigations have taken place, but it is too early to evaluate the implications of these findings for the physiology of learning [81].

While there is every reason to believe that species differences are Mendelian—indeed that inherited variation and Mendelian variation are synonomous terms—it is obvious that most species differences cannot be subjected to a direct Mendelian test. The study of behavioral differences between species must continue to rely on the Darwinian criteria for innate traits. There are a few instances where groups as divergent as species are interfertile. Such is the case for domestic breeds of dogs. This provides a valuable source material for comparative and genetic study of behavior. Scott [139] has used a number of behavioral measures to compare breeds. These behavioral measures include tests of timidity, emotionality, learning, and motor skills. In the next step various breeds such as cockers and basenjis were crossed. In many instances, Scott found a recovery of grandparental traits in the F_2 generation bred from the hybrids. In the case of the traits that were recovered, a relatively few Mendelian factors must have been responsible for the difference between breeds. In no case did the ratio suggest that one pair of alleles was responsible for the difference between breeds.

Summary

The modern study of behavior as a species character began with Darwin. Today the emphasis on taxonomy can be found in the studies of comparative ethologists. The discussion of innate behavior in Darwin's sense raises the issue of hereditary and environmental variation. Before Mendel, minimization of environmental variation was the only method available for the study of heredity. The method of restricting the environment remains an important way of determining the role of maturation. This technique is also useful for the study of continuously varying traits in a random-breeding population. The pure-line method introduced a new way of separating hereditary and environmental variation and led to the distinction between phenotype and genotype. Today the gene and the environment can be viewed as interacting and even interchangeable factors in development. This concept can be applied to behavioral phenomena such as imprinting.

The genetics of behavior is a branch of genetics in which a behavioral trait, rather than a morphological one, is found to segregate. These traits are not likely to coincide with those which psychologists have studied. Traits such as learning ability or intelligence are not likely to show simple ratios in the F_2 generation. The experimental study of the genetics of behavior does not replace the Darwinian type of species analysis, even though Darwin's notion of the mechanism of inheritance has been replaced.

The Comparative Method for Determining Physiological Mechanisms

Lorenz has suggested that the term *comparative* be restricted to studies of closely related species aimed at determining phyletic relations. He wrote in 1950:

Since the days of Charles Darwin the term "comparative" has assumed a very definite meaning. It indicates a certain rather complicated method of procedure which, by studying the similarities and dissimiliarities of homologous characters of allied forms, simultaneously obtains indications as to the phyletic relationships of these forms of life and as to the historical origin of the homologous characters in question. I need not enlarge on the details of this method which is a commonplace to biologists and physiologists. We all know perfectly well what we mean by "comparative" anatomy, morphology physiology and so on. But it is all the more misleading if psychologists who evidently are not familiar with what we mean when we speak of the comparative method, apply the same term in a very loose sense to all behaviour studies concerned with different forms of life [99, p. 239].

There is another sense of "comparative" which is as much a part of the Darwinian tradition as is the meaning favored by Lorenz. We are speaking of the use of different forms of life to arrive at an understanding of physiological mechanisms. An early example of this method is Harvey's investigation of the function of the heart. In establishing that the blood is transferred by the heart from veins to arteries, Harvey used the fish as a model. In the absence of a secondary circulation to the lungs, the passageway from veins to arteries is apparent. Harvey argued that the pulmonary circulation in mammals had obscured our realization that the function of the heart is the same in all vertebrates.

In general, we can ask what a comparative study is like when the emphasis is not primarily on taxonomy but on functional analysis. Baldwin [6], for example, posed the following problem: What mechanisms have evolved which maintain similar ionic concentration in the blood of widely diverse species—man, lobster, and fish—living in totally different environments—fresh water, sea water, or land? Baldwin discovered that all vertebrates are osmotically independent of the environment. This finding suggests that vertebrates originated in fresh water and that some returned to the sea at a later stage of evolution. In the same inquiry, Baldwin asked what mechanisms have evolved to make blood more efficient in carrying oxygen to the tissues. The answer to the question may be found by a comparison of the respiratory pigments. The distribution of these pigments is a matter of great zoological interest. Chlorocruorin, hemerythrin, and hemocyanin are each restricted to limited groups of animals, but hemoglobin is widely distributed in a haphazard fashion. It is present in all vertebrates, a few holothurians, several crustaceans, at least two insects, many annelid worms, two species of Platyhelminthes, etc. As a partial explanation for this curious distribution, Baldwin pointed out that all cells are capable of synthesizing heme pigments in connection with the manufacture of cytochrome. The heme of cytochrome b is very like that found in hemoglobin. Presumably, when the need arises the capacity for heme production can be directed to the production of hemoglobin.

Our purpose in discussing these two examples in some detail is to show how taxonomic groupings enter into comparative physiology. The conventional system of taxonomic classification forms the backdrop for these studies, but their concern is not primarily with determining phyletic relations.

If psychologists hope to relate the phylogeny of behavior to important changes in the history of the nervous system and thereby gain insight into basic physiological mechanisms of behavior, it is clear that they cannot rely solely on comparison of closely related species. When we look over the whole of the animal kingdom and ask what are the major mechanisms by which the behavior of organisms is adapted to the environment, the distinction between instinct and learning comes to mind. It is often said that nature had two plans for adaptive behavior. One provides for highly developed innate equipment and the other provides for maximum flexibility. Lashley [94] has questioned whether these modes are fundamentally different in their underlying physiology.

In any case, one major problem for comparative psychology has concerned the relative learning capacity, or intelligence, of different kinds of organisms. Comparative psychologists approached the question by the invention of behavioral tasks. Many of these tests—for example, the maze—became in a later generation the testing grounds for the conflicts between various theories of learning. Their primary purpose in the beginning was not to test theories of learning, but to provide common objective scales for comparing various groups of animals. Observation of organisms in their natural habitat may maximize opportunity for noting intelligence, but is unsatisfactory from the point of view of objectivity. A number of difficulties arise in the use of objective tasks for determining relative learning capacity. First, there are the variations in acuity and agility. One cannot compare the learning capacity of a rat and a monkey by employing a task which requires free use of hands. It is not easy to find a laboratory task equally suited to sensory-motor capacities of widely varying groups. A more subtle difficulty was emphasized by Lashley [94]. He pointed out that when an animal fails on a task it is not safe to conclude that he lacks capacity. A failure can be taken as a sign that the task is beyond the animal's capacity only when we can make sure the question was properly asked. Lashley gives the example of a chimpanzee who was faced with the problem of pulling in one of two stimulus boxes in order to secure food. She solved the problem by holding one rope with her feet before pulling the other rope with both hands. Needless to say, this method was successful every time.

A number of experiments have been done with simple tasks aimed at minimizing differences in sensory-motor capacity. The conclusions from these studies have been reviewed in several places [85, 114]. In general, simple learning tasks have failed to differentiate higher and lower mammals. The rate of formation of simple conditioned habits is about the same for widely separated species [127]; rats and men learn mazes with about equal facility [85]; domestic animals are slightly superior to chimpanzees in the learning of visual discriminatory tasks [51].

Not all laboratory tasks have failed to differentiate species. Lashley [94] reported an experiment in which the learning capacity of a spider monkey was compared with that of a chimpanzee. The task was to select either a red or green square, depending on the color of a third or model square. For example, when the model was red, the correct choice was the red square. The spider monkey failed to solve this task. However, it was easy for a chimpanzee, and a macaque could eventually solve the problem, but only after many trials. The basis for the difficulty faced by the spider monkey was investigated by changing the position of the model. When the model was shifted so that it touched the correct square, learning occurred in a dozen trials. The model could serve as an indicator only by pointing to the correct choice. Color as such was not important because the spider monkey did just as well when a white card pointed to the correct choice. Lashley concludes from this type of experiment that "it is not the fact of learning but what is learned that differentiates animals in the evolutionary scale. The learning of higher animals involves a perception of relations which is beyond the capacity of the lower" [94, p. 30].

Nissen [115] came to a somewhat similar conclusion. He developed the notion that the perceptual world becomes more complex in an ascending series of mammals. As an example of perceptual complexity, Nissen cited experiments on conditional discrimination. A chimpanzee was rewarded for selecting the larger of two square white plaques, and the smaller of two black squares. Following this training, square plaques were replaced by triangular ones. The rules were changed with these new stimuli. The smaller white triangle and the larger black triangle were correct. It was found that the chimpanzee can utilize five different cues in order to solve a conditional problem. The limit for the monkey appears to be four, while carnivores have great difficulty when the number of different cues exceeds two.

There appears to be some agreement among comparative psychologists that the greater problem-solving capacity of higher animals is made possible by the increased complexity of their perceptual world. As opposed to mere sensory acuity, this perceptual capacity involves the perception of relations. An example of a perceptual relation is the notion of "the middle." In a more complex relation, one event may symbolize something not present in the sensorium. Studies of arthropods under natural conditions have revealed behavior which depends on the perception of symbolic relations. Thorpe [153] who has distinguished several kinds of learning—adaptation, habituation, imprinting, conditioning, trial-and-error learning, and insight—points out that all of them are present in bees. The fact that bees as well as primates have the capacity to use symbols suggests a further question: To what degree is this perceptual capacity fully developed at birth?

To the extent that the capacity for perception is limited by phylogenetic level, we would argue that the perception of relations is innate. At the same time, even in bees this capacity could hardly be called "blind instinct," since it functions to keep the organism in tune with changing conditions in the environment. Cognition, however, seems to develop differently in bees and in primates. From the work of Riesen, it is clear that a prolonged training period is required for maturation of perception in chimpanzees. On the other hand, the role of experience in the development of perceptual capacity in bees may be different. We seem to have returned to the commonplace that nature has two plans for adaptive behavior, but to characterize these plans in a word is not easy. The dichotomies genetic versus experience or fixed versus plastic have a part of the truth but would have to be greatly qualified.

As a further step, the phylogeny of behavior can be related to the evolution of the nervous system. We shall conclude this section with a brief introduction to this area of research. The aim of relating behavior to the evolution of the nervous system is to determine the structural bases of function, a goal which this method has in common with the ablation method. It is evident that comparative psychology covers a range of studies from genetics, taxonomy, and phylogeny to those which might be classified either as comparative or physiological psychology.

The evolution of the nervous system and behavior. There are a number of steps in the phylogeny of the nervous system that might be expected to coincide with different levels of behavioral organization. The major innovations in nervous organization as one ascends the phylogenetic tree are the nerve net, synaptic conduction, and the dorsal cord. Each of these steps ultimately provides the basis for more highly integrated nervous mechanisms. But, according to Lashley—

None of these changes seems to have introduced anything new in behavior, when it first appeared. The behavior of hydra is no better coordinated than that of some of the suctoria. The synapse perhaps conferred on the nerve net the capacity for independent reflexes, but paramecium and the hypotricha have independent reflexes as well as coordinated movements of groups of cilia [94, p. 32].

Lashley's argument suggests that nervous systems grossly different in structure may be similar in behavioral accomplishments. However, if similar behavioral outcomes depend on different neural mechanisms, surely there must be some circumstances that would reveal a basic difference in the behavior itself. Recent electrophysiological studies of chemoreception in flies provide results contrasting greatly with those of similar studies in mammals [68]. Potentials recorded from a single labellar hair are of two sorts: small spikes correspond to one receptor neuron (S) and large spikes correspond to the other receptor neuron (L) innervating the hair. S responds only to sugar and leads to a feeding response. L responds to a variety of salts and acids and leads to a rejection response. Both S and L receptor cells are also fired by mechanical stimulation of the hair or temperature changes as small as .1°C. The receptor mechanism seems to be designed to discriminate the acceptability of the stimulus rather than its quality. If it were definitely established that the principles of receptor specificity are different in mammals and arthropods, the implication for the comparative study of neural organization would be far-reaching. Entirely different central neural mechanisms may be present in arthropods and vertebrates.

In the next section, we shall consider in some detail the evolution of the cerebral cortex in vertebrates. This line of phylogenetic development more than any other, it would seem, has the promise of revealing the neural basis of learning capacity.

PART II. THE EVOLUTION OF CORTEX AND THALAMUS

The Origin of Cortex

The development of the cerebral cortex holds special fascination not only because of man's interest in his own nature, but because the change in the nervous system is the outstanding feature in vertebrate evolution. The following account of the phylogeny of the vertebrate cortex is taken from Herrick's 1933 paper [65].

The entire cortex emerged from the olfactory forebrain of the primordial fish. In amphibians no cortex is present but a number of non-olfactory fibers can be found in the pallium. These fibers carry visual, auditory, and somatic impulses to the forebrain. Cortex first appears in reptiles. This layer of cells on the surface of the forebrain can be divided into three regions: hippocampus, pyriform cortex, and a dorsal region which Herrick calls "general cortex." General cortex may be further specified as general sensory cortex since it receives input from the non-olfactory exteroceptive systems. However, the reptilian general cortex is not sharply separated from olfactory regions and olfactory influences remain everywhere in the cortex. A distinguishing feature in mammalian neocortex is the degree of its differentiation from olfactory cortex. In a primitive mammal such as the opossum, one can readily distinguish neocortex from hippocampus medially, and primary olfactory cortex laterally. Further, each of the nonolfactory exteroceptive systems—auditory, visual, and somatic—has a representation in its own exclusive cortical area. As one ascends the scale of mammals, the striking change is the growth of neocortex relative to olfactory cortex.

The Diencephalon

Since the cortex appears to develop by the increasing penetration of sensory fibers into the pallium, and since sensory systems directed to the cortex relay in the thalamus, one would expect a parallel evolution of telencephalon and diencephalon.

Le Gros Clark [35] has described the changes in the diencephalon in an ascending series of vertebrates. In primitive vertebrates the diencephalon is divisible into a dorsal region, the epithalamus, and a ventral region, the hypothalamus. A functional distinction between these regions is suggested by the source of their afferent fibers. Fibers to the habenula are exteroceptive, while those to the hypothalamus originate in the visceral nuclei of the brain stem. Throughout vertebrate history the separation of external sensory from vegetative or internal functions is an important principle of organization. To some degree this functional difference remains associated with the spatial separation of dorsal and ventral diencephalon. In all vertebrates the various regions are linked by cells and fibers of the periventricular region. In the brain of fishes, an increasing number of somatic impulses enter the dorsal diencephalon, and a new structure, the thalamus proper, shows signs of differentiating just below the epithalamus. Afferent fibers from the tectum, from the reticular system of the midbrain and from the optic tract, reach the thalamus of amphibians and, in turn, the cell bodies of the thalamus send fibers into the pallium. By the time a reptilian level is reached, a number of well-defined nuclear masses are present in the thalamus proper.

The Organization of the Mammalian Thalamus

Rose and Woolsey [133] have studied the organization of the mammalian thalamus, utilizing, in addition to comparative anatomy, observations of embryonic development and experimental results of retrograde degeneration. They distinguish three areas in the dorsal diencephalon of a rabbit embryo, two of which, the epithalamus and the ventral thalamus, differentiate early in the ontogeny of the embryo. The epithalamus consists of the habenula, the paraventricular and the pretectal nuclei; the ventral thalamus includes the reticular nucleus and the ventral lateral geniculate body. The remaining subdivision, the dorsal thalamus, is the last to develop, suggesting a more recent phylogenetic origin.

The dependence of a nucleus on the cortex provides another way of estimating its phylogenetic level. Whether or not a thalamic nucleus projects to a cortical area can be determined by the study of retrograde degeneration. Ablation of a cortical region produces degeneration of the cell bodies that send their axones to the ablated region. Rose and Woolsey point out that the epithalamus remains intact after total removal of the endbrain. It is reasonable to conclude that this subdivision has not been of importance in the evolution of cortex. In contrast, both the reticular nucleus of the ventral thalamus and all of the dorsal thalamus are dependent on the endbrain. Localized lesions of the neocortex result in retrograde degeneration in the reticular nucleus, and the site of the degeneration varies with the locus of the lesion [26]. The field of projection of the entire reticular nucleus is very widespread and may include all of the neocortex. The effects of restricted lesions of the endbrain on nuclei of the dorsal thalamus will be described below.

The dorsal thalamus is divisible into a number of groups which can, in turn, be classified in a number of ways [35, 129, 162]. No single classification is the appropriate one for all purposes. Each classification points to some facts important for an understanding of function. Rose and Woolsey have made the important distinction between extrinsic and intrinsic nuclei. The classification rests on whether or not the nucleus receives afferents from extrathalamic sources. The sensory relay nuclei, that is, the lateral and medial geniculate bodies and *n. ventralis posterior*, are included in the extrinsic group, while those nuclei which project to the association cortex fall into the intrinsic class. Since the intrinsic nuclei depend on the extrinsic nuclei for their afferent supply, it would appear that the intrinsic nuclei constitute a further stage in the elaboration of sensory input. This evidence is one part of Rose and Woolsey's argument leading to the conclusion that the intrinsic group represents a higher functional level. The functional significance of the various classes of nuclei in the dorsal thalamus is the major theme of the discussion that follows. In this section, we will consider the evidence from comparative anatomy and experimental neuroanatomy and neurophysiology. In the following section, we will turn to ablation studies.

A review of some general concepts in comparative neuroanatomy may serve as an introduction. The term *homology,* of course, implies a common phylogenetic origin. For example, the superior colliculus of mammals is homologous to the tectum of lower vertebrates, which is to say that the superior colliculus has an ancient origin preceding that of mammals. We raise this elementary notion because it comes up in connection with the meaning of lower and higher functional levels. It has been suggested that some nuclei in the dorsal thalamus of mammals are homologous to thalamic nuclei in reptiles [35]. However, since these attempts to draw homologies have not been accepted by all comparative neuroanatomists, the conservative conclusion is that the method of homology has failed to establish with certainty a more primitive origin for any group in the dorsal thalamus. If we turn from a comparison of mammals and reptiles to a series of mammals, then there is little difficulty in determining homologies between individual nuclei and classes of nuclei in the dorsal thalamus. Further, there is consensus that each of the major classes in a primate dorsal thalamus is present in a more primitive mammal such as the opossum, rat, or rabbit [15, 90, 131].

The important point for arriving at a view of functional organization is that these classes do not develop uniformly with the evolution of neocortex. Some nuclei—the anterior nuclei, for example—remain stable throughout a series of mammals, while others, like the pulvinar, increase greatly in primates. The contrast between the development of the pulvinar in a monkey and in a cat suggests that this nucleus has an important role in the neural functions that differentiate primates from other mammals. Evidence of differential development is cited by Rose and Woolsey [133] in their study of the relation between intrinsic and extrinsic nuclei. In general, the conclusion that the intrinsic nuclei of primates represent a higher level of organization is supported.

The kind of uneven development described above almost certainly has been going on from the beginning of mammalian evolution. Even in the opossum, some nuclei of the dorsal thalamus may have undergone considerable differentiation from the time of the first mammals. It is well to keep in mind that mammals are believed to have differentiated at a very early stage in reptilian evolution, long before the age of dinosaurs. If some thalamic nuclei remained stable throughout all of mammalian history, they may exhibit a very primitive organization not unlike that of thalamic regions of the amphibian-reptile ancestor of mammals. We have already pointed out that such a conclusion cannot be supported by homologies with present-day reptiles. This is not surprising in the light of the specialization of reptiles since the divergence of mammals.

There are, however, other ways of estimating whether a class of nuclei represents a primitive or advanced state of organization. We have already mentioned that the degree and manner of dependence of the nucleus on the neocortex can be taken as some indication of its functional development. A second kind of evidence for functional level is provided by the character of the afferent tracts to the thalamus. In the discussion that follows we shall consider both types of evidence, taking advantage of recent anatomical and electrophysiological studies. In every instance, the starting point for our analysis is the 1949 paper by Rose and Woolsey.

The intralaminar and midline nuclei. The intralaminar and midline nuclei seem to be the most primitive division of the dorsal thalamus, on the grounds of their relation to neocortex. Little or no retrograde degeneration is found in the midline and intralaminar nuclei after lesions confined to neocortex. However, lesions of the internal capsule produce cell loss and gliosis in the intralaminar nuclei, *n. ventralis anterior,* as well as the reticular nucleus of the ventral thalamus [111].

Recently the intralaminar nuclei have been intensively studied by neurophysiologists, and this area of investigation has become vast and complex. For our purposes, we wish to emphasize a few facts that are relevant to the question of functional level. The outstanding property of the intralaminar nuclei discovered by Morison and Dempsey [108] is their capacity to control the electrical rhythms of widespread areas of the cerebral cortex. Thus in the pioneer studies of these workers, and later Jasper and his group [71], low-frequency repetitive stimulation of the intralaminar nuclei led to the recruiting response throughout the neocortex covering both sensory and association areas. Destruction of the extrinsic sensory nuclei or the intrinsic association nuclei does not affect the recruiting response. It is apparent that there is a system in the thalamus with a widespread cortical projection, overlapping the projection areas of the extrinsic sensory and intrinsic association nuclei. The pathway taken to neocortex from the diffuse thalamic system is unknown; perhaps the reticular nucleus of the ventral thalamus is the final relay station. This nucleus of the phylogenetically old ventral thalamus must be classified with the intralaminar and midline nuclei of the dorsal thalamus on the basis of its capacity to produce the recruiting response. The fact that the intralaminar nuclei have functional properties in common with the ventral thalamus is a second reason for considering this group the most primitive part of the dorsal thalamus.

A discussion of the functional properties of the diffuse thalamic projection system is beyond the scope of this paper. However, some reference must be made to the relation between this thalamic system and the brain stem reticular formation. Electrical stimulation of the reticular formation reproduces the changes in the cortical EEG observed in the transition from sleep to wakefulness [38]. Stimulation of the reticular formation produces EEG arousal or activation, even after the lemnisci have been transected just before these tracts enter the thalamus. Thus both the diffuse thalamic system and the brain-stem reticular system appear to have a connection with widespread areas of the cortex, a connection which is independent of the main afferent pathways. [38. See especially papers by Magoun and Jasper.] It was natural to ask whether these two systems are parts of the same mechanism. Some evidence suggests that the cortical effect of reticular stimulation is mediated by the thalamic recruiting system, but the degree to which the reticular formation and the diffuse thalamic recruiting system can be regarded as a functional unit remains a conjecture. The notion that the reticular formation projects to the intralaminar nuclei has received support from recent anatomical studies [112].

Whatever the relation between the recruiting response and the EEG arousal, it is clear that the diffuse thalamic system and the reticular formation are anatomically linked. One further anatomical point should be raised at this time. Both the reticular formation and the diffuse thalamic system were thought to receive collaterals from the lemnisci and the optic tract. This concept of collateral projections organizes a number of facts, including the fact that sensory stimuli can activate the EEG. With a picture of different kinds of sensory information feeding into it, the central core of the brain stem could be viewed as an integrative center elaborating sensory impulses, a conception not unlike the functional concept of association cortex a generation ago. However, the presence of collaterals has never been proved by anatomical methods. Evidence will be presented below which suggests that the medial lemniscus does not give off collaterals as it ascends the brain stem to its target in the dorsal thalamus.

In general, we do not know what it means from a behavioral point of view to conclude that a neural structure represents a primitive level of organization. Some of the functions attributed to the diffuse systems, such as control over wakefulness, certainly would be included in the repertoire of lower vertebrates. In any event, the intralaminar nuclei do not increase in size in an ascending series of mammals. It is not likely then that the phylogeny of mammalian behavior can be directly correlated with the development of the diffuse thalamic projection system. On the other hand, the special behavioral achievements of neocortex appear to be related to the specific sensory nuclei, GM, GL, and VP,[3] and the adjacent nuclei *n. lateralis posterior* and the pulvinar.

[3] See a list of abbreviations used at the end of this article.

The anterior nuclei and n. medialis dorsalis.   Before returning to a discussion of extroceptive functions, we shall consider briefly parts of the thalamus not linked with exteroceptors, the anterior group and *n. medialis dorsalis*. The anterior nuclei receive their afferent supply from the hypothalamus and project to the transitional cortex of the medial surface of the cerebral hemisphere. Le Gros Clark [35] believes that the mammillo-thalamic tract is derived from the old periventricular system linking hypothalamus with thalamus. Whether or not the anterior group is homologous to any well-defined reptilian nuclei, there appears in a series of reptiles a progressive differentiation of a tract from the mammillary bodies to the thalamus.

Papez [119] was the first to emphasize that the connections of the anterior nuclei form part of a circuit between the hypothalamus and the cortex. The transitional cortex of the midline receives fibers from the anterior nuclei and sends projections to the hippocampus, which in turn projects to the mammillary bodies via the fornix. The circuit is completed by the pathway from the mammillary bodies to the anterior nuclei. Because of its connection with the posterior hypothalamus, Papez argued that the circuit which now bears his name is concerned with emotion. Ever since Bard [7] showed that the transection of the brain-stem rostral to the posterior hypothalamus led to a lowered threshold for rage, there has been a search for the part or parts of the forebrain which are the source of restraining impulses on the hypothalamus.

It was natural that this search was guided by the phylogenetic subdivision of the cerebral cortex into new and old cortex. The old cortex, pyriform area and hippocampus, and related structures such as the amygdala are parts of a system of olfactory connections. However, this olfactory system is more extensive than would be expected if it served only in the limited function of olfactory discrimination. Herrick [65] postulated that the old brain may act on exteroceptive systems as a nonspecific activator, a function which may be suggested by psychological terms like *motivation* and *emotion*. Herrick argued that some part of the nervous system must relate to the internal state adjustments to the external environment, and the olfactory brain is a good candidate for this function. The neural circuit associated with Papez emphasizes that the old cortex may be closely tied with the hypothalamic functions. The extensive literature on the effect of stimulation and ablation of hippocampus, amygdala, and other structures of the old brain upon emotional and instinctive behavior supports, in a most general way, the view which Herrick and Papez had suggested, namely, that the olfactory brain is not limited to olfactory functions. It would be impossible to be more specific in a few words, since all structures of the so-called "limbic system" are by no means equivalent or equally important in instinctive and emotional behavior, and the role of these structures may be quite different in different species [78].

The position of *n. medialis dorsalis* in mammalian evolution is ambiguous. On the one hand, it is well developed in many mammalian groups such as carnivores and primates. On the other hand, the cortical projection field of *n. medialis dorsalis*—frontal granular cortex—is limited in carnivores and greatly expanded in primates. The effects of ablation and stimulation of frontal cortex and *n. medialis dorsalis* has also become a field in itself, one which we cannot begin to consider in the present context. We shall merely note that very recently Pribram [124] suggested that *n. medialis dorsalis* might be considered with the anterior nuclei as an internal core of the thalamus, possibly having some functional unity.

Fiber Size and the Development of Sensory Systems

A recent paper by Bishop [12] has provided new insight into the phylogeny of sensory systems. This paper reinterprets the significance of fiber size and presents evidence that has radical consequences for our understanding of intrinsic and extrinsic nuclei. The starting point for Bishop's inquiry was his own electrophysiological studies of the visual system. Employing the established relation between thresholds, rate of conduction, and fiber size, Bishop concluded that in the cat only the largest fibers of the optic tract reach the cortex via the lateral geniculate body [13]. The next lower-sized fibers relay through layer B of the lateral geniculate to *n. lateralis posterior* of the thalamus. The smallest fibers terminate in the superior colliculus of the phylogenetically older midbrain. Since differences in the size of visual fibers have never been identified with differences in the quality of visual sensation, Bishop reexamined the significance of fiber size in cutaneous nerves and in the spinal cord. His working assumption was that peripheral nerve fibers tend to increase in diameter with the evolution of higher species. The selective advantage of larger fibers might result from larger and faster traveling-action potentials. The activity of a single neuron is more significant when one or a few can excite the next neuron. In the case of small fibers with correspondingly smaller potentials, the activity of a large group must be summed in order to be effective. The evidence from the cat's visual system suggests that larger fibers, when they first appear, will join the smaller fibers in their projection to lower brain-stem centers; but as higher targets are available in the thalamus and cortex, the larger fibers will bypass phylogenetically older centers.

The generally accepted view of the functional significance of fiber size grew out of the work of Gasser and Erlanger [52, 53] and Bishop [11] in the twenties and thirties. These studies first showed that the compound action potential recorded from a nerve trunk was a function of fiber size—the earlier waves representing the larger fibers and the later waves representing the smaller fibers. Further, the progressive loss of sensation following nerve block was correlated with the order of disappearance of these waves. In a pressure block, sensitivity to touch is affected before pain, and correspondingly the primary wave is the first portion of the action potential to show a decrement. Thus pain was identified with smaller fibers, and touch with larger fibers.

Earlier it had been shown by Ranson [126] that the dorsal root is divided into two portions. The fibers of the medial division are of large caliber and, after entering the cord, ascend in the dorsal columns. The fibers of the lateral division are thinly myelinated or unmyelinated and, after entering the cord, synapse in the posterior horn. A second-order neuron usually crosses the cord and ascends in the contralateral lateral column. From these two lines of investigation, it follows that different spinal tracts carry impulses of different modality. Sensory dissociation following lesions in the cord is, of course, a common neurological finding. Even before this chapter in neurophysiology, Sherrington had located the pathway for pain in the lateral columns by his study of the nociceptive reflex after partial sections of the cord.

The dorsal- and lateral-column systems.   The requirements of the doctrine of specific nerve energy provided a rationale for the spatial arrangement in the cord. The analysis into various sensory qualities accomplished by the receptors is maintained by spatially separated pathways. Comparative anatomy puts a new light on the significance of the dorsal and lateral columns. Only in mammals, according to Herrick and Bishop [66], is there a true medial lemniscus originating in the gracile and cuneate nuclei. In a recent study employing the Nauta technique for detecting degenerating fibers, Bowsher [17] showed that all of the fibers in the medial lemniscus of the monkey terminate in *n. ventralis posterior* of the thalamus. No collaterals were found to the brain-stem reticular formation or to the diffuse thalamic projection system. One may conclude that the dorsal-column system is composed of low-threshold, large fibers that bypass the phylogenetically older structures of the brain stem and reach the neocortex via the somatic-relay nucleus VP. All of Bishop's requirements for a recent phylogenetic origin are fulfilled.

The pathway of the lateral columns is quite a different story. Nauta and Kuypers [112] traced degenerating fibers produced by a lesion of the lateral columns in the cat. Terminal degeneration was widespread throughout the medial tegmental region of the medulla, and the periaqueductal gray, superior colliculus, and reticular formation of the midbrain. Further, rostrally the diffuse path terminates throughout the intralaminar nuclei of the thalamus as well as regions of the subthalamus. In the same paper, Nauta and Kuypers reported that lesions of the brain-stem reticular formation also produce terminal degeneration in the intra-laminar nuclei. They described a second area of the cat's thalamus re-ceiving fibers of the lateral column. Lateral to the diffuse path to the intralaminar nuclei, terminal degeneration was found in VP and in a region medial to the medial geniculate body. The area medial to GMp includes what has commonly been called "the magnocellular division of the medial geniculate and the suprageniculate nucleus." These regions, GMp and adjacent nuclei, can be seen in Fig. 1. It should be noted that in presenting our own results, the terminology of Rose and Woolsey [135] was followed. They classify the suprageniculate nucleus and portions of the medial geniculate as a part of the posterior group (Po). Findings very similar to those of Nauta and Kuypers are reported by Anderson and Berry [5]. These authors also traced two paths to the thalamus of the cat, following lateral-column section. They concluded that a diffuse medial pathway projects to the intralaminar nuclei, while a lateral path-way projects to VP. From the sections shown by the authors, it is likely that a part of the region they label "VP" is not the primary somatic-relay nucleus to SI but is anterior Po of Rose and Woolsey [135]. We shall return to this point below.

According to Herrick and Bishop [66], the diffuse path taken by some lateral-column fibers to the reticular formation and to the intra-laminar nuclei has precursors in amblystoma, while only in mammals do some fibers of the lateral-column system digress and terminate in VP. In other words, it is the oldest portion of the lateral column which pro-jects to the intralaminar nuclei. We concluded above that, of the various groups in the dorsal thalamus, the intralaminar nuclei have developed the least with the evolution of mammals. It makes sense that the portion of the thalamus reflecting a primitive stage of organization receives fibers that have an early phylogenetic origin.

To summarize: The lateral column sends fibers to the reticular for-mation which in turn projects to the diffuse thalamic system. Some fibers of the lateral column enter a diffuse pathway direct to the intralaminar nuclei. Other fibers of the lateral column terminate in Po of the thalamus. Finally, still other fibers of the lateral columns reach *n. ven-tralis posterior* of the thalamus.

The conclusion seems inescapable that the dorsal-column system is entirely of recent origin, while the lateral-column system is composed of tracts of varying age. The diffuse portion may be as old as the am-phibian stage in vertebrate history, while the classical spinothalamic tract may originate with mammals.

Another implication of these studies is that sensory input to the brain-stem reticular formation need not depend on collaterals from neocortical sensory systems. Such collaterals have not been demonstrated anatomically, and the view that primitive sensory systems project to the reticular system may be the simplest interpretation of electrophysiological findings. In this connection, the results of Collins and O'Leary [36] are relevant. They found that stimulation of large, low-threshold peripheral fibers elicited responses in VP, while stimulation of the smaller gamma and delta fibers activated responses in the midbrain reticular formation and in the vicinity of the intralaminar nuclei. Section of the lateral columns abolished the medial responses, and section of the dorsal column greatly reduced the VP response.

The phylogenetic interpretation of fiber size implies that within the bodily senses, modality differences may be the result of phylogenetic development. This conclusion is reminiscent of Head's theory of two types of sensation mediated by two kinds of peripheral mechanisms—a primitive or protopathic sense and an advanced or epicritic sense. (The reader may refer to Rose and Mountcastle [132] for a discussion of Head's views. The distinction between epicritic and protopathic is analyzed in the light of present-day evidence for modality specific receptors and for two neural systems—dorsal column and lateral column.) While sensations mediated by the two systems differ, e.g., no pain in the epicritic sense, there is some overlap between epicritic and protopathic sensibility, as might be expected from the way the systems originated. By the same token, we may expect some overlap, as well as some difference, between the functions of the dorsal-column lemniscal system and the lateral-column projection system. Duplication in the function of the two systems is suggested by studies now in progress. Cats are able to learn habits based on discriminating the location of a bodily stimulus after removal of sensory-motor cortex plus a complete section of the dorsal columns. (See studies in progress on the effect of cortical and spinal lesions on somatic discrimination in cats by I. T. Diamond, W. Randall, and L. Springer.)

Further Analysis of the Difference between Extrinsic and Intrinsic Nuclei

The method of evoked potentials has greatly advanced our understanding of the organization of sensory projection systems. Sensory areas of the cortex or of subcortical structures have been determined by the presence of short latency potentials evoked by external sensory stimuli or by electrical stimulation of peripheral sensory tracts. The following discussion is based on studies of evoked potentials in the cat.

It is possible to divide the responsive cortex of the cat into a sensory core and a surrounding belt. The core corresponds to the first sensory areas of Woolsey [168, 169], auditory area I or A I, visual area I or V I and somatic area I or S I. Each of these three sensory areas shows a similar topographic organization. If a cortical point is defined by its best stimulus (for example, the best frequency continues to elicit responses at intensities below the threshold for all other frequencies) the result is a map which replicates the spatial order of the receptor surface [148, 170]. Spatial organization is also present in the adjacent cortical belt [171]. In somatic area II a face, arm, and leg area can be localized [2]. Visual area II constitutes a mirror image of visual area I [147]. In one very important respect, the belt differs from the core. The responsive cortex surrounding the first sensory areas is not modality specific. Auditory as well as somatic stimuli elicit responses in S II [158]. Both auditory and visual stimuli can evoke potentials in the middle suprasylvian gyrus [102, 60, 152]. A composite sensory area is reported in the anterior suprasylvian gyrus [104, 98].

When these secondary areas were first discovered, the question arose as to whether or not they were excited by cortico-cortical fibers from the first areas. A negative answer was suggested by the latency of the responses and was established by the failure of lesions in the first areas to abolish potentials in the belt [147]. Attention was then drawn to the thalamic nuclei which project to these areas. If we make certain required modifications in the definitions of the classical relay nuclei, it turns out that, in general, the belt receives afferent fibers from the intrinsic nuclei, LP, Pul, and Po, while the first areas receive projections from the relay nuclei, GL, GM, and VP. The question now to be considered is this: How can the intrinsic nuclei be responsible for the independence of responses in the belt cortex if they receive no independent afferent input from receptors?

A partial answer is suggested by the following data. Figure 1 shows the brain of an animal in which we removed cortical areas A II, S II, and the insular-temporal cortex. In orther words, the belt cortex below and between A I and S I was ablated. Below the reconstructed surface depicting the primary lesion are drawings of the thalamus, showing retrograde degeneration. Thalamic degeneration is located in anterior Po, the magnocellular division of GM, posterior Po, and the posterior tip of GM. From other studies, we know that neither the magnocellular division nor the posterior tip of GM is part of the thalamic relay system to A I [134, 40]. Indeed, in the opossum, the posterior tip of GM does not project to any part of the neocortex [15; studies in progress by I. T. Diamond and J. Utley]. The thalamic degeneration then surrounds, but essentially spares, the relay nuclei VP and anterior GMp. For our present purpose, the important feature of this experiment emerges from a comparison of the region of retrograde degeneration with the region of

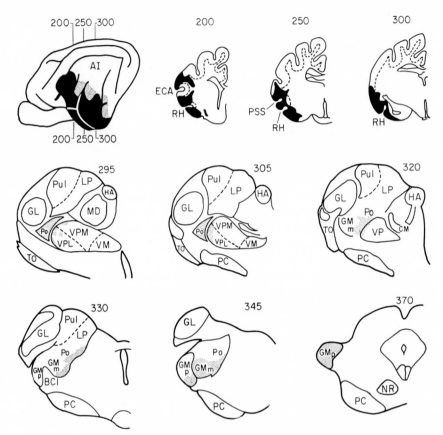

Fig. 1. Thalamic degeneration following removal of cortical areas A II, S II and the insular-temporal area. In the reconstruction of the lateral surface, the primary cortical lesion is depicted by solid black. In addition to the intended removal, the lesion invaded paleocortex below the rhinal fissure. Stippling indicates that the cortex was undercut. For example, in frontal section 200, the depth of the anterior ectosylvian sulcus is preserved, but the fibers to this cortical area have been interrupted. In the sections through the thalamus, stippling indicates cell loss and gliosis. It is to be noted that in sections 295 and 305, the nucleus labeled "Po" has in the past been called "GM" or "VP." The present terminology is based on the studies of Rose and Woolsey [135]. The anterior portion of GMp is preserved, as would be expected from the sparing of A I. Similarly, VP is largely intact, as would be expected from the sparing of S I. The degeneration then is confined to Po, the magnocellular division of GM, and the posterior tip of GMp.

termination of the spinothalamic tract as described by Nauta and Kuypers [112] and Anderson and Berry [5]. There is a striking overlap in the area which supplies the belt cortex and the area which is supplied by some fibers of the lateral-column system. From these results, one may infer that the belt of cortex surrounding A I and S I may receive afferent impulses originating in the phylogenetically older lateral-column system.

A comparison of the functional properties of VP and Po is consistent with the conclusion that the former receives projections from the dorsal-column system, while the latter receives projections from the lateral-column system. Poggio and Mountcastle [122], employing microelectrode techniques, reported that each responsive neuron in VP was specific in regard to both modality and place. A given neuron was excited either by light cutaneous stimuli or by kinesthetic stimuli, but not by both. Further, each neuron was excited by a limited field, such as the side of the wrist, and stimuli outside this area failed to produce a response. In contrast, neurons in Po were activated by large areas, often including regions on both sides of the body. Many of these neurons were found to be sensitive to several kinds of stimulation such as light touch, deep pressure, and pain. It is especially noteworthy that Po is activated by painful stimuli because of the identification of pain with the lateral-column system. Mountcastle states that the majority of units in Po were excited only by intense stimuli which may be regarded as destructive of tissue. Perhaps of even greater interest is that some neurons in Po responded to auditory stimuli as well as somatic stimuli. This fits the view that Po projects to a polysensory cortical region, S II, and the anterior ectosylvian gyrus.

We have attempted to summarize the somatic projection systems in the diagram shown in Fig. 2. Can we expect to find a similar organization for the visual and auditory system of the cat? Does the pulvinar, for example, which probably projects to V II receive visual impulses directly from the optic tract? Earlier studies by Barris and others [8] failed to find such a pathway, but recently J. Altman and M. B. Carpenter, using the Nauta technique, have traced fibers from the superior colliculus to the pulvinar (Altman, J. Personal communication). Presumably such fibers would carry visual impulses.[4]

We must conclude that it is too early to make a generalization about afferent tracts to all of the intrinsic nuclei. However, it would appear

[4] Since this writing we have learned that the results on the projections of the superior colliculus will soon be published: Altman, J. & Carpenter, M. B. Fiber projections of the superior colliculus in the cat. *J. comp. Neurol.*, in press.

Further unpublished results on the visual system of the cat by these experimenters have a direct bearing on the present argument. Using the Nauta technique, J. Altman and M. B. Carpenter found that, after cutting the optic nerve, no degenerating fibers or collaterals are present in reticular formation. However, a lesion in the superior colliculus produces excessive degeneration in the reticular formation. This seems to suggest a two-part division of the visual system which is roughly analogous to the two parts of the somatic projection system.

Further evidence based on optic-tract lesions indicates that the pulvinar may receive a few direct fibers from the optic tract.

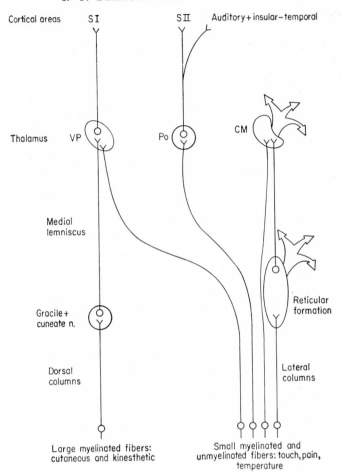

Fig. 2. The projections of the dorsal and lateral columns. The special point to be noted is the contrast in these two systems. The dorsal-column system is composed of a single path to cortical area S I. The lateral-column system is composed of many paths. A second point is that the three thalamic nuclei show varying degrees of specificity in their projections. Based on electrophysiological evidence, CM has the most diffuse or widespread projection. At the other extreme, the projection of VP is confined to one cortical area, S I. Po is intermediate in the specificity of its projections.

worthwhile to investigate the possibility of unmyelinated paths from the distance receptors to LP, Pul, and Po. One other possibility for an independent pathway to the pulvinar and *n. lateralis posterior* might be mentioned. When V I and its surrounding belt are removed, there are still cells remaining in the lateral geniculate body (see Diamond, I. T. &

Neff, W. D., thalamo-cortical relations in the cat, unpublished manuscript). Only the larger, deeper-staining ganglion cells degenerate, leaving smaller, lightly staining cells intact. We have earlier mentioned Bishop's finding a small fiber route to LP via the lateral geniculate body.

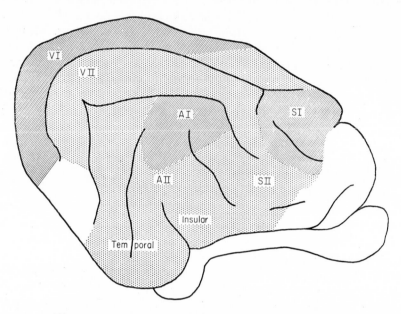

Cortical areas receiving essential projections from sensory relay nuclei GL, GM, and VP

Cortical areas without essential projections from the thalamus

FIG. 3. Thalamocortical relations in the cat. This diagram summarizes the results obtained from a study of retrograde degeneration by I. T. Diamond and W. D. Neff. Small lesions in various parts of the region shown by stippling failed to produce retrograde degeneration in the thalamus. Some of this stippled area, and perhaps all of it, receives sustaining projections from the thalamus, including the intrinsic nuclei, LP, Pul, and Po. This conclusion is based on the evidence from combination lesions. For example, the pulvinar shows severe degeneration when the cortical lesion includes V I, V II, and the middle suprasylvian gyrus; anterior Po shows severe degeneration when the cortical lesion includes S I, S II, and the anterior ectosylvian gyrus.

Perhaps it is the small cells of GL which project to LP and Pul. It has been suggested that optic-tract fibers of small diameter terminate predominantly in the smaller cells, while fibers of large diameter terminate in larger cells of GL [61]. A small-fiber, small-cell pathway might then be independent of a large-fiber, large-cell pathway to V I. It must be admitted that if this surmise is correct, it is likely to have only limited applicability. In both rats and monkeys, all of the cells of GL degenerate with the ablation of visual cortex [90].

Essential and sustaining projections to the cortex.   In cats, a difference can be found in the way the different nuclei of the thalamus project to the cortex. Small cortical lesions in V I, A I or S I produce sharp focal degeneration in their respective thalamic sources. This type of projection is called "essential" [135]. Thus the preservation of S I is essential to the preservation of VP. On the other hand, small lesions in the belt cortex do not produce any degeneration in the thalamus. In a study in progress, Diamond and Neff have made small lesions in S II, V II, the middle suprasylvian gyrus, and in other regions outside the first sensory areas. Figure 3 shows A I, V I, and S I, and the regions surrounding these primary sensory areas. In no case did a small cortical lesion outside V I, S I or A I have an effect on the thalamus. However, large lesions combining several cortical areas often produced degenerative changes. For example, when a lesion of V II was combined with ablation of V I, the pulvinar shows severe retrograde changes. Removal of either V I or V II alone did not lead to severe degeneration in the pulvinar. This type of projection is called "sustaining." Sustaining projections from the posterior medial geniculate to A I, A II, and the temporal-insular cortex have been established [135, 39]. Similarly, S II is found to receive sustaining projections from Po [135, 19]. If a lesion includes auditory cortex in addition to S II, then anterior Po will degenerate. Recently we have found degeneration in anterior Po after lesions of S I, S II, and the anterior ectosylvian gyrus. These results show that Po and Pul in the cat have a widespread projection which may overlap with the projection areas of the classical sensory relay nuclei.

Summary

Three sensory projection systems to the cortex can be distinguished in the cat. First, there is a diffuse projection to the entire cortex from the intralaminar and midline nuclei and the reticular nucleus. Second, there is a set of specific projections from GL to visual area I, from anterior GM to auditory area I, and from VP to somatic area I. A third projection system appears to be intermediate to the first two in its diffuseness. This third system involves the intrinsic nuclei, LP, Pul, and Po. All of the cortex responsive to external stimuli can be divided into a few extensive sectors. Starting from V I and extending toward the somatic and auditory areas is a region which receives its afferents from the dorsal part of the intrinsic complex, the pulvinar and *n. lateralis posterior*. Lying between auditory area I and somatic area I and extending ventrally below both of these areas is a region which receives its afferent supply from the ventral part of the intrinsic complex, the posterior group. We have retained the term *intrinsic* although its original meaning has been modified. The intrinsic nuclei may receive an extrathalamic input after all.

It is tempting to speculate that the three projection systems represent three stages in mammalian development. Perhaps the diffuse thalamic system is an outgrowth of the amphibian level in which impulses from the reticular formation, the tectum, and the hypothalamus mingle in a common diencephalic pool and then spread diffusely into the pallium. This thalamic system might serve in the perception of the stimulus and at the same time register its survival value. The function of the primitive thalamus might have been to link perception of an external object with a specific releasing mechanism or general level of arousal. Some selective advantage may have depended on a further separation within the thalamus of cognitive and conative functions.

We imagine that the common ancestor of reptiles and mammals possessed a thalamic region which was exclusively sensory, and the projection area of this sensory thalamus was restricted to one portion of the pallium. In reptiles this area became the general cortex. In mammals a further subdivision took place and modality-specific systems emerged within the general sensory field. These modality-specific systems may be the basis for the most refined or epicritic cognitive functions. Whatever functions are made possible by the differentiation of modality-specific thalamic nuclei, it would appear from anatomy that the separation between these nuclei and the intrinsic nuclei, LP, Pul, and Po, becomes more and more sharply drawn in an ascending series of mammals—opossum, rabbit, cat. In the opossum GL, GM, and VP merge without sharp boundaries into adjacent regions.

The argument so far only applies up to the carnivore stage of mammalian evolution. An additional development in thalamocortical projection systems is introduced by primates. The intrinsic nuclei, especially the pulvinar, develop greatly in size and achieve the specificity of cortical projections found chiefly in the extrinsic nuclei of subprimates.

These closing paragraphs of speculation could be taken seriously only if support is received from behavioral studies employing the methods of ablation and stimulation. The difficulty in arriving at any general conclusions about the function of intrinsic versus extrinsic thalamocortical systems will be apparent in the next section.

PART III. SENSATION AND LEARNING: THE PROBLEM OF SENSORY AND ASSOCIATION CORTEX

The Classical View of Sensation and Perception

A most interesting effect of cortical disorder is *mental blindness*. This consists not so much in insensibility to optical impressions, as in *inability to understand them*. Psychologically it is interpretable as *loss of associations* between optical sensations and what they signify; and any interruption of the paths between the optic centres and the centres for other ideas ought to bring it about. Thus, printed letters of the alphabet, or words, signify certain sounds and certain articulatory movements. If the connection between the articulating or auditory centres, on the one hand, and the visual centres on the other, be ruptured, we ought *a priori* to expect that the sight of words would fail to awaken the idea of their sound, or the movement for pronouncing them. We ought, in short, to have *alexia*, or inability to read: and this is just what we do have in many cases of extensive injury about the fronto-temporal regions, as a complication of *aphasic disease* [70, pp. 48–50].

This passage, taken from the *Principles of psychology* by William James, contains the view of learning and sensation which not only prevailed in James's time, but in the succeeding generations. Even today, after these ideas have been discredited to some extent by results of ablation experiments, no other ideas of equal comprehensiveness have replaced the old view of the function of sensory and association cortex.

The resilience of the classical theory of cortical function is based on many factors. In the first place, a happy congruence of anatomy and psychology was achieved by identifying sensation with sensory cortex and perception with association cortex. In James's time, the existence of regions of the cortex receiving afferent impulses from the main exteroceptors was well established. For example, the hearing region of the dog depicted by Luciani or the visual center described by Munk correspond well with our present notions. Indeed, as early as 1884, Munk reported that ablation of both occipital lobes produced blindness in his experimental dogs. [70; see James for references to these early experiments.] Nothing seemed more natural than to assign the function of forming associations and storing memory traces to the cortical regions between primary sensory and motor cortex. A further parceling was accomplished by putting visual association in the region next to visual cortex, and so on.

A second reason for the acceptance of the classical neurology of sensation and learning lies in the merit of the distinction between sensation and perception. Parenthetically, it should be noted that this view merely states where learning takes place; it does not offer an explanation of the law of effect, or law of contiguity, or some other law of learning in terms of neural events. The psychologist's purpose in defining sensation was to isolate an element of consciousness not affected by differences in past experience. If this could be achieved, it was hoped that mental content could be specified in terms of the physical dimensions of the stimulus. After establishing a relation between, for instance, wave length and hue, the next step was to look to the physiology of the receptor. The physiology of the receptor might explain both the correspondence and the lack of correspondence between stimulus and sensation. Thus an explanation for negative afterimages, an instance of a lack of correspondence, might be sought in some physiological process of adaptation [155].

Electrophysiology and the Concept of Sensory Quality

The advent of new techniques for electrical recording from the receptor and the nervous system permitted a test of many of the speculations about peripheral physiological analysis. The notion that differences in elementary sensory qualities correspond to differences in receptors was, on the whole, supported. For example, Granit [58] concluded that the mechanism of color reception is peripheral and depends on a limited number of color-sensitive elements, each sensitive to a different portion of the spectrum. The conclusion that electrophysiological results support the concept of sensory quality must be justified. Strictly speaking, electrophysiology has confirmed the specificity of receptors, not the view of sensory elements. Yet there is a close linkage between the traditional view of sensation and the role of receptor analysis. This linkage can best be seen in the light of the gestalt criticism of sensory elements.

The gestalt view of sensory quality. Köhler [80] discovered that transposition or generalization was based on the relation between a pair of stimuli, rather than on any absolute qualities of either member of the pair. This kind of transposition does not appear to be a higher or derived mental function; it is within the capacity of a chicken. Yet no retinal cells correspond in any obvious way to "darker than" or to "curvilinearity." A relation such as "darker" does not seem to depend on learning nor does it have anything to do with specificity of receptors. This finding led Koffka [79] to repudiate the entire notion of an elementary sensory quality corresponding to the physical dimensions of the stimulus. While there are no known mechanisms—peripheral or central—to explain transposition, it does not follow that all sensory dimensions are unrelated to the receptor. Indeed, neurophysiological studies of individual neurons show that the first stage of sensory analysis bears a striking relation to the old sensory qualities. For example, in the eighth nerve or cochlear nucleus, different frequencies of sound will activate different populations of neurons [48]. Beyond the cochlear nucleus, an inhibitory mechanism has been discovered which may serve to sharpen frequency discrimination [164]. In the case of audition the analysis into sensory qualities comes closer to the analysis provided by the receptor than do any other psychological terms.

Revisions in the meaning of sensation. The term *sensory quality*, as currently used in the physiology of sensation, does not carry with it all of its old connotation. The introspectionists held that the firing of some cortical neurons is the physical counterpart of conscious experience—a view that has been called "psychophysical parallelism." The concept of structure and function has generally replaced a mind-body dichotomy. For example, the difference between daylight and night vision seems to depend in a first approximation on the difference between rods and cones. We may speak very loosely of daylight vision residing in the cones, but it is commonly accepted that a structure-function relationship is all that is implied. A function requires certain structural arrangements, but the latter is not the physical counterpart of the former. Capillary walls do not comprise or constitute exchange, nor do the functions implied by the concept of internal environment reside in capillary walls. A similar statement can be made about the relation between genotype and phenotype. The gene for red flowers is not the physical counterpart for a red appearance or even a red pigment.

The view of a one-to-one relation between nerve fiber and sensory quality has also been revised. Pfaffmann [121] has recently reviewed the main issues in the physiology of sensory quality. His own research in the physiology of taste suggests the following scheme:

In the two-fiber example . . . low concentrations of salt will discharge only A, higher concentrations will discharge both A and B, but activity in A will be greater than that in B. Low concentrations of sugar will activate only B, higher concentrations will activate both B and A, but B will be greater than A [121, p. 231].

A sensory quality is determined by the pattern of fibers excited rather than one specific type of fiber. But the units in the pattern are fibers and their receptors; and the differential sensitivity of the receptor can be described only in terms of the physical dimensions which correspond to the sensory qualities—sweet, sour, bitter, and salt.

We conclude that a lasting feature in the traditional psychology of sensation and perception was its concern for receptor analysis. Many of the ideas associated with introspectionism have, of course, been rejected. The effort to create a consistent systematic viewpoint for psychological study led to curious self-imposed limitations. For example, by insisting that mental content was the only proper subject matter, the introspectionists reduced attention to an attribute of sensation clearness. The alterations in the power of concentration observed in brain-damaged patients could not even be described by someone with a position like Titchener's [155]. It is also questionable whether animal experimentation would be admitted by introspectionists as a test of their view of sensory and association cortex.

Clinical Evidence for and against the Theory of Memory Loss

The quotation from James indicates that the chief empirical support for his sensation-perception view of cortical functioning came from the neurological clinic. Since that passage was written, has the view received further support from the clinic? This cannot be given a simple answer. On the one hand, many years after James, there appeared a study of human brain damage by Nielsen [113], supporting the traditional view of agnosia, alexia, and apraxia. Not only did Nielsen report dissociation of memory from sensation, but he described patients with modality-specific memory losses, that is, patients with good vision who could not understand what they see but could understand what they hear.

On the other hand, some neurologists, notably Goldstein [56, 57], have denied that loss of memory explains any symptoms from brain damage. The reason patients fail on certain behavioral tasks is their inability to free themselves from the concrete and particular aspects of their environment. As an example of the loss of capacity for abstraction, Goldstein describes the patient who had no concept of a map or a floor plan. The patient was at a loss when she discovered she was on a floor different from that of her hospital room. She was unable to take a route identical to the one she had taken on innumerable occasions without the specific cues associated with her floor.

Earlier Head [62] described aphasia as a loss in vigilance rather than memory. He pointed out that patients may fail at first to understand a sentence, but if it is repeated several times, eventually the meaning is grasped. According to Head, the cerebral cortex is the organ by which we can focus attention upon the changes evoked by sensory impulses.

After many years of studying the behavioral effects of brain damage in man, Teuber is unable to accept the classical view of modality-specific agnosias [150]. At the same time he does not entirely reject the concept of agnosia. His results point to the distinction between modality-specific losses in sensory discrimination and some more general cognitive loss that is unrelated to the locus of the lesion.

As an example of sensory loss, Teuber decribed the effects of lesions in the pre- and post-Rolandic areas. Patients suffering damage in the somatic sensory and motor areas showed an impairment in position sense, touch thresholds, two-point discrimination, and point localization on the side contralateral to the lesion. The same patients were also tested for their capacity to recognize an object by touch. In an object-recognition task, the patient is asked to palpate a solid form, such as a cylinder or a pyramid, and then to try to find a replica among an array of objects. The experimenter, of course, prevents the subject from viewing the objects. If some patients showed a deficit in object recognition without suffering any change in touch threshold or other purely sensory tasks, then the classical view would be supported. At least it would be supported if we assume that recognition of the shape of objects is a perception in the Wundtian sense of that term. A most unexpected outcome emphasizes the complexity of the data. Teuber reported that all patients who failed in object recognition also showed some sensory loss; that is, a dissociation of symptoms was *not* found. However, while the sensory disturbances were restricted to one side of the body, the perceptual defect was in both hands—ipsilateral as well as contralateral to the lesion.

The syndrome resulting from damage to the somatic cortex clearly could not be reproduced by a lesion of peripheral pathways. Yet this syndrome is not entirely free from symptoms associated with peripheral damage. Similarly, the syndrome produced by damage to the occipital lobe could not be reproduced by a lesion of the retina or optic tract; yet a lesion in the visual cortex produces a scotoma [150]. To test for perceptual changes in vision, Teuber used a task which requires finding a simple line figure embedded within a complex figure. Patients with occipital lesions showed impairment in this test of visual perception. The same deficit was also found in patients with lesions outside the visual cortex. Therefore the defect in visual perception cannot be the unique result of damage to the visual cortex.

In conclusion, the symptoms produced by injury to the parietal or occipital lobes are not adequately described by the terms *sensation* and *perception* as these terms were used in traditional psychology. Further, the distinction between sensation and memory is not likely to determine the direction of research. Future studies are suggested by particular findings such as the difference between symptoms restricted to one side and those present on both sides of the body. Nevertheless, it remains useful to consider the degree to which the results deviate from the classical views of sensory and memory loss.

Experimental Studies of Sensation and Perception

The traditional views of tactile agnosia form the background of an experimental ablation study by Blum [14]. She investigated the effect of lesions in the posterior association cortex. Her behavioral measures were dictated by the distinction between a loss of sensation and agnosia. A sensory loss is one which duplicates the effect of peripheral damage. A tactile agnosia is the failure to recognize the meaning of the object from its feel alone. It is not certain how form discrimination or localization on body surface should be classified. If form is learned in the same way that meaning is learned, then the loss of form discrimination might appropriately be called "agnosia." It is more likely that a loss of form discrimination results from a spatial or temporal disorganization. However, the role of learned and unlearned factors in the development of temporal and spatial organization is itself an unsettled issue.

With these ideas in mind Blum trained monkeys to discriminate differences in temperature, roughness, weight, hardness, and form. The pair of objects used in form discrimination were a diamond versus a square-ended prism. A conditional discrimination was included as a test for higher-level cognitive functions, as were latch-box problems and the delayed-alternation task. In the conditional test, the stimulus objects were a hollow square versus a cross. In the presence of a framework of wooden strips, the cross was the correct choice. Without the framework, the hollow square was correct. After the animals had learned the various habits, a large cortical region between the primary somatic, visual, and auditory area was removed. This region receives its projections from the pulvinar. The animal with the largest lesion failed to relearn form discrimination, weight discrimination, and the conditional reaction. This monkey was able to relearn a roughness discrimination and a habit based on distinguishing sponge rubber from wood, although a longer time was required to relearn the hardness discrimination than was necessary for the original preoperative learning. No deficit was shown in temperature discrimination. These changes were not accompanied by a general intellectual decline, since the latch-box habit—e.g., removing a plug and lifting a lid—and the delayed-alternation habit were unaffected by the lesion. Two animals with small lesions showed little or no deficit in the various behavioral measures, while a fourth animal with a large lesion was intermediate in postoperative behavior. In none of the animals did the primary relay nucleus VP show degeneration. The temperature-discrimination habit, which comes closest to being a test for sensory quality, was unaffected by the lesion. In discussing the nature of the deficit, the author argued that neither a specific sensory loss nor a deficit in general intellectual factors alone can explain the symptoms. Further, the sensation-memory dichotomy does not describe the disorganization in behavior. Yet it is clear that these distinctions are not totally irrelevant to the discussion of the deficit.

It is premature to suggest that sensory cortex duplicates some of the functions of association cortex, but it is noteworthy that lesions in primary somatic cortex (S I) also produce a deficit in form discrimination [116]. After S I lesions, monkeys had considerable difficulty in relearning a habit based on distinguishing a cone from a square-based pyramid. The difficulty was not caused by a permanent sensory incapacity as might result from a peripheral lesion, since the animals were able to distinguish different grades of sandpaper and eventually did discriminate the cone from the pyramid.

There is considerable evidence that the visual loss produced by removal of visual cortex is more severe than modality-specific sensory losses produced by lesions of auditory or somatic cortex. Klüver [77] showed that monkeys deprived of the visual cortex could only discriminate the total amount of light energy, the luminous flux. In a manner of speaking, the animal is reduced to a photoelectric cell. Discrimination of all characteristics of the stimulus other than energy—e.g., color, form, and position—were lost, including brightness. Klüver's method for demonstrating the loss of brightness discrimination has become a classic in the annals of ablation studies. Following the striate lesion, monkeys lost a brightness-discrimination habit but were able to relearn. However, if the area of the brighter stimulus was reduced so that both members of the stimulus pair were identical in luminous flux, then the discrimination broke down. In other words, the animals were not discriminating brightness in the precise sense of this term, for the judgment of brightness clearly does not depend on size.

Ablation studies of the auditory cortex in carnivores. While the receptor surface is topographically represented in the visual, somatic, and auditory cortex, only in the auditory system does space correspond with sensory quality. It is natural to ask whether frequency discrimination is disturbed by removal of the auditory cortex. In cats the capacity to respond to a change in frequency was found to be unimpaired after ablation of A I and cortical areas surrounding A I [19, 40, 55]. There can be no question that the negative findings were the result of incomplete lesions, since in several cases all of the posterior dorsal thalamus had degenerated—LP, Pul, Po, and GL, in addition to GM. In all of these studies, animals were trained to remain at rest during presentation of a single tone repeated at regular intervals. At any time from one-half to several minutes, the neutral stimulus was replaced by the warning stimulus, which was the signal for the animal to cross a partition. This warning consisted of the introduction of a new tone alternating with the old. If the animal failed to cross in 15 sec, shock was delivered through the grill floor. As soon as the cat escaped shock or avoided shock by a conditioned response (CR), the warning signal was replaced by the neutral signal. The stimuli were thus presented continually. This sequence of neutral and warning stimuli is depicted in Fig. 4.

An entirely different result is obtained when neutral and warning stimuli do not succeed each other. If the stimulus conditions are changed so that a period of silence intervenes between neutral and warning signals, then similar cortical lesions produce an irreversible loss in discrimination [103, 151]. In the studies by Thompson, Meyer, and Woolsey, the animals were required to respond to two alternating tones and withhold response to one repeating tone. Either of these signals would appear after a silent interval. After the operation, the cats could respond to the sequence of two alternating tones, but they also responded to the single tone. When the response to the single tone was punished by counter-shock, all conditioned responses disappeared.

Similar findings were reported some years ago by Allen [4]. He trained dogs to flex the leg within 7 sec of the onset of a positive signal, a bell tapped once per second. The animals were required to inhibit movement for 10 to 15 sec when a negative stimulus was presented. All animals were trained on two negative stimuli, a cup tapped once per second, and a bell tapped three times per second. Removal of auditory cortex as described by Tunturi had the following result: The animals had

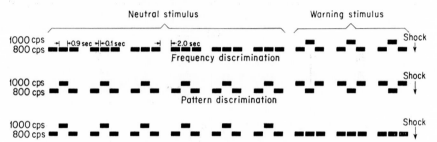

Fig. 4. Diagram of the sequence of tones used in frequency and pattern discrimination. The neutral or negative stimulus is varied in duration to prevent temporal conditioning. The interval between the first tone of the warning stimulus and the last tone of the neutral stimulus is the same as between any two groups of three tones. Shock is given at a fixed point after the onset of the warning or positive stimulus. As soon as the animal responds, the warning stimulus is replaced by the neutral stimulus, and a new trial is begun. The unlabeled sequence of tones is discussed in the text. It should be noted that in this third task the warning stimulus of the first sequence becomes neutral, while the neutral stimulus of the first sequence becomes the warning stimulus.

no difficulty in relearning the CR to the positive stimulus, but the same proportion of leg flexions were made to the negative stimulus as were made to the positive. After many punishments for the incorrect response to the negative stimulus, the animals were able to inhibit the leg flexion. However, at this point they inhibited the positive response to the positive stimulus as well. Therefore the deficit does not seem to be an inability to inhibit responses as such.

The difference between the frequency discrimination that can be re-learned and the frequency discrimination that cannot be relearned must be sought in the perceptual relations between negative and positive cues. Operated animals can relearn when it is possible to become habituated to the neutral tone. To respond correctly, they need only wait for the appearance of a new or different tone. The perceptual problem is reduced to one tone on a neutral background. When both positive and negative stimuli are presented on a background of silence, there is no opportunity for habituation to one stimulus. Both stimuli arouse the animal and he must then determine whether the signal is positive or negative, whether it contains one or two tones. Is it possible, using the continuous method of presenting stimuli, to ask the animal to decide whether the stimulus contains one or two tones? By the continuous method, we mean the method in which neutral and warning stimuli are continuous and succeed each other. We feel this condition is met when the neutral stimulus consists of two frequencies in sequence, while the warning stimulus consists of only one of these tones. The bottom sequence of stimuli in Fig. 4 shows this discrimination. In contrast to the sequence labeled "frequency discrimination," the animal cannot solve the problem by habituating to

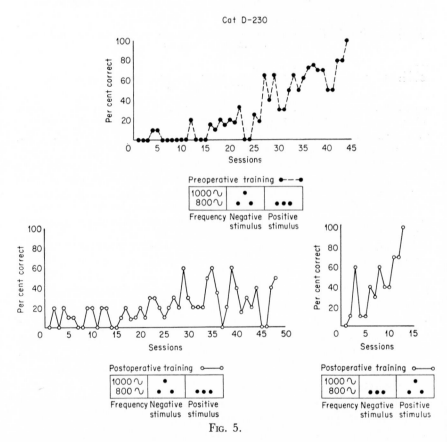

Fig. 5.

Figs. 5 and 6. Pre- and postoperative performance curves for two animals trained with the sequence of stimuli shown in the third line of Fig. 4. In both animals auditory areas I and II were removed bilaterally after preoperative learning. The postoperative training sessions are shown consecutively. That is, G-333 relearned a frequency discrimination after failing on the original task and then failed once again on this original task. For both animals, the failure to relearn the original habit is one tone and waiting for a different one to appear. The animal must perceive whether one tone repeats itself or whether two tones alternate. Indeed, it was found that this third task is more difficult for normal animals than is frequency discrimination. (The results were obtained in unpublished experiments by I. T. Diamond, J. Goldberg, and W. D. Neff.)

On the average, it required 36 training sessions (of 10 trials each) for an animal to reach learning criterion in the third discrimination, while the discrimination labeled "frequency" in Fig. 4 is usually mastered in less than one-third of this number of sessions. Further, it was found that, when A I and surrounding cortical areas had been completely removed bilaterally, these animals were unable to reach preoperative learning criterion. The pre- and postoperative learning curves for two animals are shown in Figs. 5 and 6. Our conclusion is that it is

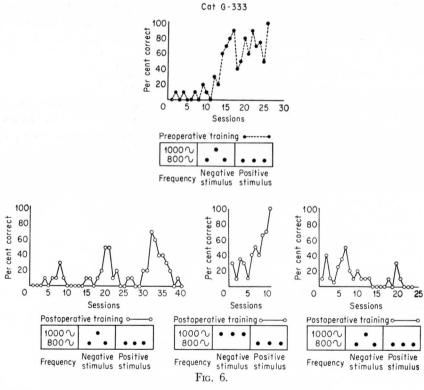

Fig. 6.

more complete then may be suggested by the performance curves. On those sessions in which a number of CR's were recorded, the animal was spontaneously crossing back and forth from one compartment to the next. Training was stopped when the animal was showing no further improvement. These results are from unpublished experiments analyzing the behavioral deficit following temporal lesions in cats by I. T. Diamond, J. Goldberg, and W. D. Neff.

not training method as such which determines the fragility of a frequency discrimination. Rather, the perceptual requirement of the task appears to be the factor which determines whether or not the task will be affected by lesions of auditory cortex.

One further clue to the nature of the perceptual deficit following auditory lesions is provided by a study of pattern discrimination [40]. In this experiment, animals were also trained in a double-grill box using the continuous method of presenting stimuli. The same two tones were presented sequentially in both neutral and warning stimulus and the signal to respond was a change in the order of the sequence. The middle sequence in Fig. 4 shows this discrimination. For example, low tone, high tone, low tone may be the neutral stimulus; while high tone, low tone, high tone is the warning cue. After ablation of A I and surrounding belt cortex, cats that had learned the discriminatory habit before the operation lost the habit and never relearned.

The essential perceptual requirement of those tasks which depend on the auditory cortex remains unknown. We may ask whether the capacity to perceive temporal patterns in audition is similar to the capacity to recognize spatial forms in the tactile or visual modality. Perceptual complexity certainly is a factor in the fragility of both auditory and somatic tasks. For example, Ruch, Fulton, and German [137] reported that, following ablation of the posterior parietal cortex, a chimpanzee relearned a habit based on discriminating between a cone and a pyramid. The same chimpanzee was unable to discriminate between a wedge and a pyramid even after extensive retraining.

These ablation experiments indicate the difficulty in assigning receptive and integrative functions to sensory and association cortex. No behavioral syndrome revealed by ablation studies can be interpreted as a purely sensory or a purely integrative disturbance. Research in this field has become less concerned with any given behavioral distinction as such, and more concerned with particular problems in the relation of structure and function. The discussion in the next two sections is aimed at amplifying this point.

The Pavlovian View of Association Cortex

This discussion was introduced with James's theory of association cortex because the ideas of sensation and perception continue to form the historical backdrop for ablation as well as electrophysiological studies of the afferent systems. No mention has been made of another important tradition, the one which stems from Pavlov [88]. In one noteworthy respect, the two traditions are similar. Both looked to the association cortex for the engram. Of course, Pavlov did not hold that memory was localized in cortical areas. Instead he pictured the association cortex as a vast switchyard with the potentiality of rerouting incoming impulses supplied by sensory cortex. The neural basis for the unconditioned reflex or unlearned reflex was pictured as a pathway from receptor to sensory cortex and from there to motor cortex via association cortex. The analogy to Sherrington's spinal reflex is apparent. Sensory cortex takes the role of the dorsal-root ganglion, while motor cortex is the substitute for ventral-horn cell. Association cortex replaces internuncial neuron with the all-important synapses. The process of conditioning was viewed as a shifting of the connections made in the association cortex, presumably by some change in synaptic resistance. Now, if the pathway from sensory to motor cortex was interrupted by some lesion in the association cortex, then the conditioned reflex should be lost. As long as the input to the sensory cortex and output from the motor cortex are preserved, however, the potentiality for establishing new connections between sensory and motor areas should remain. Restitution of function was interpreted as a reeducative process resulting in the formation of new paths.

Just on the face of it, any view that analogizes all central nervous functions to the spinal reflex must be limited. Certainly Sherrington himself was greatly opposed to extending the principles of reflex organization either literally or analogically to the entire nervous system. In a simple spinal reflex, the receptor acts as a selector. This selection depends only on the property of differential sensitivity. For the organism as a whole, such selection depends on factors other than peripheral sensitivity. The problems of set or attention cannot be easily explained in terms of receptors. In complex or interacting reflexes, the concept of final common path is introduced. A given muscle cannot do two things at the same time; its contraction or relaxation depends on the outcome of competition for ventral-horn cells. However, the responses of an organism are not simply motions, but can be executed in a number of equivalent ways. Therefore, which particular final common paths are excited seems less critical than some more central pattern of organization.

Lashley's Study of Learning

In spite of its limitations, the concept of the conditioned reflex provided a general framework for the study of physiology of learning. A good part of Lashley's experimental program was designed to test the implications of Pavlov's model of learning. Of course the sensation-perception view, considerations from phylogeny, and evidence from neurology all pointed to association cortex as important in learning.

Lashley has reviewed his major conclusions in a 1950 paper, *In search of the engram* [95]. The view that learning consists of the formation of reflex paths from sensory areas of the cortex to motor areas was refuted by a series of experiments. In these experiments, the motor cortex was removed, or its connections to the sensory cortex were severed in either rats or monkeys. Rats with a lesion separating visual from motor cortex were able to learn the most difficult habit for a rat, a visual conditional reaction. After the operation, the animals were taught to jump to a white triangle and to avoid a white cross when both figures were on a black background; but if the background was striped the animals were taught to select the white cross [91]. In another experiment, rats were trained on the maze and then knife cuts were made through the cortex and underlying fibers, separating various functional areas [92]. The lesions had no effect on the retention of the maze habit unless the afferent path to the sensory cortex was involved. Some animals were operated on before training and the rate of initial learning of the maze was compared with the performance of normal animals. Again, no difference was found between normal and operated groups. In one of Lashley's earlier experiments, he removed the motor and premotor cortex in monkeys [83]. The animals had previously been trained to open various latch boxes. When the animals had sufficiently recovered from the temporary paralysis, they were returned to the test apparatus. On their first contact with the test the animals promptly opened the boxes. The lesion did not affect the recognition of the box or the memory for such movements as turning a crank. Later Sperry crosshatched a large cortical sector in monkeys, including sensory and motor areas [145]. Such animals showed no incoordination of movement, even though most of the fibers connecting cortical regions with each other were destroyed.

The relationship between the deficit and the lesion. Even before Lashley's program had ruled out the reflex-like pathway as the neural unit for learning, his own data had forced his attention to particular problems in the relation of neural structure and function. Some of his experiments showed that the degree of deficit was a function of the size of cortical lesion irrespective of locus. Small cortical lesions had little or no effect on the rats' habit for traversing a maze without error [84]. With larger lesions, the maze had to be relearned and the degree of savings was correlated with the amount of cortex removed. Similarly, the ability of rats to learn how to open a door by working a latch—pulling a chain, for example—was disturbed by large but not by small cortical lesions. As a matter of convenience, the term *mass action* was coined to describe this correlation between degree of deficit and amount of brain damage. These data at the same time imply that various parts of the cortex are equipotential.

Lashley's studies of the visual cortex in rats revealed a different relation of structure and function. The habit of brightness discrimination was affected only by the complete removal of striate area. Lesion of other cortical sectors had no effect on this learned discrimination. Further, within the striate cortex, the preservation of a small percentage of tissue will prevent a temporary loss of the discriminatory habit. Since this preserved island of tissue might be anywhere within the anterolateral surface of the striate cortex, we can say that various parts of this cortical sector are equal with respect to their potentiality for maintaining a visual discriminatory task [87].

In a later experiment, Lashley [89] pursued the problem of the functioning of a small remnant of visual cortex. Rats were trained to jump against one of a pair of stimulus cards, the correct choice resulting in food, the incorrect choice resulting in a fall. Several pairs of visual figures were presented, such as an upright versus an inverted triangle. After the animals had learned the discrimination, they were subjected to an operation in which the entire right visual cortex was removed. All of the left visual cortex was removed except the projection of the binocular field, a small portion of the lateral margin of the striate area. Following the operation, the animal's capacity for detail vision was tested with a variety of stimulus pairs, both old and new. Histological examination of the lateral geniculate permitted Lashley to estimate the size of the minimal area required for pattern vision. Lashley concluded that discrimination of visual figures is possible with only one-fiftieth of the number of neurons normally present in GL.

Ablation studies, in general following Lashley's lead, have been less concerned with testing some general neural model. More and more of them are based on relations which were first uncovered by previous ablation studies. This shift of emphasis can be viewed as a growing respect for the unique contribution of each of the parts of the nervous system. The concept of "structure-function" may be clarified by describing the alternative which conceives of the nervous system as something linking a receptor to a muscle. Watson said that the nervous system was needed because the connection between S and R would take too long in a big animal. But both phylogeny and the method of ablation show that the function of a part of the nervous system depends on its internal organization. The difference in function between cortical and midbrain centers for vision is not confined to the differences in opportunities afforded for establishing connections to motor neurons. Both visual cortex and superior colliculus eventually connect with any of the muscles. Both receive fibers from the eye, but there the similarity ends. Clearly the kind of integration accomplished in visual cortex is not possible for the superior colliculus.

This shift in viewpoint enables the investigator to study the behavioral role of a neural structure without having to justify the research as a test of some neural model of behavior. The view that association cortex is a switchyard available for conditioning is rejected. Nevertheless, behavioral alterations can be produced by lesions in primate association cortex. Several review articles have attempted to summarize the conclusions of these studies [31]. We wish to devote the remainder of this section to an illustration of the way in which further ablation studies follow up the leads provided by earlier studies.

The Loss of Learned Visual Discrimination Following Ablation of the Temporal Lobe in Monkeys

One line of research was initiated by Klüver's discovery that bilateral removal of the temporal lobe produced amnesia for learned visual tasks [78]. Many experiments have since been done to determine the nature of the visual deficit and to define the limits of the temporal cortical lesion which produces the loss. The first group of studies attempted to discover whether habits other than visual ones were affected by the lesion and whether lesions in areas other than temporal cortex could duplicate the syndrome. The attempt to establish the unique function of a part of the nervous system can be considered as the first goal of the ablation method.

The reasoning underlying the deficit method for establishing structure-function relations has been analyzed by Teuber [149]. Teuber's own studies may be used to illustrate the ablation method. It was found that lesions of the visual cortex in man produce a defect in visual perception. However, one cannot conclude from this relationship that the unique function of visual cortex involves visual perception. Perhaps the same deficit will result from a lesion in cortical areas other than visual—an alternative which turned out to be the correct one. When a deficit has been shown to be the result of a specific lesion, the question of the nature of the deficit must be faced. Ablation of somatic cortex, for example, may disturb roughness discrimination because the operated animal has lost sensitivity to touch stimuli or because the operated animal no longer understands the test situation. The second alternative could be eliminated by showing that a discrimination of visual patterns was not disturbed by the same operation. The aim of the investigator is, then, to demonstrate that lesion A will affect task a but not b, while lesion B will affect task b but not a. The term *double dissociation* was invented by Teuber to describe this goal of ablation studies.

In most of the early studies of the temporal lobe the following procedures were used: The monkeys were first trained on two-choice simultaneous visual discriminations. In a two-choice visual discrimination, an animal is shown a pair of objects, such as a red plaque and a green plaque, or a black disk and a black diamond. Food is always placed under one stimulus of the pair, and the animal's task is to select this positive stimulus each time the pair of stimuli is presented. The trials are continued until some learning criterion is reached, usually 90 per cent correct in 30, 60, or 100 trials. Each monkey, prior to the surgery, was trained on a number of such visual discriminations. Selected cortical areas were then ablated bilaterally in one stage, and the animals were tested on the same tasks after the postoperative recovery period. The results showed, in general, that following ablation of the middle and inferior temporal gyri the animals forgot the preoperatively learned visual habits, but they could relearn these habits with further training [23, 107]. Lesions in other regions—the preoccipital cortex, the frontal cortex, the parietal cortex, and the cortex on the medial surface of the temporal lobe—had no such effect [105, 25, 166]. Chow and Hutt [31] have discussed what may appear to be exceptions to the conclusion that visual habits are uniquely affected by lesions of temporal neocortex [118].

The deficit produced by temporal cortical injury appears to be specific to visual tasks. At least other behavioral tasks, such as delayed response and somesthetic discriminations, were unaffected by the ablation of temporal cortex [123, 166]. Furthermore, the visual deficit was apparent whether the stimuli were presented successively or simultaneously [125]. In the method of successive presentation, only one of two stimuli is presented in any given trial. The monkey is required to respond to the positive stimulus and to withhold response to the negative stimulus. Thus further experiments could accept as a starting point that learned visual discriminations are uniquely affected by lesions of the temporal neocortex, and that the deficit from this lesion is specific to visual habits.

Further experimental analysis proceeded along two lines. One problem was to determine the role of anatomical pathways to the temporal cortex either from visual cortex or from subcortical nuclei. The only known cortico-cortical fibers from the visual area are short axon fibers that connect the visual area with the adjacent preoccipital cortex. Monkeys subjected to a partial ablation of preoccipital cortex still retained the learned visual tasks [25, 93]. The anterior temporal cortex receives fibers from the medial pulvinar nucleus and sends corticofugal fibers back to this thalamic area [22, 165]. Bilateral, partial lesions of the medial pulvinar nucleus did not affect the monkey's retention of visual tasks [28]. A lesion which combined a part of the preoccipital cortex and a part of the medial pulvinar similarly failed to duplicate the effect of bilateral removal of the temporal cortex.

Since in none of these cases was there a complete lesion of the preoccipital cortex or a complete lesion of the medial pulvinar, two other types of surgical intervention were attempted [29]. It is possible to eliminate all of the fibers from the pulvinar and still preserve cortico-cortical connections by undercutting the temporal cortex. After such a lesion, monkeys retained habits based on visual discrimination. It is possible to disrupt all cortico-cortical fibers and still preserve thalamocortical fibers by crosshatching the temporal cortex. After such a lesion, monkeys failed to retain habits based on visual discrimination. As far as we know, this visual deficit is the same as that produced by ablation of temporal cortex. Thus, whatever the role of impulses from visual centers in the temporal cortex syndrome, the path taken by such impulses must be via cortico-cortical fibers.

These results may resolve the apparent contradiction in experiments reported by Ades [1], Lashley [93], and Chow [25]. In contrast to the latter two experiments, Ades found that monkeys with preoccipital lesions failed to retain visual discriminations. If the lesions made by Ades were complete and had interrupted all cortico-cortical fibers, while lesions made by Chow and Lashley spared some of these connections, then the reported difference in the behavioral effects of the lesions is understandable.

Another line of studies deals with the nature of the visual deficit following bilateral temporal removals. The first question asked was whether the deficit in visual discrimination was caused by a reduction in visual acuity or a scotoma. To test for a scotoma, animals were presented with a horizontal row of small pieces of food. It is known that in cases of scotoma, monkeys will miss some pieces in the defective region of their visual field. Animals with temporal lesions showed no such defect. Also temporal animals were able to locate thin threads. The performance on these visual tasks suggests that the animals did not suffer from some change in visual acuity. The effects of temporal lesions on visual discriminations do not then appear to be an expression of a sensory deficiency.

Pasik and others, however, disputed this interpretation [120]. They found that monkeys with temporal lesions could learn a form discrimination at a normal rate, provided the visual stimuli were large in size. Furthermore, some of their monkeys showed difficulty in learning a tactile problem. Thus, they felt that the effect of temporal lesion may be accounted for by visual-field defects, such as amblyopia, plus a general disturbance of learning and memory.

The conclusions of Pasik and others were not supported by a recent study of Wilson and Mishkin [167]. These authors designed an experiment to demonstrate the dissociation of visual-sensory defects following lesions of visual areas, and visual-learning defects following lesions of the temporal cortex. They found that monkeys with lateral occipital lesions had difficulty in learning string-pattern problems and colored-pattern discrimination. Monkeys with temporal lesions were deficient in acquiring form-discrimination and object-learning set. The string-pattern problem was considered a measure of visual-field defects. Both the form-discrimination and learning-set problems were considered to be tests of learning ability. The form-discrimination test, however, can be interpreted as a measure of perceptual organization, not necessarily dependent on learning as that term has been used in connection with agnosia.

The level of performance on the learning-set problem has been shown to be positively correlated with phylogenetic level [130, 142]. In this task the animals are not required to remember specific discriminations but to arrive at a general rule. The animal must discover that whatever member of a pair is correct on the first trial will be correct thereafter. Hundreds of pairs of visual stimuli were presented to the animals, each for only a few trials. The animals must use the first trial to find out which of the two visual stimuli contains food reward, and to react appropriately on the very next trial. After training on two or three hundred problems, a normal monkey will select the correct stimulus 80 to 90 per cent of the time on the second trial. Monkeys with temporal lesions performed at a significantly lower level than did normal animals [130]. Thus, the separation of visual sensory and learning functions appears to correspond with the distinction between visual-sensory cortex and temporal-association cortex. However, the temporal-lobe deficit does not fit precisely the traditional agnosia. Clearly, learning set cannot be equated with perception as that term was employed by Wundt, James, and Titchener.

Accepting the conclusion that the syndrome of the temporal neocortex cannot be explained by some sensory disturbance, further studies were undertaken to explore the behavioral mechanisms underlying the symptom of amnesia. One study asked whether the postoperative memory deficit may be due to a lack of comprehension of the testing procedure [27]. Monkeys were trained preoperatively to form learning sets with pairs of three-dimensional objects and with pairs of forms painted on cards. After temporal-cortical ablation, they retained the former but lost and could not relearn the latter. As stated earlier, the learning-set task requires the animal to understand the general principle that determines which member of a pair is correct. The retention of the learning set under some conditions indicates that the animals understood what they were supposed to do in the testing situation. They were not deficient in the capacity to form a learning set. Why then did they lose the learning set when the stimuli were painted forms? This puzzling finding may be related to the more abstract character of painted forms. In any event, the form-discrimination learning set is a more difficult problem if difficulty is defined as the percentage of correct responses in a certain number of trials.

Further studies designed to test whether the temporal lesions cause monkeys to fail on difficult tasks yielded conflicting results. Mishkin and Hall [106] found that normal monkeys made more errors in learning to discriminate between two circles when the difference in the size of the circles was small than when the difference in size was large. Thus the degree of difficulty in this discrimination is correlated with size differences. After temporal ablation the animals retained a discrimination between circles of different sizes when the difference was large. However, they failed when the difference in size was small. The study of Pasik and others [120], cited earlier, reported a similar role of size differences in the temporal-lobe deficit. In another study, difficulty of the task as defined by the percentage of correct responses was not a crucial factor in the amnesia for visual habits. Chow and Orbach [32] trained monkeys with pairs of stimuli, such as a black cross versus a black disk. Each pair was exposed for different durations. The percentage of correct responses made by normal monkeys decreased as the exposure time was shortened. A gradient of difficulty is clearly correlated with exposure time. Monkeys with temporal lesions performed this task as well as normal animals, regardless of the duration of the stimulus exposure.

The question of whether the postoperative transient loss of learned visual discriminations indicates a loss of particular memory traces was also studied. When monkeys were given new visual discriminations to learn during their recovery from the operation, they sometimes retained visual discriminations originally learned before removal of temporal cortex [24]. In other words, the postoperative recovery of a habit did not depend on practicing that specific habit. The finding of spontaneous recovery without practice is reminiscent of the arguments raised by the opponents of the memory-image theory of aphasia. In other studies, a monkey was given several visual discriminations preoperatively. On some of these discriminations, training continued only until the animal attained a criterion level of 90 per cent correct in 30 trials. But with other discriminations, several hundred additional trials were given after the criterion was reached. Following bilateral temporal ablation, the same animal forgot a discrimination learned just to criterion, but retained one on which additional training had been given [34, 117].

Further experiments have explored the neural basis for relearning following removal of temporal cortex. After animals had relearned visual discriminations, they were subjected to a second cortical ablation. In some cases, but not in all, ablation of frontal and parietal association cortex produced a second loss of the visual habits.

Results from these studies show that the visual defect following the removal of temporal cortex in monkeys cannot be attributed to a sensory change. Further, it is not the result of the animal's failure to comprehend the testing procedure. Nor can the loss be attributed to a complete disappearance of specific memory traces corresponding to specific visual habits. What actually happens to the monkey's visually guided behavior after surgery remains a challenging question.

It is apparent that these attempts to discover the mechanisms underlying the visual defects following temporal neocortical ablation fall short of an explanation at the neuronal level. This review serves to indicate, however, the type of experiments that are currently in progress, and the complexity of the findings. At present, further analytic studies along the lines illustrated above offer the only feasible approach to the temporal-lobe problem. It is hoped that such lines of study will eventually lead to an explanation of the visual defect at a neuronal level. However, this long-run goal need not be the immediate concern of the investigator.

Conclusion

A major problem of biological psychology is to discover the function of the cortex in mammals. The study of the phylogeny of behavior and the phylogeny of the nervous system and the study of behavioral changes following cortical injury each contributes to an understanding of cortex. Interaction between the several approaches is clearly fruitful. For example, an experimental program employing the ablation method looks to comparative anatomy for concepts about neural organization, and to comparative psychology for ideas about the kind of behavioral tests that might reflect greater complexity in behavioral organization. The studies of Lashley provide a good example of how all three methods can be used to achieve a single goal. It is natural to wonder whether the results of the several approaches are pointing in the same direction to one or a few main conclusions. However, there does not seem to be any simple way of applying the conclusions of one approach to the others. Obviously a lesion of neocortex does not transform the behavioral level of one species to that of another species lower in the phylogenetic scale. The question of the behavioral achievements of more recent neural structures, such as neocortex, is probably not separate from the puzzling question of the function of older parts which have homologues in more "primitive" species. It is difficult to conceive of the relation between the function of the optic midbrain in fish and in primates and of the changes in the function of midbrain visual centers brought about by the development of new visual centers in the diencephalon and cortex.

Our purpose in emphasizing the complexity of the problem of cortical function has not merely been to suggest that a general conclusion is premature. There is a basic methodological point to be made in connection with the nature of the complexity. The central nervous system can be subdivided in a variety of ways, as may be suggested by sets of distinctions: dorsal and ventral roots, sympathetic and parasympathetic divisions of the autonomic system, neocortex and paleocortex, intrinsic and extrinsic thalamic nuclei, cortex and midbrain, sensory and association cortex. Many and perhaps all of these distinctions have behavioral significance. The view that anatomical separations have functional importance can be thought of as a premise of the structure-function method. The only alternative to a step-by-step working out of structure-function relations is to bypass the great wealth of facts about the anatomy, physiology, and phylogeny of the nervous system. However, efforts to develop models of neural functioning which at once explain intelligence, the cortex, and the difference between higher and lower species have not proved fruitful. For example, the attempt to account for the capacity to learn in terms of a hypothetical property of the nervous system, such as the number of neural pathways available for switching reflex arcs, is no longer helpful even as a hypothesis for generating research.

PART IV. THE EEG AND LEARNING

Introduction

Newer methods in electrophysiology have renewed the hope for some direct approach to the physiological correlates of learning. Electroencephalographic (EEG)[5] records can be obtained from waking or sleeping animals by means of permanently implanted electrodes. This enables the investigator to seek correlations between ongoing behavior and changes in electrical rhythms of the brain and in evoked potentials. It should be noted that EEG records are not suitable for analyzing the short latency potentials evoked by sensory stimuli in anesthetized preparations. The evoked potentials used in classical studies of mapping sensory areas in the cortex and in the subcortex are best observed by triggering the sweep of an oscilloscope with the external stimulus. Deflections that systematically occur with a constant latency and wave form are called "the evoked potential." The EEG method of recording is better suited for observing relatively slow changes in potential, the spontaneous brain rhythms, and the secondary diffuse evoked potentials. All of the experiments cited below use the method of EEG recording.

Out of the extensive literature which has accumulated in the past few years, a few studies have been selected to illustrate the various methods. For reviews of this literature, the reader can refer to papers by Rusinov and Rabinovich [138], Yoshii [175], Chow [30], and those included in the Moscow International Colloquium on Electroencephalography of Higher Nervous Activity [73]. In the method we shall describe first, EEG changes are recorded during the learning process. In a second method, the change in the EEG plays the role that the response does in conditioning experiments. After a procedure of pairing stimuli, the

[5] For convenience, EEG is used here to include both electrical recordings from the scalp by conventional silver-disk electrodes and recordings from the cortex and subcortical regions by implanted electrodes.

conditioned stimulus produces the EEG effect originally elicited only by the unconditioned stimulus. In a third method, the application of electric shock through the implanted electrode serves as a conditioned or unconditioned stimulus. A fourth group of studies uses electric shock applied to various neural structures to disrupt learning or memory.

EEG Changes during Learning

Most of the studies of the first group begin by habituating the EEG response to some sensory stimulus. Galambos and co-workers [49, 63], for example, found that the EEG potentials evoked by a click gradually decreased in amplitude and finally disappeared if the click was repeated for a long period. In one experiment, 11 clicks (with a few seconds' interval between clicks) were presented to cats every 8 min for many days. The animals were in a quiet room during the experiment and the EEG was recorded from electrodes implanted in various areas of the brain. A gradual decrease was noted in the amplitude of the potentials evoked by the clicks. In the next step, painful shock was delivered to the chest immediately after the train of clicks. After a few pairings of shock and clicks, the size of the evoked potentials increased. When shock was withdrawn and clicks alone were presented, the evoked potentials again decreased. This waxing and waning of the evoked responses was recorded not only in the auditory pathway such as cochlear nucleus and auditory cortex, but also in other structures, such as the caudate nucleus and the hippocampus. There seems little question that the pairing of shock and the click was the cause of the potential change. However, does the change in potential directly reflect a neural mechanism of learning or does it reflect the increased significance of the stimulus? If habituation is a progressive loss of attention, the pairing with the shock can be said to reverse the effect of habituation and reestablish the attention value of the stimulus. Needless to say, the importance of the finding is not diminished by this interpretation which is indeed one of the alternatives suggested by Galambos [47].

What is the significance, we may ask, of the decrease in amplitude of the evoked response? It need not mean less firing of individual neurons. Desynchrony would have the same effect as fewer impulses. In a different type of experiment, Sharpless and Jasper [141] studied the habituation of the arousal response. Cats were presented with a 500-cps tone after they had fallen asleep. The signal awakened the animals and induced the EEG activation pattern. This procedure was repeated until the tone failed to awaken the animals or alter the EEG. At this stage, evoked potentials in the auditory cortex were recorded using a cathode-ray oscilloscope. It was found that the voltage of the evoked responses had increased rather than decreased. The authors point out that the relationship between the habituation of the arousal reaction and the habituation produced by prolonged, continual stimulation is obscure.

The following four studies illustrate somewhat different aspects of the method, but they have in common an initial period of habituation. In a study by John and Killam [75], the rhythmic potentials induced by a flickering light were first habituated. Following habituation, a training period began. The cats were trained in a double-grill box to avoid shock in response to the flickering light. The rate of flicker was approximately ten per second. During the initial stages of training, rhythmic potentials reappeared in the visual cortex, lateral geniculate body, superior colliculus, and reticular formation. When the animal began to avoid shock by crossing from one to the other compartment, the photic driving or rhythmic response diminished in the visual system and the reticular formation, but appeared in the hippocampus and amygdala. When the animal reached a performance level of 100 per cent correct in a training session, the appearance of EEG waves in synchrony with the stimulus was confined to *n. ventralis anterior* of the thalamus. The authors report that multiples of the stimulus frequency reappeared in the visual area, lateral geniculate, and amygdala.

In the following experiment by Worden [172], animals were trained in a food-reward situation. Again the first step of the experiment consisted of habituating the electrical response, this time the response evoked by tone bursts. Following habituation, a training period ensued. With the tone on, lever pressing was rewarded by food; with the tone off, there was no reward. In the early stage of training, the evoked response reappeared throughout the auditory system—cochlear nucleus, trapezoid body, inferior colliculus, and medial geniculate. When learning had been firmly established, the response disappeared everywhere except in the trapezoid body.

It is not clear why EEG responses are found in some neural structures but not in others. Even when the responses are found in sensory structures, which we might expect to be involved because of their role in the reception of the conditioned or unconditioned stimulus, the significance of the waxing and waning of the response is not certain. A further point concerns the nature of the EEG response. The data reveal where changes are taking place in the nervous system as the result of learning, but not what these changes are. In other words, what is being studied is functional localization. This area of research is therefore comparable to the study of functional localization, using the method of ablation. When it is recognized that EEG studies are not dealing with cellular events, then certain findings which might otherwise appear paradoxical are quite reasonable. We would not expect, for example, that the basic cellular changes underlying learning could be undone, so to speak, by overtraining. Yet after prolonged training, the EEG response returns to its appearance prior to any learning. This is puzzling only if the EEG response and cellular change are equated. When an alteration in response appears in some structure and then at a later stage disappears, it must mean that the role of the structure in behavior is different in the two stages.

Most of the points raised so far apply to the next experiment by Beck, Doty, and Kooi [10]. These authors employed a Pavlovian conditioning process. In the first step of the experiment, the EEG arousal or activation pattern was habituated. Tones which initially produced the EEG arousal response were presented repeatedly to cats until the response disappeared. The animals were then given Bulbocapnine hydrochloride to assure slow, high-voltage waves as a sharp contrast to the activation pattern. The conditioned stimulus (CS) was a 500-cps tone, 2 sec in duration. The unconditioned stimulus (US) was a shock to the toe. The US elicited leg flexion. After many pairings of CS and US, the conditioned leg flexion (CR) appeared in anticipation of the shock. Before the appearance of the CR and after only a few pairings of CS and US, the EEG showed the low-voltage fast or "arousal" pattern in response to the CS. These EEG changes occurred in all leads, cruciate, ectosylvian, and marginal gyri long before changes in respiration or the conditioned leg flexion. With overtraining, the EEG response tended to diminish, despite the continuation of the CR. This eventual waning of the response with continued training is similar to that obtained in the studies of instrumental conditioning.

In contrast to the above studies, Yoshii and co-workers [176] reported EEG changes which became more pronounced as training proceeded. Repeated presentations of flashing light or buzzer were preliminary to the conditioning procedures. After this habituation, the light or sound was paired with food or shock to leg to establish the classical conditioned salivary or defensive reflexes. Following a few CS-US pairings, the CS induced EEG-evoked potentials and the arousal response in many areas. In some instances, the CS augmented the cortical background fast waves. These EEG changes preceded the behavioral CR and were maintained throughout the entire course of conditioning.

The last study we shall describe followed a procedure different from all of the others. This experiment reported by Verzilova [159] did not depend on an initial habituation period. The experimental animals were dogs. Metronome beats served as the CS and were paired with shock to the leg (US). The metronome produced in auditory cortex a rhythmic wave with the same frequency of the metronome beat. As conditioning proceeded, the waves appeared in motor cortex as well as auditory cortex, and when the CR was established, the waves were restricted to the motor areas. The results of this study come the closest to some of our traditional concepts about learning. It would be interesting to determine whether the shifting of stimulus-induced waves expresses the formation of connections between auditory and motor area. Repeating the experiment after severing cortico-cortical connections is an obvious suggestion.

To sum up:

1. The appearance and disappearance, and the change in locus of various EEG responses to the CS have been correlated with stages of instrumental learning.

2. In classical conditioning experiments, the CS has been shown to induce diffuse evoked potentials, stimulus-driven rhythmic waves, EEG arousal and augmentation of fast brain waves before the onset of the US.

3. Whether or not the EEG change persists throughout the learning period must be considered in interpreting the significance of the change.

4. The EEG response has been located in structures other than the classical motor and sensory pathways.

5. The EEG change may reflect a change in the animal's attention to the stimulus rather than a process of learning or association. It may be misleading, however, to oppose attention and learning. At least some psychologists have argued that learning and changes in perception of the stimulus are closely related.

In evaluating this new and intriguing type of study, one point should be kept central. At the present time we do not know the neuronal basis of the potential changes observed on the EEG. Therefore, correlations between EEG and behavior cannot tell us in terms of neurons how the nervous system is altered by learning. On the other hand, by revealing where changes are occurring at different stages of learning, these studies provide invaluable insights into the relations between structure and function.

Conditioning the EEG

In a number of studies, alterations in the EEG pattern play the role that the response does in behavioral experiments. In a sense the EEG is conditioned, rather than a behavioral response. The earlier studies of Jasper [72] have established that the blocking of the alpha rhythm may be conditioned in humans. By analogy to a conditioned reflex, a light served as the US; in other words, in the absence of training, light will block the alpha rhythm. When a formerly neutral sound stimulus (CS) was paired with the light repeatedly, the sound itself blocked the alpha rhythm. Recently Morrell, Jasper, and others have demonstrated this type of conditioning in monkeys, cats, and rabbits. Morrell and Jasper [109] used sound or touch as the CS and flickering light as the US. The sound was first presented to the animal until it no longer produced EEG arousal. After habituation, the sound was paired with the flickering light; the sound was turned on 2 sec before the light, and both stimuli were turned off 5 sec later. The first sign of conditioning was a generalized desynchronization of all cortical areas prior to the US. At a later stage of conditioning, the CS induced repetitive waves in the visual areas before the onset of the US. During the last stage of conditioning, the CS caused a localized desynchronization restricted to the visual areas only.

To date, most of the research in this field has attempted to demonstrate that the EEG can be conditioned. Only a few investigations, and these recent ones, have attempted to cast light on the mechanisms involved in conditioning the EEG. Morrell, Roberts, and Jasper [110] showed that epileptogenic lesions placed in the cortical area of the CS (auditory or somatic areas) prevented the formation of the conditioned EEG response, but lesions in the area of the US (visual area) facilitated the conditioning of the EEG. Studies by Chow (unpublished) indicated that cortical lesions abolished the formation of conditioned photic driving. However, subcortical lesions in the rostral thalamus, in *n. centrum medianum* or in the brain stem reticular formation had no effect on the formation of conditioned photic driving. Furthermore, photic driving occurred only when the background EEG showed slow 5 per sec waves. It may be suggested that the locus for the photic driving is confined to the cortex.

Conditioning by Means of Direct Stimulation of the Central Nervous System

It is an old idea that bypassing the peripheral pathways with direct shock to the central nervous system might serve to restrict the possible locus of learning. A comparable kind of restriction is accomplished by ablation. Thus one of Sherrington's great achievements was to isolate the spinal cord and thereby locate the mechanism of the reflex in the synaptic connections of the gray matter of the cord. This identification of the anatomical place of integration invited further neurophysiological studies of processes of excitation and inhibition. In the earlier literature, Loucks reported that successful conditioning could be obtained by replacing the CS with a shock to the nervous system [100]. At that time, the method for delivering shock was an inductorium, and the possibility that meningeal blood vessels were stimulated could not be ruled out.

Taking advantage of recent and better methods for electrical stimulation, Doty, Rutledge, and Larsen [43] succeeded in establishing a conditioned avoidance reflex in response to direct shocks to the marginal, suprasylvian, and ectosylvian gyri in cats. The CS was a train of 2-msec pulses, 50 pulses per sec for 2 sec. The US was a shock to the hind leg overlapping the last 50 msec of the CS. Possible extraneous factors were controlled by sectioning the trigeminal nerve bilaterally and by avoiding cortical areas 3 to 5 mm around the midline. The investigators also monitored skin resistance. They felt that pain in extracortical tissue would be reflected in some change in skin resistance. Stimulation of the cortical tissue alone did not lead to changes in skin resistance. The number of trials necessary for conditioning (about three hundred) was of the order of magnitude required to establish classical conditioned reflexes.

It is also possible to establish conditioned reflexes by using direct brain stimulation as the US. For example, Segundo, Roig, and Sommer-Smith [140] stimulated *n. centrum medianum* and the midbrain reticular formation to elicit stereotyped motor responses. When such brain stimulation was paired with a neutral tone (60 to 600 repetitions) the tone itself elicited the motor responses. The authors have not discussed the possibility that nonneural tissue was excited, or the possibility that an afferent input secondary to the motor acts serves as the US.

Doty and Giurgea [41] reported the formation of conditioned reflexes by pairing electric shock to visual and motor cortex. The stimulus to the motor cortex originally produced leg flexion. As a result of the conditioning process, the stimulus to the visual cortex had a similar motor effect. In a sense, both CS and US were replaced by the electric shocks applied to the cortex.

Doty and Rutledge [42] have begun an investigation of the mechanism of this type of conditioned reflex. They found that after a stimulus to one point in the cortex has been established as the CS, a little pairing of a second point of stimulation with the US was all that was required to make the second cortical point effective in eliciting the CR. This second point might be in the same or opposite hemisphere as the first. Such a phenomenon would be called "transfer of training" or "generalization" if environmental stimuli were used instead of brain stimulation. The analogy is clear enough to say that the effect of conditioning one point transfers to other regions of the brain. The transfer across hemispheres was not prevented by sectioning the posterior *corpus callosum* and hippocampal commissure prior to the conditioning procedure. In further experiments, the cortex at the site of the CS was partially undercut or circumsected. These lesions caused only a transient depression of the CR. Furthermore Segundo and others [140] found that a small lesion at the site of the US electrode did not affect the CR. These results are reminiscent of the effects of ablation on conditioned reflexes in the usual sense of that term. Both lines of study suggest that there is no restricted pathway for conditioning.

Disruption of Learning by Electrical Stimulation of the Brain

Many studies have reported that learned performances are disrupted by electric stimulation of brain structures. Chiles [21] trained cats in a

Skinner box to press a lever in order to receive food. After a steady response rate was reached, electric shocks (biphasic 1-msec pulses, 300 pulses per sec) were delivered to the posterior hypothalamus, the medial nucleus of the thalamus, or *n. centrum medianum*. The animals showed slower rate and greater variability in their responses under stimulation. The author suggested that factors such as emotional changes and extraneous responses are responsible for this effect. The disruption was produced in three places that were stimulated, and no place was stimulated that failed to produce disruption.

Rosvold and Delgado [136] applied 60 cps shock, 2 sec in duration, to a variety of neural structures. They found that stimulation of the caudate nucleus disturbed the monkey's performance on delayed-alternation tests. This behavioral effect was specific, since the monkey's performance on visual discrimination was undisturbed. Stimulation of the other areas—the putamen, the septal area, and the medial and orbital cortices—had no effect on either of these two behavioral tests. The attempt to find tests that are unaffected and to discover sites which fail to produce the disruption adds to the value of the study. Unless these steps are taken, it cannot be established that the learning task is localized in a particular structure. For example, the electrical shock may produce its disrupting effect by causing widespread seizure-like discharges.

One way of determining the extent of the afterdischarge is to monitor the EEG during and after stimulation. Employing this technique, Chow determined that the afterdischarge in the cortex was limited to the area of the stimulus shock, in this case, the temporal cortex (unpublished manuscript). Monkeys who were tested during the afterdischarge failed to learn or retain visual discriminations. Unilateral temporal afterdischarges or afterdischarges in the hippocampus and visual cortex did not reproduce the disorganizing effect. Bilateral temporal-lobe afterdischarges seem to produce the same deficit in visual discrimination that is produced by ablation of temporal cortex. The electrical stimulation method can be used as a kind of reversible ablation.

Conclusion

From our survey, we conclude that the study of EEG and learning is at the "organ level" of analysis. The idea that there may be one or a few kinds of cellular change which constitute the basis for learning does not appear to play a major part in current research. It is not even known what relation there is between the action potentials of individual neurons and the rhythmic changes in potential called "brain waves." This does not mean that there is any want of research problems relating neurophysiology to behavior. It does suggest that neurophysiology is itself very largely a study of organs. The method of evoked potentials has supplemented purely anatomical techniques for delimiting structure. In addition, the method of evoked potentials has provided knowledge of function by determining what kinds of stimuli excite a given region of the brain. The area of the EEG and learning is an extension of this type of study, made possible by the use of unanesthetized preparations. If there is any purpose in conceiving of subdivisions in the biological sciences, the lines should not be drawn between anatomy, physiology, and biological psychology. It would make better sense to view all the ways of studying the parts of the nervous system at the organ level as one science. All of the experiments on the function of a structure, the pulvinar, for example, have a common subject matter and a common purpose whether the nervous substrate is ablated or stimulated, whether anatomical or physiological techniques are used to define boundaries.

PART V. BIOLOGICAL PSYCHOLOGY AND LEARNING PSYCHOLOGY

The conclusion of our survey is that the biology of learning is not a single field dominated by one or a few unifying concepts and purposes. We have attempted to show that the genetics of behavior shares its methods and problems with genetics proper, the distinguishing feature being that the phenotype studied is a behavioral rather than a morphological trait. In general, the concern of comparative psychology is not so much with learning per se as with the relation between learned and unlearned behavior, and the investigator is led to whatever aspect of behavior is significant in phylogeny. Similarly, the ablation method is not primarily concerned with learning as such or, for that matter, with sensation or emotion or thought. Rather, the goal of this method is to discover the orderly breakdown of behavior following removal of parts of the central nervous system. It is believed that this will lead to an understanding of the function of the nervous system, as well as the organization of behavior. The newer methods of EEG recording will focus the attention of the experimenter on any behavioral measures which correlate with changes in brain waves.

On the other hand, there is an area of psychology which inquires into questions such as: Can a rat learn a maze without reward? Experiments are done in which rats are permitted to explore a maze without receiving food at the goal box. A clear difference in subject matter and purpose is evident between this type of inquiry and biological psychology. Yet, in spite of the obvious difference in subject matter, learning psychology and biological psychology are not two separate sciences, as are chemistry and physiology.

At one time, biologists took sides on some issues that divided learning theorists. Reflexology was objectionable to biological psychologists as long as it offered a view of neural organization. The S-R diagrams popular in the 1930s, depicting stimulus substitution, provide little insight into the integration between afferent and efferent neurons. In so far as behavior can be used as a starting point to the study of the nervous system, the closer we approximate the stimulus as it appears to the organism, the better we can state the requirements for nervous integration. For this reason, the facts of perception and stimulus equivalence, in Klüver's terms, have played an important part in the thinking of biological psychologists. Lashley was fond of calling attention to the perceptual constancies—an object appears to be the same object, whether viewed in an upright or tilted position. As learning and behavior theorists concentrated on the lawfulness of S-R relations without regard to the nervous system, the details of their continuing debates became less the direct concern of biology.

Lashley was one of the first to suggest that learning theorists give up neurologizing. In 1930 he pointed out that no explanation is achieved simply by substituting neural language for behavior conclusions:

In more technical treatises the neurological explanations are made up mostly of assumptions concerning the properties of the nerve cell which have no counterpart in physiological experiment. Thus we find the superiority of distributed over concentrated practice seriously "explained" by the "fact" that successive passage of neural impulses over a synapse reduces its resistance least when the impulses come in quick succession [86, p. 2].

The Hierarchy of the Biological Sciences

Physiological explanation appears to be a central issue in the relation of biological psychology and learning psychology. The biological view of this issue is best understood on the background of the organization of the biological sciences. It is common to distinguish a number of sciences intermediate to physicochemical events on the one hand and behavior on the other hand. This resulting hierarchy of fields is suggested by the units which characterize each level of analysis: enzyme, gene, cell, organ, organism [174]. While such a subdivision is clearly artificial, in any single instance it is usually possible for an investigator to specify the level of his approach. For example, Sherrington [143] separated three methods of studying the physiology of the nervous system: (1) a metabolic level dealing with nutritional problems, for the most part common to all cells; (2) a tissue level dealing with nerve-cell conduction, a feature peculiar to neurons; (3) an organ level dealing with the integrative action of groups of neurons.

Since the separation into levels is an abstraction in the first place, general statements about the relations between levels are likely to be empty. In particular cases, however, it can be shown that great advances were achieved through the application of physics and chemistry and molecular levels to the molar levels. Bernard's concept of internal environment permitted physiologists to formulate many of their problems in terms of physical science. Krogh's analysis of the role of diffusion in the transport of O_2 is a notable example [82]. By considering all organs in terms of their role in the exchange between blood and tissue fluids, organ physiology was essentially replaced by a physiology of transport mechanisms. In the evolutionary sciences, great advances were made by the application of genetics to the study of the mechanism of evolution. The problem of speciation was reduced to statistical genetics by treating populations of individuals in terms of populations of genes [173]. Even where unification of fields has been achieved, the problems and terms at a molar level have not been entirely replaced, as is attested by the continuing recognition of many biological sciences.

In addition to instances where two separate areas of experience are unified by a deeper point of view, similarities between fields may be suggested by an analogy. For example, morphogenesis has been described in terms of self-duplicating gene products competing in the cytoplasm [161]. This effort to explain development at a cellular level shows a similarity between populations of individuals competing for ecological niches and autocatalytic gene products. However, embryology remains largely at an organ level with terms like *induction, field,* and *differentiation.* Progress is being made toward understanding differentiation at the cellular level, and various analogies and models may be helpful in achieving this goal.

The history of biological science also reveals the formation of new fields with the discovery of a unique unit or relation. It is probably true that any new unit must eventually find its place in the hierarchy, making contact above or below. As long as Mendelian factors remained mathematical constructs useful in prediction, it was not clear what contribution this type of study could make to biology. Prediction of phenotype by itself was not sufficient to establish the field, and besides, the concept of blending inheritance derived from Galton had at least as much predictive value under a number of circumstances. The discovery that chromosomes behave like Mendel's units put an end to all debate [146].

The main conclusion we wish to draw is that there are many senses of explanation in biology corresponding to the several levels of analysis. At the organ level, high blood sugar is explained by the removal of the pancreas. At the cellular level, high blood sugar is explained by the role of insulin in carbohydrate metabolism. The explanation of behavior in terms of neural structure is clearly at the organ level. We have attempted to show that what is being explained by structure is function and that function must be revealed by the difference method.

The difference method. The parts of an intact organism function so harmoniously that it is difficult to determine their roles or even their identity. The first step, then, in biological analysis is the location of differences—differences between this part and that part, between a function at this time and at that time, between this condition and that condition. Intervention by the experimenter is often required to bring out these differences. For example, keeping wild species in captivity alters certain behavior patterns. These patterns would probably not even be recognized if the comparison between normal and captive animals were not available [99]. The biological psychologist often begins by noting kinds of behavior that emerge in states of relative disorganization. For example, monkeys can see light but not objects after lesions of the striate cortex [77]; cats are easily provoked to rage after transections of the brain-stem rostral to the hypothalamus [7]. Differences in behavioral disorganization can be readily attributed to differences in structural changes. That the picture of parts obtained from study of disorganization will cast some light upon normal organization scarcely requires defense.

The Behaviorists' Organization of Science

There is an entirely different intellectual tradition in psychology, exemplified in modern times by Watson but preceding him by centuries. In this view, the subject matter of all natural science is motion—change in place. In an effort to make psychology a natural science, Watson reformulated the central problem of psychology: How do certain motions in the environment come to elicit motions in the organism? Any kind of behavior, irrespective of complexity, might be included under the term response. Between stimulus and response, Watson pictured other motions, currents running up and down nerve tracts. Thus, when a poem is written, impulses are streaming into the fingers of the hand.

Later psychologists who were sympathetic, in general, to the way Watson formulated the problems of psychology recognized that his neurologizing was dispensible. One of these, Skinner, suggested the phrase "conceptual nervous system" to emphasize the imaginary character of the neural events inferred from behavior [144]. This phrase might have served to make the point that a translation of the facts of behavior to neurological language is merely analogical when the possibility of an independent test of the neural events is remote. Certainly the point which Lashley had earlier made about physiological explanation is contained in Skinner's analysis of the relation between psychology and neurology. However, Skinner also included as an instance of the conceptual nervous system the structure-function method. Skinner argued that Sherrington's concept of the synapse is an example of the conceptual nervous system, since the properties of synapse were not directly observed but were inferred from responses. Since this has confused rather than clarified the relations between biological and learning psychology, it may be worthwhile to consider Sherrington's method in some detail.

Sherrington's methods. In Sherrington's time, neurophysiologists studied the properties of nerve trunks or axones by a nerve-muscle preparation. The nerve was stimulated and the muscle response—its latency, strength, etc.—was taken as a sign of nervous activity. The activity of nerves was inferred from the movements of muscles. Later, with the advent of improved instruments, electrical activity recorded from the nerve replaced the muscle movement as the sign of nervous impulses. The newer methods are more direct and are surely more refined, but the nerve impulse is inferred nonetheless. There does not seem to be any purpose in insisting that these inferred neural events are imaginary, unless the philosophical point is being made that all scientific knowledge is derived from experience. Sherrington's problem was to determine the function of the gray matter in the spinal cord. This is the region where incoming neurons meet with internuncial and efferent neurons. Sherrington's method was to compare nerve-trunk conduction with spinal-cord or reflex conduction. The differences in function could then be attributed to the anatomical differences between the two kinds of preparation. The structural difference between the two preparations is clear. In the study of nerve-trunk conduction, there is just an efferent nerve and the muscle. A spinal preparation consists of the receptor, the afferent nerve, and the gray matter of the cord, in addition to the efferent nerve. It should be noted that the brain is cut off to restrict the anatomical locus of the difference. Sherrington attributed some of the differences between nerve-trunk and reflex conduction to the selective activity of the receptor. Other differences such as one-way conduction, fatigability, and afterdischarge were attributed to the gray matter, the place where neuron joins neuron. "In view, therefore, of the probable importance physiologically of this mode of nexus between neurone and neurone it is convenient to have a term for it. The term introduced has been *synapse*" [143, p. 17]. Later Sherrington's students and others, using electrical recording techniques, were able to confirm many of Sherrington's ideas about the properties of synapses [44].

Many of the advances in neuropsychology have been made by this structure-function or difference method. Bard's discovery of the function of the hypothalamus may serve as our final example of the difference method [7]. A cat, prepared by a transection of the brain stem above the superior colliculus, exhibits the pseudaffective reaction to noxious stimulus. Sherrington described this reaction as having components of emotional behavior without its being sustained and directed [143]. Bard showed that if the transection is directed rostrally so that the mammillary bodies are in front of rather than behind the section, then the animal is easily provoked by a noxious stimulus into a tantrum of rage. The difference between sham rage and the pseudaffective response is attributed to the difference between the two lesions. In the caudal transection, the posterior hypothalamus is included in the portion removed, while in the rostral transection, the posterior hypothalamus is not included.

Conclusion. We conclude that "conceptual nervous system" as employed by Skinner loses much of its significance by lumping Sherrington with a kind of neurologizing that learning psychology has appropriately discarded. The important distinction to be made, in our view, is the character of the inference from data. If Pavlov's explanation for stimulus generalization, the theory of irradiation, be called "conceptual," then surely we would want another term for Sherrington's theory of the synapse.

We do not feel that the organ level of analysis was overlooked accidently by Watson and other behavior theorists of the same mind. A part of this philosophical tradition seems to be that biology is synonomous with the application of physics to the body. In this organization of science, there is no place for the concepts of structure and function; thus neurophysiology in this view is either the study of membrane potentials or it is conceptual. Biologists, on the other hand, are impressed by the fact that even analysis at the cellular level eludes a complete description in terms of mechanics. With respect to the ultimate relation between biology and physics, most biologists would accept the views of the physicist N. Bohr:

> On the one hand, the wonderful features which are constantly revealed in physiological investigations and differ so strikingly from what is known of inorganic matter, have led many biologists to doubt that a real understanding of the nature of life is possible on a purely physical basis. On the other hand, this view, often known as vitalism, scarcely finds its proper expression in the old supposition that a peculiar vital force, quite unknown to physics, governs all organic life. I think we all agree with Newton that the real basis of science is the conviction that Nature under the same conditions will always exhibit the same regularities. Therefore, if we were able to push the analysis of the mechanism of living organisms as far as that of atomic phenomena, we should scarcely expect to find any features differing from the properties of inorganic matter [16, p. 457].

Summary

We have tried to show that biological psychology is a "molar" biological science and that the biology of learning is a study of organs. In the first section, it was argued that species differences reveal behavior traits which organisms possess as they possess organs. In the sections on the methods of ablation and electrical recording, we argued that the study of learning is more like organ physiology than it is like cellular physiology. We have provided examples of the organ level in fields other than biological psychology. Prior to the study of carbohydrate metabolism at a biochemical level, a number of investigators reported the effects of various ablations, singly or in combination, on blood-sugar level. The result was the picture of a complex integrated system involving pancreas, liver, and pituitary. In this final section, we have selected one philosophical tradition in the psychology of learning to demonstrate that the organ level, e.g., the interrelations of pancreas, liver, and pituitary, is not any more imaginary than the biochemical level, the analysis of insulin's activity inside cells.

We have chosen this particular tradition to contrast with biology because the relation between biological psychology and learning psychology has been confused by the idea that physiological explanation is a reduction of behavioral laws to physiology. Unification has a clear meaning within the biological sciences because, to start with, a number of levels can be recognized. Further, particular instances of unifying trends are provided by history; and, finally, the direction in which future unification may take place can be anticipated. For example, the study of the structure of nucleoproteins promises to solve problems in many areas of biology. The questions of gene replication, of virus infection, and of the control exercised by the nucleus suggest some of these areas. Biological psychology, however, is not an attempt to reduce any other level. It would be just as correct and just as misleading to say that behaviorism is a reduction of biology to mechanics as to argue that biological psychology is a reduction of psychology to physiology. Function is not reduced by being related to structure. At the same time, a unification of organ neurophysiology and neuropsychology and cellular neurophysiology is a long-run goal of present research.

It appears that a number of questions about learning can be answered only by methods now employed by learning theorists. These involve behavioral and environmental variables such as reinforcement, temporal intervals between stimuli, and the like. In this sense, learning psychology and biological psychology are two different subject matters. Nonetheless, a difference in intellectual tradition can be found between biologists and some learning psychologists. This difference can be characterized as the search for the unique organization of parts versus the search for laws or orderly relations between variables. Some have argued that all science must follow one of these patterns. As pluralists, we see no need to force all inquiry into one mode. Scientists will undoubtedly follow their own interests, regardless of which philosophy of science prevails.

Our final thoughts are these: Today we know of no cellular or biochemical changes which correspond to, are produced by, or underlie
learning. If at some future time a neural change is discovered which
provides a final solution to the neurophysiology of learning, then we
should expect that the relations between biology and psychology could
be reexamined with profit. We do not expect the organization of science
to remain fixed.

ABBREVIATIONS IN FIGURES AND IN TEXT

A I	auditory area I
A II	auditory area II
BCI	brachium of the inferior colliculus
CM	*n. centrum medianum*
ECA	anterior ectosylvian sulcus
GL	lateral geniculate body
GM	medial geniculate body
GMm	magnocellular division of the medial geniculate body
GMp	principal division of the medial geniculate body
HA	habenular complex
LP	*n. lateralis posterior*
MD	*n. medialis dorsalis*
NR	red nucleus
PC	cerebral peduncle
Po	posterior group of nuclei
PSS	pseudosylvian sulcus
Pul	pulvinar
RH	rhinal fissure
S I	somatic area I
S II	somatic area II
TO	optic tract
V I	visual area I
V II	visual area II
VM	*n. ventralis medialis*
VP	*n. ventralis posterior*
VPL	*n. ventralis posterolateralis*
VPM	*n. ventralis posteromedialis*

REFERENCES

1. Ades, H. W. Effect of extirpation of parastriate cortex on learned visual
   discriminations in monkeys. *J. Neuropath. exp. Neurol.,* 1946, **5,** 60–65.
2. Adrian, E. D. Double representation of the feet in the sensory cortex
   of the cat. *J. Physiol.,* 1940, **98,** 16P.

3. Adrian, E. D. Afferent discharges to the cerebral cortex from peripheral sense organs. *J. Physiol.,* 1941, **100,** 159–191.
4. Allen, W. F. Effect of destroying three localized cortical areas for sound on correct conditioned differential responses of the dog's foreleg. *Amer. J. Physiol.,* 1945, **144,** 415–428.
5. Anderson, F. D., & Berry, C. M. Degeneration studies of long ascending fiber systems in the cat brain stem. *J. comp. Neurol.,* 1959, **111,** 195–229.
6. Baldwin, E. A. *An introduction to comparative biochemistry.* London: Cambridge Univer. Press, 1948.
7. Bard, P. A diencephalic mechanism for the expression of rage with special reference to the sympathetic nervous system. *Amer. J. Physiol.,* 1928, **84,** 490–515.
8. Barris, R. W., Ingram, W. R., & Ranson, S. W. Optic connections of the diencephalon and midbrain of the cat. *J. comp. Neurol.,* 1935, **62,** 117–153.
9. Beale, G. H., Robinson, G. M., Robinson, R., & Scott-Moncrieff, R. Genetics and chemistry of flower color variation in *Lathyrus odoratus. J. Genet.,* 1939, **37,** 375–387.
10. Beck, E. C., Doty, R. W., & Kooi, K. A. Electrocortical reactions associated with conditioned flexion reflexes. *EEG clin. Neurophysiol.,* 1958, **10,** 279–289.
11. Bishop, G. H. Neural mechanisms of cutaneous sense. *Physiol. Rev.,* 1946, **26,** 77–102.
12. Bishop, G. H. The relation between nerve fiber size and sensory modality: phylogenetic implications of the afferent innervation of cortex. *J. nerv. ment. Dis.,* 1959, **128,** 89–114.
13. Bishop, G. H., & Clare, M. H. Organization and distribution of fibers in the optic nerve of the cat. *J. comp. Neurol.,* 1955, **103,** 269–304.
14. Blum, J. S. Cortical organization in somesthesis: effects of lesions in posterior associative cortex on somatosensory function in *Macaca mulatta. Comp. Psychol. Monogr.,* 1951, **20,** 219–249.
15. Bodian, D. Studies on the diencephalon of the Virginia opossum. Part III. The thalamo-cortical projection. *J. comp. Neurol.,* 1942, **77,** 525–576.
16. Bohr, N. Light and life. *Nature,* 1933, **131,** 421–423, 457–459.
17. Bowsher, D. Projection of the gracile and cuneate nuclei in *Macaca mulatta. J. comp. Neurol.,* 1958, **110,** 135–151.
18. Burt, C. The inheritance of mental ability. *Amer. Psychologist,* 1958, **13,** 1–15.
19. Butler, R. A., Diamond, I. T., & Neff, W. D. Role of auditory cortex in discrimination of changes in frequency. *J. Neurophysiol.,* 1957, **20,** 108–120.
20. Carmichael, L. The development of behavior in vertebrates experimentally removed from the influence of external stimulation. *Psychol. Rev.,* 1926, **33,** 51–58.

21. Chiles, W. D. Performance during stimulation of the diencephalic activating system. *J. comp. physiol. Psychol.*, 1954, **47**, 412–415.
22. Chow, K. L. A retrograde cell degeneration study of the cortical projection field of the pulvinar in the monkey. *J. comp. Neurol.*, 1950, **93**, 313–340.
23. Chow, K. L. Effects of partial extirpations of the posterior association cortex on visually mediated behavior in monkeys. *Comp. Psychol. Monogr.*, 1951, **20**, 187–217.
24. Chow, K. L. Conditions influencing the recovery of visual discriminative habits in monkeys following temporal neocortical ablations. *J. comp. physiol. Psychol.*, 1952, **45**, 430–437.
25. Chow, K. L. Further studies on selective ablation of associative cortex in relation to visually mediated behavior. *J. comp. physiol. Psychol.*, 1952, **45**, 109–118.
26. Chow, K. L. Regional degeneration of the thalamic reticular nucleus following cortical ablations in monkeys. *J. comp. Neurol.*, 1952, **97**, 37–60.
27. Chow, K. L. Effects of temporal neocortical ablation on visual discrimination learning sets in monkeys. *J. comp. physiol. Psychol.*, 1954, **47**, 194–198.
28. Chow, K. L. Lack of behavioral effects following destruction of some thalamic association nuclei in monkeys. *Arch. Neurol. Psychiat.*, 1954, **71**, 762–771.
29. Chow, K. L. Anatomical and electrographical analysis of temporal neocortex in relation to visual discrimination learning in monkey. In J. F. Delafresnaye (Ed.), *Brain mechanisms and learning.* Oxford: Blackwell, 1961.
30. Chow, K. L. Brain functions. *Annu. Rev. Psychol.*, 1961.
31. Chow, K. L., & Hutt, P. J. The "association cortex" of *Macaca mulatta:* a review of recent contributions to its anatomy and functions. *Brain,* 1953, **76**, 625–677.
32. Chow, K. L., & Orbach, J. Performance of visual discriminations presented tachistoscopically in monkeys with temporal neocortical ablations. *J. comp. physiol. Psychol.*, 1957, **50**, 636–640.
33. Chow, K. L., Riesen, A. H., & Newell, F. W. Degeneration of retinal ganglion cells in infant chimpanzees reared in darkness. *J. comp. Neurol.*, 1957, **107**, 27–42.
34. Chow, K. L., & Survis, J. Retention of overlearned visual habit after cortical ablation in monkey. *Arch. Neurol. Psychiat.*, 1958, **79**, 640–646.
35. Clark, W. E. Le Gros. The structure and connections of the thalamus. *Brain,* 1932, **55**, 406–470.
36. Collins, W. F., & O'Leary, J. L. Study of a somatic evoked response of midbrain reticular substance. *EEG clin. Neurophysiol.*, 1954, **6**, 619–628.
37. Darwin, C. *The origin of species.* New York: Random House.
38. Delafresnaye, J. F. (Ed.) *Brain mechanisms and consciousness.* Oxford: Blackwell, 1954.

39. Diamond, I. T., Chow, K. L., & Neff, W. D. Degeneration of caudal medial geniculate body following cortical lesion ventral to auditory area II in cat. *J. comp. Neurol.*, 1958, **109**, 349–362.

40. Diamond, I. T., & Neff, W. D. Ablation of temporal cortex and discrimination of auditory patterns. *J. Neurophysiol.*, 1957, **20**, 300–315.

41. Doty, R. W., & Giurgea, C. Conditioned reflexes established by coupling visual and motor cortex stimulation. *The Physiologist*, 1958, **1**, 17.

42. Doty, R. W., & Rutledge, L. T. "Generalization" between cortically and peripherally applied stimuli eliciting conditioned reflexes. *J. Neurophysiol.*, 1959, **22**, 428–435.

43. Doty, R. W., Rutledge, L. T., & Larsen, R. M. Conditioned reflexes established to electrical stimulation of cat cerebral cortex. *J. Neurophysiol.*, 1956, **19**, 401–415.

44. Eccles, J. C. The development of ideas on the synapse. In C. M. C. Brooks & P. F. Cranefield (Eds.), *The historical development of physiological thought*. New York: Hafner, 1959. Pp. 39–66.

45. Emerson, A. E. Termite nests: a study of the phylogeny of behavior. *Ecol. Monogr.*, 1938, **8**, 247–284.

46. Ephrussi, B. The interplay of heredity and environment in the synthesis of respiratory enzymes in yeast. In *The Harvey lectures*. Springfield, Ill.: Charles C Thomas, 1952.

47. Galambos, R. Electrical correlates of conditioned learning. In M. A. B. Brazier (Ed.), *The central nervous system and behavior*. Transactions of The First Conference. New York: Josiah Macy, Jr. Foundation, 1958.

48. Galambos, R., & Davis, H. The response of single auditory nerve fibers to acoustic stimulation. *J. Neurophysiol.*, 1943, **6**, 39–57.

49. Galambos, R., Sheatz, G., & Vernier, V. G. Electrophysiological correlates of a conditioned response in cats. *Science*, 1956, **123**, 376–377.

50. Galton, F. *Natural inheritance*. London: Macmillan, 1889.

51. Gardner, L. P., & Nissen, H. W. Simple discrimination behavior of young chimpanzees: comparisons with human aments and domestic animals. *J. genet. Psychol.*, 1948, **72**, 145–164.

52. Gasser, H. S., & Erlanger, J. The role played by the sizes of the constituent fibers of a nerve trunk in determining the form of its action potential wave. *Amer. J. Physiol.*, 1927, **80**, 522–547.

53. Gasser, H. S., & Erlanger, J. The role of fiber size in the establishment of a nerve block by pressure or cocaine. *Amer. J. Physiol.*, 1929, **88**, 581–591.

54. Ginsburg, B. E. Genetics as a tool in the study of behavior. *Perspectives Biol. Med.*, 1958, **1**, 397–424.

55. Goldberg, J. M., Diamond, I. T., & Neff, W. D. Frequency discrimination after ablation of cortical projection areas of the auditory system. *Fed. Proc.*, 1958, **17**, 216. (Abstract)

56. Goldstein, K. *The organism*. New York: American Book, 1939.

57. Goldstein, K. *Human nature in the light of psychopathology*. Cambridge, Mass.: Harvard Univer. Press, 1940.

58. Granit, R. *Receptors and sensory perception.* New Haven, Conn.: Yale Univer. Press, 1955.

59. Hall, C. S. The genetics of behavior. In S. S. Stevens (Ed.), *Handbook of experimental psychology.* New York: Wiley, 1951. Pp. 304–329.

60. Harmon, P. J., & Berry, C. M. Neuroanatomical distribution of action potentials evoked by photic stimuli in cat fore- and midbrain. *J. comp. Neurol.,* 1956, **105**, 354–416.

61. Hayhow, W. R. The cytoarchitecture of the lateral geniculate body in the cat in relation to the distribution of crossed and uncrossed optic fibers. *J. comp. Neurol.,* 1958, **110**, 1–63.

62. Head, H. *Aphasia and kindred disorders of speech.* New York: Macmillan, 1926.

63. Hearst, E., Beer, B., Sheatz, G., & Galambos, R. Some electrophysiological correlates of conditioning in the monkey. *EEG clin. Neurophysiol.,* 1960, **12**, 137–152.

64. Hebb, D. O. *The organization of behavior.* New York: Wiley, 1949.

65. Herrick, C. J. The functions of the olfactory parts of the cerebral cortex. *Proc. Nat. Acad. Sci.,* 1933, **19**, 7–14.

66. Herrick, C. J., & Bishop, G. H. A comparative survey of the spinal lemniscus systems. In H. H. Jasper et al. (Eds.), *Reticular formation of the brain.* Boston: Little, Brown, 1958. Pp. 353–360.

67. Hess, E. H. Imprinting. *Science,* 1959, **130**, 133–141.

68. Hodgson, E. S. Chemoreception in arthropods. *Annu. Rev. Entomol.,* 1958, **3**, 19–36.

69. Horowitz, N. H. Genetic and non-genetic factors in the production of enzymes by neurospora. *Growth,* 1951, **11**, 47–62.

70. James, W. *The principles of psychology.* Vol. I. New York: Holt, 1890.

71. Jasper, H. H. Diffuse projection systems: the integrative action of the thalamic reticular system. *EEG clin. Neurophysiol.,* 1949, **1**, 405–420.

72. Jasper, H. H., & Shagass, C. Conditioning the occipital alpha rhythm in man. *J. exp. Psychol.,* 1941, **26**, 373–388.

73. Jasper, H. H., & Smirnov, G. (Eds.) *EEG clin. Neurophysiol.,* Suppl. 13, 1960.

74. Johannsen, W. *Concerning heredity in populations and in pure lines.* Chicago: Univer. of Chicago Press, 1953. (Translated by H. Gall and E. Putschar of *Ueber Erblichkeit in Populationen und in reinen Linien.* Jena: Gustav Fischer, 1903.)

75. John, E. R., & Killam, K. F. Electrophysiological correlates of avoidance conditioning in the cat. *J. Pharmacol. exp. Ther.,* 1959, **125**, 252–274.

76. Klüver, H. *Behavior mechanisms in monkeys.* Chicago: Univer. of Chicago Press, 1933.

77. Klüver, H. Functional significance of the geniculo-striate system. *Biol. Sympos.,* 1942, **7**, 253–299.

78. Klüver, H., & Bucy, P. C. An analysis of certain effects of bilateral temporal lobectomy in the rhesus monkey, with special reference to "psychic blindness." *J. Psychol.,* 1938, **5**, 33–54.

79. Koffka, K. Perception: an introduction to Gestalt theory. *Psychol. Bull.*, 1922, **19**, 531–585.
80. Köhler, W. *Gestalt psychology.* New York: Liveright, 1947.
81. Krech, D., Rosenzweig, M. R., Bennet, E. L., & Krueckel, B. Enzyme concentrations in the brain and adjustive behavior patterns. *Science*, 1954, **120**, 994–996.
82. Krogh, A. *The anatomy and physiology of capillaries.* New Haven, Conn.: Yale Univer. Press, 1929.
83. Lashley, K. S. Studies of cerebral function in learning. V. The retention of motor habits after destruction of the so-called motor areas in primates. *Arch. Neurol. Psychiat.*, 1924, **12**, 249–276.
84. Lashley, K. S. *Brain mechanisms and intelligence.* Chicago: Univer. of Chicago Press, 1929.
85. Lashley, K. S. Learning. I. Nervous mechanisms in learning. In C. Murchison (Ed.), *The foundations of experimental psychology.* Worcester, Mass.: Clark Univer. Press, 1929. Pp. 524–563.
86. Lashley, K. S. Basic neural mechanisms in behavior. *Psychol. Rev.*, 1930, **37**, 1–24.
87. Lashley, K. S. The mechanism of vision. XII. Nervous structures concerned in the acquisition and retention of habits based on reactions to light. *Comp. Psychol. Monogr.*, 1935, **11**, 43–79.
88. Lashley, K. S. Factors limiting recovery after central nervous lesions. *J. nerv. ment. Dis.*, 1938, **88**, 733–755.
89. Lashley, K. S. The mechanism of vision. XVI. The functioning of small remnants of the visual cortex. *J. comp. Neurol.*, 1939, **70**, 45–67.
90. Lashley, K. S. Thalamo-cortical connections of the rat's brain. *J. comp. Neurol.*, 1941, **75**, 67–121.
91. Lashley, K. S. The mechanism of vision. XVII. Autonomy of the visual cortex. *J. genet. Psychol.*, 1942, **60**, 197–221.
92. Lashley, K. S. Studies of cerebral function in learning. XIII. Apparent absence of transcortical association in maze learning. *J. comp. Neurol.*, 1944, **80**, 257–281.
93. Lashley, K. S. The mechanism of vision. XVIII. Effects of destroying the visual "associative areas" of the monkey. *Genet. psychol. Monogr.*, 1948, **37**, 107–166.
94. Lashley, K. S. Persistent problems in the evolution of mind. *Quart. Rev. Biol.*, 1949, **24**, 28–42.
95. Lashley, K. S. In search of the engram. *Sympos. Soc. exp. Biol.*, 1950, **4**, 454–482.
96. Lehrman, D. S. A critique of Konrad Lorenz's theory of instinctive behavior. *Quart. Rev. Biol.*, 1953, **28**, 337–363.
97. Lehrman, D. S. On the organization of maternal behavior and the problem of instinct. In P.-P. Grassé (Ed.), *L'Instinct dans le comportement des animaux et de l'homme.* Paris: Masson, 1956. Pp. 475–520.
98. Lombroso, C. T., & Merlis, J. K. Suprasylvian auditory responses in the cat. *EEG clin. Neurophysiol.*, 1957, **9**, 301–308.

99. Lorenz, K. Z. The comparative method in studying innate behavior patterns. *Sympos. Soc. exp. Biol.*, 1950, **4**, 221–268.

100. Loucks, R. B. Studies of neural structures essential for learning. II. The conditioning of salivary and striped muscle responses to faradization of cortical sensory elements, and the action of sleep upon such mechanisms. *J. comp. Psychol.*, 1938, **25**, 315–332.

101. McDougall, W. *Psychology: the study of behavior.* London: Butterworth, 1912.

102. Marshall, W. H., Talbot, S. A., & Ades, H. W. Cortical response of the anesthetized cat to gross photic and electrical afferent stimulation. *J. Neurophysiol.*, 1943, **6**, 1–15.

103. Meyer, D. R., & Woolsey, C. N. Effects of localized cortical destruction upon auditory discriminative conditioning in the cat. *J. Neurophysiol.*, 1952, **15**, 149–162.

104. Mickle, W. A., & Ades, H. W. A composite sensory projection area in the cerebral cortex of the cat. *Amer. J. Physiol.*, 1952, **170**, 682–689.

105. Mishkin, M. Visual discrimination performance following partial ablations of the temporal lobe. II. Ventral surface vs. hippocampus. *J. comp. physiol. Psychol.*, 1954, **47**, 187–193.

106. Mishkin, M., & Hall, M. Discrimination along a size continuum following ablation of the inferior temporal convexity in monkeys. *J. comp. physiol. Psychol.*, 1955, **48**, 97–101.

107. Mishkin, M., & Pribram, K. H. Visual discrimination performance following partial ablations of the temporal lobe. I. Ventral vs. lateral. *J. comp. physiol. Psychol.*, 1954, **47**, 14–20.

108. Morison, R. S., & Dempsey, E. W. A study of thalamocortical relations. *Amer. J. Physiol.*, 1942, **135**, 281–292.

109. Morrell, F., & Jasper, H. H. Electrographic studies of the formation of temporary connections in the brain. *EEG clin. Neurophysiol.*, 1956, **8**, 201–215.

110. Morrell, F., Roberts, L., & Jasper, H. H. Effect of focal epileptogenic lesions and their ablation upon conditioned electrical responses of the brain in the monkey. *EEG clin. Neurophysiol.*, 1956, **8**, 217–236.

111. Nashold, B. S., Hanbery, J., & Olszewski, J. Observations on the diffuse thalamic projections. *EEG clin. Neurophysiol.*, 1955, **7**, 609–620.

112. Nauta, W. J. H., & Kuypers, H. G. J. M. Some ascending pathways in the brain stem reticular formation. In H. H. Jasper et al. (Eds.), *Reticular formation of the brain.* Boston: Little, Brown, 1958. Pp. 2–30.

113. Nielsen, J. M., & FitzGibbon, J. P. *Agnosia, apraxia, aphasia: their value in cerebral localization.* Los Angeles, Calif.: Los Angeles Neurological Society, 1936.

114. Nissen, H. W. Phylogenetic comparison. In S. S. Stevens (Ed.), *Handbook of experimental psychology.* New York: Wiley, 1951. Pp. 347–386.

115. Nissen, H. W. Problems of mental evolution in the primates. *Hum. Biol.*, 1954, **26**, 277–287.

116. Orbach, J., & Chow, K. L. Differential effects of resections of somatic areas I and II in monkeys. *J. Neurophysiol.*, 1959, **22**, 195–203.

117. Orbach, J., & Fantz, R. L. Differential effects of temporal neo-cortical resections on overtrained and non-overtrained visual habits in monkeys. *J. comp. physiol. Psychol.*, 1958, **51**, 126–129.

118. Orbach, J., & Fisher, G. J. Bilateral resections of frontal granular cortex, factors influencing delayed response and discrimination performance in monkeys. *AMA Arch. Neurol.*, 1959, **1**, 78–86.

119. Papez, J. W. A proposed mechanism of emotion. *Arch. Neurol. Psychiat.*, 1937, **38**, 725–743.

120. Pasik, P., Pasik, T., Battersby, W. S., & Bender, M. B. Visual and tactual discriminations by macaques with serial temporal and parietal lesions. *J. comp. physiol. Psychol.*, 1958, **51**, 427–436.

121. Pfaffmann, C. The afferent code for sensory quality. *Amer. Psychologist*, 1959, **14**, 226–232.

122. Poggio, G. F., & Mountcastle, V. B. A study of the functional contributions of the lemniscal and spinothalamic systems to somatic sensibility. *Johns Hopkins Hosp. Bull.*, 1960, **106**, 266–316.

123. Pribram, H. B., & Barry, J. Further behavioral analysis of parieto-temporo-preoccipital cortex. *J. Neurophysiol.*, 1956, **19**, 99–106.

124. Pribram, K. H. Comparative neurology and the evolution of behavior. In A. Roe & G. G. Simpson (Eds.), *Behavior and evolution*. New Haven, Conn.: Yale Univer. Press, 1958. Pp. 140–164.

125. Pribram, K. H., & Mishkin, M. Simultaneous and successive visual discrimination by monkeys with inferotemporal lesions. *J. comp. physiol. Psychol.*, 1955, **48**, 198–202.

126. Ranson, S. W. The course within the spinal cord of the non-medullated fibers of the dorsal roots: a study of Lissauer's tract in the cat. *J. comp. Neurol.*, 1913, **23**, 259–281.

127. Razran, G. H. S. Conditioned responses in animals other than dogs. *Psychol. Bull.*, 1933, **30**, 261–324.

128. Riesen, A. H. Plasticity of behavior: Psychological aspects. In H. F. Harlow & C. N. Woolsey (Eds.), *Biological and biochemical bases of behavior*. Madison, Wis.: Univer. of Wis. Press, 1958. Pp. 425–450.

129. Rioch, D. McK. Studies on the diencephalon of carnivora. Part I. The nuclear configuration of thalamus, epithalamus and hypothalamus of the dog and cat. Part II. Certain nuclear configurations and fiber connections of the subthalamus and midbrain of the dog and cat. *J. comp. Neurol.*, 1929, **49**, 1–154.

130. Riopelle, A. J., Alper, R. G., Strong, P. N., & Ades, H. W. Multiple discrimination and patterned string performance of normal and temporal-lobectomized monkeys. *J. comp. physiol. Psychol.*, 1953, **46**, 145–149.

131. Rose, J. E. The thalamus of the sheep: cellular and fibrous structure and comparison with pig, rabbit and cat. *J. comp. Neurol.*, 1942, **77**, 469–524.

132. Rose, J. E., & Mountcastle, V. B. Touch and kinesthesis. In J. Field, H. W. Magoun, & V. Hall (Eds.), *Handbook of physiology.* Vol. I. Washington: American Physiological Society, 1959. Pp. 387–429.

133. Rose, J. E., & Woolsey, C. N. Organization of the mammalian thalamus and its relationships to the cerebral cortex. *EEG clin. Neurophysiol.,* 1949, **1**, 391–403.

134. Rose, J. E., & Woolsey, C. N. The relations of thalamic connections, cellular structure and evocable electrical activity in the auditory region of the cat. *J. comp. Neurol.,* 1949, **91**, 441–466.

135. Rose, J. E., & Woolsey, C. N. Cortical connections and functional organization of the thalamic auditory system of the cat. In H. F. Harlow & C. N. Woolsey (Eds.), *Biological and biochemical bases of behavior.* Madison, Wis.: Univer. of Wis. Press, 1958. Pp. 127–150.

136. Rosvold, H. E., & Delgado, J. M. R. The effect on delayed-alternation test performance of stimulating or destroying electrically structures within the frontal lobes of the monkey's brain. *J. comp. physiol. Psychol.,* 1956, **49**, 365–372.

137. Ruch, T. C., Fulton, J. F., & German, W. J. Sensory discrimination in monkey, chimpanzee, and man after lesions of the parietal lobe. *Arch. Neurol. Psychiat.,* 1938, **39**, 919–938.

138. Rusinov, V. S., & Rabinovich, M. Y. Electroencephalographic researches in the laboratories and clinics of the Soviet Union. *EEG clin. Neurophysiol.,* 1958, Suppl. 8, 1–36.

139. Scott, J. P. *Animal behavior.* Chicago: Univer. of Chicago Press, 1958.

140. Segundo, J. P., Roig, J. A., & Sommer-Smith, J. A. Conditioning of reticular formation stimulation effects. *EEG clin. Neurophysiol.,* 1959, **11**, 471–484.

141. Sharpless, S., & Jasper, H. Habituation of the arousal reaction. *Brain,* 1956, **79**, 655–680.

142. Shell, W. F., & Riopelle, A. J. Progressive discrimination learning in platyrrhine monkeys. *J. comp. physiol. Psychol.,* 1958, **51**, 467–470.

143. Sherrington, C. S. *The integrative action of the nervous system.* New York: Scribner's, 1906.

144. Skinner, B. F. *The behavior of organisms.* New York: Appleton-Century-Crofts, 1938.

145. Sperry, R. W. Cerebral regulation of motor coordination in monkeys following multiple transection of sensorimotor cortex. *J. Neurophysiol.,* 1947, **10**, 275–294.

146. Sutton, W. S. The chromosomes in heredity. *Biol. Bull.,* 1903, **4**, 231–247.

147. Talbot, S. A. A lateral localization in the cat's visual cortex. *Fed. Proc.,* 1942, **1**, 84. (Abstract)

148. Talbot, S. A., & Marshall, W. A. Physiological studies of neural mechanisms of visual localization and discrimination. *Amer. J. Ophthal.,* 1941, **24**, 1255–1264.

149. Teuber, H.-L. Physiological psychology. *Annu. Rev. Psychol.,* 1955, **6**, 267–296.

150. Teuber, H.-L. Some alterations in behavior after cerebral lesions in man. In *Evolution of nervous control*. Washington: American Association for the Advancement of Science, 1959. Pp 157–194.

151. Thompson, R. F. Function of auditory cortex of cat in frequency discrimination. *J. Neurophysiol.*, 1960, **23**, 321–334.

152. Thompson, R. F., & Sindberg, R. M. Auditory response fields in association and motor cortex of cat. *J. Neurophysiol.*, 1960, **23**, 87–105.

153. Thorpe, W. H. The concepts of learning and their relation to those of instinct. *Sympos. Soc. exp. Biol.*, 1950, **4**, 387–408.

154. Tinbergen, N. Social releasers and the experimental method required for their study. *Wilson Bull.*, 1948, **60**, 6–52.

155. Titchener, E. B. *A textbook of psychology*. New York: Macmillan, 1910.

156. Tryon, R. C. Genetic differences in maze-learning ability in rats. In *Thirty-ninth Yearbook of the National Society for the Study of Education*. Bloomington, Ill.: Public School Publishing, 1940. Pp. 111–119.

157. Tryon, R. C. Individual differences. In F. A. Moss (Ed.), *Comparative psychology*. Englewood Cliffs, N.J.: Prentice-Hall, 1942. Pp. 330–365.

158. Tunturi, A. R. Further afferent connections to the acoustic cortex of the dog. *Amer. J. Physiol.*, 1945, **144**, 389–394.

159. Verzilova, O. V. Changes in the cortical electrical activity of the dog in the region of the auditory and motor analysers during the formation and reversal of motor defensive reflexes. *Pavlov J. higher nerv. Activity*, 1958, **8**, 410–420.

160. Waddington, C. H. Canalization of development and the inheritance of acquired characters. *Nature*, 1942, **150**, 563–565.

161. Waddington, C. H. The genetic control of development. *Sympos. Soc. exp. Biol.*, 1948, **2**, 145–154.

162. Walker, A. E. *The primate thalamus*. Chicago: Univer. of Chicago Press, 1938.

163. Watson, J. B. *Behaviorism*. New York: Norton, 1925.

164. Whitfield, I. C. The physiology of hearing. *Progr. in Biophys. biophys. Chem.*, 1957, **8**, 1–47.

165. Whitlock, D. G., & Nauta, W. J. H. Subcortical projections from the temporal neocortex in *Macaca mulatta*. *J. comp. Neurol.*, 1956, **106**, 183–212.

166. Wilson, M. Effects of circumscribed cortical lesions upon somesthetic and visual discrimination in the monkey. *J. comp. physiol. Psychol.*, 1957, **50**, 630–635.

167. Wilson, W. A., & Mishkin, M. Comparison of the effects of inferotemporal and lateral occipital lesions on visually guided behavior in monkeys. *J. comp. physiol. Psychol.*, 1959, **52**, 10–17.

168. Woolsey, C. N. Patterns of sensory representation in the cerebral cortex. *Fed. Proc.*, 1947, **6**, 437–441.

169. Woolsey, C. N. Organization of somatic sensory and motor areas of the cerebral cortex. In H. F. Harlow & C. N. Woolsey (Eds.), *Biological*

and biochemical bases of behavior. Madison, Wis.: Univer. of Wis. Press, 1958. Pp. 63–81.

170. Woolsey, C. N., & Fairman, D. Contralateral, ipsilateral and bilateral representation of cutaneous receptors in somatic areas I and II of the cerebral cortex of pig, sheep, and other mammals. *Surgery,* 1946, **19,** 684–702.

171. Woolsey, C. N., & Walzl, E. M. Topical projection of nerve fibers from local regions of the cochlea to the cerebral cortex of the cat. *Johns Hopkins Hosp. Bull.,* 1942, **71,** 315–344.

172. Worden, F. G. Discussion in M. A. B. Brazier (Ed.), *The central nervous system and behavior.* Transactions of the Second Conference. New York: Josiah Macy, Jr. Foundation, 1959. Pp. 271–291.

173. Wright, S. The statistical consequences of Mendelian heredity in relation to speciation. In J. Huxley (Ed.), *The new systematics.* London: Oxford Univer. Press, 1940. Pp. 161–183.

174. Wright, S. Genes as physiological agents. *Amer. Naturalist,* 1945, **79,** 289–303.

175. Yoshii, N. Methodological principles of electroencephalographic investigation on conditioned behavior. *Folia psychiat. neurol. Jap.,* 1956, **9,** 341–365.

176. Yoshii, N., Natsumoto, J., Maneo, S., Hasegawa, Y., Yamaguchi, Y., Shimokochi, M., Hari, Y., & Yamazaki, H. Conditioned reflex and electroencephalography. *Med. J. Osaka Univer.,* 1958, **9,** 353–375.

EXPERIMENT AND THEORY IN PHYSIOLOGICAL PSYCHOLOGY

R. C. DAVIS*
*Department of Psychology
Indiana University*

Introduction 242
What Is Meant by "Physiological Psychology"? 242
Experimental Work 246
Theorists 256
    Mathematical biophysics 257
    Binary digital theory 259
    Pattern theory 263
    Hebb's theory 266
    Pribram's synthesis 269
Theory and Experiment 270
References 278

INTRODUCTION

Physiological psychologists are not often philosophers. Whatever convictions they may entertain on the scientific role of their work, their public expressions are rare and usually brief. To find their points of departure, their intentions, and their rules of procedure, we must look more at their deeds than at their words. More exactly put, we must consider *words* to be more than words about words. Important consequences—both good and bad—follow from their lack of philosophical awareness, as I shall try to show.

WHAT IS MEANT BY "PHYSIOLOGICAL PSYCHOLOGY"?

Naturally a great deal of what one might say about the field hangs upon a decision about what territory is properly named "physiological

*It is with deep regret that the editor records the death of Dr. Davis on February 23rd, 1961. Dr. Davis had finished the final work on his manuscript in March, 1960. He died only a few weeks before the publisher's copy editor completed preparation of his essay for press. Dr. Roger Russell and other close colleagues at Indiana were good enough to assist in dealing with the copy editor's queries.

242

psychology." No Vienna congress has ever settled the boundaries for us—and maps with names and no division marks look more like Antarctica than like Europe. Some work is physiological psychology by general consent. But in the case of many contributions, one feels uncertain about claim to the adjective; in many others, about a claim to the noun. It is doubtful whether collation of common usages would define even the central area in any fashion simple enough to be useful.

In the days of the founders, the common doctrine of mind-body parallelism dictated a meaning for the new term. According to philosophical supposition, every event was dual—mental and corporeal—and anyone who ventured a complete account was engaged in physiological psychology. With two "event chains" running parallel, the same experimental data could be used for both, for an event of one kind was thought to reflect a corresponding event of the other. To separate the data into two treatises, experimental and physiological, would have been pointless. The hybrid title as Wundt [37] used it signifies less a field of psychology than the author's idea of what general psychology should try to be. The distinction implied by the name seems one more of doctrine than of field.

Although parallelism as a profession of faith no longer lives, its progeny remain. There are several proposals to assign an area for physiological psychology which is coordinate with one or more kinds of non-physiological psychology. We may think of division by level, by kind of subject matter, or by method.

Fine-scale description is sometimes proposed as the proper task of physiological psychology. Woodworth [36] has favored this view, and it seems to be the intention of some who speak of the molar-molecular division of psychology [33]. Of course, the naming of a trait like "fineness of description" does not of itself establish two classes, and as some have used the phrase, very likely it is not intended to. The dimension needs more qualification if it is not to include in physiological psychology a detailed description of external events, and "fineness of description" is not a matter of just two levels. From the movement of armies to the movement of electrons surely there must be many levels; only a firm believer in some further doctrine would feel he was transgressing by using descriptions as fine or as coarse as he thought helpful. Nevertheless, there are those who feel that certain levels—the molar, the molecular or whatever—have a completeness which needs no supplement and a charm it would be foolish to avoid. So a devotee of molarism may feel he ought to restrain himself from wandering afield [29]; the molecular psychologist may feel a spinal shudder at any but the simplest experimental variables. The postulate of completeness at certain levels perhaps deserves more exposition than it has been given; it is not obvious what the levels are or that our universe is, in fact, a logical layer cake.

To the authors of the usual texts on physiological psychology [7, 23], the contrary position on this point looks self-evident. Conditions and events within the organism, considered molecular by some, are thought to obtrude themselves into sequences whose outcome is some kind of behavior. Physiological psychology is therefore taken to be a treatment of certain subject matter, the internal determiners of behavior. Plausible though it seems, this assignment leads to an inconvenience and an ambiguity.

If we recognize two branches of psychology—one to study effects arising in the interior, one devoted to external influences—we probably intend that the two branches should add up to produce the whole of psychology. But the interactions between the internal and the external are left out of the reckoning. Doubtless these exist—stimulus A, for example, leading to response B when the internal condition is C, but producing response M when the condition is D, etc. It would be most awkward to examine everything three times, once for stimulus effects, once for internal effects, and finally for the combination effects.

Nor is it very clear how to separate the internal from the external. No one has any doubt that the immediate precursor of any item of behavior is a muscular contraction, or that any "experience"—if such a term be recognized—follows certain processes within the body. Study of these would be physiological psychology in the subject-matter sense. Yet these immediate predecessors also have their antecedents; sooner or later, if we retrace the chain of events, we should expect to find some segment which lies outside the boundary of the organism. In this fashion we should arrive at the stimulus or some more general external determiner. Whether we should always arrive at such an external segment is interesting to speculate; it is certain that we often would.

To manipulate the organism's condition as an experimental variable, the investigator must establish artificial control of the chain of events at some point; sometimes it is outside the organism, sometimes inside. Whatever this point may be, in the nature of the case, what the experimenter does actually introduces a controlling condition from *outside* the organism—a condition which results in a change *inside* the organism before a change in behavior (or experience) is produced. Because the external and internal variables are in chain rather than in parallel, all experiments manipulate both and qualify as physiological and nonphysiological by the touchstone of where the variable is located. Knowledge of the internal effects of an experimental procedure will naturally vary from one case to another. We can be sure it is never perfect; on the other hand, it is not likely to be wholly wanting. There is no clear division of this sort; if there were, no one would care to distinguish a branch of psychology by anything so trivial and fleeting as our ignorance of it.

As long as patience remains, one may continue the exploration of possible boundaries for physiological psychology—lines such as stimulus differences, response differences, differences of method—but the questions would be moot, and there seem to be no advocates. Perhaps there *is* no proper field for physiological psychology in the broad territory of psychology. The outcome might have been foreseen since, without some recognized discontinuity in the universe, there can be no clear subdivisions in the science which describes it; the investigator may well let his thoughts follow wherever questions lead.

This very principle of *nil obstat* may be the trade-mark of physiological psychology. Among psychologists there is a difference of creed on this point; if one likes, it can be taken to separate the physiological psychologist from others. Rather paradoxically, it may be said that the non-physiological psychologist is one who looks upon his subject as a distinct and independent science. The physiological psychologist, on the other hand, does not feel that he is clearly separate from scientists in general or confined to any special territory. Apparently without reflecting on the matter very much—or at least without being very articulate about it—he follows his strong and simple faith that an event, like a piece of machinery, is best understood by taking it apart [25, 32]. His inclination is to dissect and analyze everything into smaller components—reflexes, nerve impulses, impinging forces, chemical reactions, and so on—and he finds his work mingling with that of other disciplines. This analytic trend is certainly a common one in science, and one finds in each discipline a tendency to move downward: The physiologist turns to biochemistry, the chemist turns to physics, and the sciences all spill over at their lower edges.

The kind of analysis which concerns—and so defines—the physiological psychologist is literal, as it is for the chemist. He would expect as a result of his analysis to come upon smaller parts which reveal themselves for his observation. If one thinks of the subject matter of psychology as the study of the responses of physical systems in the organism and across it, then, for the physiological psychologist, analysis is a separation of the complete system into smaller ones. The separation can be longitudinal or transectional. In the former case, the investigator would concern himself with possibly one channel—though he knows others are also functioning—so he might study certain muscular contractions during performance of a task. In the latter case, he would in some way interrupt a pathway of the system and study what occurs at just one end or in the middle of a normal response channel. In either case, he isolates a subsystem from the normal. Analysis then means a division into partial systems which are presumed to take part in normal response. In a sense, logical conveniences and mathematical abstractions can be counted as analytic, but these would generally have limited appeal to those who think of themselves as physiological psychologists. The connotation of another phrase, "the experimental analysis of behavior" [28], is nearer their own practice: Work under that title is indeed a sort of dissection. But to a group working strictly in that area, only stimuli seem to be worth dissecting—a limitation that some physiological psychologists would think hampering.

The psychologist who is not physiological in this analytic sense may argue that the procedure of dissection is naïve, for obviously this teasing out of parts produces new structures which no longer act like the original. The physiological psychologist may indeed be guilty of the fallacy of reduction; he is generally heedless of it, probably convinced that reduction *is* no fallacy. For this conviction, no doubt, a philosophical foundation can be provided [4], but the physiological worker seems content without one for the most part.

Far from being a subsection of general experimental psychology, in this view physiological psychology simply becomes the less-circumscribed way of viewing the whole subject. It is not set off from other types of psychology by a set of boundaries but travels in carefree—sometimes careless—ways through molar and molecular, inside and outside the organism, advancing itself by heterogeneous methods. The old term thus comes full circle, meaning, as it once did, a point of view—albeit now a view quite different.

EXPERIMENTAL WORK

If physiological psychology is a point of view rather than a subject matter, no field of data lies outside its range. The unhappy problem of whether one is working outside or inside the organism can be dismissed, for variables anywhere will be subject to analysis and definite observations of whatever level will contribute to it. In systematic general writing, it will be obvious whether the work is analytic or not. But for us, there is extreme difficulty in deciding what body of experimental work should be considered. There would be little value in trying to guess a writer's own purposes, which are seldom expressed—it would be more to the point to ask what his contribution is good for.

Does it, one may ask, further a program of the analysis of psychological events into smaller ones? There are a good number of studies in which a variable which is analytic as well as psychological is manipulated or observed. These, of course, would not make up the whole of physiological psychology. (An inference about the cochlea, for example, is as analytic and physiological when it comes from stimulus-response data as when it is derived from anatomical facts.) Such studies might, however, be taken as representative and they can be identified, though in a rather backhanded fashion. An experiment can be said to involve a nonpsychological variable by either of these criteria: (1) Some observed responses (dependent variables), though produced by the organism, are other than skeletal movements or verbal responses of S; and (2) the organism is subject to an unnatural condition (an independent variable) which is presumed to isolate a subsystem.

By the first qualification, one would count studies which include observations on blood chemistry, electroencephalogram (EEG), heart rate, or action potential, for example—even under conditions which are about normal for the organism. The investigator may compare these with the behavior or verbal response of S or he may leave such a comparison to inference or later study. Even though he professes no interest in the psychological, it is still possible that others may consider his work pertinent to their analytic endeavor. If it so happens, we should include the work.

By the second qualification, one would count studies in which, for example, cortical areas are removed (by intention or by accident), drugs or electroconvulsive shock (ECS) administered, or electrical stimuli delivered to the nervous system.

To sample experimental studies, we have used two sources: the papers appearing in the *Journal of Comparative and Physiological Psychology,* 1947 to 1954 and 1956 to 1958, and the abstracts appearing in the 1955 and 1958 *Psychological Abstracts* under the classifications "Physiological psychology" and "Receptive and perceptual processes." (The abstracts were examined for appropriate titles listed under other headings and there appeared to be very few.) From each of these sources, experiments which met either of the above criteria were selected. The first source yielded 208 items for the earlier period and 151 for the later; the second, 192 and 176. Of course, there were difficult decisions, particularly about what counts as a condition of ordinary life. By fiat, variations of ordinary variables, such as food intake, were not admitted to the sample (they do not always bear on the sort of analysis referred to); qualitative changes, like variation of glutamic acid intake, were included. Being rigid on this point had an odd effect, requiring inclusion of studies of electroconvulsive shock but exclusion of studies of audiogenic seizures, unless some other condition had been varied. In most instances, this was the case. With these interpretations, the selection went rather smoothly.

There is some doubt that the abstracts of 1958 fairly represent the publications of the period. But even in a biased sample, the proportion of publications in Russian is striking. Of the total listings under "Physiological psychology" and "Receptive and perceptual processes," Russian titles comprise 21 per cent. Russian interests, being rather concentrated, therefore influence the distribution pattern considerably. In the earlier year, the listings from the Russian are almost negligible in number, but one cannot be sure that this is more than an editorial accident.

Analyzing these groups would be much easier if psychology consisted of a gridwork of ready-made subdivisions. One looks wistfully at sciences which are supposed to be better organized. Certainly, in psychology there is no set structure one could use as a frame of reference. Indeed, it may be the essence of science that pigeonholes are very temporary structures. In the absence of the ideal, a practical expedient was to let the studies group themselves into clusters rather than attempt to group them by rigid classifications.

Studies were first grouped by the physiological variables they contained—the variables which entitled them to inclusion in the first place. According to the criteria, these could be either dependent or independent variables in the experiments. The following groupings seemed distinguishable on examination of the list:

1. Damage to the nervous system
2. Electroconvulsive shock
3. Administration of drugs and chemicals
4. Manipulation or observation in the somatic sector
5. Manipulation or observation of receptor structures or processes
6. Direct stimulation of the nervous system
7. Recording of neural processes
8. Irradiation (X ray and other)

A second sort of classification was more difficult. As each experiment must have at least one other variable in addition to that used in the first grouping, a cross-classification was tried. Here the variables are either those which the physiological variables were supposed to influence or those which were supposed to influence them. Included, therefore, are responses, stimuli, individuals, general conditions, and additional physiological variables. Study soon showed that the basic problem was response classification; in the 400 experiments, other classes of variables—except stimuli—did not need separation from one another. So far as possible, the behavior tested was classed according to the particular activity used in the experiment rather than according to a broad psychological category. Thus "maze learning" was preferred to "learning." Most authors also follow this practice. Especially in the first group, however, many particulars had to be thrown together to make a large enough number. The groupings used were as follows:

1. "Ready-made" behavior. This covers behavior which is produced without training of the subjects by the experimenter. It includes drive

behavior, social behavior, locomotor behavior, work, and audiogenic seizures.

2. Maze and runway learning and retention. Lever-box studies are almost negligible in number in the earlier period and are also included.

3. Choice and discrimination behavior. This includes experiments in which the relation of alternative responses to alternative stimuli is in question. Discrimination with delayed response is counted here.

4. Conditioned avoidance. Anxiety reactions, as well as actual avoidance are included.

5. Physiological variables. Experiments whose second variables were of the kinds mentioned in the first list are here combined.

6. Conditioned limb or glandular response.

7. Test scores and ratings.

8. Verbal learning and mental work.

9. Stimuli and environment.

Granting a certain margin of error to these labels and assignments, they may still be useful. The distribution resulting from the cross-classification is given in Tables 1 and 2. The column totals (for the most part) show the kinds of behavior the experimenters have most often tried to unravel; the row of totals show the favored means; and the numbers in the cells disclose the hypotheses most often at stake.

On first impression, the display is ragged and distressing, it must be admitted. Of course, the very construction of the table would comb any pattern there may have been to a mere crisscross, but some features do stand out clearly.

One of them is the almost universal experimental design. In Table 1 the "other variable" of the experiments turns out to be almost always some form of behavior. The experimenter has nearly always manipulated the physiological variable or used it somehow as an independent variable, and observed its effect upon a chosen response. The complementary sort of experiment, in which the origins of the physiological variable are sought, makes up only the 10 per cent listed in categories 5 and 6. In Table 2, on the other hand, the typical experiment is concerned with the effect of external conditions, such as stimuli upon one of the physiological variables.

Both types of "other variable" might be used in the same experiment, but they very seldom are in either group of studies. Indeed, any sort of experiment with more than two variables is uncommon. (In half a dozen studies in the later period, there seems to be a second manipulated variable. Each of these is entered twice in the tables, once for each independent variable.) Yet it is very likely that interactions between determining conditions are of the highest importance. A physiological variable could undoubtedly have an effect on behavior under one set of stimulus conditions but have a different effect, or none at all, under another set. Experimenters usually recognize that possibility and properly limit their conclusions to one set of conditions, one organism, etc. But experiments are usually not planned to cover more than a very narrow territory, and increasing the number of simple experiments is not a very good substitute for experiments of broader scope. Difficulties of technique may discourage complex experiments, or it may be that ideas have not yet advanced enough to produce complex hypotheses.

Among the physiological variables in Table 1, there is high and about equal concentration on the first four in the early period. The reasons for the attention given nervous system damage, usually ablation, are easy to understand. Few would agree with Kantor [13] that results from "mutilated organisms" throw no light on the normal; the experiments are evidently based on the hypothesis that brain events are powerful determiners of behavior, and that removal experiments are a means of discovering the particulars of their influence. New knowledge of brain areas and improved surgical techniques open exciting vistas to explore.

With a little less enthusiasm, the same may be said of the somatic manipulations. The hypotheses about the relation of somatic structures to response are not always so clear, but one can hardly doubt the need for them. The state of the body does vary in the course of nature, and experimental variations can be taken as special cases illuminating the behavioral effects of all.

The prominence of ECS and of drugs and chemicals probably comes from practical interests. Particularly in the earlier years, ECS was a favorite therapeutic measure, with no particular rationale. The experiments were no doubt a commendable attempt to provide one. Yet it is questionable whether they ought even to be counted as physiological psychology in the analytic sense, since the electric shock is so difficult to connect with physiological processes. The same observation applies to some of the drug studies, though here there are more opportunities for analytic results. Pharmacological agents whose physiological effect is known or is discovered by the experiment can be a means of entering a response system at an unusual point and analyzing it.

Among the studies in Table 2, three of these same physiological variables receive a good deal of attention. Electroshock convulsions, however, turn out to be a preoccupation peculiar to psychologists—at least, in the years tabulated they received nothing like the same amount of attention from other experimenters. On the other hand, two new variables have a large representation here: the electroencephalogram (EEG) and receptor processes. Work on both of these seems now to be pursued by groups of specialists.

In Table 1, among the "other variables," mainly behavioral, there are also strong favorites. In view of the preoccupation of so many psy-

TABLE 1.*

	Unlearned behavior (1)	Maze, etc. (2)	Discrimination (3)	Avoidance (4)	Physiological (5)	Stimuli (6)	Conditioned response (7)	Tests (8)	Abnormal (9)	Verbal learning (10)	Total
Ablation	4.3	2.4	9.6	1.9		1.4	2.4	1.0		.5	23.5
	4.0	*1.3*	*13.2*	*2.6*	*.7*		*.7*	*.7*		*1.3*	*24.5*
ECS	1.4	9.1	4.8	4.8		1.4	.5	.5			22.6
	7.3	*3.3*	*2.6*	*2.0*	*.5*			*.7*			*10.6*
Drugs	9.6	6.2	1.0	2.9	.7	1.0	.5	.7			21.6
	6.0	*2.6*	*3.3*	*2.0*	*.5*	*1.3*					*17.8*
Somatic state	12.0	1.0	.5	2.0	2.6	2.4	1.0	1.0		1.0	19.7
	8.6	*2.6*	*1.3*	*.5*	*.5*	*2.6*				*6.6*	*23.8*
Receptor state	3.0	.5	3.0		2.0	1.9	.5				8.7
					.5	*.7*					*3.3*
Stimulation of nervous system	2.0									2.6	1.9
		1.0	*2.0*	*1.3*						*.7*	*9.3*
Record from nervous system		4.6	.5		.7						1.0
			.7								*7.3*
Radiation	1.3	1.0	3.3			.7				.7	1.0
		3.3								*1.4*	*9.3*
Total	29.3	20.7	19.2	10.1	1.4	8.1	4.8	2.2		.7	
	21.3	*17.9*	*24.9*	*7.9*	*6.4*	*4.0*	*.6*	*1.2*		*12.5*	

* Per cents of articles in *J. comp. physiol. Psychol.* in various categories during two periods. Italic numbers for later period, roman for earlier.

251

TABLE 2.*

	Unlearned behavior (1)	Maze, etc. (2)	Discrimination (3)	Avoidance (4)	Physiological (5)	Stimuli (6)	Conditioned response (7)	Tests (8)	Abnormal (9)	Verbal learning and verbal report (10)	Technique (11)	Total
Ablation	5.2	.5	4.1		4.1							14.0
	3.4		*2.8*		*2.3*							*8.5*
ECS	.5				1.0							1.6
					.6							*.6*
Drugs	4.1		3.1		6.2		1.0			1.0		15.5
	1.7		*.6*		*6.2*	*2.3*	*2.8*			*.6*		*14.2*
Somatic state	2.1		1.0		3.6	5.7	1.0		.5	.6		14.5
	2.8		*1.7*		*5.7*	*5.1*	*9.1*	*.5*				*24.4*
Receptor state						17.0		.5			.5	18.0
					.6	*8.0*						*8.5*
Stimulation of nervous system	2.6	.5			5.2	.5					.5	9.3
	1.7				*2.8*	*.6*						*4.5*
Record from nervous system			3.1		3.6	12.5	.5		3.1	1.6	1.6	26.0
	5.1		*.6*		*6.8*	*19.3*	*2.3*			*.6*		*34.6*
X-ray					.5							.5
	.6				*1.7*		*2.3*					*4.5*
Total	14.5	1.0	11.4		23.8	36.0	26.0	.5	3.6	2.6	2.6	
	14.8		*5.1*		*26.7*	*35.2*	*16.5*			*1.7*		

* Per cents of articles in *Psychol. Abstr.* in various categories for two years. Italic numbers for 1958, roman for 1955.

chologists with learning, the number of papers on ready-made behavior is a mild surprise. In these there is usually no assertion that the behavior in question is unaffected by learning: The classification means only that the experiment is not concerned with the learning or unlearning of responses. We may infer that the major proportion of work in our sample is not very directly related to any of the theorizing about learning which has attracted so much attention in the period. This is understandable enough, since the more popular learning theories have nothing to say about the analysis of behavior into physiological components.

Experimenters represented in Table 1 choose maze-running and stimulus-choice behavior (discrimination) about equally often. The second of these may be taken as simple examples of important psychological categories; for the complex and special performance brought out in a maze, the most apparent rationale is that here is something animals can learn. In view of theoretical elaborations of the conditioned response, and the physiological experiments Pavlov and others have conducted on it, the current low popularity is hard to justify or even understand.

In Table 2 there are but two behavioral variables substantially represented in the earlier years: unlearned and discriminative behavior. Some of these contributions are, of course, from psychologists, and for the study of the others psychologists seem to receive little outside help.

Looking at the body of Table 1, the population within the various cells shows how often the possible kinds of hypotheses have been studied. There are four special favorites, each being about 10 per cent of the total:

1. Discrimination is affected by neural destruction.
2. Maze learning is affected by electroconvulsive shock.
3. Unlearned behavior is affected by drugs and chemicals.
4. Unlearned behavior is affected by a somatic modification, such as excision of a structure.

As a general proposition, each of these sounds pretty obvious, but these are generalities by nature—it is the particulars which are interesting. The second category, however, does not seem really to belong with the rest of the family because it is already particular. Its prominence may come from a thorough exploration of a special subject.

In Table 2, one observes a special concentration on just two relationships, those of stimuli to receptor process and to electroencephalogram. These may be considered an attack on the organism from the input side, as the predominant groups in Table 1 attempt to trace an output. One may guess the reason—these are the most accessible areas, and they are better understood already. The tables make clear that much remains to be done to connect the one area with the other, probably by means of experiments with more than one dependent variable. It is unfortunate, though not unexpected, that experimental design and statistical methods for this sort of experiment have not yet been developed very far.

The earlier and later figures in the two tables show some changes in the direction of research effort. In Table 1, the sharp fall in the attention given ECS is most striking. With less than half its earlier percentage, however, it is still among the four leading topics. Among the physiological variables, the most notable increases in the *Journal of Comparative and Physiological Psychology* articles are in the papers dealing with direct stimulation of the nervous system and in those dealing with radiation effects. The first increase evidently shows interest in self-stimulation techniques; the second may be simply another applied topic, for the most part. Beyond this, the drop in the number of papers on receptors probably is nothing more than a change in publication policy, and the other variations are rather small. In the second group of categories, there is some shift of interest from studies of ready-made behavior to work on discrimination learning, and a surprising fall in the already small percentage claimed by conditioned-response (CR) studies.

In the main, Table 2 shows much the same distribution for the earlier and later periods. The principal change is in the representation of CR work. The substantial increase in this is entirely due to the great amount of Russian work included in 1958, and, of course, may mean no more than an accident of editing.

The cross-classification of the tables raises one's curiosity about certain absences. Naturally there is no reason why all cells should be equally populated. When there are few studies or none within a cell, it may be the result of a conscious decision that the two variables are not closely connected; it might come from lack of particular ideas on the subject; or from want of technique to test them. The idea of the receptors having a special effect on avoidance behavior would probably strike an experimenter as one he would not care to investigate at the moment. On the other hand, lack of studies on the subject probably does not mean lack of interest in the effects of cortical stimulation in conditioning. But nothing about absences can be proved by guesswork like this; we must simply say that the table describes operations, not theories. We may ask whether extension of study into other areas might not repay a good deal of effort. Without an extraordinary faith in some rational system, one cannot very well write prescriptions for discovery.

Where relations have been the subject of experiments, one can with more reason look for an underlying logic. The choice of the experimenter implied certain ideas. There is, of course, the common defining idea that behavior processes can with advantage be taken apart. A result of this idea, it has been argued [4], is that variables will be identified by their physical characteristics, in the common language of science. The labels appearing in the tables, derived as they are from experimenters' titles and statements, show that physiological psychologists do in fact follow such a practice. It seems to us, at least, that very little psychological sophistication is required to comprehend these experiments. Terms like *maze learning, avoidance behavior,* and *left temporal ablation* are of low order, and refer to physically defined events—even terms like *discrimination* and *drive behavior,* when they are used, almost always clearly refer to certain physical operations specified in the experimenter's text. The only trouble a biologist, for example, might have in understanding the reports would be in getting rid of some "psychological ideas" he might read into the experimenter's words. We have, therefore, a body of literature in which the problems set and the explanations sought are in the ordinary language of science. The device of the intervening variable, widely welcomed in learning theory of this period, is seldom openly acknowledged by the writers of this group.

Beyond these prolegomena, the experiments surveyed probably share no rational system. A few are designed to test some implication of a general system, as Sperry's experiment [31] does for Hebb's theory, and Miller and Kesson's experiments [22] do for Miller's. But on the whole, there is not much sign of full-fledged hypothetical-deductive procedure in the choice and execution of experiments. Instead the choice seems to come, probably without formal logic, from rather limited generalizations. An experimenter, for example, has found that hypophysectomy does or does not influence the learning of a particular maze; thereupon he or another investigator experiments with other mazes, other tasks, and other animals and he probably has no strong predictions about how the new experiments should come out. About the only implication seems to be that such variables have been found influential in other situations and may be so in this one. The procedure is probably much like the one that Skinner [28] defends.

Therefore we find many limited and rather unrelated hypotheses. According to the subject of study, there seem to be two directions of inquiry. Studies of the nervous system, predominantly concerned with learning, concentrate heavily on the localization question. Ablation studies could be expected to discover where something happens—what happens or how would be rather out of range for the method. On the other hand, in somatic studies, typically of nonlearning behavior, localization does not seem to be much of an issue. (It may not even seem to be a sensible question.) At any rate, the question is more likely to be about contributing influences. This distinction of question may reflect a presumption that responses, or response changes, have their primary correlates at some region of the central nervous system (CNS), which somatic variables modify. Even on such a view, it must be admitted that a determination of focus still leaves important questions without answers.

If experiments are chosen, as they seem to be, because of leads from other experiments, there is some danger of building good roads to no destination. Looking back at the psychological topics chosen for investigation, one suspects that tradition has been a frequent guide. The behaviors studied, now carefully particularized by operational definitions, probably entered the experimental repertory as examples of broad psychological functions in a day when psychologists had greater faith in their ability to divide all behavior offhand into an assortment of mental functions. Could one but know, for example, that all behavior displays the operation of sensation, perception, learning, memory, motivation, thinking, and so on, then some particular performance could be chosen as an exemplar of each. Then a thorough study of each typifying case would lead to an understanding, not too far over the horizon, of all those things an organism can do. To the founders of psychology, the world may have looked as small as that—had it not, they might well have been discouraged from ever setting foot upon the journey.

But now this faith of our forbears no longer supports us, and the skeptical experimenter often contents himself, so it seems, with any niche or cranny that offers a toe hold, without much thought of the forbidding dimness of view in all directions. We still have, consequently, the repertory of classical situations from which an experimenter is likely to choose, while the original reasons for being interested in them are lost.

Here we come upon a dubious result of the concern of the physiological psychologist for hard facts and his reluctance to venture upon general speculation. Yet a wholehearted empiricist might still defend the practice by postulate and example. The science of genetics seems to do very well with its fruit-fly tradition, and visual physiology flourishes on Limulus. On a most sanguine view, nature is so much of one piece that any specimen will display the same structure. Or, oddly enough, the same indifference to forethought could mean a deep despair that natural chaos can yet be brought to order by feeble human wits. On a view so rosy or one so dark, an experimenter would do quite well to begin his research by selecting some well-tried device from the shelves of the storeroom. A day of reckoning may well await a distant tomorrow. On the other hand, there is the possibility of adding to one's stature by taking thought.

THEORISTS

Rather surprisingly, there are a number of efforts at system building in physiological psychology, though they have little visible influence upon experiments. A complete survey would be more tedious than necessary for our present purpose. An examination of a few prominent theories may bring out enough of their nature.

Mathematical biophysics. One of these—in fact, Rashevsky's mathematical biophysics—seems to be the first application of formal mathematical deductive procedure to a psychological area. The chosen domain of mathematical biophysics is, of course, much wider than anyone would claim for physiological psychology: It includes a mathematical attack on the problems of general physiology. But, in the approach to psychological problems, the reasoning takes a fresh start and depends but little on the preceding argument. At this point, a set of definitions and postulates which originally seemed to refer to the impulses in neurons and synapses is introduced. But, upon finding that the constructs were in poor accord with neurophysiology, Rashevsky [27] works in both directions from them. He goes backward, as it were, to show that the conceived properties could belong to certain combinations of neurons and synapses which, taken singly, would behave as experiments show they do, and goes forward to deduce from his constructs the outcome of certain classical psychological experiments.

The postulated characteristics of these intermediate elements are consequently the basis of the system. To paraphrase the formal statement they are as follows:

1. The central nervous system is composed of a very large number of these elements, arranged in geometrical positions.

2. These elements are irritable.

3. They are of two kinds: those whose activation has an exciting effect on others, and those whose activation has an inhibiting effect on others.

4. There is an intensity of excitation for each element which is proportional to the product of impulse frequency and impulse size, when the stimulus is constant.

5. This proportion varies among elements, but is usually to be taken as a constant for a single element.

6. Each element has a threshold.

7. Excitation in an excitatory element produces at its end an excitatory factor whose increase with time is equal to the excitation (times a constant) minus a constant.

8. Excitation in an inhibitory element produces an inhibitory factor with the same relations.

9. An element will be excited if, impinging on it, the excitatory factor minus the inhibitory factor is greater than its threshold.

It seems also to be taken implicitly that elements conduct at finite velocity and in one direction. Combining the propositions above, Rashevsky secures a series of nine equations which he thinks "adequate to describe quantitatively any situation arising from the interaction of any number of neurons arranged according to a definite geometrical pattern." Actually, at least one more postulate is used, a postulate that, to the algebraic sum of excitatory and inhibitory factors, there must be added algebraically a quantity which fluctuates at random.

A striking fact about this set of assumptions is that it contains no learning postulate, although Rashevsky and his collaborators propose to deal with learning situations and data. They find it possible, in other words, to derive learning from the postulates given, under the general topic of "hysteresis." This is a rare, if not a unique, feat in system construction.

Mathematically considered, the postulates amount to a number of linear functions, with positive or negative sign, exponentials of positive or negative sign with time exponents, and a function to represent random variation. Each function has at least one associated parameter. These functions, as it were, constitute the raw material for the system builder. The first postulate is to be understood, further, as giving him liberty to make further postulates of geometrical configurations of any size and shape, largely *ad hoc,* one would suppose. Algebraically this choice of geometrical configuration means that the postulated functions may be combined in any number and in many ways, as the systematist may desire. No doubt, there is an assumed limitation that the network imagined shall be plausible to anatomy, but this is not a galling restriction in the present state of knowledge.

Following this program, Rashevsky and his associates have developed equations to correspond to data in some of the principal areas of experimental psychology: intensity discrimination, form constancy, reaction times, conditioning, choice learning, and aesthetics, and for certain other psychological processes on which they are not able to offer corresponding data. The plots of theoretical functions fitted to experimental data show extremely close fits.

The experimental data and the other phenomena analyzed are naturally at a much higher level of complexity than the processes the theory takes as elementary. To reach them requires a considerable piling up of functions and parameters. The equation for the learning of choice behavior, for example, involves the logarithm of a ratio which includes three exponential functions. It uses four parameters. The equation for reaction time as a function of fore period has one less exponential but two more parameters. The lines given by such equations have considerable flexibility, and might give a reasonable fit to a great variety of data. (Oddly enough, what seems to be the greatest discrepancy occurs when a six-parameter equation is fitted to a set of six data points.) There is the further technical difficulty that nothing prevents the systematist from complicating an equation still further by elaborating the network, if still better agreement is desired.

Experimental evidence at the level of the postulates or at the levels in between the postulates and the psychological data would help a great deal. For networks and network states, no amount of mathematical ingenuity can be expected to substitute for a good set of facts. Although so far there seems to have been little interaction between this system and experimenters, it is still possible that experimenters will devise ways of testing and revising some of its conceptions.

Beyond the nature of the explanation is the question of what a system is designed to explain—the dependent variable, as it were. Mathematical developments in the Rashevsky system work toward the establishment of a quantity of excitation in some varied but unspecified locale. Where experimental data are to be fitted, this quantity is, in most cases, further related to frequency, time, or number of responses, chiefly by means of the probability function mentioned. In the particular case of aesthetic judgment data, it is not so related. Rather there is the assumption that the quantity of excitation, somewhere or everywhere, is directly related to pleasure and the judgments are taken to be direct expression of the entity. (Excitation is equated to pleasure on the grounds that excitation, in the analysis of choice learning, was coordinated with reinforcement, and that anything reinforcing is pleasant.) Where no attempt is made to match experimental data, the quantity of excitation is identified with consciousness, memories, anticipations, perceptions, will, and so on, these being differentiated from one another by locus. These mental-faculty concepts are of ancient vintage but, psychologists would probably judge, without their onetime bouquet.

Binary digital theory. Mathematical construction, but of a different sort, is the foundation of the system expounded most fully by McCulloch [18, 20]. Whereas Rashevsky converts the neural discontinuity of "all-or-none" action into a continuous variable by one of his first postulates, McCulloch offers a model in which, as in a digital computer, discontinuity is the principle of operation. Consequently, the mathematics appropriate to his networks is Boolean algebra rather than differential and integral calculus.

Ranging from general to particular, there seem to be postulates of three levels in McCulloch's model. There is first the broad presumption that the organism, particularly its nervous system, ought to be treated as a physical system which transforms certain inputs to certain outputs, a presumption which is not unique of course, but not universal either. Associated with this first assumption are certain ideas about what constitutes inputs and outputs. At a second level is the assumption that the system operates primarily by quantal jumps, each with a mathematical place value and taking place in an independent element; finally and most specifically, McCulloch proposes a set of particular network mechanisms to perform the transformations he considers crucial. The felicity of these, or their lack of it, is given a good deal of attention by the discussants in the Hixon symposium [18]. The author thinks their chances of being wholly correct are almost nil, but believes that they can be studied experimentally.

In constructing a system on the binary digital plan, McCulloch has deliberately chosen to make the most of certain neural behavior which seems discrete or is needed for a quantal mode of operation—"the brevity of latent addition, the requirement of spatial summations, the irreciprocity of conduction, the occurrence of direct inhibition and the duration of delay, which characterize synaptic transmission, and the all or none response with subsequent refractiveness of the component neurons." He mentions neuromuscular behavior of other sorts, such as facilitation and inhibition among adjacent cortical points and the summating effects of muscle, but assigns these merely the adjunct role of "smearing in time" the results of binary calculation. Other known, continuously varying states, such as neuron polarizations, are neglected or assigned a role only reluctantly. More recent knowledge of such states [3] would either need to be played down or allowed to revise the whole plan.

On the postulate of binary digital action rests the structure of Boolean algebra applied to the nervous system, and the quantification made possible by information theory. The latter gives rise to the argument attributed to Wiener [35] that the information, unless it be misinformation, in a system or its output is never greater than that in the input. (It would seem to be a modern dress for the old maxim *"Nil in intellectu quid non prior in sensu."*) The period of time over which the input is regarded as reaching is not specified; in view of acknowledged "storage" possibilities, it would seem necessary to make it cover the organism's previous life at least. Further, McCulloch and Pitts [20] use the quantification method to compute the information capacity of input and output. Finding the latter much smaller, they conclude there must be a loss of information (corruption) of all but 1 or 2 of every 100 million units of information put into the organism (presumably at maximum input). Similarly, a number of other deductions follow from the quantification.

McCulloch and Pitts offer a demonstration that, in imagination at least, some network of neurons, having the properties they postulate, can be constructed to realize any conceivable proposition inherent in the input. This seems to mean a network whose output corresponds to any that can conceivably exist in the input. The reasoning is, principally, that anything inherent in the input can be stated in algebraic logic, and that the operations of this logic can be performed by relay circuits. This is probably the feature of the system McCulloch has in mind when he refers to his "underlying theory" as a "glorified tautology."

On his most general level of postulation, McCulloch refers to outputs he is seeking to explain as "mind," "ideas," "purposes," "finality," "form," and so on (though he especially abjures "consciousness"). But these words are probably best understood as traditional gewgaws to decorate a new structure. For each, to the dismay of some of his critics, a special meaning is selected. Purpose is identified with the operation of a system which responds to the difference between an initial and a terminal state. "Ideas," he writes, "are to be construed as information." The intention is, it seems, to give a physical meaning to these terms.

The word "information," often used in the theory, clearly needs reduction itself if it is to have such a meaning. It is, according to Wiener [35], "orderliness," and is to be measured by the logarithm of the reciprocal of the probability of a state. For the case at hand, the logical probability of excitation for one neuron is said to be $\frac{1}{2}$ and that of a number of neurons at the same level is $\frac{1}{2}^n$, which is the reciprocal of the number of different states possible, place being counted as a difference. By using this value and logarithms to the base 2, one simplifies the definition of information; it is equal to the number of independent elements, or in McCulloch's interpretation of the nervous system, the number of neurons at a given level. Apparently, it follows that a given ensemble of neural elements always contains the same amount of information. So far as the definition goes, "truth" and "falsity" would in no way apply to this information.

McCulloch does, however, wish to distinguish the true from the false, and does so by adding the proposition, or perhaps definition, that the state of a cell considered as information "is false if it arises from any source other than the adequate, or proper, excitation of the cell." (A corresponding proposition about the nonexcited state of a cell may be implied.) The "proper" excitation of a cell is explained only by an example: Visual phosphenes are said to be false. Difficult as it is to establish a canonical stimulus for a receptor, it is even harder to know what such a thing is for a central cell. One would probably not wish to identify it as the commonest source of excitation and should be on guard against defining it as the true source. The problem is serious for the theory, for the application of simple logical algebra requires that an excitation state imply (truly or falsely) its correct antecedent. Without such a favorite, all propositions in the nervous system are disjunctive, implying any one of all possible antecedents with greater or lesser probability.

There are some hazards in the special definition of such a common word as "information," and the theorists themselves are not always able to avoid them. "Information" has a quantitative measure; "true information" does not; yet sometimes the one is taken for the other [18, p. 58]. Excitation in a neuron ("a proposition on the move") should not be identified with information or a proposition; absence of excitation is just as much information. With so handy a formula for assessing information, there is quite a temptation to number magic.[1] The comparison of quantities of information in different kinds of systems depends on how large a unit is regarded as discrete and countable. With continuous variables like time, space, and intensity, the choice has a good deal of the arbitrary about it. McCulloch and Pitts calculate the maximum possible output of a piano player as two units of information per millisecond. To secure this figure, they assumed that there are 10 degrees of force a finger may apply to a piano key. Actually, the force seems to be a continuous variable, and the finger may be said to run through an infinite number of steps in a single movement. Any number could be used as an approximation and any number obtained as an answer. The place of the response is likewise arbitrarily bounded; a *real* piano player moves more than his fingers and may even sing to his accompaniment. The information content of a stretch of speech per second, used as part of the same argument, is likewise indeterminate for lack of natural units. Units are chosen on the basis of the intelligibility of the speech, which surely confounds the input capacity of the listener and the phonemic significance of states with their mere number, which is supposedly being assessed.

The information concept turns out to be most useful in the present connection when it is applied to bivalent discrete mechanisms. For them the question of how much information means simply: How many independent bivalent elements are there? Although the theorists have generally given an answer based entirely on histology, the question needs and deserves experimental answer.

As systematists of this school implicitly acknowledge, study of information in their technical sense is by no means the whole problem of physiological psychology or neurophysiology. The number of possible states is perhaps not as important to know as their relations. The information present in an invariant (shape, musical interval, etc.) is necessarily much less than that in the multitudinous input from which it is abstracted—in fact, it would seem necessarily to be exactly one unit. Yet the occurrence of the invariant is the principal point of the story. These invariants are consequently the second problem addressed

---

[1] It is strange that McCulloch does not use the measure of "transmitted information" rather than the simple measure of amount possible. But if he were to do so, there would be no means of estimating its value from mere anatomy.

by the theory. It supplies, one might say, an imagined mechanism for Helmholz's famous "unconscious inference." The invariances are presumably known from what psychologists would call the "constancy phenomena" in the behavior of organisms or in their experience. The theory, however, does not carry matters any further than the output of certain networks somewhere in the cortex; the relation of these to behavior or experience is unexpressed.

The third topic addressed by this theory, on the other hand, *is* a type of movement, inasmuch as purpose is interpreted as movement under control of negative feedback. How wide a domain this is, there is no attempt to say. A final answer to the question of what the theory is about must therefore be: It is a theory concerned with the fineness of structure in the response system, with the derivation of invariants in the nervous system, and with movements controlled by input-output differences.

In the Hixon symposium one of the discussants (Liddell) called McCulloch's ideas "a theory in search of some facts," by contrast with the many experimental facts needing theoretical treatment. McCulloch is himself concerned with experiments which might grow from the theory which was constructed, he explains, to tell him where to place electrodes. He would probably agree that the system is constructed by certain selection and "idealization" of both neurological and behavioral events. Examination of facts known even now would probably raise questions of how far behavior is really an embodiment of purpose and idea as McCulloch conceives them. There is some danger of explaining the behavior of some character of fiction who is wearing the dress of a man of real flesh.

Pattern theory. The ideas of Köhler [14] and Lashley [16], both presented from time to time during the last three decades, are diverse in detail but have much to tie them together.

A good deal of the diversity between the two arises from the kind of neurophysiology each uses to construct explanations. Lashley, more conventional here, builds on the basis of conducted impulses in a neural network. Köhler, on the other hand, proposes that the cerebral cortex, at least, works by means of electrical gradients generated by various concentrations of electrolytes produced by stimulation, a notion which today seems more tolerable to neurophysiology than it did when he offered it in 1921. Historically, Köhler was led to a pattern theory of neural action by his interest in the form constancies of perception; Lashley was led to the same sort of theory by the outcome of his early ablation experiments.

For both writers, the problem that stands in the focus is: How can experience or behavior contain certain relations? Both have been concerned with the constancy of experience or behavior when the input patterns are constant only in spatial relations, both have turned to the problem of temporal structuring, and both foresee relations of other sorts, such as object-attribute, as problems for the future. For both the solution of the problem is an analogue pattern somewhere in the cerebral cortex.

The choice of the problem of relations would not be considered by either as hypothetical at all. Apparently both are convinced that all behavior and all experience are dominated by a structural pattern. They offer many striking examples of the constancy of a pattern whose constituents are subject to great variation. Yet even a large number of chosen examples falls short of proving that structure is ubiquitous and omnipotent. It is not difficult to think of conditions like those of brightness-constancy experiments in which the outcome is sometimes in accord with relationships, sometimes with an absolute value, and typically somewhere in between the two. Of course, these outcomes may still be considered structured. Unhappily, even though the idea has been discussed for more than forty years, it is still not easy to say just when something has a structure. At the risk of forcing examples into the wrong gestalt, one may propose that a structure exists when the number of degrees of freedom in an ensemble is less than the number of parts, leaving to arbitrary decision how the parts are to be counted [1]. In that case, the question about structure could also be: With how fine a division into parts does one find a less-than-corresponding number of degrees of freedom?

In a time sequence, events at two points somewhere lose complete independence as the points approach one another; similarly, in a spatial series, the selection of points closer and closer together will eventually lead from independence to identity. At some point, it would seem, any series or sequence would take on a structural character by such a definition. A question of importance would be: Just how soon in a process of subdivision does this happen? The answer given by the pattern theorists may be "Very soon indeed." Their interest, of course, extends to dependencies which are not functions of proximity alone, and they seem to be calling special attention to those which are not monotonic functions of proximity. That dependencies of both kinds are present, hardly anyone would doubt, and all seem agreed on the further point that the relation between two parts is not always one of complete dependence.

In stating the problem as the analysis of structures, there is a restriction of the subject to a sort of limiting case, that in which dependencies are perfect, or nearly so. Though the case may be very important, it is not, by the above analysis, universal.

Though their reasons differ, both Köhler and Lashley locate the physiological analogue of a structure in the central sector. With experience taken as the subject of theory, it would, of course, be eccentric to place it elsewhere, and Köhler's problem is to provide the isomorph of experience. For Lashley, the whereabouts of the agent of structure is a matter of evidence, because of his interest in explaining behavior. He is persuaded, perhaps too easily, that peripheral responses—seen or unseen —cannot contribute to the spatial and temporal structures of behavior; they are only driven by a central agency. In either case, as McCulloch puts it, "The mind is in the head." There is a defense of the tradition that what we can see and hear of the person's actions is but the shadow and the echo of a drama played on another stage. A change of venue, of course, does not solve the problem, but, if it must be settled in terms of the old dichotomy, the sooner one turns to it, the better.

Both writers are well aware that the presence of an internal analogue is not enough to explain their chosen phenomena. It is still a question of how such an analogue is generated by what happens to the individual. Köhler goes further toward answering this question, for the principle of the isomorphism of experience and brain field gives, he thinks, a ready access to the field structure of the brain. Lashley seems unwilling to be guided by isomorphism of this sort, and indeed it is hard to see how it would help with problems of animal behavior. His theorizing is also checked by the recognition he gives to neural impulses as the substance of a field, for according to present understanding, these lead to field structure less readily than areas of electrolytic concentration in a volume conductor. Lashley's main point about the organizers of behavior is that they cannot be confined to small areas of the cortex, and he seems disinclined to take very seriously his own further speculations on how they might be formed.

The argument for analogue patterns in the brain rests upon one or more negative propositions. Köhler [14] remarks, after citing some experimental results, "Can this conclusion be reconciled with present views about the behavior of nerve impulses? Apparently this is not the case. . . . Then we must find another process by which it is actually caused." Discussing the temporal patterns of language, Lashley [15] writes, "From such considerations, it is certain that any theory of grammatical form which ascribes it to direct associative linkage of the words of a sentence overlooks the essential structure of speech. . . . The order is imposed by some other agent." Of Washburn's ideas about kinaesthetic feedback he writes, "Attempts to confirm these peripheral theories by mechanical (Thorson) or electrical (Max) recording of muscular tensions have given no valid evidence in support of them." Later he writes, "There are, behind the overtly expressed sequences, a multiplicity of integrative processes which can only be inferred from the final results of the activity." When the negative statement is about experimental results it means, of course, an acceptance of the null hypothesis. An inference is a bit unsteady resting on a nullity. (Unless one has some idea of the magnitude of a hypothesized event, it is not easy to say whether an experiment has been precise enough to disprove its existence.) Negative statements about constructions, on the other hand, might conceivably be demonstrated, but the assertion that no explanation in these terms can be made because one has not been able to make one invites a contest of wits.

Lashley's interpretations have probably stimulated more experimentation in physiological psychology than any other theory of the period. The sweeping denial of localization in his early work [15] offered what seemed to be an easy mark to shoot at. Because of its breadth and negative form, any positive finding about localization would be crucial. Köhler, with a theory which proposes a particular cortical process, seems to have provoked little investigation on the physiological level, though its psychological implications have interested many experimenters, of course. The results Köhler has reported on steady potentials in the cortex, in contrast to the earlier reports of the Berger rhythm, have made curiously little impression on experimenters. It may be that their origin in an unpopular theory has kept experimenters from exploring further.

Hebb's theory. By far the most thoroughgoing and comprehensive system of physiological psychology in several decades is D. O. Hebb's *Organization of behavior* [10]. His field is psychology, rather than a physiological annex to the subject, and he offers a physiological or analytic type of theory because he considers it the best strategy for a general advance. As a program, he proposes "learning as much as one can about what the parts of the brain do [primarily the physiologist's field], and relating behavior as far as possible to this knowledge [primarily for the psychologist]; then seeing what further information is to be had about how the total brain works, from the discrepancy between (1) actual behavior and (2) the behavior that would be predicted from adding up what is known about the action of the various parts."

The physiological properties which Hebb makes use of are therefore of two sorts, those which have been demonstrated for nerve tissue, and those which are thought to be reasonable inferences from the facts of behavior and his analysis of them. Properties of the first sort are, of course, *selections* from the experimental results and neurophysiology of the time of writing, selections of properties which promise to combine into something which will relate to behavior. In the *Organization of behavior*,[2] Hebb uses a set of properties much like that of Rashevsky.

[2] More recently Hebb [11] recognizes the importance—and advantage—for psychological theory of the dendritic properties reported by Clare and Bishop [3].

He chooses, that is to say, discrete elements as his building blocks: neurons, which are discrete in space, and nerve impulses, which are discrete in time. It is hard to decide whether some of the properties imputed to these come from physiological observations or from behavioral inferences, since it is clearly necessary for the author to extrapolate from the limited neural observations. The alpha rhythm, for example, is taken to be summation of spike potentials, though this is by no means certain. A clear example of a behavioral inference is the principle that a "growth process or metabolic change takes place" [10, p. 62] when one neuron repeatedly or persistently takes part in firing another. Such a postulate has long been criticized for its use of physiological terms in the absence of physiological facts. Yet everyone, including the pattern theorists, who recognize physiological reduction as a proper undertaking, comes at last to very much the same notion. As Hebb frames it, there are no contradictory facts, at least, and it would have quite as much evidence as do entities like cortical fields. To this and similar ideas taken as hypotheses needing verification, it is hard to raise objection.

Hebb argues that the stimulus-response formula cannot serve for the analysis of behavior in general. Although psychologists may profess the stimulus-response principle as an article of faith, he observes, much of what they say—using terms like *expectancy, attention, need, intention,* and so on—is quite incompatible with the original profession. In this dilemma, he proposes that we forswear stimulus-response (S-R) and clearly acknowledge expectancy, attention, need, and so on. He chooses this alternative because the stimulus-response principle, as he sees it, means that all the organism's actions are controlled by the environment immediately present. (Defenders of the principle would unquestionably object to this version of it.) Since behavior is not controlled by stimuli or even stimulus pattern of the immediate present, we are forced to terms like those mentioned, the argument runs.

In his introductory remarks, Hebb seems to raise a banner in the cause of central versus stimulus control of behavior, but on the level of his neural hypotheses, at least, no battle actually takes place. Broadly put, these propose that processes go on in the nervous system and other parts of the organism prior to any given stimulus, and that the process following a stimulus is a resultant of the foregoing one and the effect of the stimulus. He seems to say that the ongoing process is modulated by the effects of the stimulus—one could, with the same meaning, say the effects of the stimulus are modulated by the ongoing process. The relative power of the two factors, naturally, varies from one instance to another, and can hardly be fixed a priori.

The manner of combination of the old and new process or, for that matter, of two old or two new processes is a problem which demands a theorist's attention. Can one discover any rules to predict the outcome, or must one take whatever comes and hide his discontent with words like "interaction effect"? Hebb proposes that there are three cases of interaction: one in which the consequences of two processes are similar, one in which they are incompatible, and one in which they are mutually indifferent. So far as they go, these are impeccable categories, though they may not be numerous enough to account for the diversity of effects. In fact, Hebb finds it necessary to recognize two grades of incompatibility, the lesser resulting in pleasure and the greater in disorganization (emotion).

In the case of incompatibility (conflict), of either high or low degree, special effects—other than simple algebraic addition—are supposed to exist. These would be neural effects of the hypothesized rather than the observed variety, since there seems to be no direct evidence that excitations having diverse consequences will generate any "exploding" effects when combined. The hypothesis is indeed convenient in accounting for behavior when it is said to be disorganized. Some theorists [21], for the sake of simplicity, have nevertheless preferred to avoid it, with the argument that the disruption of one activity means the institution of another which the experimenter considers inferior, and so requires no special mechanism.

From the crowd of available psychological constructs, Hebb selects a set which he evidently thinks designate the important features of behavior. The principal terms he uses, as noted, are *perception, expectancy, attention, intention, abstraction, insight, motivation, pleasure, emotion.* All these have a yellowish look of age, and the halos of either good or bad angels. But Hebb's intention is plainly to rejuvenate them with new meanings. He intends that each shall have an *empirical* (behavioral) and a *theoretical* (neural) meaning and both shall be called "definitions"; in one case "emotional behavior" and "emotion" distinguished these meanings. These definitions are sometimes made explicit. "Attention," for example, "refers to a selectivity of response" [10, p. 104], and likewise to a certain state of affairs in the hypothesized neural configurations. For other terms, *abstraction,* for example, the empirical meaning seems to be taken as understood. The two definitions for each term are assumed to be equivalent, and the neurological is taken as a clarification of the behavioral meaning. "An immediate dividend," Hebb remarks, "is the possibility of clearly stating, in physiological terms, the meaning of words like abstraction or similarity which are necessary to describe behavior, but which have had, to say the least, a touch of mystery about them." (A behavior description with a touch of mystery is puzzling; the reference is probably to use of the terms in some explanatory sense.) Such a proposition seems to depend upon the correctness of neural construction.

It seems as though Hebb feels some obligations to make use of these traditional psychological terms. They are, as he makes very clear [10, p. 162], names for inferences from behavior, not for kinds of behavior. For some (e.g., motivation and emotion) he is dissatisfied with existing inferences and contributes a very careful analysis of his own. From these, it turns out that there are too many original terms. *Intelligence, insight,* and *motivation* are found to refer to the same thing; *attention* and *expectancy* differ hardly at all; and other terms coalesce or overlap. As Hebb puts the question to himself: "Given this collection of old words, what can we intelligently do with them?" But the words, of course, are not universally thought necessary and sufficient for psychology. The author probably regards as beyond the scope of his endeavor the more open question: What terms should be used?

Pribram's synthesis. Since the foregoing was written, there have been a number of partial physiological systems offered for the interpretation of behavior, and quite recently Pribram [26] has designed a rather large-scale construction.

The physiological principles which Pribram has used are easy to identify; they include certain discoveries in neurophysiology of the last decade, a number of speculations about more complex relations, and the familiar idea of homeostasis. In brief, he proposes that the brain is in a state of activity even when not receiving external stimuli and regulates their reception; that the brain-stem nuclei are sensing points for homeostatic adjustments; that the nearby reticular formation adjusts the equilibrium point of the homeostats; that the dorsal part of the cerebrum receives inputs, computes invariants in the association areas by virtue (somehow) of steady dendritic potentials (see McCulloch), and acts homeostatically to maintain a congruence of these with dispositions already present; and that the forward part, including the limbic system, performs similarly except that the dispositions it tries to match are, so to say, templates for patterns of action, coordinating the homeostats of the brain stem. The functions attributed to the brain stem and reticular formation are fairly close to known facts. The role suggested for the limbic system is reached by a tour de force—finding the common element in experiments which point to motivational effects and observations which suggest retention effects. The operation of the congruence-homeostasis principle in the association areas is more purely speculative.

The behavioral facts which these mechanisms are related to are not so easy to identify—they are for the most part not explicit. By implication it seems they are (1) the mixture of homeostatic and antihomeostatic reactions to be seen in behavior and somatic response, (2) what might be called "cognitive-drive effects," the seemingly self-motivating inquiries into the environment, (3) goal-terminated sequences of behavior of both long and short range. These classes of behavior are probably not intended to be exhaustive. The class of learning modifications is notably absent, and Pribram has little discussion of the subject.

Like Hebb, Pribram attacks "stimulus-response reflex-arc concept." His point is that efferent control of the input has been demonstrated. But whether one regards the S-R conception as covering enough ground to include this sort of thing or chooses a new term seems a matter of no great import, except that there still seems to be some patriotic allegiance or opposition to the term because of its association with a cherished or despised behaviorism.

Pribram proposes a new general position on the status of brain processes: "Brain processes and psychological processes are thus not identical, nor parallel. . . . Specification of the properties of the component elements of this organization [the psychological], while a proper pursuit of science in its own right, must not be confused with the search for specification of all the properties of the more complex organization" [26, pp. 22–23]. From the example which follows, it appears that Pribram is thinking of the psychological process as an interaction between environment and neural state.

On such grounds he is opposed to attributing psychological functions to parts of the brain. Though it affects sex behavior, the amygdaloid complex is not to be considered as a sex center. This principle perhaps makes Pribram less burdened than Hebb with the traditional psychological concepts. His search for the common element—in the divergent results on the paleocortex, for example—leads him to an analysis of behavior and a different psychological category: following out a planned sequence. Such an approach, *de novo,* considering both psychological and physiological facts in a fresh light, offers good hope for the future. The guesses may be wrong, the facts are certainly fewer than one would like, and the psychological analysis could be more extensive and explicit, but if theories are to be constructed, a certain boldness and freedom from old ideas are to be commended.

THEORY AND EXPERIMENT

How experiment and theory stand toward each other may be shown in the case of two major discoveries of the past decade. The influence of reticular-system activity and the reinforcing effects of electrical stimuli applied to certain parts of the brain have been given a good deal of attention during this period and may exemplify the present mode of work.

First, both these phenomena, it seems, were brought to light by accident. Reticular effects on the cerebral cortex were seen in a transection experiment performed for another purpose; the positive reinforcing effects of stimulation in the septal region came as a surprise. Neither was the outcome of an experiment designed to test a hypothesis specifically concerning the phenomena which eventually turned up. Of course, it can be said that the experiments actually operated on the broad hypothesis that the manipulations would have important consequences and would not have been performed unless the experimenters had some specific hypotheses about another sort of outcome. At any rate, the two experiments strengthen Hebb's plea for freer exploratory experiments.

There has been research on these two topics by investigators in several academic fields. Collections of papers [2, 9] dealing chiefly with these subjects include contributions by anatomists, physiologists, embryologists, biochemists, pharmacologists, and psychologists. The techniques of these several scientists are apparently understood and largely shared by all, and it would be hard to say in many instances whether a particular experiment had been done by one sort of worker or another. There is certainly no clear separation of interest.

Neither experiment has yet produced much in the nature of a new theoretical structure; the results tend to be fitted to some common psychological constructs and considered as correlates or explanations of them. To reticular effects, the names "activation" and "alerting" have been applied [17] because the effects of reticular stimulation are not specific to sensory area and seem to be adjuvant to normal sensory stimulation. These properties are traditionally attributed to attention or vigilance, and invite the application of the old construct. One interpretation of limbic effects [24] uses the conceptions of motivation, adaptation, need, perception, memory, and reinforcement. It is not easy to limit the theoretical penumbra of some of these terms, as Olds evidently takes their meaning to be well established. Another discussion [5], however, illustrates how varied the understanding of a term like *positive reinforcement* can be, ranging from "subjective pleasure" to "productive of adient behavior" and "increasing response probability" or a "stamping-in process."

The terms used for both the reticular and limbic effects come from current psychological usage, or, strangely enough, from a psychological vocabulary of the past. Neither *attention* nor *subjective pleasure* figures very largely in current psychological writing. How those constructs fit together, whether they are all necessary, or whether they are the best constructs for the science—these are questions which have not come up yet. This complacent attitude is well expressed by E. R. John [5]: "For me, as a psychologist, the identification of brain changes which relate to concepts derived from psychology like conditioned response, meaning, memory, value, motivation are the essence of the problem before us. I want to know what in the brain corresponds to these things." Suggesting fresh attack upon the issue, however, are some remarks in the discussion following Doty's paper [5]. In the course of these, Galambos, looking at psychology from the outside, proposes that the processes psychology sets up for physiological study are only three—learning, motivation, and attention. Olds later commented that the reticular formation contributes to the latter two. This facing of the fundamental issue seems to be rare either in connection with the two phenomena under discussion or in the whole field of physiological psychology. An exception needs to be made for the analysis offered by Pribram, which has already been described. There is in it certainly an attempt to match new facts with new ideas.

The pitfalls presented by an array of loosely defined psychological constructs are obvious, but hard to avoid. The words seem to connote agencies—though perhaps unintentionally—and setting the problems in terms of psychological agencies seems to call for an answer in terms of physiological agencies. "The hypothalamus produces emotional states." "Memories are located in the temporal lobe." Such propositions can but yield a new phrenology with only the labels changed. The reification of constructs into subjective agents still happens at times. An explicit adoption of such neurological language [8] is proposed by Sperry [30]: " . . . one wonders if any physiological model of the conditioned response that fails to include the subjective properties is not bound to end up with some kind of a gap in the chain of cerebral events." If such terms are to be used, they must be taken apart into elements which belong to the same universe as the physiological facts before they are studied physiologically. And one may doubt the wisdom of synthesizing the constructs and then analyzing them before getting to business. Hebb [12], however, warmly assures us that they are essential.

The need for analysis is clear to some outside the field of psychology, as well as to those within it. Tower [34] gives the following quotation from G. H. Bishop:

On the other hand we should have mental behavior broken down into components capable of corresponding to practically recordable patterns of neural behavior. That such a breakdown should be possible follows from the premise that mental behavior is a function of nervous tissue. It is difficult to conceive of a neural pattern corresponding to anxiety, or to a dissociation from reality; if there were one it must be too hopelessly complex to be recorded by any current apparatus. There must be simple mental components conceivable, as there will certainly be more complex electrical recording possible, in terms of which the neurophysiologist and the psychologist can find a common ground; but this common ground must be approached from both directions.

Although, as a result of physiological experimentation, certain nuances may have been added to the constructs from the standard repertory, it is hard to discern any real innovations in general theory. Nor do experiments often concern testing some deduction made from principles (or simply constructs) of general psychology. The common condition is rather a *post hoc* collation of morsels of psychology put together to care for the arrival of an unexpected fact.

In physiological psychology, experiment and theory seem far apart, although they are expected to march side by side. They are fortunate to be in shooting distance of one another. Each can say, "Here is the way," but neither seems able to say where "here" is. Yet such remarks should not be taken as strictures upon past performance, since enlightenment seldom comes from lamentation and castigation. But we may look for reasons and consider the next steps.

General theory of a physiological sort has a hard task, because the facts it must join together are so far apart. On the one hand are facts about the action of neurons and synapses (chiefly in isolation), about reflexes, knowledge of general and neural anatomy and the functional relations of some parts of the nervous system, as well as certain points about electrical brain waves. These, with the possible addition of some principles of physical chemistry, are the materials usually chosen for a theory. On the other hand is the appalling number of observations on behavior and situations. Direct observations of events between these two extremes are rare, except perhaps on processes in the soma, which most theorists can find little use for. To make the behavior data more manageable, the theorist takes a set of concepts which seem to him to summarize the multitude of facts. He then builds toward the concepts by piling up the known neural processes as far as necessary. Any plausible solution to the problem deserves admiration.

The experimenters' neglect of certain areas has not, of course, been merely willful. In some part it is forced by lack of technical methods. So far, there is no means known for direct observation of many of the processes theorists have thought may be present. "Phase sequences" (Hebb), "brain fields" (Köhler) "interference patterns" (Lashley), "true information" (McCulloch), and similar possible states of the brain —all are themselves out of reach at present, though microelectrode techniques may be getting close. The consequences they imply could possibly be derived and tested; yet if these are rather remote consequences, the experimenter would find himself testing predictions which do not discriminate much between theories.

The experimenter's preference for the beaten path is easy to understand. If he chooses to experiment on the learning of certain mazes by rats, for example, he is studying something once thought to be important

by someone and endorsed by the practice of many. For the manipulations he shall perform, his choice is limited by what is known and what is
possible. In all this, the psychological investigator is probably acting
much as do experimenters in other fields, for most experimentation
probably means the application of familiar techniques to accepted
problems. It is hardly to be expected, nor wholly to be desired, that
each laboratory worker should lay down anew the groundwork of his
science.

A survey of the logical and scientific status of a subject, if it is a
successful one, ought to bring questions to light and illuminate hidden
alternatives. When it does so, accomplishments may seem to be viewed
with cynical eyes. But of course it is not reprehensible per se to adopt an
assumption which may be questioned, follow an unrationalized practice,
or draw a conclusion which is not beyond cavil. In fact, psychologists
may be too much concerned with the protocol of science.

To improve the state of the science, there seems to be but one
prescription—more science; one may reasonably suspect that any particular recipe for general improvement is a nostrum. The problems are
quite numerous and, for their solution, need a large number of good
ideas and a good many experiments.

The gap between theory and experiment may in time be closed by
work from both directions. The advance of experimental work into new
areas depends most of all upon technical invention. There has, of course,
been a great deal that is new in techniques, instrumentation, and analytic
methods in the past quarter of a century. There may be still other techniques, already in use elsewhere, which would serve well in psychology—
psychologists themselves might devise some for their own purposes. Instruments and methods which add convenience and accuracy are to be
desired, for they increase the possible scope of investigations. But most of
all, we should profit by inventions which would take us into some un-
explored territory. The urge to obtain experimental results may retard
new developments of this sort which, in the long run, would profit more
than additional results of familiar kinds.

On the other side, the theorist may help by devising theories which
come closer to the experimental range. It might be possible to carry a
very general theory a few steps farther and reach a point of contact with
experimental work. But, of course, this would still leave a good deal of
the theory untested. A theory of limited range describing the relation
between several measurable variables would offer a chance of more complete verification. At present, the best-understood segments of the response
mechanism are the more peripheral ones, afferent and efferent—a possible mode of progress would be the extension of knowledge inward, step
by step, from both directions.

Nevertheless there is always imminent peril in the piecemeal approach; if some process sought for is not found at site A, there is a strong temptation to conclude that it must be located at a certain spot somewhere else. ("It is not in the nerve fiber, therefore it is in the synapse." "It is not in the afferents, therefore it must be central.") Beyond the difficulty of establishing a negative, there is the need to consider whether an effect has so sharp a locus. In principle, the interaction of parts is readily recognized as possible, though it seems easy to forget when small-scale data are in point. Of course, it should not be—though a machine is always built part by part, even the mechanic knows that he is producing a combinational effect.

Before their first steps through the jungle of behavioral fact, both theorist and experimenter would like to have a taxonomic guide.[3] The facts, as always, are many and various, so much so as to discourage thought. The only hope of a general account seems to be a system which will reduce the multitude to the limits of reason. If the observations already made are correct, theorists and experimenters have tried to work with types of behavior categories—types like perception, emotion, ability, learning, etc. Though terms like these have long histories, each being interpreted in many ways, there are no clear answers to several questions about them. How many are necessary to give a good general account? In what way may the universe of behavior best be apportioned among them or some others? Where should lines be drawn or types centered? A full treatment of these basic questions seems to be lacking in both physiological and nonphysiological theory. Even the methods by which an answer might be given have yet to be devised.

It is a serious question whether we are not, in our desire for these answers, just idly wishing we knew more than we do. Ought we to try for the answers, or simply proceed in a hit-or-miss way, trusting that, through variety, our experiments will eventually touch upon everything important? We follow neither course, in fact, for variety is confined by custom. Therefore, even though our reasoning process should always go astray among the high-level abstractions, we should have been helped by being led into new paths. Impetus from other sources may have the same effect to be sure. The demand for the solution of practical problems—the determination of the human operator's characteristics, for example—may lead to discoveries of general importance. It would sometimes be hard to justify disdain for work on a response of practical import in favor of something more general—it might be hard to show that one is more general than the other.

[3] Both H. F. Harlow and A. W. Melton referred to this matter in their discussion of the future of physiological and experimental psychology. (American Psychological Association meeting, 1955.)

No good solution can be expected out of hand from rational analysis of a problem so broad. Nevertheless, several reflections may be ventured. There is first a question whether the best or only way to organize the data of behavior is to classify (or typify) them. When this most familiar procedure is applied, the divisions which look so clear on paper usually turn out to be quite indistinct among the facts. All facts are likely to be tinted, at least a little, with the colors of all categories. Using the category called "discrimination," one finds that all behavior discriminates to some degree; using the category called "motivated behavior," one finds all behavior somewhat motivated, and so on. By fiat a line could be drawn at some point, of course, producing neatness at the cost of common sense. There may be a better way to organize data; one might consider that we have but one type or class—responses, for example—and try to find what dimensions and how many would provide a good specification of the class members. It seems as though the data would be more amenable to a schema of dimensions than to one of classes. Independent variables would probably be treated in the same way, and the relationships found would be between a number of continuous variables. This mode of thought is, naturally, no innovation; in present thought it seems to exist in unplanned mixture with the older mode.

There are two requirements for constructs which are both desirable but sometimes conflicting: one would like to have constructs which can be the subject of laws, and which have clear domains at the same time. Some psychological theorists seem to incline to one, some to the other ideal, being very exacting in making their constructs fit their favored requirement, and each group facing the other with simple optimism. So, in "habit strength" we have a construct which is usually lawful by definition, but hidden under behavior by several blankets of other constructs, whereas in "test intelligence" we have something easily identifiable but probably not subject to simple laws.

If physiological considerations are included in the construct, they may help in reaching the best compromise. In medical science, diagnosis and treatment do not rest wholly on external signs. It is recognized that a cough and a fever can result from a number of quite different pathologies, and the patient is treated for pneumonia, tuberculosis, or something else, according to the results of physiological tests. Cough medicine and the febrifuge are no longer in the best scientific standing. (Even when a diagnosis is made in the absence of tests, knowledge of diseases coming from physiological research plays its part.) It seems a fair guess that behavior constructs too might be improved were they to include some specifications of physiological state. Physiological events are, of course, identifiable, and at the same time seem very likely to bind together those external events which are subject to common laws.

The facts of response equivalence are sometimes thought to prove that such is not the case. At first glance, it seems as though there are behavior events with different bodily origins which are, nevertheless, products of the same history and subject to a common fate. But this is to think in terms of absolute sameness and differentness and to prefer, perhaps, the most bizarre combination of them. Of course, the supposed equivalents are not absolutely identical in their functions or absolutely different in their physiology, in all probability. A man with injured hands may write with his toes but probably not so well or so often as he did with his hands. When he does try, he will assuredly use much of the same neural system he built up in originally learning to write; he will probably even use the same widespread set of muscles, though with a shifted pattern. It is still possible that the functional and physiological sameness are actually the same.

A final suggestion might be called "armchair experimentation." In the nature of the case, one could not expect to organize data well on wholly a priori grounds if the object is to form a schema convenient and economical for data handling. Further, it is probably too much to expect that anyone could hold all the facts in mind and, by careful thought, derive a solution he could prove was the best. New facts, of course, will complicate the problem still more. Therefore, there may be more to hope for in a successive-approximation sort of thinking. The theoretical controversies in the field may be taken as poor and primitive examples of the trial-and-error process. In more sophisticated form, there could be more cold-blooded comparison of more alternatives. (It would probably help in such an endeavor to draw names for concepts only from the psychologists' lists of nonsense syllables—best of all, from the lower end of it.) Here, too, prudence would argue for original simplicity. Even though one feels sure that behavior has more than a few aspects, the trial of a small number ("amount" and "variety,"[4] for example) would make a good start. But, as the point to be settled is the relative merits of sets of terms, the armchair experimenter will need to be on guard against a favoritism for his first-born. We may take it for granted that data may be ordered in more than one way; the mere elaboration of another would entertain the mind, without necessarily advancing a decision. In this enterprise of organization, the methods of operating and the bases of decision have yet to be thought out. But there seems at least as good a chance of success if one tries to work at the problem first and discover the methods later. Any solution, however, should be thought temporary, for new facts should produce new ideas, and new ideas, new facts. The experimenter's desire for a pre-

[4] These particular terms might refer to the concepts offered by Duffy [6].

formed set of constructs and the theorist's hope for a representative set of facts—both are likely to fail of satisfaction in the human world.

REFERENCES

1. Attneave, F. Some informational aspects of visual perception. *Psychol. Rev.*, 1954, **61**, 183–193.
2. Brazier, Mary A. B. (Ed.). *The central nervous system and behavior.* Transactions of the First Conference. Josiah Macy, Jr. Foundation, New York: 1958.
3. Clare, M. H., & Bishop, G. H. The properties of dendrites. *EEG clin. Neurophysiol.*, 1955, **7**, 85–98.
4. Davis, R. C. Physical psychology. *Psychol. Rev.*, 1953, **60**, 7–14.
5. Discussants. In [2, pp. 270–273].
6. Duffy, E. The concept of energy mobilization. *Psychol. Rev.*, 1951, **58**, 30–40.
7. Freeman, G. L. *Physiological psychology.* New York: Van Nostrand, 1948.
8. Harlow, H. F. Behavioral contributions to interdisciplinary research. In [9, pp. 3–23].
9. Harlow, H. F., & Woolsey, C. M. *Biological and biochemical bases of behavior.* Madison, Wis.: Univer. of Wis. Press, 1958.
10. Hebb, D. O. *The organization of behavior.* New York: Wiley, 1949.
11. Hebb, D. O. Drives and the C.N.S. (conceptual nervous system). *Psychol. Rev.*, 1955, **62**, 243–254.
12. Hebb, D. O. Alice in wonderland, or psychology among the biological sciences. In [9, pp. 451–467].
13. Kantor, J. R. *Problems of physiological psychology.* Bloomington, Ind.: Principia, 1947.
14. Köhler, W. Relational determination in perception. In L. Jeffress (Ed.), *Cerebral mechanisms in behavior.* New York: Wiley, 1951.
15. Lashley, K. *Brain mechanisms and intelligence.* Chicago: Univer. of Chicago Press, 1929.
16. Lashley, K. The problem of serial order in behavior. In L. Jeffress (Ed.), *Cerebral mechanisms in behavior.* New York: Wiley, 1951.
17. Lindsley, D. B. Emotion. In S. S. Stevens (Ed.), *Handbook of experimental psychology.* New York: Wiley, 1951.
18. McCulloch, W. S. Why the mind is in the head. In L. Jeffress (Ed.), *Cerebral mechanisms in behavior.* The Hixon Symposium. New York: Wiley, 1951.
19. McCulloch, W. S. *Finality and form.* Springfield, Ill.: Charles C Thomas, 1952.
20. McCulloch, W. S., & Pitts, W. How we know universals. *Bull. Math. Biophys.*, 1947, **9**, 127–147.
21. Meyer, D. R. The interaction of simultaneous responses. *Psychol. Bull.*, 1953, **56**, 204–220.

22. Miller, N. E., & Kesson, M. L. Reward effects of food via stomach fistula compared with those of food via mouth. *J. comp. physiol. Psychol.,* 1952, **45,** 555–564.

23. Morgan, C. T., & Stellar, E. *Physiological psychology.* New York: McGraw-Hill, 1950.

24. Olds, J. Adaptive function of paleocortical and related structures. In [9, pp. 237–262].

25. Patton, R. A. Physiological psychology. *Annu. Rev. Psychol.,* 1954, **5,** 247–262.

26. Pribram, K. H. Theory in physiological psychology. *Annu. Rev. Psychol.,* 1960, **11,** 1–40.

27. Rashevsky, N. *Mathematical biophysics.* (rev. ed.) Chicago: Univer. of Chicago Press, 1948.

28. Skinner, B. F. Are theories of learning necessary? *Psychol. Rev.,* 1950, **57,** 193–216.

29. Spence, K. W. The postulates and methods of behaviorism. *Psychol. Rev.,* 1948, **55,** 67–78.

30. Sperry, R. W. Discussion. In [2, p. 421].

31. Sperry, R. W., Miner, N., & Myers, R. E. Visual pattern perception following subpial slicing and tantalum implantations in the visual cortex. *J. comp. physiol. Psychol.,* 1955, **18,** 50–58.

32. Teuber, H. L. Physiological psychology. *Annu. Rev. Psychol.,* 1955, **6,** 267–296.

33. Tolman, E. C. *Purposive behavior in animals and men.* New York: Century, 1932.

34. Tower, D. B. The neurochemical substrates of cerebral function and activity. In [9, pp. 285–366].

35. Wiener, N. *Cybernetics.* New York: Wiley, 1948.

36. Woodworth, R. S. *Psychology: a study of mental life.* New York: Holt, 1921.

37. Wundt, W. *Grundzuge der Physiologische Psychologie.* Leipzig: W. Engelmann, 1874.

PSYCHOPHYSICS AND NEUROPHYSIOLOGY

BURTON S. ROSNER

*West Haven Veterans Administration Hospital and
Yale University School of Medicine*

Introduction 281
Neurophysiology 282
   Electrical Properties of Single Neurons 282
      Intracellular recording of action potentials 282
      Intracellular postsynaptic potentials 285
      Extracellular records from single neurons. 288
      Sampling biases of microelectrodes 289
   Extracellular Records from Neuronal Pools. 290
      Response of whole peripheral nerve 290
      Multineuronal activity in central nervous system 291
   Measures of Neuroelectric Responses 293
   Independent Variables in Neurophysiology. 296
Psychophysics. 297
   Behavioral Definition of Psychophysics 297
      Individual and species differences in psychophysics 298
   Empirical Variables of Psychophysics 299
      Sets of stimuli 299
      Programs for presentation of stimuli 301
      Instructions 302
      Sets of responses. 303
   Computational Devices in Psychophysics 304
      S statistics 305
      R statistics 306
   Forms of Psychophysical Functions 307
      First-order invariances 308
      Second-order invariances 309
   Experiential Terminology in Psychophysics. 310
      The classical psychophysical model and its failures 311
      The psychophysics of intensity. 313
Interrelationships between Psychophysics and Neurophysiology. 318
   Empirical Relations 318
      Absolute sensitivity 319

"Submodality" specificity 320
Temporal interactions 320
Differential sensitivity 321
The Psychophysiological Preparation 321
Measurement, Theory, and the Assumption of Linearity 325
Concluding Remarks 327
References 328

INTRODUCTION

Physiological psychology investigates the ways in which bodily processes determine the forms of psychological laws. Interrelationships between psychophysics and neurophysiology constitute a relatively advanced sector of this discipline. These interrelationships form the subject of this paper. Psychophysics studies the functional relation of discrimination to properties of stimuli; neurophysiology offers parallel observations on the effects of environmental events upon electrical activity of the nervous system. Since neuroelectric responses must intervene temporally between stimuli and discriminative behavior, interrelationships between empirical findings from the two fields should illuminate the neural control of psychological processes.

A psychophysical and a neurophysiological function of a given parameter of stimulation may show varying degrees of resemblance. The significance of such resemblances, however, goes beyond a purely empirical level and depends upon some implicit assumptions in physiological psychology. These assumptions or "models" also lie at the base of explicit neurological theories which attempt to explain psychophysical findings. This paper therefore gives due attention to both the empirical and theoretical aspects of the interplay between psychophysics and neurophysiology.[1]

The first section of this paper reviews modern neurophysiology. The terms *neurophysiology* and *electrophysiology* will act as interchangeable labels for the experimental study of neuroelectric activity. The second part of the paper takes up the empirical variables of psychophysics and some general theoretical approaches to psychophysical processes. Discussion of current and possible future relationships between the two disciplines occupies the final section of this article.

[1] This work was supported in part by Grant M–1530 from the National Institute of Mental Health. William R. Goff and Truett Allison made many helpful suggestions during the preparation of this paper. They also participated in collection of data reported here, as did Ethel Matin and Stanley Novak. My wife, Sue R. Rosner, gave far more aid in development of this article than mere acknowledgment in a footnote can indicate.

NEUROPHYSIOLOGY

Electrical Properties of Single Neurons

The neuron doctrine states that the nervous system is built of structurally discrete units or neurons. These neurons generate electrical potentials which are recorded as neuroelectric activity. A neuron consists of a cell body, containing a nucleus and other microstructures, together with all elongated processes which arise from the cell body. Any standard textbook of neuroanatomy [74] discusses the histological and embryological evidence for the concept of the neuron. The typical multipolar neuron of the central nervous system has a single axon and many arborizing dendrites attached to the cell body (see Fig. 1). A continuous membrane encloses the entire unit. The axon is histologically distinct from cell body and dendrites, which together seem homogeneous under the microscope. Axonal membrane lies inside one or more sheaths, which may include a fatty white covering of myelin. No sheath surrounds the membrane of a cell body and its dendrites.

Certain neurons differ markedly in structure from the multipolar type. A monopolar spinal afferent neuron, which may supply skin, muscle, or deep tissue, emits a single bifurcating axon but no dendrites from the cell body. The peripheral branch of the axon ultimately breaks into unspecialized afferent terminals or makes contact with specialized receptors; the central branch of the axon enters the spinal cord. The bipolar type of neuron, such as that constituting acoustic nerve, sends out two axons and no dendrites. The peripheral axon of a neuron of acoustic nerve goes to the hair cells of the cochlea, while the central axon runs to the brain stem.

FIG. 1. Pyramidal cell from the cerebral cortex of a mouse. The axon *e* gives off a collateral *c* before entering white matter *b*. Basal dendrites *a* and a profusely branching apical dendrite *l* arise from the cell body. The apical dendrite terminates near the surface of the cortex *p*. Golgi method; after Cajal [74].

Intracellular recording of action potentials. Diameters of peripheral axons in vertebrates range from less than 1 μ to about 20 μ. Fortunately for neurophysiologists, certain invertebrates have evolved "giant" unmyelinated axons. The giant motor axon of the squid, for example, may exceed 500 μ in diameter. It thus has become a favored object of study. One can dissect out a fair length of this fiber and record from it in isolation in a bath of sea water. The axon is spacious enough to accommodate one or two fine glass or wire electrodes inserted longitudinally. Measurements show that the inside of the resting squid giant axon is polarized about 50 to 60 mV negative with respect to the outside. This difference is the *resting potential* of axonal membrane.

Application of a very mild electrical stimulus to the axon produces a small, transient depolarization of the membrane around the site of stimulation. This small response does not propagate down the length of the axon. As intensity of the shock increases, the response grows larger until the membrane reaches a critical threshold level of depolarization. At this level, the membrane goes on to develop a monophasic propagating action potential or *spike*. Figure 2 shows the resting potential and the action potential of the membrane of a squid giant axon. The action potential involves a rapid total depolarization of the membrane. This depolarization continues over to a reversal of the resting polarity of the membrane, so that the membrane at the peak of the spike is electropositive on the inside. The membrane potential then swiftly returns to its original polarity and eventually reestablishes its resting level. The action potential in Fig. 2 lasts about 1.5 msec.

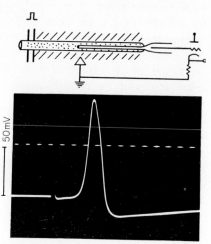

Fig. 2. Resting and action potential of giant axon of squid. Diagram at top represents experimental arrangement, with stimulating electrodes at left, "active" pipette electrode inserted longitudinally into the axon, and indifferent (grounded) electrode in bath of sea water holding the preparation. Horizontal broken time marker indicates 0.5-msec intervals and also shows "zero" potential difference between indifferent electrode and active electrode when the latter also lies in sea-water bath. Before stimulation, indicated by brief interruption in tracing of membrane potential, the membrane resting potential is about 55 mV electronegative on the inside. After stimulus, membrane generates an action potential with an overshoot of about 45 mV [97].

Although subthreshold responses of axonal membrane are not self-propagating, the action potential does propagate by acting as a strong electrical stimulus to portions of the membrane just ahead of its own wave front. (Conduction velocity depends on many factors; for the largest myelinated axons in mammals, it is about 120 m/sec at most.)

The action potential also obeys the "all-or-none" law: Under constant conditions, the amplitude of the spike is independent of the intensity of a suprathreshold stimulus. The amplitude of a subthreshold response varies with intensity of stimulation. During an action potential, axonal membrane is absolutely refractory and cannot respond to a stimulus with another spike. A relative refractory period then ensues, in which the membrane has an elevated threshold for generation of a spike. Refractoriness limits the frequency at which an axon can discharge spikes. The intimate details of generation and propagation of action potentials by axons are a subject of some disagreement. Eccles [20], Nachmansohn [69], and Tasaki [97] present three partly different views on these problems.

Recordings obtained with extremely fine microelectrodes from mammalian central nervous system resemble findings from intracellular studies of isolated axons. The tips of these microelectrodes are less than 1 μ in diameter; Frank [22] discusses the special problems of constructing microelectrodes and of compensating for their peculiar electrical properties through electronic devices. Penetration of the central nervous system (the neuraxis) with a microelectrode is a blind procedure. When the electrode first contacts neural tissue, there is essentially no potential difference between its tip and an indifferent point elsewhere on the preparation. As operation of a micromanipulator slowly drives the electrode deeper into the nervous system, a steady negative potential of about 60 to 80 mV may suddenly appear between the electrode and the indifferent point. Neurophysiologists interpret this voltage as the resting potential of neuronal membrane and therefore as the sign of entry of the tip of the microelectrode into a single neuron. (This resting potential is of the same order of magnitude as the resting potential of an isolated invertebrate axon.) Stimulation of the preparation in various ways often causes a brief, all-or-none action potential at whose peak the microelectrode is positive with respect to the indifferent point. The action potential thus shows an "overshoot" or reversal of resting-membrane polarity, which incidentally is somewhat smaller than the corresponding overshoot of the propagated action potential of an isolated squid giant axon.

These and other properties of certain records obtained from the neuraxis with fine microelectrodes suggest that the potentials represent transmembrane events in single neurons. The experimenter cannot see directly or verify histologically the precise location of the electrode tip. "Intracellular" potentials from the mammalian neuraxis therefore are a compound of observation and inference. The inference is so compelling, however, that the term *intracellular potentials* will appear throughout this paper without further qualification.

Intracellular postsynaptic potentials.   Within the central nervous system and autonomic ganglia, axons terminate by breaking into fine branches which finally impinge upon cell bodies and dendrites. These regions of approximation are termed *synapses.* Presynaptic fibers may end in specialized *boutons terminaux* (see Fig. 3) or, as in cerebral cortex, may lack specialized terminations. Impulses in presynaptic fibers affect the activity of postsynaptic neurons by means of "transmission"

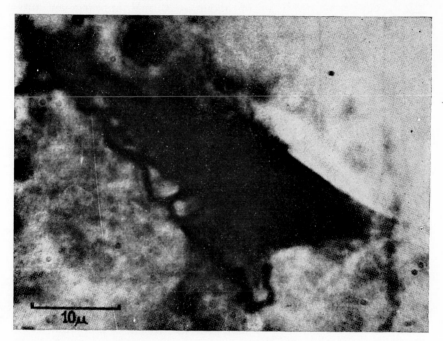

Fɪɢ. 3. Presynaptic fiber ending in *boutons* along the large dendrite and cell body of a neuron of the magnocellular nucleus of the brain stem reticular formation. Dendrite extends toward the upper left. *Boutons* appear as stubby enlargements at the end of short terminal collaterals from fiber, which courses down the dendrite and cell body. Rapid Golgi method on young cat [84].

across synapses. This transmission is one-way, so that a postsynaptic neuron normally conducts a spike away from its cell body and down the axon. Intracellular recordings from central nervous system have registered graded[2] responses which apparently signal activity of postsynaptic membrane [21]. These graded responses may lead to generation of a propagated action potential by the postsynaptic neuron.

[2] Throughout this paper, the term *graded response* operationally refers to any neuroelectric response whose amplitude is a continuous function of intensity of stimulation. A graded response stands in contrast to an all-or-none action potential, whose amplitude is a step-function of intensity.

Studies on spinal motoneurons exemplify these results particularly well. The ventral horn of the spinal cord contains the cell bodies of spinal motoneurons which send efferent axons to skeletal-muscle fibers. Electrical stimulation of a ventral root antidromically fires the cell bodies of the motoneurons in the segment of the cord from which the root arises.

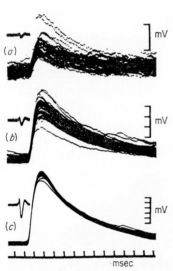

When a microelectrode penetrates the cell body of a motoneuron, a resting potential of about −70 mV appears; an antidromic stimulus then produces a single action potential having an overshoot of perhaps 10 to 20 mV. Large afferent axons which supply the sensory spindles of a skeletal muscle originate from monopolar spinal afferent neurons. The central branches of these axons synapse in part directly onto motoneurons which send efferent axons to the same muscle. This monosynaptic pathway mediates the stretch reflex. Stretching of a muscle discharges afferent fibers which supply muscle spindles. Impulses in the large afferents synaptically excite motoneurons which then activate the muscle and relieve tension on the spindles.

FIG. 4. Excitatory postsynaptic potentials recorded through an intracellular electrode in a motoneuron supplying biceps-semitendinosus muscle. Stimulation of large-muscle afferents sets up dorsal-root volleys shown in insets at left of a-c; these volleys were recorded at constant amplification for which no calibration is given. Psp increases as afferent volley grows. All records formed by superimposition of about forty faint traces. Positivity upward [12].

Electrical stimulation of large-muscle afferents produces brief graded intracellular potentials in the cell bodies of motoneurons which supply the same muscle. These potentials signal transmission across the monosynaptic link of the pathway for the stretch reflex. They depolarize the membrane of the motoneuron cell body and increase in size as the presynaptic volley grows (see Fig. 4). When depolarization becomes sufficient, the motoneuron develops an action potential (see Fig. 5j). Graded depolarizing potentials thus represent excitatory activity in postsynaptic membrane of a normal cell. Stimulation of afferents which supply an antagonist muscle may produce graded postsynaptic potentials (psp's) of opposite, hyperpolarizing sign in a motoneuron which supplies a given muscle (see Fig. 5). These latter potentials hinder depolarization of the cell-body membrane of the motoneuron to a level necessary for spike generation and therefore are inhibitory. Various electrical and pharmacological properties of psp's favor the theory that synaptic transmission requires release of chemical transmitters from presynaptic terminals.

Many properties of psp's need further investigation. In general, however, the available evidence presents approximately the following picture of activity in a single neuron. Electrical spikes in presynaptic fibers

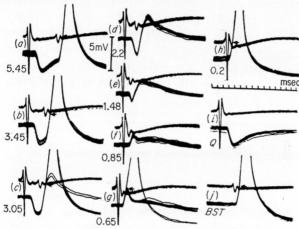

FIG. 5. Upper records in each set show afferent volleys recorded from *L6* dorsal root; lower records show intracellular responses from a biceps-semitendinosus motoneuron. *i* shows a hyperpolarizing inhibitory postsynaptic potential following stimulation of afferents of the antagonistic quadriceps muscle; *j* is response to stimulation of biceps-semitendinosus afferents at an intensity which leads to an action potential. Remaining records (*a-h*) show inhibition of action potential when quadriceps volley precedes biceps-semitendinosus afferent volley. Numbers at lower left show intervals between the two volleys in milliseconds. Motoneuron fails to generate a spike at intervolley intervals of about 0.65 to about 3.05 msec. Note probabilistic behavior of spike at these two extreme intervals. All records formed from superimposition of about forty faint traces. Arrows in *a-h* indicate approximate threshold voltage for initiation of spike. Positivity upward. Calibration of 5 mV for all intracellular records shown in *a* [13].

cause ejection of chemical transmitters from presynaptic terminals. Excitatory transmitters depolarize postsynaptic membrane, while inhibitory transmitters tend to prevent depolarization from reaching a critical level. A large fraction of the membrane of a cell body and its dendrites is postsynaptic and generates nonpropagating graded psp's upon stimulation by synaptic transmitters. Depolarization of postsynaptic membrane electrically stimulates nearby nonsynaptic membrane to depolarize. When the latter in turn depolarizes sufficiently, it generates an action potential which propagates down the axon of the postsynaptic neuron.

Grundfest [39, 41] has reviewed evidence that postsynaptic membrane itself is electrically inexcitable. According to this argument, postsynaptic membrane can produce only graded responses and cannot support an action potential. Grundfest's thesis makes chemical transmission at synapses mandatory. Certain observations also suggest that membrane of sensory receptors and of afferent terminals is electrically inexcitable and produces only graded responses [38, 39].

Extracellular records from single neurons. Under favorable conditions, extracellular electrodes will detect brief spike potentials which obey the all-or-none law. These spikes represent the *external fields* established by momentary action potentials in single neurons. The dis-

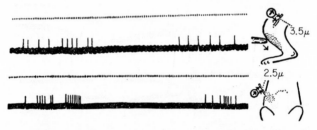

Fɪɢ. 6. Spike discharges from two single cutaneous fibers in cat. Each fiber responds to light touch in stippled region of skin in drawings on right. Fibers have unusually wide receptive fields. Negativity upward; time marker, 10 msec [64].

tinction between transmembrane potential variations and their resultant extracellular potential fields is fundamental for neurophysiology. Extracellular fields are small in maximum potential difference relative to the size of transmembrane potential changes. Extracellular fields also may show some properties which do not match the course of transmembrane events. For example, the action potential of an axon is a monophasic change in membrane potential, while the resultant external field of the action potential in a volume conductor is triphasic [58, 65]. Extracellular fluid, of course, is a volume conductor. The time course of changes in extracellular potentials therefore does not necessarily follow faithfully the sequence of transmembrane events.

Surgical paring down of a peripheral sensory nerve permits registration of extracellular all-or-none action potentials from single sensory fibers whose afferent terminals are intact. Such spikes, which are recorded through gross extracellular electrodes supporting the remaining strand of nerve, are usually only tens of microvolts in size. Figure 6 shows spikes from single peripheral cutaneous fibers isolated by this procedure. These records come from fibers which innervate relatively large areas of skin. Most cutaneous fibers have much smaller receptive fields. (The receptive field of a neuron is simply that region of a sensory surface within which stimulation alters the rate of firing of the neuron.)

Penetration of central nervous system with microelectrodes also permit extracellular recording of action potentials from a single neuron. Figure 7 shows action potentials from a neuron in a cat's medial geniculate body in response to an acoustic click. Two signs indicate that such spikes are extracellular. First, the responses are relatively small and rarely exceed 5 to 10 mV. Second, there is no large resting potential between the electrode and an indifferent point. The slow waves in Fig. 7 represent summated extracellular potentials from numerous neurons (see below). Extracellular microelectrodes may have tips up to about 10 μ in diameter. Experience indicates that they record activity from cell bodies in preference to activity from axons.

In general, discharge patterns from single central units are more complex than those from single peripheral fibers. Single peripheral and central neurons frequently show spontaneous discharge of spikes in the absence of external stimulation. External stimuli usually raise the frequency of firing of a single peripheral fiber above its spontaneous level. Labyrinthine afferents are one exception; stimulation may inhibit their spontaneous rate of firing [59]. Central neurons may increase or decrease their spontaneous rates of discharge following an external stimulus. Spontaneous activity in a single central unit sometimes may reach fairly high frequencies. Furthermore, one location of a peripheral stimulus may increase the rate of firing while another location may lower the rate [68].

Sampling biases of microelectrodes. Intracellular and extracellular recordings with microelectrodes from single neurons may preferentially show activity of larger cell bodies. A small cell body offers a less favorable target for an intracellular microelectrode and probably could not withstand damage due to penetration by the electrode. Therefore, neurons with large cell bodies, such as spinal motoneurons (maximum

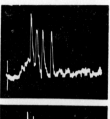
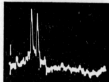

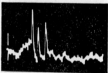

10   20
msec

Fig. 7. Spike discharges from single neuron in medial geniculate body of cat in response to clicks. Records from top to bottom show first four and eleventh responses to train of clicks at 1/sec. Note multiple discharge and variability in number of spikes to each click. Negativity upward [26].

breadth of 75 μ), have been most extensively studied intracellularly. Extracellular microelectrodes may have a similar bias. These electrodes presumably register more easily activity in neurons which set up extracellular fields of relatively large potential. Since considerable evidence shows that the action potentials of larger-diameter axons establish larger extracellular fields, it seems reasonable to suppose that larger cell bodies also produce external fields of higher potential. The external field of the action potential of a cortical cell body may have a vertical extent of about 100 μ altogether [67]. Usually, a microelectrode must be considerably closer to the cell for favorable recording. This also suggests that extracellular microelectrodes record mainly from neural elements which generate relatively high external potential fields.

Exact assessment of sampling biases in microelectrodes is currently very difficult, since no histological method can identify the particular unit which yielded a given recording. Sections through the region of the nervous system which a microelectrode has traversed will show the electrode track. In conjunction with depth readings from the micromanipulator used to drive the electrode, the sections show the sorts of cells encountered. Sometimes the electrical records themselves may help to identify the type of cell which produced them. For example, large pyramidal cells in cerebral motor cortex send axons into the pyramidal tracts. Electrical stimulation of the medullary pyramids antidromically fires such cells [56]. Further work may clarify the extent of sampling biases in microelectrodes.

Extracellular Records from Neuronal Pools

Records obtained with gross electrodes from whole peripheral nerve or from central nervous system represent summated extracellular potentials from groups or pools of neurons. The recording surfaces of these "macroelectrodes" are hundreds of square microns in area; the tips of macroelectrodes often exceed 1 mm in diameter. Neuroelectric responses recorded with such electrodes do not obey the all-or-none law, often show several peaks, and may last for many milliseconds. Gross electrode records from central nervous system may also show spontaneous potential fluctuations which tend to obscure transient responses to external stimuli. A basic problem in neurophysiology is the analysis of graded activity from pools of neurons into contributions from individual elements. The most successful example of such an analysis concerns the compound action potential of whole nerve.

Response of whole peripheral nerve. Electrical stimulation of a whole peripheral nerve produces a graded compound response at a gross recording electrode (see Fig. 8). This response is the sum of extracellular action potentials from individual active fibers in the nerve.

(The initial positivity in Fig. 8 before the large negativity is typical of the external field of the action potential of an axon.) Various data show that axons of smaller diameter have higher thresholds to electrical stimulation, slower conduction velocities, and smaller external spike potentials. As intensity of a shock to a whole nerve is increased, smaller fibers discharge spikes. The compound response therefore gets larger and progressively longer and may develop several distinct peaks. Each peak signals activity in a relatively large subgroup of fibers of about the same

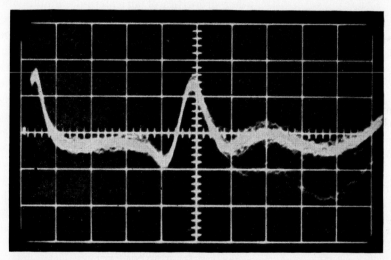

Fig. 8. Response of whole median nerve in man recorded through surface electrodes at wrist to stimulation of the nerve in the upper arm. Impulses conducted distally. Negativity upward. The second negative peak may partly represent activity in some slower fibers, according to preliminary evidence. The first positive-negative part of the response shows activity in larger, faster fibers. Calibrations: 1 msec and 10 μV per major division.

diameter and conduction velocity. From data on the spectrum of fiber diameters in a whole nerve and the relations between fiber diameter, spike potential, and conduction velocity, neurophysiologists have theoretically reconstructed the compound action potential [29, 30]. The predicted and observed responses agree closely. This reconstruction shows that the compound response consists of summated extracellular spikes from simultaneously stimulated fibers in whole nerve.

Multineuronal activity in central nervous system. Environmental stimuli evoke graded extracellular responses in different parts of the central nervous system. Activation of a given modality, such as vision or somesthesis, produces responses throughout the corresponding afferent pathway defined by neuroanatomists. In addition, evoked responses also appear in other structures which lie outside anatomically determined afferent pathways: "second" cerebral cortical areas [106], cerebellum [18], and brain stem reticular formation [23]. All respond to environmental stimuli. Figure 9 shows an evoked potential from cerebral somatosensory cortex of an anesthetized cat. Extracellular microelectrodes as well as macroelectrodes can pick up such graded evoked potentials. (See the slow negative waves in Fig. 7 which represent summated extracellular potentials.) Variations in the locus, frequency, intensity, or other properties of an external stimulus alter the quantitative features of these responses.

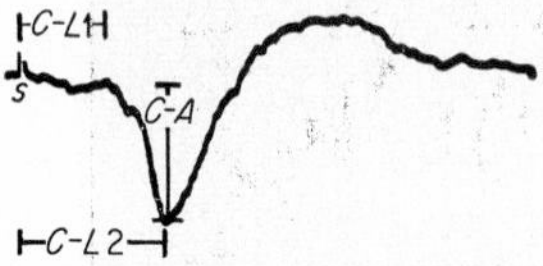

FIG. 9. Potential recorded from pial surface of cat's cerebral somatosensory area I following a brief electrical shock to contralateral forepaw. Negativity upward. Stimulus artifact at s; C-L1 is onset latency (12.5 msec); C-L2 is peak latency of positive deflection (19.5 msec); C-A is amplitude of positive deflection (125 μV).

Certain graded extracellular responses from central nervous system seem to comprise summated spikes from individual axons. Records from optic tract [7] and from other fiber bundles fit this interpretation. Passive spread of potentials evoked elsewhere in the brain may contribute slightly to such records, although this effect hardly seems serious. Graded extracellular responses from nuclear[3] regions of the brain, such as thalamus or cerebral or cerebellar cortex, are much harder to decompose. Theoretically, these records could contain a mixture of extracellular action potentials and extracellular postsynaptic potentials from numerous neural elements. It is hardly surprising, then, that analysis of such responses from nuclear regions of the brain is a subject of some disagreement.

Eccles [19] originally had proposed that these graded potentials consist of extracellular psp's; more recently, he seems to favor a somewhat more complex theory [21, chap. 6]. Clare and Bishop [10] suggest that decrementally propagating graded responses in apical dendrites (see Fig. 1) contribute to cortical evoked potentials, while Chang [9] believes that apical dendrites support slowly conducting action potentials. Grundfest [40] and Purpura [73] have stressed the role of extracellular psp's in creating graded responses from nuclear regions. These authors suggest that extracellular spikes contribute relatively little to such responses.

[3] The term *nuclear region* will serve in this paper as a convenient label for regions of the central nervous system which consist of cell bodies and dendrites, terminal presynaptic fibers, and the first parts of efferent fibers leaving the region. The nuclei of the cranial nerves, for example, are nuclear regions, as are cerebral, cerebellar, and hippocampal cortex.

One difficult problem in treating extracellular graded responses from a nuclear region concerns their temporal relationships to extracellular spikes recorded from single neurons. The phase relations between these two types of responses to a given stimulus are quite complex [73]. A second source of difficulty is lack of any precise data on the extracellular field of a psp of a single neuron in a volume conductor. Mauro [65] presents some reasons for believing that the extracellular field of a psp may not always behave like the external field of an action potential. In part, current theories of the origin of slow potentials from nuclear areas include hypotheses about the distribution of extracellular fields of graded responses in single neurons. Despite the ambiguities, however, the discovery of psp's in single neurons has opened significant new possibilities for analysis of graded extracellular responses. This discovery also has influenced theories of the origin of spontaneous activity, such as the electroencephalogram. On balance, current opinion apparently leans toward emphasizing the contribution of summated extracellular psp's to graded responses from nuclear regions.

Anatomical considerations also complicate the interpretation of extracellular potentials from nuclear areas. Macroelectrode recordings from central nervous system tap activity in a pool of neurons whose extent is not known exactly. Stereotaxic instruments which assign a three-dimensional set of coordinates to each locus in the brain facilitate reliable placement of deep electrodes in acute and chronic preparations [79]. Final determination of the site of an electrode tip, however, requires histological sections showing the end of the electrode track. (Specification of the location of an electrode on the surface of the brain usually calls for direct visual inspection only.) Anatomical description of the position of an electrode still does not delimit the pool of neurons which produced a given record. To some degree, systematic depth recordings and "bipolar" recording between electrodes whose tips lie close together can help to define the geography of an active pool. Together with anatomical data, these procedures aid in determining the probable major sites of generation of multineuronal responses.

Measures of Neuroelectric Responses

Physical instruments for recording of neuroelectric activity include equipment for amplifying and displaying small potentials. Biological amplifiers must have a high input impedance, high total gain, low internal noise, and a flat response from direct current or very low frequencies up to several thousand cps. The usual display instruments which these amplifiers drive produce a record of neuroelectric activity which shows voltage plotted against time (Figs. 2, 4 to 9). Voltage and time therefore are the fundamental physical scales for measurement of neuroelectric activity. Frequently reduction of raw records to more convenient numerical representation is desirable. Various measures of neuroelectric responses serve this purpose.

For any kind of neuroelectric response, one can specify values of parameters of stimulation which produce a detectable response. These "positive-stimulus" measures do not depend critically upon physical scales of time and voltage for display of neuroelectric activity. Many monotonic nonlinear transformations on those scales would not affect the value of a positive-stimulus (P-S) measure. The receptive fields plotted in Fig. 6 illustrate P-S measures. Each plot shows locations of stimuli which produced a detectable response in a single cutaneous fiber.

A second major class of measures of neuroelectric response are immediately tied to physical measures of time and voltage. These amplitude and time (A-T) measures differ somewhat for various classes of neuroelectric responses. For present purposes, we need only to consider A-T measures for extracellular action potentials from single neurons and for graded multineuronal responses. Since action potentials from a single neuron obey the all-or-none law, temporal measures are most useful for describing records of spikes from a single unit. These measures include time from onset of stimulation to the first (or any succeeding) spike, time between successive spikes, and number of spikes following a transient stimulus. (Time between successive spikes is equivalent to frequency of firing.) Since single units often discharge spontaneously, detection of an effect by external stimulation requires demonstrating a change in the pattern of firing following a stimulus. Responses of single units to external stimuli thus are shifts away from basal firing patterns. Positive-stimulus measures for activity in single neurons depend on detection of such shifts.

Measures of amplitude as well as measures of time are useful for describing graded extracellular responses. These responses may represent summated action potentials, summated psp's, or both. Temporal measures show time from a stimulus to the beginning or to some selected peak of a graded extracellular response. (See C-$L1$ and C-$L2$ in Fig. 9.) Measurements of amplitude usually show the size of a deflection from base line (zero potential) to peak (see C-A in Fig. 9). Occasionally, peak-to-peak measurements have replaced peak measurements. Amplitude measures on multineuronal responses usually are converted to dimensionless numbers by expressing them as percentages of the amplitude of a maximal reference response. Absolute amplitudes reflect the distance of a macroelectrode from an active source as well as local conditions at the electrode tip and therefore are not very meaningful for multineuronal responses.

A neurophysiological function often displays the relationship of a measure of response to a stimulus variable. Figure 10 shows how three different measures of a graded extracellular response from cerebral somatosensory cortex of a cat change with increasing intensity of a peripheral electrodermal shock. The three measures are represented in Fig. 9. The functions in Fig. 10 show that onset latency (*C-L*1) and latency of the first positive peak (*C-L*2) decrease while amplitude of

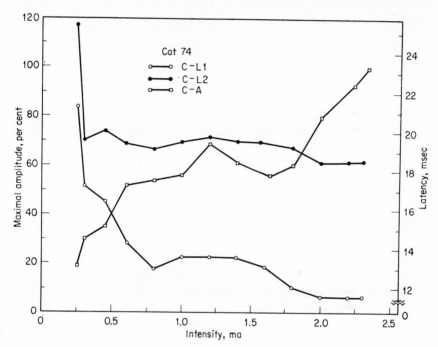

FIG. 10. Effect of intensity of peripheral electrodermal shock on onset latency (*C-L*1), peak latency (*C-L*2), and amplitude (*C-A*) of positive deflection of evoked cortical response of Fig. 9. Note that all three functions have two distinct limbs, due to activation of two sets of peripheral nerve fibers of different diameters.

the positive deflection (*C-A*) increases. All three functions show two distinct limbs. The measures of amplitude are dimensionless since they all have been referred to the amplitude of the response to maximal stimulation. Since neuroelectric responses to a series of identical stimuli often show some variability, electrophysiological functions may be based on statistical summary of a measure of response over such a sample. For example, each point in Fig. 10 is the median of 25 measurements.

Different measures on the same response are not equally sensitive to changes in a stimulus variable. Some measures show relatively large changes as a property of stimuli is varied over a wide range while other measures show relatively limited changes. Figure 10 shows that amplitude of a multineuronal response is a more sensitive indicator of the effects of intensity of stimulation than are onset and peak latencies. In general, onset latencies of single-unit and multiunit responses are less sensitive to parameters of stimulation than are other measures. Thus, intercorrelations between different measures of a given response tend to be nonlinear. These intercorrelations, however, turn up repeatedly in observations on neuroelectric activity from different recording loci.

Independent Variables in Neurophysiology

Two classes of independent empirical variables in neurophysiology are directly relevant to this paper: sets of stimuli and type of physiological preparation. The detailed discussion of sets of stimuli in the following section on psychophysics is directly applicable to specification of stimuli in neurophysiology. The other class of independent variables, type of preparation, requires brief comment here.

Neurophysiological preparations range from excised single axons through anesthetized animals to unanesthetized, intact animals and humans. Various observations show good agreement between results on excised fibers and on peripheral fibers studied *in situ*. Experiments on central nervous system, however, run into problems arising from the type of preparation. Traditional acute neurophysiological preparations have required use of general anesthetics or transections of the neuraxis at various levels. More recent work on unanesthetized, neurally intact animals shows that older acute techniques may influence experimental findings. Anesthetics, for example, can abolish evoked multineuronal potentials in the brain stem reticular formation [24]. Repetition of the same experiment on central nervous system in two different kinds of preparations therefore may yield divergent results. To obviate such problems, neurophysiologists gradually have shifted to preparations with chronically implanted electrodes or to acute control of experimental animals through local anesthetics and neuromuscular blocking agents. Traditional types of preparations, however, remain useful for many purposes.

Any acute procedure influences total bodily functioning and may produce secondary effects on neuroelectric activity. For example, many acute techniques upset normal respiration which ensures adequate oxygenation of the brain. Acute experimentation therefore must include methods of compensating for or preventing any abnormalities in the internal environment of the animal. These methods seek to maintain the preparation in a "steady" state. A somewhat analogous problem may occur with chronic, unanesthetized preparations. These latter preparations may exhibit "habituation" [49, 85] or other progressive changes in neuroelectric responses to fixed external stimuli. The state of unanesthetized preparations may become a problem of growing concern in neurophysiology.

PSYCHOPHYSICS

As a branch of experimental psychology, psychophysics has felt the impact of debates over the nature of psychological data. A behavioristic view of psychophysics, to which Johnson [52, 53], Graham [32, 33, 34], and Bergmann and Spence [5] have contributed heavily, seems to command wide allegiance today. For example, Guilford [42] and Stevens [87, 90] couch their recent definitions of psychophysics in S-R terminology. The publicly observable responses of organisms to environmental stimuli clearly contribute to the empirical material of psychophysics. The present analysis of psychophysics therefore begins from a behavioristic viewpoint.

Behavioral Definition of Psychophysics

According to behaviorism, experimental psychology studies stimulus-response relationships of the form $R = f(S)$. A brief review of a typical psychophysical experiment delineates the particular subclass of S-R functions which psychophysics investigates. A psychophysicist may wish to study differential sensitivity to lifted weights or, in these more modern times, he may want to establish a category scale for lifted weights. The experimenter (E) first chooses a set of stimuli which, in this case, are weights of various values. He then instructs a subject (O) to lift pairs of weights and to indicate whether the left-hand or right-hand member of each pair is heavier; or he instructs O to lift single weights and to place each stimulus in one of a fixed number of "equally spaced" categories. In the latter instance, O's responses usually are integers.

The psychophysical experiment proceeds trial by trial. On each trial, E presents a stimulus or a pair of stimuli and O makes one of the responses which the instructions permit. The stimuli occur over successive trials according to a predetermined program; each stimulus or pair of stimuli occurs on several trials. The experimenter records each trial as a joint event consisting of a known condition of stimulation and O's immediately succeeding response. After the experimental session, E reduces the raw data to manageable form through some computational devices, such as difference limens or scale values. These devices rest on a common assumption: Any psychophysical statistic would converge to a single value if E gave O progressively more trials under identical conditions. This assumption is the key to the nature of psychophysical data.

The concept of conditional probability offers a more precise characterization of the S-R relationships studied by psychophysics. Many psychophysical computational procedures first require determination of conditional probabilities of response. A conditional probability of response $p(R_k|S_i)$ is simply the relative frequency of R_k on all those trials which began with S_i. For example, R_k might be the category rating "four" and S_i a weight of 100 g. Then $p(R_k|S_i)$ would be the ratio of trials on which O called the 100-g weight as "four" to all trials on which that weight occurred. A simple "relative-frequency" interpretation of probability [70] therefore describes psychophysical data from a single subject.[4] This interpretation does not hold for data from one subject in an experiment on discrimination learning until performance reaches asymptote. Psychophysical measurement becomes possible at precisely that point.

The psychophysicist assumes that the probabilities $p(R_k|S_i)$ are convergent over successive trials, so that more and more identical trials with S_i would yield continually better approximations of $p(R_k|S_i)$ to its "true" value based on an infinite number of trials. A test of this assumption clearly is impossible. Nonetheless, psychophysicists can achieve sufficient experimental control to justify treating their data with some simple but powerful mathematics which assume convergence. Furthermore, since each $p(R_k|S_i)$ is "stable" over identical trials, its value is a function of the parameter of stimulation i. The main task of psychophysics therefore is to study the influence of properties of stimuli upon conditional probability of response. The functional slogan for psychophysics becomes $p(R_k|S_i) = f(i)$, which is a special case of $R = f(S)$. The requirement of stability of $p(R_k|S_i)$ over "identical trials" covers experiments such as those on dark adaptation. In the latter experiments, probability of response to one stimulus changes progressively over successive trials. The experimenter does not calculate one conditional probability for each response across all trials. Instead, he obtains a separate $p(R_k|S_i)$ for each stage of adaptation. Thus, S_i is really a function of i and of time t starting at t_0. The psychophysical function becomes $p(R_k|S_{i,t}) = f(i,t)$, $t \geqq t_0$. For most experiments, t is not an effective variable.

Individual and species differences in psychophysics. The traditional concentration of psychophysics on the study of individual sub-

[4] In certain experiments, the conditional probabilities represent pooled results from several subjects. Practical difficulties may sometimes prevent the experimenter's obtaining sufficiently stable discriminative performance from single subjects. The experimenter treats pooled data as representing time-invariant performance by an average subject. Use of several subjects, however, is usually unnecessary to get orderly data on stable discriminative responses.

jects expresses a fundamental attitude of this discipline. Psychophysical laws summarize some common and widespread features of discriminative behavior. These features in turn reflect basic properties of the nervous system. A variety of formal and informal observations supports this outlook, which traces back to the historical origins of psychophysics from biology. On certain occasions, however, psychophysicists do study interindividual differences, such as defects in color vision. These experiments contribute to the testing and refinement of neurological theories of psychophysical phenomena. Similar profits derive from psychophysical investigations on animals with neural lesions and from comparative studies on different species. Experiments on animals with pure rod as against pure cone retinas illustrate the comparative approach. Nonetheless, psychophysics ultimately remains oriented toward sources of uniformity in behavior. Differential and comparative studies may aid in teasing out the separate processes which contribute to the uniformities.

Empirical Variables of Psychophysics

The major independent empirical variables of psychophysics are sets of stimuli, programs for presentation of stimuli, and instructions. Sets of responses comprise the dependent empirical variables in psychophysical experiments. Choices of variables for a given experiment depend on the aims of the experiment and on limiting interrelationships among the experimental variables themselves. For example, selection of a set of responses determines certain aspects of instructions. Finally, computational devices for summarizing results reflect the structure of a particular experiment.

Sets of stimuli. Physical methods play an essential role in many psychophysical experiments by providing highly reproducible stimuli and scales for measuring these stimuli. Physical specification of a stimulus involves determining its value on each of a relatively small number of independent dimensions. For example, a flash of light may have a certain area, duration, intensity, and dominant wavelength. A set of stimuli for a psychophysical experiment has fixed values on several physical dimensions. The stimuli differ among themselves by assuming unique combinations of values on one or more variable dimensions. Apparatus for generating and controlling stimuli permits a stimulus to assume a wide range of values on one dimension, irrespective of its values on others. The experimenter thereby can study the behavioral effects of a single physical dimension of stimulation at a time. Given the physical properties of a set of stimuli, another experimenter can reproduce the stimuli with maximum assurance of success. Physical measurement thus permits accurate reproduction of a wide variety of environmental events by the use of a small number of independent terms.

Closer inspection of psychophysical practices, however, shows that purely physical knowledge never suffices to specify a set of stimuli. Certain quantitative measures of stimuli depend immediately upon biological or psychophysical information. As examples, visual angle would be a fairly meaningless measure without some knowledge of physiological optics; psychophysical observations are necessary to specify intensity of sound in sensation-level units, which are referred to the subject's own absolute threshold. Even beyond cases like these, psychophysical and biological knowledge enter into specification of stimuli in other ways. Stimuli are events in a subject's environment and must occur in some definite, reportable relationship to the subject. The experimenter must therefore direct stimuli at a particular receptor organ, such as the ear or the skin. Achievement of this arrangement requires that E know something about the superficial appearance of these organs and about psychophysical responses to their stimulation. Some of these biological and psychophysical facts are the property of most adult humans and long have been common knowledge. Their widespread currency may obscure the role which they necessarily play in specification of stimuli.

Some perfectly acceptable psychophysical experiments involve stimuli for which no useful physical measurements exist at present. Studies on the intelligibility of speech are a good example. Among the stimuli for these experiments are utterances such as nonsense syllables or monosyllabic words. The experimenter distinguishes these linguistic stimuli on the basis of his own acoustic discriminations [57]; judges other than the experimenter make virtually the same distinctions. Lack of efficient physical measurements for the utterances themselves has not prevented the securing of reproducible data on intelligibility of speech under various conditions of communication.

Experiments like those on the intelligibility of speech emphasize the role of the experimenter's own discriminations in specification of stimuli. It is a truism that he discriminates whenever he specifies stimuli, even through physical means. Physical measurements rely on classes of human discrimination which afford a high degree of interobserver consensus. The success of physical science shows that such discriminations exist but hardly proves that they are exclusive to physical practices. Full resolution of theoretical problems in specification of stimuli may await a theory of scientific measurement which orders classes of discriminations according to the probability of agreement between observers. In the meantime, psychophysics will continue to rely upon physical measurement to the greatest possible extent.

Other aspects of a set of stimuli besides its variable properties may affect secondarily the outcome of a psychophysical experiment. A set of stimuli is a finite sample from an infinite population having the same fixed and variable properties. A sample of stimuli has a particular size and composition; it also has a range over any quantitatively measured variable. The size, range, and composition of a set of stimuli may themselves influence experimental results. "Anchoring" and "context" effects [105, chap. 9] show that a subject's response to a given stimulus may depend partly upon the other stimuli used during an experiment.

Programs for presentation of stimuli. Psychophysicists have devised numerous programs for presentation of stimuli. Under single-stimulus programs, E administers one "variable" stimulus at a time to O. At the start of a session, E may expose certain "standard" stimuli and O then must judge the variable stimuli relative to the standards. For example, E begins a category-rating experiment by showing the extremes of the range of stimuli to O, who then must divide this range into "equally spaced" categories. With the method of absolute judgments, in contrast, there is no standard stimulus at all.

Multiple-stimulus programs require E to present two or more stimuli on each trial to O, who then responds to some relationship between the stimuli. The members of a multiple-stimulus combination must occur in some fixed spatial or temporal order. These spatial or temporal relationships have systematic effects on O's responses and result in so-called space or time "errors." Multiple-stimulus programs compensate for these effects by counterbalancing order within a given combination across trials. In turn, counterbalancing requires E to translate O's overt responses into a new set of responses before treating the data. For example, the classical experiment on differential sensitivity to lifted weights involves presentation of a standard weight to one hand and a variable weight to the other hand of the subject. The subject does not know which weight is standard and which is variable. He must respond by indicating which hand holds the heavier weight. The experimenter counterbalances the spatial order of standard and variable weights over successive trials. Before any computations on the data, E translates each overt response of "left-hand weight heavier" and "right-hand weight heavier" into a response of "standard heavier" or "variable heavier," depending on which weight he had placed on the side called "heavier." The set of translated responses cannot be larger than the set of permissible overt responses; and each translation must yield a unique result.[5]

---

[5] Blackwell's [8] "forced-choice" methods also require translation of O's responses. In these methods, O indicates in which of several possible spatial or temporal positions a stimulus occurred. The experimenter translates each response into "correct" or "incorrect" and thereby partials out the effect of time or place of occurrence of stimuli. Blackwell's methods present some secondary problems of their own. For example, the number of possible choices confronting O may influence probability of a correct response.

Programs for presentation of stimuli also fix the time between trials and the order of stimuli (or combinations of stimuli) over successive trials. These two factors also can influence experimental results. Most programs for presentation of stimuli use randomized blocks of successive stimuli; a few, such as the method of limits, determine the sequence of stimuli on the combined basis of O's responses and the order of the stimuli along a physical dimension. The need for ascending and descending series in the method of limits results from behavioral effects due to ordering of stimuli over successive trials.

Instructions. Verbal instructions which define the subject's task are the hallmark of psychophysical experiments on man. Comparison of verbal instructions with corresponding operations in psychophysical experiments on animals brings out the behavioral role of instructions. Psychophysical studies on animals generally require establishment of a discrimination, so that the subject makes one response to one subset of stimuli and a different response to another subset. Definition of a task therefore involves two major behavioral aspects of instructions. First, the instructions delimit for O the set of permissible responses. For human psychophysical experiments, the responses may be utterances such as "left-hand weight greater" or "six." In such cases, the experimenter exploits a repertory of responses which the subject already brings to the experiment. The second main aspect of instructions is that they induce O to use a given response (or subset of responses) with high probability under certain conditions of stimulation. For example, the instructions may bring O to press key A when a stimulus is present and to press key B when a stimulus is absent. The instructions could just as well make O use these two responses in the opposite way.

Psychophysical experiments on animals often use differential reinforcement in order to establish and maintain a stable relationship between a response and various stimuli. The experimenter may differentially reinforce the subject's behavior on every trial. Alternatively, he may reinforce only certain S-R relations and rely on stimulus generalization to mediate others. The S-R linkages picked for reinforcement must be capable of a high probability of occurrence, in order to avoid purely random responding by the subject. Experiments on human psychophysical subjects generally have not used differential reinforcement. Research inspired by signal-detection theory [95, 96] provides a significant exception and demonstrates the effect of different payoff conditions on human discriminative behavior.

Even in the absence of explicit differential reinforcement in human experiments, verbal instructions seem to rely on a process quite analogous to stimulus generalization in psychophysical experiments on animals. The instructions assure a high probability of a given response or subset of responses to certain stimuli and place looser restrictions on O's choice of responses under other stimulus conditions. The many studies on *Einstellung* and set have pointed up the subtleties (and ambiguities) of this procedure. Under certain conditions, differential reinforcement could buttress or even replace verbal instructions in human psychophysics. Differential reinforcement, however, is possible only when *E* can classify *O*'s responses as "correct" or "incorrect" with respect to the variable properties of preceding stimuli. For example, responses of "left-hand weight heavier" in a study on lifted weights are correct whenever the left-hand weight is physically heavier than the right-hand one. Responses of "right-hand weight heavier" are correct under the opposite conditions. Given such a classification, *E* can differentially reinforce at least some correct responses. Application of these methods of behavioral control which have been developed in animal experiments to certain human psychophysical work might reduce some ambiguities in verbal instructions.

In certain other experiments on human subjects, however, a reinforcement approach to instructions would yield trivial results. An example is magnitude estimation of loudness, where *O* must call a standard stimulus by a certain number, say "ten," and assign each variable stimulus a number proportionate to its loudness relative to the standard. The subject must say "ninety" to a variable stimulus which sounds nine times louder than the standard. Now *E* might try to classify *O*'s responses as correct or incorrect on either of two grounds. He might reinforce *O* for responses which match the ratios of physical intensities between stimuli. This procedure would train *O* to commit the "stimulus error," which occurs when the subject tries to guess the physical value of a stimulus. Alternatively, *E* might reinforce *O* for making the same response on each trial which *E* would have made if he were the subject. This experiment would be a bizarre combination of a guessing game and paired-associates learning.

Although differential reinforcement may be impossible in psychophysical experiments where *E* cannot unambiguously classify *O*'s responses as correct or incorrect, these experiments yield nontrivial and orderly results. Verbal instructions such as those for magnitude estimation establish relationships between responses and aspects of a subject's experiences. Under instructions which contain experiential terminology, subjects do behave in an orderly fashion. One might argue that subjects have learned in the past to associate particular numbers with particular physical values of stimuli. Since many subjects who give consistent results do not know a decibel from a doorbell, this argument seems totally unconvincing. We will defer temporarily a more detailed discussion of the role of experiential terminology in psychophysics.

Sets of responses. The set of permissible responses for a psychophysical experiment usually is finite and may include the null class, "no response." This set forms a sample from an infinite population of the same generic type. A set of responses, like a set of stimuli, has a certain size, composition, and sometimes a definable range. These sampling characteristics and the generic type of a set of responses may affect psychophysical findings. Permissible responses for some experiments form a theoretically infinite set of a certain generic type. For example, O may use any positive real number in making magnitude estimations. Experiments which use reaction time as the dependent variable also permit a theoretically infinite set of responses, since E treats each value of reaction time as a different response.

On each trial of an experiment, E must distinguish which response O actually made. The experimenter can do this by direct observation or by noting the output of some physical device upon which O's behavior operates. Many psychophysical experiments require O to adjust a variable stimulus to some criterion, such as equality, relative to a standard. The subject's responses are the stimulus settings at the end of each trial. The subject has available a theoretically infinite set of responses. Conditional probabilities of response for adjustment experiments are the ratio of trials which ended with particular settings of the variable stimulus to all trials which began with a given value of the standard.

Restrictions on the set of permissible responses differentiates psychophysical data from introspective or phenomenological protocols. These restrictions help to ensure the repeatability of a psychophysical experiment. Absence of replicable and stringent limitations on responses enormously complicates the problem of deciding whether two experiments have yielded similar or contradictory results. The history of introspectionism speaks eloquently on this point. The stimuli in many introspective experiments were carefully presented; the instructions were detailed and precise. The subject, however, was free to give a copious set of verbalizations to each stimulus. Comparison of results from replications of an experiment became virtually impossible. This glut of responses contributed to the ultimate demise of introspectionism.

Computational Devices in Psychophysics

Quantitative methodology in psychophysics aims at reduction of S-R observations to a small set of summary numbers. These numbers permit mathematical representation of experimental results. There are two distinct classes of computational devices in psychophysics, which will be denoted respectively as S statistics and R statistics. S statistics are measured in stimulus units and include such contrivances as thresholds, point of subjective equality, and average settings in adjustment experiments. R statistics yield scale values for a set of stimuli; these scale values rest on assumptions about probability functions of responses over an abstract space.

S statistics. Computational routines for liminal psychophysics produce S statistics which describe the distribution of a given response to various stimuli. For example, an experiment on absolute thresholds requires O to indicate on each trial whether a stimulus is present or absent. As intensity of stimulation increases from zero, the likelihood of the response "present" grows. In terms of conditional probabilities, the absolute threshold is the intensity at which the conditional probability of a positive response reaches some chosen level, usually 0.50. Difference limens similarly describe distributions of conditional probabilities of responses of "greater than" or "less than" which result from judging variable stimuli against a given standard. The point of subjective equality is another such statistic. It may be the mode of a distribution of equality judgments or the intersection of probability functions for responses of "greater than" and "less than."

When conditional probabilities of any liminal response (except "equal") are plotted against the values of a variable stimulus applied in combination with a given standard, the resulting distribution is a *psychometric function*. (For experiments on absolute thresholds, the standard is a stimulus of zero intensity.) The psychometric function thus is a monotonic function of the variable dimension of stimulation. When this function follows a convenient mathematical form, thresholds acquire even greater significance. If the psychometric function is a normal distribution (the so-called "normal cumulative curve"), the threshold is one of two parameters which suffices for reconstruction of the entire distribution. The other parameter expresses variability and has appeared in the older literature in the guise of the measure of "precision" or as a measure of differential sensitivity itself. The importance of the phi-gamma [101] and phi-log-gamma [99] hypotheses rests on these considerations. The former hypothesis states that the psychometric function is a normal distribution of the variable dimension of stimulation; the latter hypothesis states that the distribution is normal against the logarithm of the variable dimension. When either hypothesis is correct, two statistics completely summarize the entire psychometric function. In practice, it usually is impossible to discriminate between the two hypotheses for a given set of data, since the range of variable stimuli over which probability of a liminal response changes is very small.

Psychophysicists generally have tried to apply the phi-gamma hypothesis in treatment of distributions of liminal responses. The physical quantum approach to visual thresholds [72] and the theory of the neural quantum [94] are relatively recent developments which propose abandonment of the phi-gamma hypothesis. Both departures result in mathematical forms for the psychometric function which are simpler than the normal distribution. The phi-gamma hypothesis assumes continuity on both the physical and the psychological sides. The physical quantum approach relaxes this assumption on the physical side and the theory of the neural quantum does the same for hypothesized psychological processes.

S statistics also summarize data obtained by a wide variety of adjustment methods in psychophysics. In the usual method of adjustment, O sets a variable stimulus equal to a standard; bisection methods require him to set a variable stimulus so that it divides the interval between two standards exactly in half; ratio production poses the task of setting a variable stimulus to a specified "apparent multiple" of a standard, and so forth. The median or mean setting in relation to a given standard summarizes results from such experiments. Successive cumulation of number of equal intervals from bisection and equisection procedures has produced psychophysical scales. So has successive cumulation of number of just noticeable differences (jnd's), on the now tarnished assumption that jnd's are psychologically equal. More direct methods of scaling, however, utilize R statistics.

R statistics. In direct methods of scaling, a subject may use a relatively large number of responses. For example, he may place stimuli in perhaps a dozen or more categories, or he may use any positive real number to describe the subjective ratio between two stimuli. The experimenter treats the resulting S-R observations by reducing them to scale values. A scale value for a stimulus helps to summarize the distribution of conditional probabilities of different responses to that stimulus. R statistics thus are the converse of S statistics, which deal with the distribution of a given response to different stimuli.

To scale a set of stimuli, E must first assign a numerical "R value" to each response. The R values embed the responses in some abstract space. The experimenter then can form probability functions of responses to each stimulus over that space. (Technically, he forms density functions of conditional probabilities, since the integral of each probability function is unity.) For most supraliminal experiments, the space is unidimensional and the R values impose a unique order on the responses. Multidimensional psychophysics [100] seeks a Euclidean space of least dimensionality, which allows an internally consistent embedding of responses.

Two different approaches now exist to rules for assigning R values. Thurstone [98] proposed the first approach, which embeds responses in a Euclidean space where the probability density function of R values to any stimulus is Gaussian ("bell-shaped"). Distance is the fundamental property of a Euclidean space. Thurstone's methods make the scale distance between two stimuli equal to the distance between the R values of the most probable (modal) responses to those stimuli. By a well-known statistical theorem, the variances of the Gaussian density functions of the R values play an essential role in determining this distance. Successive cumulation of scale distances yields scale values which E can plot against the parameter of stimulation. The scale values are unique up to a linear transformation of the form $y = ax + b$ and therefore at best lie on a scale which permits measurement of intervals only. Behaviorally, the scale values contain information about both the modal response and variability of responses to each stimulus. The experimenter can recover the original density functions of R values from the scale values.

From work on category rating and magnitude estimation, Stevens [88, 90] has evolved a very different approach to assignment of R values. In these experiments, O places stimuli in equally spaced categories or judges the apparent ratio between two stimuli. His responses are numbers which the experimenter treats as differences or ratios in the field of real numbers. This procedure assumes that O has an internal measuring device which can generate intervals and ratios and that O's responses are linear functions of subjective intervals or subjective ratios. The experimenter simply computes the median response to each stimulus and plots the medians as real numbers against the parameter of stimulation. The scale values for a set of stimuli then are linear or scalar transformations of the median R values of responses to each stimulus. A measure of variability of responses to a given stimulus does not enter into determination of the scale value for that stimulus. This fact reflects choice of an algebraic rather than a Euclidean-Gaussian geometric model for representation of R values.

Psychophysical experiments which use reaction time as the dependent variable [54] are formally similar to experiments on scaling. The experimenter treats each reaction time as a separate response, computes the median reaction time to each stimulus, and plots the results against the variable dimension of stimulation. This routine actually is a predecessor of Stevens' methods. The median reaction time summarizes the distribution of different responses to each stimulus. This parallelism suggests that systematic exploration of relationships between reaction time and other supraliminal results might prove worthwhile.

Forms of Psychophysical Functions

Psychophysics is primarily concerned with functions which relate probability of response to parameters of stimulation such as sound intensity, concentration, visual angle, etc. These parameters of stimulation are first-order independent variables. The dependent variables in psychophysical functions are S statistics or R statistics which summarize distributions of probabilities of response. The empirical variables of psychophysics also include numerous second-order independent variables which often influence experimental findings. Among the second-order variables are size, range, and composition of a sample of stimuli; programs for presentation of stimuli; reinforcement or "payoff" conditions in instructions; and size, range, composition, and generic class of a set of responses. Psychophysical functions thus express two kinds of invariances. First-order invariances show regularities in relationships between probability of response and parameters of stimulation despite changes in second-order variables. Second-order invariances show regularities in the effects of second-order variables on conditional probability of response.

First-order invariances.   For a given type of task, changes in second-order independent variables may affect a psychophysical function which relates S statistics or R statistics to a parameter of stimulation. A first-order invariance occurs when the form of this function remains constant despite changes in second-order variables. At least two experiments with different arrangements of second-order variables are necessary (but hardly sufficient) to establish a first-order invariance. The precision of a first-order invariance depends on the particular problem under study. Some experiments are relatively insensitive to the effects of second-order variables, while the outcomes of others notably reflect the operation of second-order variables. Figure 11 shows a restricted but instructive example of a first-order invariance. The figure shows that changing permissible responses from numbers to adjectives hardly affects category ratings of loudness. (The category ratings in this instance are plotted against the sone scale of loudness derived from magnitude estimations.)

There are two types of first-order invariances. A first-order invariance of type 1 relates probability of response to a single parameter of a population of stimuli. A first-order invariance of type 2 is an empirical law relating probability of response to a similar parameter of several populations of stimuli. Weber's law, Fechner's law, the power law [89], and general hypotheses about the shape of the psychometric function all are attempts to establish first-order invariances of type 2. These latter statements relate a systematic dependent variable ("difference limen," "subjective intensity," "probability of a response of greater than") to a systematic independent variable ("intensity," "parameter of stimulation"). The systematic variables assume concrete meanings only in particular experiments. Intensity may mean sound pressure level, concentration of sodium chloride, etc. Correspondingly, difference limen or subjective intensity may refer to loudness, saltiness, etc. First-order invariances of type 1 greatly extend the empirical significance of those of type 2. Without the former, the latter would cover experiments conducted only under very specific arrangements of second-order variables.

Second-order invariances. These describe regularities in the behavioral effects of independent empirical variables other than properties of stimuli. At least four experiments are necessary to uncover a second-order invariance. For example, changes in the composition of a sample of stimuli affect category ratings of loudness [93]. A similar effect occurs in category ratings of apparent visual size. Two category-rating experiments with auditory stimuli and two with visual forms are necessary to

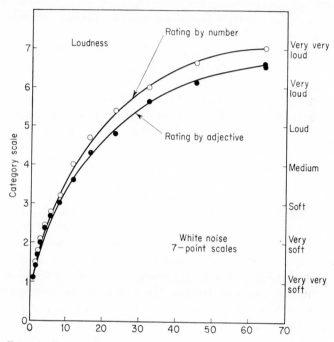

FIG. 11. Seven-point category scales of loudness for white noise plotted against magnitude estimations of loudness in sones. Filled circles show rating by adjective (right-hand ordinate) and open circles rating by numbers (left-hand ordinate). General form of function remains unaltered despite changes in characteristics of permissible responses [93].

show regular behavioral effects of the second-order variable of composition of a sample of stimuli. Psychophysicists have not devoted much effort to general quantification of second-order invariances. Certain aspects of Helson's theory of adaptation level [48] constitute one such attempt. Second-order effects tend to be more prominent in supraliminal than in liminal problems. The recent growth of work on scaling may encourage further systematic accounts of second-order invariances.

Experiential Terminology in Psychophysics

Statements of first-order psychophysical invariances often contain such terms as *hue, brightness, loudness,* or *subjective intensity,* which apparently refer to experiences of subjects. These terms also play a necessary role in verbal instructions to human subjects in many successful experiments. Dropping experiential terms from the vocabulary of psychophysics would seriously hamper or perhaps prevent communication between experimenters. Furthermore, it would eliminate from psychophysics many orderly behavioral results obtained through verbal instructions.

Behavioristic analyses of psychophysics have recognized these facts and have never suggested that psychophysicists cease using experiential terms in verbal instructions and in scientific communication. Instead, these analyses have tried to justify this dual usage on the grounds that experiential terms have rather different meanings for the experimenter and for the subject. Bergmann and Spence [5] argue that observed S-R relationships provide operational definitions of experiential terms in the experimenter's "pragmatic metalanguage." Graham takes a similar tack in proposing that such terms are the psychophysicist's labels for or constructs from his experimental results. All of these authors imply that the subject has different meanings for experiential terms. Bergmann and Spence mention the "object language" of the subject while Graham suggests that experiential terms in verbal instructions "control a subject's activity."

The fact remains that the experimenter can communicate with the subject through verbal instructions. The experimenter therefore has access both to his scientific meanings and to the subject's meanings for experiential terms. Furthermore, the subject's meanings necessarily form part of the experimenter's scientific meanings for such terms. The reason for this is quite simple. In many parts of experimental psychology, the distinction between experimenter and subject is unequivocal. Experimenters build boxes for animals but animals cannot retaliate in kind. In human psychophysics, however, the distinction between experimenter and subject breaks down. The experimenter can and usually does serve as a subject, formally or informally. The experimenter's observations as a subject inevitably enter into his scientific meanings for experiential terms. The very success of verbal instructions often depends on the experimenter's prior acuteness as his own subject. The object language of the subject and the pragmatic metalanguage of the experimenter therefore share some important denotations in common.

Statements of first-order invariances which contain experiential terms rest on a complex correlation between the psychophysicist's experiences as a subject, including observations of his own overt behavior as a formal subject, and his observations of the overt responses of other subjects to experimental stimuli. Confirmation of these statements may occur in various ways. A psychophysicist may set up a demonstration for his colleagues and be rewarded with verbal responses of "Ah, yes" (or be chagrined by rather different sorts of verbal responses). A psychophysicist may replicate another worker's stimulus conditions and literally see (or hear or smell) for himself. Another kind of confirmation comes from repeating on new subjects the behavioral observations of another experimenter. Finally, and perhaps most importantly, the experimenter can replicate on other subjects an experiment which he already has carried out on himself. This requires that he establish a set of permissible overt responses and appropriate instructions. His own observations as a subject may be upheld in different ways. Confirmation may involve agreement between S statistics or R statistics based on other subjects' behavior and estimates of those statistics from the experimenter's prior observations as a subject. At the other extreme, confirmation may represent duplication between the behavior of other subjects and the experimenter's behavior as a formal subject run by someone else.

Experiential statements in psychophysics are acceptable only when they rest on agreement between different modes of confirmation. Furthermore, behavioral observations on other subjects must represent first-order invariances. The experimenter must check for second-order effects; alternatively, he may use arrangements of second-order variables which are known to produce minor effects. The requirement of first-order invariances is the outgrowth of certain failures of the classical model of the psychophysical subject.

The classical psychophysical model and its failures. Behavioral data from a psychophysical experiment form alternating stimuli and responses in a chain. As a subject, the psychophysicist notices a chain of experiences alternately ascribable to environmental stimuli and to his own overt responses. This strongly suggests a representation of another subject in a psychophysical experiment which runs $S_i \epsilon_l R_k S_j \epsilon_e R_l S_i \epsilon_r R_m$ . . . where S and R represent stimulus and response respectively and ϵ represents aspects of the subject's experience. For example, ϵ_l might be feeling a weight in the left hand as heavier than one in the right, ϵ_r might be the opposite, and ϵ_e might be feeling the two weights as equal. So far, the psychophysicist is doing no more than everyone does in everyday life. The scientific problems arise when the psychophysicist assigns to the S-ϵ-R chain quantitative properties which have some implications for observed S-R relationships. This assignment partly consists of characterizing the conditional probabilities which link S, ϵ, and R. Classical psychophysics made two strong assumptions about these probabilities:

(1) The conditional probabilities $p(R_k|\epsilon_i)$ are unity, zero, or $1/w$, where w is the size of a subset of permissible responses; and (2) the entire chain depends only on first-order conditional probabilities, so that $p(R_k|S_i) = \sum_j p(R_k|\epsilon_j)p(\epsilon_j|S_i)$. These two assumptions have implications which some behavioral data contradict.

Largely because of assumption 1, the model implies that behavioral results obtained with n permissible results should directly forecast results obtained with a subset of m of those responses, where $m < n$. The quarrel over the use of equality judgments [105, chap. 8] in obtaining difference limens stemmed from the failure of this implication. According to the model, subjects allowed only responses of "Greater Than" and "Less Than" in an experiment on differential sensitivity should use these responses with equal probability when two stimuli seem equal. Thus, three-category results where responses of "Equal" are allowed should predict two-category results in a very simple way. Experimental tests showed that this is not the case. Subjects seem to have preferences for one or another response in the two-category situation.

Assumption 2 has encountered even graver difficulties. It implies, for example, that serial-response probabilities $p(R_l|R_k)$ should not differ from $\sum_i p(R_l|S_i)p(S_i|R_k)$. An extensive set of findings shows quite the opposite [102, 103]. Furthermore, the assumption has difficulty in accounting for anchoring and context effects. These effects show that a subject's response on a given trial may depend partly on stimuli which occurred on preceding trials. Various failures of the classical model thus have driven psychophysicists to rely on first-order invariances of type 1. These invariances permit some estimate of quantitative relationships between S and ϵ. The precision of the estimate varies inversely with the degree to which second-order variables contaminate experimental results.

The present status of the classical psychophysical model is therefore rather complicated. This model, or some variant of it which retains assumption 2 intact, seems defensible for experiments in which second-order effects are negligible or essentially linear. This often happens in studies on liminal problems. For example, the form of the scotopic or the photopic luminosity curve seems quite insensitive to second-order variables. Again, the relationship of $\Delta I/I$ to I (intensity) within a given modality is quite constant. The function is always higher for lower values of I. The discovery of nonlinearities in second-order effects certainly does not justify the conclusion that such effects are inherently nonlinear. It only means that second-order effects require investigation in order to assess their magnitude and nonlinearity, if any. This essentially is another way of stating the need for first-order invariances as support for statements which contain experiential terminology.

The psychophysics of intensity. Recent discoveries in supraliminal psychophysics also indicate that some variant of the classical psychophysical model is valid for certain classes of experiments on scaling. This version of the model retains assumption 2 intact and also assumes in effect that R statistics are linear functions of scale values for ϵ. The model essentially requires second-order effects in scaling experiments to be linear. Stevens [88] and Stevens and Galanter [93] adduce considerable evidence that this is indeed the case for magnitude estimations

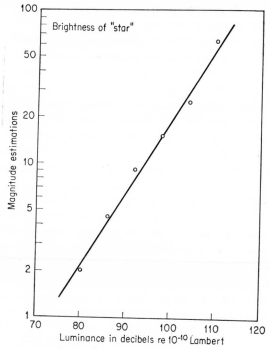

Fig. 12. Magnitude estimation scale for brightness of a small target (about 1.5 min of arc) which simulates a star [93].

of stimuli which vary along certain physical dimensions. For example, changes in the composition of a sample of stimuli do not disturb magnitude estimations of apparent intensity. In contrast, such changes produce nonlinear effects on category (and other interval) judgments of apparent intensity. Magnitude estimations lead to the power law, which states that equal ratios of physical intensity produce equal ratios of subjective intensity. Figure 12 shows results for magnitude estimations of brightness of a small, starlike target. The data fall on a straight line in log-log coordinates, in accordance with the power law. The exponents of power functions for different domains of stimulation range from about 0.3 to about 3.5. Cross-modality matches confirm the exponents (and the power law) quite well [91].

Stevens has concluded that the power law provides a ratio scale of subjective magnitude. This conclusion, however, has required qualification. On a physical ratio scale, such as weight or length, both intervals and ratios are defined. Furthermore, intervals and ratios are linearly related according to the distributive law. If a and b are (real) numbers on a ratio scale and k is a positive real multiplier, then $ka - kb = k(a - b)$. For psychological scales, separate judgments

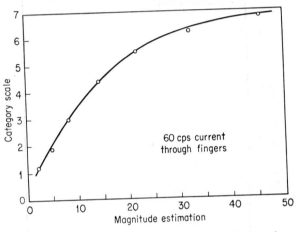

FIG. 13. Category scale plotted against magnitude estimation scale for 60 cps electrocutaneous stimuli through the fingers [92].

yield subjective intervals and ratios. If the distributive law held, interval judgments would be a linear function of ratio judgments. A mass of data shows just the opposite. Category scales are concave downward against magnitude scales of subjective intensity [93]. Figures 10 and 13 illustrate this finding. Stevens suggests that differences between weak stimuli are relatively more impressive than differences between strong stimuli, due to the assymmetry of sensitivity which also produces Weber's law. This assymmetry distorts the ratio scale of subjective intensity during category judgments, thereby preventing expression of the distributive law.

An alternative interpretation is that magnitude estimations produce scales which do not have all of the properties of physical ratio scales.[6] This interpretation may take either of two different forms. The first is

[6] The analysis offered here sprang partly from highly informal conversations with E. H. Galanter, R. D. Luce, and W. S. Torgerson.

that subjects respond only to ratios of subjective intensity and that intervals are psychologically meaningless. The second is that subjects respond only to subjective intervals and that ratios are psychologically meaningless for judgments of intensity. If the first variant is correct, then category and interval scales are really distorted measures of subjective ratios. Suppose that C is an overt response in a category-rating experiment and that $\psi(C)$ is the subjective magnitude corresponding to C. Helm, Messick, and Tucker [47] have pointed out that a subject could establish equal intervals by making $\psi(C + 1)/\psi(C) = \psi(C)/\psi(C - 1)$. Computations on C which assume that it is a linear function of subjective magnitude introduce an implicit logarithmic transformation on ψ. Galanter and Messick [28] have analyzed interval judgments of loudness in accordance with this suggestion. They find that a theoretically appropriate antilogarithmic transformation on interval-scale values makes the latter a linear function of magnitude estimations of loudness. They also point out that category scales empirically are logarithmic functions of magnitude-estimation scales.

Although these data suggest that judgments of subjective ratios are fundamental, they also support an argument with exactly the opposite implication. Suppose that category judgments gave a linear function of ψ and that subjects could not respond to subjective ratios. If $\psi(R)$ were the subjective impression corresponding to an overt ratio judgment of R, subjects could set up equal ratios by making

$$\psi(KR) - \psi(R) = \psi(R) - \psi(R/K)$$

where $K > 1$. Equal overt ratios would correspond to equal psychological intervals. A function of the form $\psi = a \cdot \log (bR) + c$ satisfies this condition. A logarithmic relationship between category and magnitude-estimation scales therefore is equally compatible with the view that subjects can only judge psychological intervals.

Two major experimental findings favor the interpretation that judgments of ratios are fundamental. First, the results of cross-modality matches of apparent intensity confirm the power law. It is hard to see how subjects could match subjective intensities of two stimuli if subjective intensity only formed an interval scale with no fixed zero point. Second, magnitude estimations are essentially unperturbed by changes in second-order variables. The exponent of the power function, which shows how rapidly subjective intensity grows, remains quite constant despite shifts in second-order variables. In contrast, second-order effects alter the slopes of category scales as functions of stimulus intensity. The form of these scales depends on spacing of stimuli and to some degree on the number of permissible responses. If interval judgments were basic, interval scales would contain an unknown, nonlinear "stretching" factor.

Furthermore, this stretching factor would not disturb magnitude estimations, which supposedly would represent further distortions of the "true" interval scales. This implication is hard to accept.

Choice of ratio judgments as fundamental therefore seems far the better alternative. This choice permits retention of assumption 2 of the classical psychophysical model and yields scales of subjective magnitude which display a high degree of invariance. These scales, however, have only the following properties:

1. For every subjective magnitude ψ produced by a stimulus on a given dimension of intensity, there is a positive real scale value $V(\psi)$.

2. For any ψ_i and any ψ_j $V(\psi_i)/V(\psi_j) = k$ and

$$V(\psi_j)/V(\psi_i) = 1/k$$

where k is a positive real number.

Under these conditions, differences simply are undefined on $V(\psi)$. Furthermore, the only permissible transformations on V are multiplication by a positive constant. Any other transformation would change the value of k in the second property. Luce's [60, 61] analysis of the possible psychophysical laws therefore still holds. In terms of algebraic theory, the numbers V lie in the Abelian multiplicative group of positive real numbers and not in the field of real numbers, where both addition and multiplication are possible and are related by the distributive law. The power law relates V to physical intensity I. Currently available data leave open the question of possible bounds on V for a given physical dimension. Intuitively, it seems hard to believe that V is unbounded; as Luce [61] points out, however, boundedness cannot be imposed simply on an arbitrary basis. The ambiguities surrounding the question of possible bounds on V make the power law and conditions 1 and 2 first approximations.

This argument also leads to a reinterpretation of Weber's law. The most adequate form of Weber's law is

$$\Delta I = aI + b \tag{1}$$

where ΔI is a just-noticeable difference and a and b are positive constants [66, 89]. This formula compensates for the universal finding that $\Delta I/I$ is larger for lower values of I and reasonably constant at higher values of I. Psychophysicists generally have presumed that just-noticeable *physical differences* necessarily imply just-noticeable *psychological intervals*. If ψ_d and ψ are respectively the subjective responses to stimuli of $(I + \Delta I)$ and I, this position states that $V(\psi_d) - V(\psi)$ determines discrimination. Fechner assumed that this difference was constant for all values of ψ and arrived at the logarithmic relationship between $V(\psi)$

and I through some unavoidably incorrect mathematics. Luce and Edwards [62] have formulated the correct derivation. If subjects only judge subjective ratios, however, then $V(\psi_d)/V(\psi)$ should determine discrimination. This idea actually is a more general form of Brentano's suggestion that psychological resolving power is relative. Stevens relates that Fechner derived the power law from Brentano's suggestion but stubbornly refused to accept the result [89]. Fechner's derivation, however, uses the old and inadequate form of Weber's law and the famous but indefensible "mathematical auxiliary principle." This principle in effect mistakenly equates difference equations to differential equations.

A simple algebraic procedure shows the relationship between the power law, Weber's law, and the assumption that resolving power is constant. A newer version of the power law [91] is

$$V(\psi) = c(I - I_o)^k \tag{2}$$

where I_o compensates for effects at low intensities. If resolving power were constant for all values of $V(\psi)$, then $V(\psi_d)/V(\psi) = D$. This is identical with Brentano's old formulation that $[V(\psi_d) - V(\psi)]/V(\psi)$ is constant; the present version does not use the undefined operation of subtraction on V. From Eq. (2), the assumption leads to

$$c(I + \Delta I - I_o)^k = cD(I - I_o)^k \tag{3}$$

and

$$\Delta I = (D^{1/k} - 1)I - (D^{1/k} - 1)I_o \tag{4}$$

There is a major discrepancy between Eq. (4) and Weber's law of Eq. (1). The additive constant in Eq. (4) is negative, since D exceeds unity and k is positive. The additive constant b in Eq. (1) is positive. The complete form of Weber's law and the power law therefore bear no simple relationship to each other. In fact, the two laws together imply that psychological resolving power gradually improves as $V(\psi)$ grows. As $V(\psi_d)/V(\psi)$ decreases, resolving power gets better. By combining Weber's law and the power law,

$$\frac{V(\psi_d)}{V(\psi)} = \frac{(I + aI + b - I_o)^k}{(I - I_o)^k} \tag{5}$$

and

$$\frac{V(\psi_d)}{V(\psi)} = \left(1 + \frac{b}{I - I_o} + \frac{aI}{I - I_o}\right)^k \tag{6}$$

Differentiation of the expression on the right shows that it has a negative slope for all values of I greater than I_o. This expression also is greater than unity for all I greater than I_o and approaches $(1 + a)^k$ as I increases. Resolving power therefore gradually improves as $V(\psi)$ grows, since $V(\psi_d)/V(\psi)$ gently decreases. The human psychophysical subject by this analysis is like an analog multiplier-divider whose accuracy gradually gets better at higher input levels. The power law and Weber's law together therefore imply that there is no simple a priori assumption by which scaling data can be derived from discriminability data. Assumptions of "equality" of jnd's as intervals or ratios cannot mediate the relationship between the two classes of data. Possibly, both Weber's law and the power law themselves are the consequence of some even more fundamental process in discrimination.

There presently are no clear grounds for choosing between Stevens's interpretation and the present analysis of recent findings in supraliminal psychophysics. The two views may very well be experimentally indistinguishable. We cannot presently conceive of an experimental procedure which would discriminate between them. Perhaps further theoretical and empirical work will bring out some substantive differences between the two analyses. In any event, the bulk of evidence in modern psychophysics increasingly testifies that Fechner's law is unconstitutional.

INTERRELATIONSHIPS BETWEEN PSYCHOPHYSICS AND NEUROPHYSIOLOGY

Empirical Relations

Examination of relationships between psychophysics and neurophysiology requires a slight reformulation of the properties of empirical functions from these two disciplines. A psychophysical function $P = f(i)$ shows the functional dependency of an S statistic or an R statistic P on a parameter of stimulation i. These statistics are based, of course, on probability of response. A neurophysiological function $N = g(i)$ shows the relation between a positive-stimulus (P-S) or an amplitude or time (A-T) measure of response and the parameter of stimulation i; in this function, N represents the measure of neuroelectric response. Attempts to "reduce" psychophysics to neurophysiology follow a common paradigm. This paradigm is to find a neurophysiological function $g(i)$ such that a linear transformation T exists between $f(i)$ and $g(i)$: $f = T(g)$. The transformation makes a behavioral measure P a dependent variable of an electrophysiological measure N. If the transformation is linear, the relation between P and N also is linear.

At best, contemporary interrelationships between psychophysical and neurophysiological functions sometimes approximate this ideal situation. Generally, empirical functions from these two disciplines show differing amounts of correspondence. A correspondence between a psychophysical and an electrophysiological function exists when the functions satisfy either of two conditions: (1) Both functions must be montonic over the same range of the parameter of stimulation; or (2) both must show maxima or minima at the same values of the parameter of stimulation. For neurophysiological functions which rest on A-T measures of neuro-electric responses, these requirements usually mean that the most sensitive measure of response generates a function with the best correspondence to a psychophysical function. A review of contemporary data will show how the precision of correspondence between functions from psychophysics and neurophysiology varies from case to case.

Absolute sensitivity. Both neuroelectric and psychophysical responses show absolute thresholds. Stimuli must lie within or exceed a certain range of intensity before behavioral or neuroelectric responses occur. There are lower bounds on the sensitivity of single neurons in the visual [2, 17, 37], auditory [1, 14], somatosensory [75, 107], and gustatory [71] systems. Furthermore, near-threshold responses from a single neuron may have probabilistic properties, as do psychophysical responses [25]. The probability of either type of response seems to be a normal distribution as a function of stimulus intensity. Similar limitations exist on the level of intensity of stimulation which produces detectable multi-unit responses [31].

Available evidence suggests, however, that electrical responses from specialized peripheral receptors and the terminal portions of afferent fibers may not have an absolute threshold in any important sense. The cochlear microphonic appears at stimulus energies below those necessary for behavioral or other neuroelectric responses to sound [14]. "Generator potentials" in crayfish stretch-receptor and mammalian Pacinian corpuscle [37, 38] arise at stimulus intensities which do not produce spikes in afferent fibers. Thus, neural barriers to psychophysical sensitivity may involve events proximal to the level of receptors and receptor-nerve junctions. This hypothesis also is consistent with the finding that a single rod probably responds to one quantum of light while several quanta are necessary for visual sensation [72].

Various parameters of stimulation have corresponding effects on psychophysical and electrophysiological absolute sensitivity. Visual adaptation [37, 44] and acoustic masking and fatigue [76] change psychophysical and electrophysiological thresholds in parallel ways. The form of the psychophysical scotopic sensitivity curve remarkably resembles observations on constant electrophysiological outputs from a dark-adapted preparation to stimuli of different wave lengths [37, pp. 116–118]. Similar data on cochlear microphonics show a general but somewhat less precise correspondence to the audiometric function which relates absolute auditory sensitivity to the frequency of sinusoidal tones [104]; the discrepancies apparently reflect in part the method used for recording the microphonics. Finally, absolute thresholds for many single-unit and multiunit responses from the nervous system are of quite comparable magnitude to psychophysical thresholds.

"Submodality" specificity. Single neural units in the visual and auditory systems do not respond in the same pattern to stimuli of different wave lengths or frequencies. These findings bear some correspondence to hue and pitch discrimination; the exact nature of these correspondences presently is not entirely clear [1, 14, 37]. Analogous submodality specificity also occurs to some degree in neuroelectric responses from different somatosensory or gustatory single neurons [6, 71, 107]. A single somatosensory fiber, for example, may be highly sensitive to cutaneous temperature and quite insensitive to mechanical stimulation of the skin. The problem of submodality specificity actually arises from psychological distinctions between different classes of subjective events, such as "touch" versus "pain." The general assumption of linear relationships between psychophysical and neurophysiological responses implies that classes of neurophysiological events should match subjective distinctions on a one-to-one basis. Neurophysiologists have sought these corresponding classes of neuroelectric events in the activity of separate classes of neurons. So far, this search has not proved completely successful.

Temporal interactions. Temporal parameters of stimulation have similar influences on psychophysical and electrophysiological functions. Intensity-time relationships for visual thresholds have appeared in both types of investigations [35, 43]. The subjective intensity of the second of two equal stimuli delivered in rapid succession is lower than that of the first one in both audition and somesthesis; neuroelectric responses in the acoustic and somatosensory pathways to the second of two successive stimuli also suffer a decline [78]. These interactions decrease as the intensity of the first stimulus decreases or as the interval between stimuli lengthens. Although precise data are lacking, neurophysiological interactions between responses to successive stimuli in anesthetized preparations may run a longer time course than psychophysical interactions. Finally, there is extensive electrophysiological and psychophysical work on visual flicker [3, 37]. The neurophysiological results show a steady decline in the size of neuroelectric responses as flash rate increases toward psychophysical critical fusion frequency. Stimulus parameters such as intensity which affect critical fusion frequency also seem to influence neuroelectric responses to a train of flashes; the quantitative relations between these parameters and electrophysiological responses to flicker are not yet clear.

Differential sensitivity. There are some good correspondences between psychophysical and electrophysiological data on spatial acuity in the somesthetic and visual systems. Cutaneous and retinal regions with the highest spatial resolving power also have the largest projections into the central nervous system [80, 81, 82, 83]. For example, the fingers and lips have a much more extensive anatomical representation in the somatosensory pathway than does, say, the trunk or the forearm. Adjacent cutaneous and retinal loci, however, overlap in their central projections. True mosaic point-to-point projection does not exist. Recent work shows that adjacent spatial stimuli exert psychophysical and electrophysiological inhibitory effects on one another [4, 45, 68]. Neural inhibitory effects may partly compensate for overlapping central projections of adjacent loci on a receptive surface. These inhibitory mechanisms also may lie behind psychophysical contrast phenomena. Currently the correspondences between psychophysical and neurophysiological data on spatial acuity thus involve several different classes of neurophysiological functions. A fairly good rank-order correlation holds between spatial acuity and the size of central projections of different parts of the retina or of the skin. The data are too few as yet to tell whether the relationship is linear.

A very different story now prevails for research on differential sensitivity to intensity. Many neurophysiological responses change in a nonlinear, monotonic fashion with intensity of stimulation. Furthermore, single temperature fibers show effects corresponding to "paradoxical" temperature sensations at fairly extreme deviations from physiological zero [107]. Existing electrophysiological data suggest correctly that subjective magnitude should be a nonlinear function of intensity of stimulation. Beyond this, however, there are no obvious correspondences between the psychophysical power law and electrophysiological functions of intensity. About five years ago, Granit [37] suggested that frequency of spikes from single peripheral afferent axon increases logarithmically with intensity of stimulation. He took this as a correspondence between neurophysiology and Fechner's equation. If, as now seems true, Fechner's equation simply is incorrect or irrelevant for psychophysics, this potentially nice correspondence evaporates. Furthermore, amplitudes of multiunit responses to stimuli of different intensity do not obey a logarithmic law in any event; apparently amplitude is some sort of exponential function of intensity.

The Psychophysiological Preparation

Up to the present time, psychophysics and neurophysiology have shared sets of stimuli as a single, common class of independent variables.

Correspondences between functions from the two disciplines therefore have concerned first-order psychophysical invariances. These empirical correspondences tend to be imprecise in many instances. This fact partly reflects lack of systematic quantitative functions from one or another of the two disciplines; in part, it also is due to use of acute preparations for obtaining many electrophysiological functions. Clearly, acute physiological techniques produce an experimental subject which is quite far removed from the intact organisms used in psychophysics.

Two recent developments in neurophysiology promise to alter this situation. Neurophysiologists have perfected various preparations with chronically implanted macroelectrodes [16, 86], so that simultaneous behavioral and electrophysiological observations are now possible on the same animal. Newer techniques even permit extracellular recording from single neurons in the brain of an unanesthetized, unparalyzed animal [50, 51]. The other development is application of high-speed computer techniques in neurophysiology. For example, observation of single oscilloscopic tracings following a stimulus often does not permit detection of evoked activity from the brain of intact man. The spontaneous activity of the brain tends to swamp these responses, which may be rather small. Computers which average neuroelectric activity at each of many successive points in time after a stimulus make possible the recording of evoked responses through scalp leads in man [11, 15]. Averaging cancels out activity which is not locked in time to the stimulus and, as Fig. 14 shows, brings out activity which is. Through computer technology, one can now obtain neuroelectric functions from human subjects, even during a psychophysical experiment. Obviously, computer processing of neuroelectric activity also is applicable to experiments on animals.

Intact electrophysiological preparations may introduce some new independent variables into neurophysiology. Neuroelectric responses in these preparations may show habituation and perhaps other changes due to a past history of stimulation of the animal [49]. These responses also seem sensitive to external reinforcement, both positive and aversive [27, 46]. The past history and momentary state of an intact preparation therefore may influence its neuroelectric responses to environmental stimuli. Psychological techniques may prove essential in order to stabilize electrical responses in such a preparation. Programs for presentation of stimuli and instructions thus may become independent variables in neurophysiology. In turn, this might tighten up correspondence between psychophysics and neurophysiology and also might yield neurophysiological data relevant to second-order psychophysical invariances. A few results hint that extrinsic control of intact neurophysiological preparations may require more complex procedures than those used in the usual psychophysical experiment.

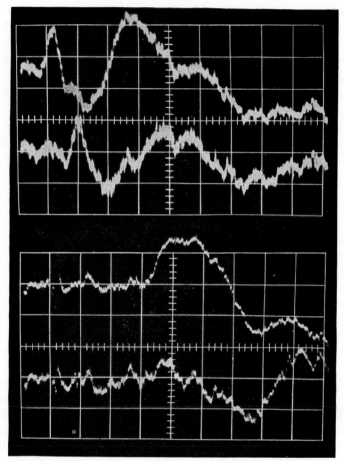

Fig. 14. Average cerebral responses from human subject to electrocutaneous shock to left index finger. First and third traces from top derived from scalp electrode over right post-Rolandic (cerebral somatosensory) area; second and fourth traces derived from scalp electrode 6 cm anterior to post-Rolandic site. Indifferent electrode on bridge of nose. Positivity upward. Top two traces are averages of 30 consecutive responses; calibrations, 50 msec and 4.2 μV per major division. Bottom two traces are averages of 60 consecutive responses; calibrations, 10 msec and 2.1 μV per major division. Stimulus occurs 10 msec after start of each trace and appears as small spike. Positive-negative sequence in fast record of third trace may be analogous to response in Fig. 9. Note absence of a similar early response at anterior site (fourth trace). Also note long, "late" responses at both electrodes in top two traces. Averaging carried out automatically on special-purpose computer for summation of evoked potentials.

Evoked neuroelectric responses arise in widespread regions of the brain in an intact preparation. Placement of recording electrodes thus raises a potentially serious problem of adequately sampling these responses. One way of facing this problem is use of large numbers of recording electrodes. The resulting data should slowly yield some picture of what constitutes an adequate electrical survey of the brain. Observations on anesthetized animals suggest that a given measure on single-unit or on multiunit responses from different neural loci will show high intercorrelations in many cases. These intercorrelations would reduce the need for widespread recordings from the brain. In other cases, however, the intercorrelations between responses from different loci in anesthetized animals are not very good. For example, recovery times at subthalamic stations along an afferent pathway are shorter than at thalamic or cortical stations [63, 77].

Another approach to sampling activity in the brain of an intact preparation is to record only from structures which ablation studies have shown to be essential for the discrimination under investigation. In many ablation studies, however, a given lesion has produced only transient effects on discriminative behavior. These results leave open the question of whether to sample areas whose removal produces only temporary behavioral deficits. A final and more radical approach would be simply to remove parts of the brain which are not essential for a given discrimination and to study neuroelectric activity in the remaining tissue. The investigator could surgically simplify an animal preparation before introduction of implanted electrodes. This procedure superficially seems very risky, since it leads to study of pathological preparations. The classical work of Sherrington's school on spinal reflexes, however, gives excellent precedent for the analytical value of this method. This work ultimately led to analysis of intracellular activity in motoneurons in the spinal animal.

Electrophysiological studies on chronic animals promise to widen and complicate theoretical and empirical relationships between psychophysics and neurophysiology. Psychophysical and neuroelectric responses to environmental stimuli also are open to study in the normal human subject. Data on neuroelectric activity in normal man, of course, are limited to recordings from superficial electrodes outside the brain. Recordings from within normal brains demand use of animal preparations. The relationships of the latter results to human neuroelectric activity and human psychophysical findings will depend partly on psychophysical studies on animal preparations. Thus, future investigation of the psychophysiology of discrimination probably will rest on psychophysical and neurophysiological data from both man and animals. Physiological analysis of neuroelectric activity also may continue to require acute animal preparations. Data from acute and chronic preparations therefore may afford still another set of intercorrelations which are relevant to psychophysics.

Perhaps one of the most formidable problems in future work will be the significance of recordings from single neurons in intact animals for the psychophysiology of discrimination. The relations between single-unit and multiunit activity presently are obscure in many respects. The wide variety of results from single neurons suggests that multiunit responses may be easier initially to correlate with behavioral data. Furthermore, sampling problems in study of activity from single units in intact animals may prove exceedingly intricate. There are so few data now on responses from single units in intact animals, however, that this suggestion is quite speculative.

Measurement, Theory, and the Assumption of Linearity

The idea of reduction of psychophysical to electrophysiological data involves the assumption or hope that a linear relationship exists between corresponding functions from the two disciplines. The same assumption also lies behind explicit neurological theories of psychophysical phenomena. Sometimes these theories almost function as labels for observed or presumed linear relations between corresponding functions. The duplex theory of vision, for example, appropriates electrophysiological observations on dark adaptation which show a two-limbed form. In other instances, such as Licklider's "triplex theory of pitch" [57], the theory sets up hypothesized neural activity of which discrimination is a linear function. The assumption of linearity thus appears at many points throughout theoretical relations between psychophysics and neurophysiology.

Review of empirical correspondences between the two disciplines raises some doubts, however, about the future status of this assumption. Existing correspondences seem fairly precise in the areas of absolute sensitivity and spatial acuity. The quantitative properties of these correspondences have not all received detailed study. The convergences between these psychophysical and electrophysiological data, however, are impressive enough to encourage the hope that a linear transformation will mediate these correspondences. Now neurophysiological sensitivity functions and maps of central projections rest upon positive-stimulus measures of neuroelectric responses. These measures show values of stimulation which produce detectable neuroelectric responses. Psychophysical sensitivity and spatial acuity functions utilize S statistics. The dependent variables in these neurophysiological and psychophysical functions thus are measured in stimulus units and are formally identical.

Other electrophysiological functions show how an amplitude or time measure of response changes with a property of stimuli. Neurophysiological functions which utilize A-T measures of response actually depend upon the distribution of an A-T measure to each value of the variable parameter of stimulation. Psychophysical scales based upon R statistics therefore are formally identical with these electrophysiological functions. Presumably, then, correspondence should obtain between psychophysical scales and electrophysiological functions which contain A-T measures. This idea forms the framework for Granit's attempt to relate frequency of discharge in a single peripheral axon to Fechner's logarithmic equation. Stevens's differentiation of prothetic from metathetic continua [89] takes a similar form. Prothetic continua, like brightness and loudness, display among other things a concave downward relationship of category to magnitude estimation scales; this relationship may be linear for metathetic continua like pitch. Stevens suggests that prothetic continua involve additive physiological processes while metathetic continua depend on substitution of excitation in one place in the nervous system for excitation in another. Prothetic continua therefore should correspond to electrophysiological A-T measures. Among such measures, frequency of firing in single neurons and amplitude of multiunit responses seem the most promising candidates for these correspondences. Both measures change monotonically over a wide range of stimulus intensities.

Current relationships between psychophysical scaling functions and neurophysiological A-T functions of intensity are nonlinear. These nonlinearities may spring from several different sources. One is that electrophysiological A-T functions give a biased or distorted picture of neuroelectrical activity. Recordings from single units may tend to pick out activity in larger neurons. Multiunit responses may reflect simultaneous operation of different physiological processes, such as excitatory and inhibitory postsynaptic potentials. Since too little is known about the extracellular fields which contribute to multiunit responses from nuclear regions, quantitative interpretation of amplitude measures on these responses is very difficult. Further neurophysiological experimentation may clarify these possible sources of distortion.

Another possible explanation of current nonlinear relations between psychophysical scales and neurophysiological A-T functions of intensity of stimulation goes much deeper and involves the very nature of A-T measures. Instrumentation for electrophysiology displays neuroelectric responses in terms of time and voltage. Both frequency of spikes and amplitude of graded potentials are measures on physical ratio scales. Amplitude measures on responses from a given locus usually are rendered dimensionless by referring these measures to the amplitude of the maximal response from that locus. Frequency of spikes properly could be made dimensionless by referring it to the spontaneous rate of firing in the single neuron under study. Luce's [61] results show that any mathematical relationship whatsoever may obtain between psychophysical scales and electrophysiological functions which use dimensionless A-T measures. The properties of dimensionless A-T measures therefore put no a priori restrictions on interrelations between psychophysics and neurophysiology.

Amplitude and time measures of neuroelectric activity, whether dimensionless or not, depend upon and have all of the formal properties of physical ratio scales. Nonlinearity in the transformation which carries an electrophysiological function into a psychophysical scaling function of intensity may mean that the nervous system does *not* produce behavior by operating linearly upon neuroelectric activity as we measure it with our particular instruments and physical ratio scales. An oversimplified example will illustrate this argument. Suppose that we assign a value of unity to spontaneous rate of firing in a single neuron and suppose further that rate of firing rises monotonically with intensity of stimulation. We plot relative frequency of firing against intensity. By its very nature, this plot implies that a change in relative frequency from, say, 3 to 4 is as important as an equal change from 20 to 21. In terms of discrimination, however, a change in relative frequency of firing from 3 to 4 may have a greater (or a smaller) effect than a change from 20 to 21. To put it another way, there is no reason to suppose that the nervous system has the exact analogue of an electronic events-per-unit-time meter. This argument suggests searching for invariant nonlinearities in relationships between psychophysical scales of intensity and corresponding neurophysiological functions based on A-T measures. The invariance of the power law over prothetic domains gives some mild hope for a successful search.

CONCLUDING REMARKS

Psychophysics and neurophysiology provide corresponding functions which show the effects of parameters of environmental stimuli. The degree of correspondence varies from case to case. The most satisfactory agreements at present obtain between psychophysical and electrophysiological functions whose dependent variables are measured in stimulus units. Weaker correspondences exist between scaling functions for prothetic domains and neuroelectric functions which rely on amplitude or temporal measures of response. Use of chronic physiological preparations may improve relationships between psychophysical and electrophysiological data. Experimental control of these preparations also may introduce some new, psychological independent variables into neurophysiology.

On a general theoretical level, relations between psychophysics and neurophysiology have implicitly involved the assumption of linear transformations which mediate the correspondences between the two fields.

At bottom, this assumption really holds that aspects of experience are linear functions of neuroelectric activity. The nature of electrophysiological measurement, however, may pose some serious challenges to this assumption. Biases in neurophysiological measurements which prevent attainment of a representative picture of neuroelectric processes are one such barrier. A more fundamental difficulty may lie in the possibility that the nervous system does not process neuroelectric activity in linear relationship to physical scales on which we measure it. Both factors may contribute simultaneously to the complexity of problems in physiological psychology. Further psychophysical and neurophysiological experimentation along with development of quantitative models of neuroelectric activity and its relationship to behavior may gradually resolve these problems.

REFERENCES

1. Ades, H. W. Central auditory mechanisms. In J. Field, H. W. Magoun, & V. Hall (Eds.), *Handbook of physiology*. Vol. 1. Washington: American Physiological Society, 1959.
2. Barlow, H. B., Fitzhugh, R., & Kuffler, S. W. Change of organization in the receptive fields of the cat's retina during dark adaptation. *J. Physiol.*, 1957, **137**, 338–354.
3. Bartley, S. H. Central mechanisms of vision. In J. Field, H. W. Magoun, & V. Hall (Eds.), *Handbook of physiology*. Vol. 1. Washington: American Physiological Society, 1959.
4. Békésy, G. V. *Experiments in hearing*. New York: McGraw-Hill, 1960. Chap. 13.
5. Bergmann, G., & Spence, K. W. The logic of psychophysical measurement. *Psychol. Rev.*, 1944, **51**, 1–24.
6. Bishop, G. H. The relation between nerve fiber size and sensory modality: phylogenetic implications of the afferent innervation of the cortex. *J. nerv. ment. Dis.*, 1959, **128**, 89–114.
7. Bishop, G. H., & Clare, M. H. Organization and distribution of fibers in the optic tract of the cat. *J. comp. Neurol.*, 1955, **103**, 269–304.
8. Blackwell, H. R. Psychophysical thresholds: experimental studies of methods of measurement. *Engng. Res. Bull.*, No. 36, Univer. of Mich., Eng. Res. Institute, 1953.
9. Chang, H.-T. The evoked potentials. In J. Field, H. W. Magoun, & V. Hall (Eds.), *Handbook of physiology*. Vol. 1. Washington: American Physiological Society, 1959.
10. Clare, M. H., & Bishop, G. H. Dendritic circuits: the properties of cortical paths involving dendrites. *Amer. J. Psychiat.*, 1955, **111**, 818–825.
11. Communication Biophysics Group, & Siebert, N. *Processing neuroelectric data*, Tech. Report No. 351, M.I.T., Research Laboratory of Electronics, 1959.

12. Coombs, J. S., Eccles, J. C., & Fatt, P. Excitatory synaptic action in motoneurons. *J. Physiol.*, 1955, **130**, 374–395.
13. Coombs, J. S., Eccles, J. C., & Fatt, P. The inhibitory suppression of reflex discharges from motoneurons. *J. Physiol.*, 1955, **130**, 396–413.
14. Davis, H. Excitation of auditory receptors. In J. Field, H. W. Magoun, & V. Hall (Eds.), *Handbook of physiology*. Vol. 1. Washington: American Physiological Society, 1959.
15. Dawson, G. D. A summation technique for the detection of small evoked potentials. *EEG J. clin. Neurophysiol.*, 1954, **6**, 65–84.
16. Delgado, J. M. R. Permanent implantation of multilead electrodes in the brain. *Yale J. Biol. Med.*, 1952, **24**, 351–358.
17. DeValois, R. L., Smith, C. J., & Kitai, S. T. Electrical responses of primate visual system: II. Recordings from single on-cells of macaque lateral geniculate nucleus. *J. comp. physiol. Psychol.*, 1959, **52**, 635–641.
18. Dow, R. S., & Moruzzi, G. *The physiology and pathology of the cerebellum*. Minneopolis, Minn.: Univer. of Minn. Press, 1958.
19. Eccles, J. C. Interpretation of action potentials evoked in the cerebral cortex. *EEG J. clin. Neurophysiol.*, 1951, **3**, 449–464.
20. Eccles, J. C. *The neurophysiological basis of mind*. Oxford: Clarendon Press, 1953.
21. Eccles, J. C. *The physiology of nerve cells*. London: Oxford Univer. Press, 1957.
22. Frank, K. Identification and analysis of single unit activity in the central nervous system. In J. Field, H. W. Magoun, & V. Hall (Eds.), *Handbook of physiology*. Vol. 1. Washington: American Physiological Society, 1959.
23. French, J. D., Verzeano, M., & Magoun, H. W. An extralemniscal sensory system in the brain. *AMA Arch. Neurol. Psychiat.*, 1953, **69**, 505–518.
24. French, J. D., Verzeano, M., & Magoun, H. W. A neural basis of the anesthetic state. *AMA Arch. Neurol. Psychiat.*, 1953, **69**, 519–529.
25. Frishkopf, L. S., & Rosenblith, W. A. Fluctuations in neural thresholds. In H. P. Yockey, R. L. Platzmann, & H. Quastler (Eds.), *Symposium on information theory in biology*. New York: Pergamon, 1958.
26. Galambos, R., Rose, J. E., Bromiley, R. B., & Hughes, J. R. Microelectrode studies on medial geniculate body of cat. II. Responses to clicks. *J. Neurophysiol.*, 1952, **15**, 359–380.
27. Galambos, R., Sheatz, G., & Vernier, V. G. Electrophysiological correlates of a conditioned response in cats. *Science*, 1956, **123**, 376–377.
28. Galanter, E. H., & Messick, S. The relation between category and magnitude scales of loudness. Memorandum EP-5, Univer. of Penna., Psychological Laboratory, Philadelphia, 1960.
29. Gasser, H. S. The classification of nerve fibers. *Ohio J. Sci.*, 1941, **41**, 145–159.
30. Gasser, H. S., & Grundfest, H. Axon diameters in relation to the spike dimensions and the conduction velocity in mammalian A fibers. *Amer. J. Physiol.*, 1939, **127**, 393–414.

31. Geisler, C. D., Frishkopf, L. S., & Rosenblith, W. A. Extracranial responses to acoustic clicks in man. *Science,* 1958, **128,** 1210–1211.
32. Graham, C. H. Psychophysics and behavior. *J. gen. Psychol.,* 1934, **10,** 299–310.
33. Graham, C. H. Behavior, perception, and psychophysics. *Psychol. Rev.,* 1950, **57,** 108–120.
34. Graham, C. H. Sensation and perception in an objective psychology. *Psychol. Rev.,* 1958, **65,** 65–76.
35. Graham, C. H., & Margaria, R. Area and the intensity-time relationship in the peripheral fovea. *Amer. J. Physiol.,* 1935, **113,** 299–305.
36. Granit, R. *Sensory mechanisms of the retina.* London: Oxford Univer. Press, 1947.
37. Granit, R. *Receptors and sensory perception.* New Haven, Conn.: Yale Univer. Press, 1955.
38. Gray, J. A. B. Initiation of impulses at receptors. In J. Field, H. W. Magoun, & V. Hall (Eds.), *Handbook of physiology.* Vol. 1. Washington: American Physiological Society, 1959.
39. Grundfest, H. Electrical inexcitability of synapses and some consequences in the central nervous system. *Physiol. Rev.,* 1957, **37,** 337–361.
40. Grundfest, H. Electrophysiology and pharmacology of dendrites. *EEG J. clin. Neurophysiol.,* 1958, Suppl. 10, 22–41.
41. Grundfest, H. Synaptic and ephaptic transmission. In J. Field, H. W. Magoun, & V. Hall (Eds.), *Handbook of physiology.* Vol. 1. Washington: American Physiological Society, 1959.
42. Guilford, J. P. *Psychometric methods.* (2nd ed.) New York: McGraw-Hill, 1954.
43. Hartline, H. K. Intensity and duration in the excitation of single photoreceptor units. *J. comp. cell. Physiol.,* 1934, **5,** 229–247.
44. Hartline, H. K. Nerve messages in the fibers of the visual pathway. *J. opt. Soc. Amer.,* 1940, **30,** 239–247.
45. Hartline, H. K., & Ratliff, F. Inhibitory interaction of receptor units in the eye of Limulus. *J. gen. Physiol.,* 1957, **40,** 357–376.
46. Hearst, E., Beer, B., Sheatz, G., & Galambos, R. Some electrophysiological correlates of conditioning in the monkey. *EEG J. clin. Neurophysiol.,* 1960, **12,** 137–152.
47. Helm, C., Messick, S., & Tucker, L. Psychophysical law and scaling models. *Educ. Testing Serv. Bull.,* 1959.
48. Helson, H. Adaptation level theory. In S. Koch (Ed.), *Psychology: a study of a science.* Vol. 1. New York: McGraw-Hill, 1959.
49. Hernandez-Peon, R., & Scherrer, H. "Habituation" to acoustic stimuli in the cochlear nucleus. *Fed. Proc.,* 1950, **14,** 71. (Abstract.)
50. Hubel, D. H. Single unit activity in the striate cortex of unrestrained cats. *J. Physiol.,* 1959, **147,** 226–238.
51. Jasper, H. H., Ricci, G. F., & Doane, B. Patterns of cortical neuronal discharge during conditioned responses in monkeys. In G. E. W. Wolstenholme & C. M. O'Connor (Eds.), *Neurological basis of behavior.* London: Churchill, 1958.

52. Johnson, H. M. Did Fechner measure introspectional sensation? *Psychol. Rev.*, 1929, **36**, 257–284.

53. Johnson, H. M. Some properties of Fechner's "Intensity of Sensation." *Psychol. Rev.*, 1930, **37**, 113–123.

54. Kellogg, W. N. The time of judgment in psychometric measures. *Amer. J. Psychol.*, 1931, **46**, 65–86.

55. Kuffler, S. W. Discharge patterns and functional organization of the mammalian retina. *J. Neurophysiol.*, 1953, **16**, 37–68.

56. Li, C.-L. Some properties of pyramidal neurons in motor cortex with particular reference to sensory stimulation. *J. Neurophysiol.*, 1959, **22**, 385–394.

57. Licklider, J. C. R. Three auditory theories. In S. Koch (Ed.), *Psychology: a study of a science*. Vol. 1. New York: McGraw-Hill, 1959.

58. Lorente de No, R. *A study of nerve physiology*. Studies from Rockefeller Institute for Medical Research, **131; 132**, 1947. Chap. 16.

59. Lowenstein, O., & Sand, A. The individual and integrated activity of the semicircular canals of the elasmobranch labyrinth. *J. Physiol.*, 1940, **99**, 89–101.

60. Luce, R. D. *Individual choice behavior*. New York: Wiley, 1959. Chap. 2.

61. Luce, R. D. On the possible psychophysical laws. *Psychol. Rev.*, 1959, **66**, 81–95.

62. Luce, R. D., & Edwards, W. The derivation of subjective scales from just noticeable differences. *Psychol. Rev.*, 1958, **65**, 222–237.

63. Marshall, W. H. Observations on subcortical somatic sensory mechanisms of cats under Nembutal anesthesia. *J. Neurophysiol.*, 1941, **4**, 25–43.

64. Maruhashi, J., Mizuguchi, K., & Tasaki, I. Action currents in single afferent nerve fibers elicited by stimulation of the skin of the toad and the cat. *J. Physiol.*, 1952, **117**, 129–151.

65. Mauro, A. Properties of thin generators pertaining to electrophysiological potentials in volume conductors. *J. Neurophysiol.*, 1960, **23**, 132–143.

66. Miller, G. A. Sensitivity to changes in the intensity of white noise and its relation to masking and loudness. *J. acoust. Soc. Amer.*, 1947, **19**, 609–619.

67. Mountcastle, V. B., Davies, P. W., & Berman, A. L. Response properties of neurons of the cat's somatic sensory cortex to peripheral stimulation. *J. Neurophysiol.*, 1957, **20**, 374–407.

68. Mountcastle, V. B., & Powell, T. P. S. Neural mechanisms subserving cutaneous sensibility, with special reference to the role of afferent inhibition in sensory perception and discrimination. *Johns Hopkins Hosp. Bull.*, 1959, **105**, 201–232.

69. Nachmansohn, D. Role of acetylcholine in axonal conduction and neuromuscular transmission. *Amer. J. phys. Med.*, 1959, **38**, 190–206.

70. Nagel, E. Principles of the theory of probability. *Int. Encycl. unif. Sci.*, 1939, **1**, No. 6.

71. Pfaffmann, C. The sense of taste. In J. Field, H. W. Magoun, & V. Hall (Eds.), *Handbook of physiology.* Vol. 1. Washington: American Physiological Society, 1959.

72. Pirenne, M. H., & Marriott, F. H. C. The quantum theory of light and the psychophysiology of vision. In S. Koch (Ed.), *Psychology: a study of a science.* Vol. 1. New York: McGraw-Hill, 1959.

73. Purpura, D. P. Nature of the electrocortical potentials and synaptic organization in cerebral and cerebellar cortex. *Int. Rev. Neurobiol.,* 1959, **1,** 47–163.

74. Ranson, S. W., & Clark, S. L. *The anatomy of the nervous system.* (9th ed.) Philadelphia: Saunders, 1953.

75. Rose, J. E., & Mountcastle, V. B. Touch and kinesthesis. In J. Field, H. W. Magoun, & V. Hall (Eds.), *Handbook of physiology.* Vol. 1. Washington: American Physiological Society, 1959.

76. Rosenblith, W. A. Acoustic masking and fatigue. *J. acoust. Soc. Amer.,* 1950, **22,** 792–800.

77. Rosenzweig, M. R., & Rosenblith, W. A. Responses to auditory stimuli at the cochlea and the auditory cortex. *Psychol. Monogr.,* 1953, **67,** No. 363.

78. Rosner, B. S. Neural factors which limit cutaneous spatio-temporal discriminations. In W. A. Rosenblith (Ed.), *Sensory communication.* Cambridge: Technology Press, 1961.

79. Ruch, T. C. Sensory mechanisms. In S. S. Stevens (Ed.), *Handbook of experimental psychology.* New York: Wiley, 1951.

80. Ruch, T. C. Binocular vision and central visual pathways. In J. F. Fulton (Ed.), *Textbook of physiology.* (17th ed.) Philadelphia: Saunders, 1955.

81. Ruch, T. C. Neural basis of somatic sensation. In J. F. Fulton (Ed.), *Textbook of physiology.* (17th ed.) Philadelphia: Saunders, 1955.

82. Ruch, T. C. Somatic sensation. In J. F. Fulton (Ed.), *Textbook of physiology.* (17th ed.) Philadelphia: Saunders, 1955.

83. Ruch, T. C. Vision. In J. F. Fulton (Ed.), *Textbook of physiology.* (17th ed.) Philadelphia: Saunders, 1955.

84. Scheibel, M. E., & Scheibel, A. B. A symposium on dendrites: formal discussion. *EEG J. clin. Neurophysiol.,* 1958, Suppl. 10, 43–50.

85. Sharpless, S., & Jasper, H. Habituation of the arousal reaction. *Brain,* 1956, **79,** 655–680.

86. Sheatz, G. Multilead electrode holders in chronic preparations. In D. E. Sheer (Ed.), *Electrical stimulation of the brain: subcortical integrative systems.* Austin, Tex.: Univ. of Tex. Press, in press.

87. Stevens, S. S. Mathematics, measurement, and psychophysics. In S. S. Stevens (Ed.), *Handbook of experimental psychology.* New York: Wiley, 1951.

88. Stevens, S. S. The direct estimation of sensory magnitudes—loudness. *Amer. J. Psychol.,* 1956, **69,** 1–25.

89. Stevens, S. S. On the psychophysical law. *Psychol. Rev.,* 1957, **64,** 153–181.

90. Stevens, S. S. Problems and methods of psychophysics. *Psychol. Bull.,* 1958, **54,** 177–196.

91. Stevens, S. S. The psychophysics of sensory function. *Amer. Scientist,* 1960, **48,** 226–253.

92. Stevens, S. S., Carton, A. S., & Shickman, G. M. A scale of apparent intensity of electric shock. *J. exp. Psychol.,* 1958, **56,** 328–334.

93. Stevens, S. S., & Galanter, E. H. Ratio scales and category scales for a dozen perceptual continua. *J. exp. Psychol.,* 1957, **54,** 377–411.

94. Stevens, S. S., Morgan, C. T., & Volkmann, J. Theory of the neural quantum in the discrimination of pitch and loudness. *Amer. J. Psychol.,* 1941, **54,** 315–355.

95. Tanner, W. P., Jr., & Swets, J. A. The human use of information. I. Signal detection for the case of the signal known exactly. *IRE Trans. on Information Theor.,* 1954, Vol. PGIT-4.

96. Tanner, W. P., Jr., Swets, J. A., & Green, D. M. *Some general properties of the hearing mechanism,* Tech. Report No. 30, Univer. of Mich., Electronic Defense Group, Dept. of Electrical Engineering, 1956.

97. Tasaki, I. Conduction of the nerve impulse. In J. Field, H. W. Magoun, & V. Hall (Eds.), *Handbook of physiology.* Vol. 1. Washington: American Physiological Society, 1959.

98. Thurstone, L. L. The law of comparative judgment. *Psychol. Rev.,* 1927, **34,** 273–286.

99. Thurstone, L. L. The phi-gamma hypothesis. *J. exp. Psychol.,* 1928, **11,** 293–305.

100. Torgerson, W. S. *Theory and methods of scaling.* New York: Wiley, 1958. Chap. 11.

101. Urban, F. M. Die psychophysischen Massmethoden als Grundlagen emperischer Messungen. I. & II. *Arch. ges. Psychol.,* 1909, **15,** 261–355; 1909, **16,** 168–227.

102. Verplanck, W. S., Collier, G. H., & Cotton, J. W. Nonindependence of successive responses in measurements of the visual threshold. *J. exp. Psychol.,* 1952, **44,** 273–282.

103. Wertheimer, M. An investigation of the "randomness" of threshold measurements. *J. exp. Psychol.,* 1953, **45,** 294–303.

104. Wever, E. G. The cochlear potentials and their relation to hearing. *Ann. Otol. Rhinol. Laryngol.,* 1959, **68,** 975–989.

105. Woodworth, R. S., & Schlosberg, H. *Experimental psychology* (rev. ed.). New York: Holt, 1954.

106. Woolsey, C. N. Organization of somatic sensory and motor areas of the cerebral cortex. In H. W. Harlow & C. N. Woolsey (Eds.), *Biological and biochemical bases of behavior.* Madison, Wis.: Univer. of Wis. Press, 1958.

107. Zotterman, Y. Thermal sensations. In J. Field, H. W. Magoun, & V. Hall (Eds.), *Handbook of physiology.* Vol. 1. Washington: American Physiological Society, 1959.

A QUANTITATIVE VIEW OF NEUROELECTRIC EVENTS IN RELATION TO SENSORY COMMUNICATION[1]

W. A. ROSENBLITH AND EDA B. VIDALE[2]
Center for Communication Sciences
Research Laboratory of Electronics
Massachusetts Institute of Technology

Introduction 334
Measurement and Analysis in Electrophysiology 336
    A statistical view of neuroelectric phenomena 339
Neural Representations of Stimulus Variables. 343
    Intensity 345
    Time 352
    Localizable representations. 354
Preliminaries to the Assessment of State Variables 357
Temporal Aspects of Responses to Discrete Stimuli 367
Concluding Remarks. 373
References. 375

INTRODUCTION

Those who study the sensory commerce in which organisms engage and those who try to correlate this behavior with events in the nervous system have often been handicapped by a lack of complementary concepts. This lack stems largely from the fact that the quantification of behavioral events has developed along lines that differ markedly from the methods of measurement and data analysis that prevail in electrophysiological experiments. Since, under these circumstances, it proved impossible to establish meaningful correspondence principles between behavioral and physiological responses by direct means, research workers

[1] The preparation of this manuscript was supported in part by the U.S. Army Signal Corps, the Air Force, Office of Scientific Research, and the Office of Naval Research.
[2] Special research fellow of the National Institute of Mental Health, U.S. Public Health Service.

interested in relating these two classes of response events have had to approach their goal indirectly. The most commonly employed detour involves the derivation of the desired response-response $(R_\psi\text{-}R_\phi)$ relation from the separate stimulus-response relationships for psychological $(S\text{-}R_\psi)$ and for physiological $(S\text{-}R_\phi)$ events. Such a procedure entails the assumption that, once the appropriate $S\text{-}R_\psi$ and $S\text{-}R_\phi$ functions have been independently established, the S term common to the two sets of relations may, in some sense, be canceled or eliminated to yield the $R_\psi\text{-}R_\phi$ relation.

Despite its simplicity and convenience, this position can today hardly be regarded as tenable, as becomes apparent from even a cursory consideration of some of the obstacles encountered by the scientist who attempts to translate across several levels of systems that are capable of "responding." The classes of events that qualify as responses may, and most often do, differ at the several levels of systems that are being studied. These responses may be discrete events, such as the occurrence or non-occurrence of a spike potential or of a given motor or verbal response; or they may consist of modifications in sets of values that vary in a continuous manner, such as graded electrical activity or temporal indicants of events, e.g., latent periods and reaction times. Working at different levels of organismic complexity, investigators tended to select as criterion responses those events whose clear-cut character, i.e., easy observability and lack of ambiguity, made them readily distinguishable. The choice of experimental stimuli or, rather, certain ways of describing sensory stimulation was then usually based on the capacity of the stimuli to elicit the preferred criterion response. While the description of the stimulus is still often given in terms of the energy changes that are associated with its delivery, concepts such as biological significance, information value, novelty, and the like are coming to be increasingly utilized in the specification of stimulus variables.[3] Indeed, there are situations, involving what Russian workers call the "orienting reflex," in which the stimulus is perhaps best characterized as a shift from one pattern of stimulation to another. As the definition of the stimulus ceases to be unique and becomes increasingly dependent upon the aspect of responding that is being studied, what remains of the hope that we shall be able to cancel

[3] There is, of course, an infinity of physical configurations that the well-instructed observer will identify as the same vowel sound (e.g., an *o*) or, to take another instance, as the same visual form (e.g., a square). This response constancy is not predictable on the basis of a description of the stimulus in CGS terms; significant information about the stimulus is more likely to be contained in certain parametric relations among aspects of the stimulus complex. In sensory communication tasks, response behavior becomes predictable if we are able to specify (1) these relational stimulus variables and (2) that ensemble of possible responses which is largely determined by the situational context.

the stimulus between the two sets of aforementioned S-R relations? Quite obviously, such an elimination procedure ceases to have any validity when stimulus descriptions become incommensurable. Equally obvious is the conclusion that the solution to this dilemma consists in finding means of observing both sets of S-R relationships under conditions that are comparable and, even more important, commensurate.

It has recently become feasible to obtain convergent psychological and neurophysiological data from behaving organisms, including man. This brings us closer to our goal of establishing meaningful correspondence principles between these event classes. Before any such *rapprochement* can be achieved, however, it is essential that we specify the units of analysis within both response domains in terms of which correspondence between them is to be sought. That this undertaking is beset by theoretical and practical difficulties, many of them still unresolved, may be gleaned from some of our foregoing remarks. Nonetheless, on the basis of some of the data that have been accumulated, general trends are discernible which may serve as guides in our search.

The significant features of neural activity may perhaps best be deciphered by studying interrelationships among electrophysiological events. That is, the important aspects of neural functioning seem to be represented by more or less complicated *spatiotemporal patterns* of neuroelectric activity and are not merely given by absolute values of electrical changes as a function of time. For our purposes, we find it useful to designate this concept of neuroelectric spatiotemporal patterning by the abbreviation NSTP. The notion of a patterning of neural events that occur at one or more places in the nervous system and that typically have different temporal characteristics is by no means a novel one; similar ideas have been expressed by others. We nevertheless consider it important to recapitulate this viewpoint and to accord it explicit emphasis, since too many accounts of nervous-system functioning fail to deal with neural patterns.

This emphasis upon the relational aspects of stimulus and of response variables is both conceptually and pragmatically useful. It provides us with a strategic orientation in the task of ordering and relating the innumerable data that can be recorded from the nervous system. We personally suspect that NSTP may well prove to be an indispensable element in the formulation of neural correlates of behavioral events.

MEASUREMENT AND ANALYSIS IN ELECTROPHYSIOLOGY

From its very outset the experimental science of electrophysiology adopted quite naturally the instruments of the physicist in order to measure both stimulus and response events. These instruments have played a more limited role in psychophysics, where their use is restricted primarily to a precise specification of the stimulus. Like other behavioral responses that are widely used, psychophysical responses are typically discrete and highly stereotyped. Thus their quantification entails little beyond counting operations, whether the purpose be to determine a threshold, to establish a scale, or to construct a confusion matrix.

It is perhaps not surprising, therefore, that psychologists, in their search for neurophysiological correlates of behavioral events, selected as their most likely candidate the occurrence or nonoccurrence of "all-or-none" spikes in a single neuron. Interest persisted in aspects of responding which were less easily classifiable into discrete categories (such as reaction times to sensory stimuli), but by and large it is in the assessment of response events that the contrast between measurement in electrophysiology and in psychophysics looms largest.

Despite—or, perhaps, because of—the fact that electrophysiologists have at their disposal the constantly improving armamentarium of physical instruments, their most persistent quandary remains: What to do with the vast amounts of data collected by means of those instruments?

In evaluating the characteristic deflections or patterns in voltage-versus-time displays that are the electrophysiologist's basic data, we are hampered by the lack of intrinsic criteria of what constitutes an adequate description of these complex wave forms. As long as we deal with d-c potentials or sinusoids, an instrument that yields one or two characteristic numbers is perfectly satisfactory, but when we attempt to assess arbitrary wave forms containing time-locked "transients" and "noise," the voltmeter (even the vacuum-tube voltmeter) ceases to be the appropriate instrument of measurement. If we decide to display the complete wave form by photographing it from the face of an oscilloscope, we must still find selective transformations upon the data that will yield meaningful descriptions while reducing the total amount of information to be handled.

When we come to consider the inferences that can be drawn from electrophysiological pointer readings, our lack of understanding of the organizational principles and of the mechanisms of the nervous system is felt more seriously. The organizational structure of this nonhomogeneous medium that consists of large numbers of highly specific elements has so far defied useful descriptions in terms of the over-all physical properties of the medium. Much effort has gone into analyzing the fine structure of its various components in terms of current biophysical and biochemical knowledge, but up to the present these efforts have failed to yield an approach that is capable of dealing with the unique properties that characterize the nervous system of higher animals. Here is a system that is composed of many interacting units (all of which are by no means alike), that is organized both flexibly and hierarchically, and that consists of subsystems (enjoying various degrees of autonomy) capable of fulfilling specific and/or nonspecific functions. Here is a system that reacts more reliably and predictably to informationally rich quasi-natural stimuli than to contrived but mathematically simple ones. Here is a system that is capable of learning and of giving reasonably reliable performance throughout an extended period of time with all the safety factors and maintenance and repair requirements that such performance entails.

What is the type of electrical activity whose study will yield the "systems neurophysiology" that underlies the behavior of information-processing organisms? What strategy should we adopt in dealing with the signals that we record from the nervous system—signals whose code is known so incompletely? Should we attempt to isolate a single neuron and study its behavior in great detail, hoping that we will pick a typical one that is capable of representing a not-too-well-defined population? Should we, at the other extreme, work only with the muffled polyneural roar that is capable of making itself "heard" through man's thick skull? Should we limit ourselves to studying recordings of the "spontaneous" activity of a neuron or of neuronal populations, i.e., the activity that we can still observe after we have turned off all of the stimulus generators that are under our control? Or should we study stimulus-response relations—those response events whose occurrence is, by some criterion, usually a temporal one, linked to the delivery of a definable stimulus? Can we assume that these latter stimulus-evoked events will always simply add to the spontaneous background activity, or must we study their interaction in different physiological states of the organism?

What are the techniques of analysis that are readily available to electrophysiologists in dealing with problems that relate to sensory communication? Let us briefly mention some sample techniques that have been used.

The mathematics of circuit analysis, at least in its simpler forms, assumes that the circuits and their components are linear, lumped, finite, passive, and bilateral [40]. It would, of course, be absurd to pretend that the nervous system has these properties, although it may be possible to find, by applying circuit theory, the manner in which the behavior of a sensory system, for instance, deviates from this model.

If we restrict ourselves to dealing with whatever wave forms may have been recorded, we must ask whether specific techniques such as Fourier analysis or correlation analysis are actually appropriate to the particular experimental question. Such techniques imply that the time series that is to be analyzed satisfies certain conditions. Obviously, the assumptions implicit in these analytical techniques are a price that we have to pay for their use. Physical scientists also pay this price. They, however, know much more about the processes that underlie the phenomena they study than we know about the mechanisms that underlie neuroelectric phenomena. Thus, in physical science there is a better chance of adjusting and correcting models than there is in neurophysiology. And yet the student of the nervous system has little choice until more appropriate techniques of analysis have been developed. He must utilize those which are available in order to find out where they cease to fit. He may, nevertheless, want to take the precaution of assembling a sufficient body of apparently consistent data before getting involved in ambitious computations.

Is there a moral that imposes itself on the basis of the preceding incomplete enumeration of problems that one faces in this type of research? We believe that there is and we believe that it can be stated in a single word, "pluralism." Only a pluralistic strategy guarantees, at this stage of our knowledge of the nervous system, that we shall not blind ourselves to useful approaches because we have oversold ourselves on one of them. The multiplicity of purposes that motivate experimenting electrophysiologists precludes our prescribing too rigidly on intrinsic grounds either experimental design or methods of data processing and analysis. We must, rather, be prepared to make our choice on the basis of extrinsic values or influences.

Our background, our biases of interest, our physical and intellectual surrounds, and the *Zeitgeist* have led us to opt for certain methods of data processing and certain types of mathematical models. We believe that these techniques are capable of coming to grips with one of the essential features of neural activity: its statistical character. Since we are dealing with a multivariate system, we are not surprised that the patterns and relationships that we find are often statistical. We have, furthermore, a preference for packaging our results in a form that is reasonably quantitative; that is, we try to express as many of our findings as we can in *some* mathematical representation without always trying to fit our data to analytical functions. Finally, it is fair to say that, while we feel more secure when we have the guiding influence of a mathematical model and of a relevant physiological mechanism in our experiments, we are not so narrow-minded as to ignore the usefulness and even beauty of a good classification scheme that relates to variables whose importance to the organism is undeniable.

A statistical view of neuroelectric phenomena. Our search for such variables leads us quite naturally to look at the performance of organisms engaged in sensory tasks [65]. Here a certain number of characteristics emerge that suggest problems for quantitative studies in the area of sensory electrophysiology. As we consider organisms engaged in communication tasks, it becomes apparent (1) that their performance is statistical in character; (2) that they need more time to handle more "information"; (3) that their capacity to discriminate and their speed of reaction depend on stimulus intensity; and (4) that their repertory of absolute identifications (Miller's [57] "span of absolute judgment") is relatively small and seemingly based upon the ability to make several rather crude discriminations simultaneously, i.e., to classify the environmental sensory inflow into some rather gross categories.

We are thus led in our studies to emphasize statistical and temporal aspects of the electrical behavior of the nervous system and to look for over-all (relatively gross and stable) patterns in this behavior. By using this quasi-thermodynamic approach, we do not intend to deprecate the complementary view which derives its inspiration from statistical mechanics. At the same time, we think it important to call attention to the hiatus that exists between what a microelectrode (particularly an intracellular one) "sees" and the multifarious role played by an entire relay nucleus in a sensory system. In so-called "ablation experiments," such a structure is often removed in order to elucidate its role; however, the logical interpretation of the resulting deficits in performance is far from being unambiguous. The interpretation hinges on one's model of the nervous system. Is it a collection of simple reflex arcs, or populated by complex feedback loops? Is function strictly localized, or are there many functionally equipotential spare parts?

No matter which aspect of the electric activity of the nervous system we study, we always face the task of defining typical events among those we observe experimentally. This task confronts the experimenter whether his concern is with responses evoked by sensory stimuli or with the electroencephalogram (EEG). He has to establish certain criteria of judgment. His criteria will be different when he records population responses with the aid of macroelectrodes from his criteria when he studies the activity of a single cell with the aid of a microelectrode. The electrophysiologist must furthermore decide whether two observations are identical. The identity-defining operation may range from identity in one aspect of the event only (such as occurrence or nonoccurrence of a so-called "all-or-none" spike) to identity in several measurable aspects (such as average spike latency and distribution of spike latencies).

In order to decide whether an event is typical or whether two events differ, we should have an expectation of the distribution of possible events. This distribution might be estimated from observations of evoked responses to a large number of identical stimuli or repeated samplings of EEG traces. Actually, experimenters rarely have this information available to them; and yet, if they are well trained, they choose "representative" records as illustrations for their papers. Nevertheless, it is necessary to realize that few, if any, systematic studies have been made that assess an experimenter's information-handling capacity as applied to his ability to view oscilloscopic traces or examine film records. In other words, we do not really know how safe our current procedures are.

We have tried to present and review elsewhere [29, 63, 66] some of the available evidence on the statistical character of input-output relations for single neurons or for responses from populations of neuronal elements. Here we shall merely summarize the essential arguments. We first faced this problem when we tried to find criteria for deciding what constitutes a typical evoked response, i.e., an electrophysiological event that is triggered by the presentation of a discrete stimulus, most often a sensory one. There exists, to our knowledge, no generally accepted operational definition of what is meant by an evoked response, although the concept has been exceedingly useful in electrophysiological and neuroanatomical studies of the nervous system.

Let us briefly look at the typical procedures for recording evoked responses. The experimenter usually controls the instant of delivery of the stimulus. He then most often establishes the presence or absence of an evoked response by either of two methods or by the two methods conjointly: (1) In recording with macroelectrodes, he detects visually the presence of a characteristic wave form or deflection; (2) in recording with microelectrodes, he detects aurally and/or visually a change in the acoustic signals that represent the electrical events "seen" by the microelectrode after these events have been appropriately amplified and transduced into sound.

As should be clear from this description, the experimenter's ability to detect changes in visual and/or aural displays depends upon the stability of these changes in relation to the patterns of background activity.[4] Detection of these changes also depends upon how soon they occur following stimulus presentation and upon how much they exceed the experimenter's just-noticeable difference for the particular sensory pattern involved.

For responses recorded with macroelectrodes there is variability both in amplitude and in time. The evoked responses of the classical sensory pathways exhibit relatively short latencies and little variability in latency. Due to this relative stability of their temporal aspects, the averaging of these responses by means of computing devices becomes both a feasible

---

[4] We mentioned above the problems of the typicality of a response and of the identity of two responses. These problems include decisions of how typical is the background activity in which these responses are embedded. That the presence of spontaneous cell discharges greatly complicates the analysis of the effects of stimulus variables has been discussed in a recent article by Amassian and his coworkers [5].

and a useful undertaking. So far no convenient techniques have been developed that yield summarizing descriptions of electrical events that have longer and more variable latencies such as the so-called "blocking of the alpha rhythm."

For responses recorded from single units with the aid of microelectrodes, the variability problem poses itself in a rather different manner. Here we are dealing with a set of discrete events that are quite comparable in wave shape and amplitude but that occur at latencies that are governed by stimulus parameters and by the prevailing sequences of spontaneous firings of the cell under study and possibly of other cells. The changes in the patterns of spontaneous firing that do occur may result in either increases (excitation) or decreases (inhibition) in average firing frequency. Thus, variability may now affect (1) changes in the number of firings per unit time (how many spikes a given stimulus elicits or inhibits); (2) "first-spike" latency (latency of the spike whose occurrence is most directly linked to the delivery of the stimulus); (3) interspike intervals, and so on.

An overview of the problems involved in adequate detection and description of evoked responses thus leads to procedures in which computers as well as experimenters are instructed to look for changes that occur in patterns of ongoing activity and that are somehow linked to the delivery of stimuli. Looking for changes in averages, such as means, or for changes in the distribution of events within several time intervals becomes a method of search in which the properly programed computer supplements human capacities.

From all that precedes, it should be clear that we must find ways of dealing with the undeniable fact that repeated presentations of the same stimulus are far from yielding identical neuroelectric responses in many physiological preparations. Instead of abdicating before this fact by declaring that neuroelectric activity is therefore not truly quantifiable, we propose to take advantage of this difficulty. The variabilities that one observes seem to have their own regularities, which are related to both stimulus and organismic variables. By constructing probabilistic models that gave economical descriptions of responses from populations of neurons, several workers [36] were able to test our understanding of certain neural events in the auditory system. In addition, their models led to experimentation that was novel and productive of further insights.

If we seek an interpretation of this statistical behavior, we must first of all consider the complexity of the system or subsystem under study, the multiplicity of possible interactions,[5] and the inadequacy of our

---

[5] Sholl [70], who has discussed the quantification of neuronal connectivity, comes to the conclusion that "Impulses arriving along a single primary visual fibre will be dispersed among the 5,000 neurons distributed around its terminal branches."

description of the "state" in which a neuron, a population of neurons, or even the nervous system finds itself at the time of stimulus presentation.

Any formulation about the behavior of the nervous system depends ultimately upon one's concept of the behavior of the neuron. Without entering into a searching discussion of the present status of neuron doctrine [19], we want to call attention to the increasing importance that graded response processes assume in the view of some of the most sophisticated neurophysiologists. At present, we possess no models of the nervous system that admit the meaningful coexistence of graded activity and all-or-none events. In view of this circumstance, it behooves us to keep in mind Bishop's [14] suggestion "that the graded response type is more general, as well as more primitive, than the all-or-none response, and that the latter probably developed when an early metazoan became too large, or underwent separation of functionally related parts to too great a distance, for graded responses to be effective as a means of communication between them." Bishop's account of neural processes and mechanisms leads him to conclude that "the chief physiological business of the nervous system is transacted in graded-response elements" and that "what we do, mentally or physically, is probably to express the state of excitability of the graded response tissue that initiates impulses in axonal conductors."

These remarks are highly relevant to anyone who seeks to quantify neuroelectric events in relation to sensory communication. There is little basis for hope of finding *one* ideal measure that will permit quantification at all levels of neural organization and for all sizes of neural aggregates. And although there will undoubtedly become available more adequate descriptions of the behavior of single neurons or of neuronal populations, there is serious doubt whether we shall, in the foreseeable future, be able to—or, indeed, want to—dispense with statistical descriptions of neuro-electric phenomena.

In the following sections, the examples chosen will often come from the work of the Communications Biophysics group at M.I.T.; such parochialism can be justified in part by the undeniable fact that experimental methods and style vary so significantly from one laboratory to another as to render direct comparison and integration of data hazardous. In addition, the Communications Biophysics group has been consistently and self-consciously concerned with the application of quantitative methods to the processing and analysis of neuroelectric data.

NEURAL REPRESENTATIONS OF STIMULUS VARIABLES

Since the beginnings of Greek philosophy, but more particularly since Müller's formulation of the doctrine of specific nerve energies, natural philosophers and experimentalists have been concerned with specific receptors, with specific sensory mechanisms, and with maps of the nervous system—all of which were presumed to reflect the specificity that characterizes the sensory performance of organisms. Quite naturally, this concern led to an emphasis upon special sensory abilities: absolute pitch, reception of ultrasonic signals, the hearing of the blind, the discrimination of odors by infrahuman animals, the detection of weak electric signals by fish, the detection of temperature variation by rattlesnakes, and so on. These special abilities point to biological filtering operations by means of which a selective mirroring of certain features of the organism's environment is carried out. It was originally assumed, and often still is [41], that the filtering operations can be accomplished most economically at or near the interface of organism and environment. Ideally, "tuned" peripheral structures will keep currently irrelevant sensory inflow from cluttering up the organism's central nervous system. The introduction of controlled stimuli into laboratory experiments led to systematic and analytic studies of representational aspects of sensory processes. The stimuli used tended to be simple—in the mathematico-physical sense—as well as spatially and temporally punctiform; by means of such stimuli, several functionally resonant structures were identified at the periphery and even in the central nervous system.

On the other hand, evidence pointing to the not-so-specific organization of the nervous system has accumulated: Lashley's [53] experiments on mass action, experience with the reeducation of brain-injured patients, as well as the outcome of many ablation experiments—all emphasized the futility of looking for a localizable structure in the nervous system whose normal functioning is indispensable to *all* discriminations within a specific sense modality. In a given modality, deficits in sensory performance that are attributable to neural dysfunction are rarely of the all-or-none type; they tend to be task-specific rather than modality-specific [56].

The representation of metathetic [72] continua (of which tonotopy is perhaps the most abundantly documented example) finds in each sensory system a somewhat special, perhaps even a unique, solution. It probably involves combinations of receptor properties, density of innervation, and neural interactions, such as afferent inhibition, centrifugal control, and the like. It seems, therefore, more appropriate to look for mechanisms common to the several modalities, particularly those dealing with the neural coding of intensive (i.e., prothetic [72]) and temporal aspects of sensory stimulation. However, even though intensity and time are of undeniable importance in determining the sensory performance of organisms, we have lately come to realize that, in nature, reliable communication generally seems to be based upon gross—one might almost say qualitative—discriminations of highly redundant, noise-resistant multidimensional patterns.

Techniques are now available for producing and controlling a variety of quasi-natural stimuli that are capable of yielding quantifiable responses. Consequently, we are witnessing a shift of emphasis in the search for neural representations. Research is tending to orient itself toward the identification of those reasonably stable spatiotemporal patterns of neural activity (NSTP) in behaving animals that can be closely tied to the organism's sensory commerce [16, 48].

This "new look" at sensory electrophysiology has up to now been productive of promising observations rather than of the systematic data that are needed for theory making. Hence, at this transition stage, we must limit ourselves to presenting those elements of sensory electrophysiology that seem likely to become incorporated into even the most avant-garde of looks.

Intensity. Response patterns of single cells and of neuronal populations convey information about the intensive aspects of physical stimuli. The records in Fig. 1, from the work of Rose and Mountcastle [62], illustrate how variations in stimulus intensity are reflected in the all-or-none discharge patterns recorded from single units by means of microelectrodes. The number of spike responses increases and the latency of the first spike decreases as the strength of the transient peripheral stimulus is increased. Measurements of intervals between spikes show that (1) the larger the number of spikes in a train of repetitive discharges, the smaller is the interspike interval; (2) the interspike interval increases throughout a train and firing ceases when the interval exceeds a certain value (e.g., 2 msec in the present instance).

Similar results, of course, can be obtained from single units in other modality-specific afferent pathways. Furthermore, some patterns of unitary discharges in sensory systems span time intervals whose length is comparable to behavioral reaction times [50].

The representation of stimulus intensity in populations of neural units can be examined by macroelectrodes at various stations in the nervous system. The potentials thus recorded represent coarse spatiotemporal averages of either spike and/or continuously graded activity. The left side of Fig. 2 depicts averaged neural responses [64] to the onset of bursts of noise of different intensities recorded by gross electrodes at the level of the auditory nerve. Quantitative measurements can be made along both the voltage and the time axes of such displays. Thus, one can measure amplitudes of deflections (either peak to peak or base line to peak) and latencies (i.e., time intervals that have elapsed since the delivery of the stimulus) of extreme values or of zero crossings. These amplitude and latency measurements may then be used to plot intensity functions, func-

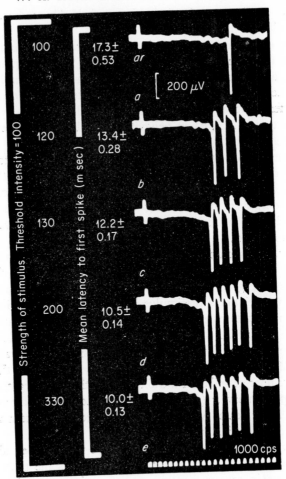

FIG. 1. Responses of single units in tactile thalamic region of the cat to transient electrical stimulation of forepaw. Position of stimulation is unchanged for all records. Numbers in column at extreme left give a measure of stimulus strength. Numbers in second column indicate mean latency to first spike and standard error of the mean for each stimulus intensity. The records in the right-hand column depict the modal value of the number of spikes that are recorded for each intensity. The short vertical line at the left of each response trace indicates the delivery of the electrical stimulus. Reproduced from Rose and Mountcastle [62, p. 260].

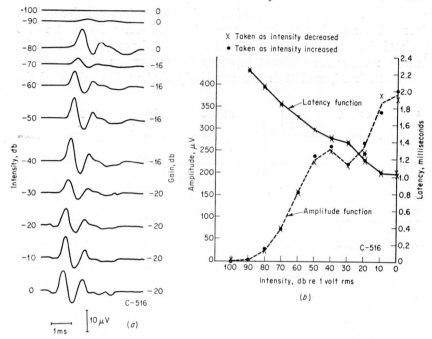

Fig. 2a. Averaged neural responses to short repeated noise bursts of various intensities recorded near the round window of an anesthetized cat. The averaging operation was carried out by an electronic computing device [64]. Relative positivity at recording electrode indicated by downward deflection. The first major negative-positive deflection in these records corresponds to the so-called "N_1 component"—the earliest and most prominent neural component that can be recorded at this location. It represents the summated action potentials from the auditory nerve. The noise bursts were 0.1 msec in duration and were presented at a rate of 5 per sec. The delivery of the stimulus coincides with the starting point of each trace. Number of responses averaged at the different stimulus intensity levels: 256 responses at -100 and -90 db, 128 at -80 db, and 64 at -70 to 0 db. The 10-μV amplitude calibration marker applies to the 0-db gain setting.

Fig. 2b. Amplitude and latency of averaged neural responses to noise bursts as a function of stimulus intensity. These intensity functions are based on the data of Fig. 2a. The values on the left-hand ordinate refer to the average peak-to-peak amplitude of the N_1 component while those on the right-hand ordinate represent measurements of the average time interval between stimulus onset and the occurrence of the negative peak of N_1. The latency values include a delay of approximately 0.4 msec that corresponds to the time that it takes for the sound to travel from the earphone diaphragm to the eardrum [60].

tions that, for example, relate the average amplitude of characteristic deflections and their average latency to the intensity of the stimulus. Such intensity functions derived from the adjacent records are shown on the right half of Fig. 2. These and similar data permit one to state the following generalizations: As the intensity of a transient sensory stimulus is increased, the average amplitude of evoked responses increases (or at least does not decrease), and the average latency of either the onset or the peak of the deflection decreases.[6] The detailed shape of these intensity functions varies for different locations in the nervous system and for different stimuli, and it is not intuitively obvious just which of the

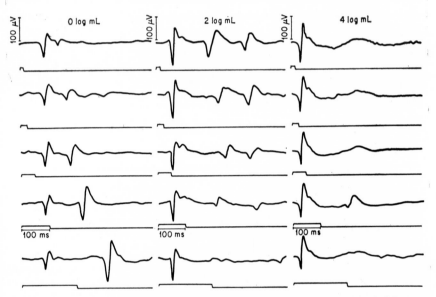

Fig. 3. Averaged evoked responses to repetitive photic stimulation recorded from a location on the visual cortex of an anesthetized cat (*Cat:Sh*). The lower of each pair of traces represents the stimulus and the upper record the corresponding averaged evoked response. The three columns represent responses at three different luminance levels. For any given luminance, flash duration was varied between the limits of 12.5 and 200 msec; averaged responses to the shortest of the stimuli appear in the topmost row, while succeeding rows depict responses to flashes having durations of 25, 50, 100, and 200 msec, respectively. Repetition rate: one flash every 5 sec. Sixty-four consecutive responses entered into the computation of each average. Surface-positive deflections are plotted downward. *Courtesy of Eda B. Vidale and O. Gutierrez-Costa.*

S-R$_\phi$ relations is the proper substrate of S-R$_\psi$ behavior, such as the loudness function.

In addition, it should be noted that this type of quantification procedure encounters difficulties when stimuli of appreciable duration are

---

[6] Comparable generalizations can, in principle, be derived for the behavior of single neural units once we have decided how to deal with such problems as spontaneous firing rate, fluctuations of responses (especially in the region near threshold), and such phenomena as inhibition, adaptation, and different types of neural interaction.

involved. Such stimuli typically elicit rather complex response patterns and, although these may exhibit systematic variations as a function of stimulus intensity, the behavior of isolated components of these response patterns cannot be represented by identical intensity functions [46].

The records of Figs. 3 and 4 serve to illustrate some of our foregoing remarks. These data represent averaged evoked responses to flashes as recorded by macroelectrodes from the surface of the visual cortex of

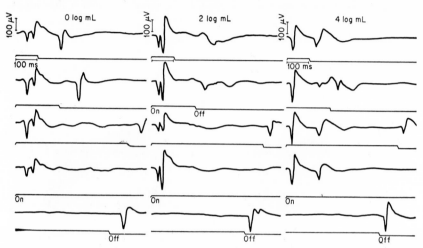

Fig. 4. Averaged evoked responses to repetitive photic stimulation recorded from a location on the visual cortex of an anesthetized cat (*Cat:Go*). Flash-duration range has been extended to span the range from 100 to 1,000 msec. For each of the three luminance levels, the first three pairs of traces represent averaged responses to flash durations of 100, 200, and 500 msec, respectively; the last two pairs of records in each column depict the response to a 1,000-msec flash whose onset and termination are indicated on the stimulus traces (i.e., the last pair of traces is a direct continuation of the preceding pair, displaced downward for display purposes). Other pertinent details as in Fig. 3.

Note the marked differences in wave form, latencies, and amplitudes of response components at comparable luminance levels and flash durations in the averaged responses of the two animals whose data are presented in Figs. 3 and 4, respectively. The latter animal was at a lighter stage of anesthesia but other factors were also involved in producing the observed differences. *Courtesy of Eda B. Vidale and O. Gutierrez-Costa.*

anesthetized cats. Both flash intensity and flash duration were systematically varied. The wave forms and temporal characteristics of the averaged responses reflect variations in these two stimulus parameters, as well as interactions between them. Separate response components that are clearly resolvable at low luminance levels fuse at higher luminances as a result of progressive decreases in their latencies; also, additional response components emerge at higher luminances and longer flash durations.

Intensity-time interaction effects may be indicated by the marked re-duction, particularly at lower luminances, in the latency of "off" com-ponents of the response as a function of flash duration. The amplitudes of separate components in the cortical response display no clear-cut systematic trend and this may reflect the greater sensitivity to various adaptation phenomena of amplitude than of latency measures.

These samples of representations of stimulus intensity in the nervous system hardly encourage one to look for a unique, or even a dominant,

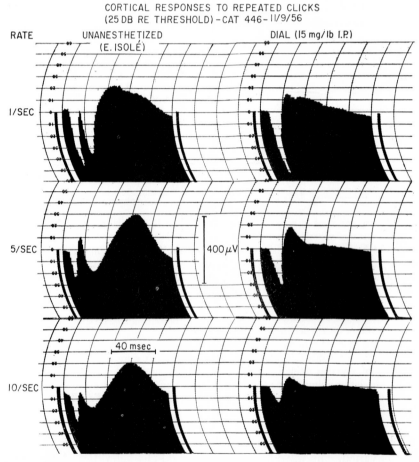

CORTICAL RESPONSES TO REPEATED CLICKS
(25 DB RE THRESHOLD) – CAT 446 – 11/9/56

Fig. 5. Averaged evoked responses to repeated clicks from the auditory cortex of a cat. Comparison of data obtained before and after anesthetization indicates cort-ical following at higher stimulus repetition rates in the unanesthetized (*encéphale isolé*) state. Note also the difference in the wave form of the response at lower repetition rates in the anesthetized and unanesthetized conditions.

In this type of display [64], the average response is the envelope of a series of intensity code. While it seems that at present we must still be satisfied with general statements—e.g., other things being equal, stronger stimuli will activate (both excite and inhibit) more neural units more vigorously and faster than weak stimuli—we can hope in the future to gain some insight into the *functional* significance of this variety of intensity codes from electrophysiological studies of the behaving animal. Multivariate coding enhances the flexibility of the nervous system. The organism can choose among the available alternatives those aspects of neural function

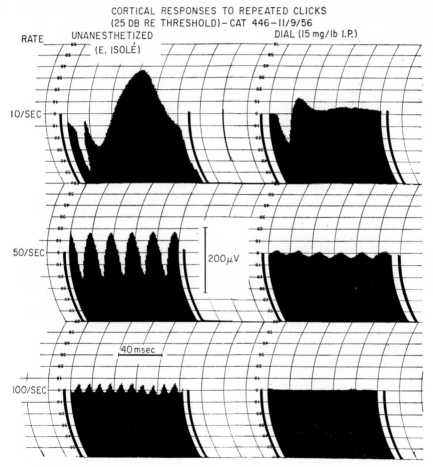

regularly spaced pen deflections. Here the pen deflections are separated by intervals of 1 msec. The delivery of the click coincides with the first of the continuous series of pen deflections. Number of responses averaged at the different repetition rates: 60 responses at 1 per sec; 300 at 5 per sec; 600 at 10 per sec; 3,000 at 50 per sec; and 6,000 at 100 per sec. After Goldstein, Kiang, and Brown [38, p. 360].

which are most relevant to his given state or task. It seems highly unrealistic to expect to find invariant representation of sound intensity in situations that differ as widely as when a laboratory subject is asked to make cross-modality matches and when a mother is to be awakened by her child's whimper.

Time. Analysis of electrical response patterns for features representing temporal aspects of stimulation is complicated by the fact that both the direct effects and the aftereffects in the evoked electrical activity outlast the duration of the stimulus in time. This fact was already apparent in the records of Figs. 1 to 4. In the experiments depicted in Figs. 3 and 4, stimulus duration was varied while repetition rate was kept constant. The temporal resolving power of various sensory mechanisms can also be investigated by varying stimulus repetition rate and looking for concomitant periodic events in electrical response patterns. One can thus determine the extent to which neural activity recorded from various sites "follows" the repetition rate of a stimulus. This general type of approach has been employed in studies of response patterns elicited at various levels and stations of afferent pathways within different sense modalities. Peake, Goldstein, and Kiang [61], for example, have recently reported that in the auditory nerve stimulus-locked neural activity, i.e., population responses, can be detected in averaged responses up to rates of nearly 3,000 per sec. The results of previous studies on following in sensory systems are not directly comparable since the data were not processed by electronic averaging techniques.

At the cortical level, evoked responses to repetitive auditory, visual, and tactile stimuli have been recorded from a number of animal species. Goldstein, Kiang, and Brown [38], using repeated clicks and repeated bursts of wideband noise, determined the range of repetition rates over which the averaged response indicated the presence of cortical following in the cat. They found stimulus-locked activity in response to clicks up to 100 or 200 per sec before anesthetization but no appreciable stimulus-locked activity above 50 per sec after anesthesia was given. Some of their data are presented in Fig. 5.

More recently, Goldstein [35] has pointed out that, because of overlapping of response components, it becomes difficult, if not impossible, to determine from macroelectrode recordings whether or not the activity of cortical elements is stimulus-locked at rates of 200 per sec and beyond. Comparable studies in single cortical cells are not yet available, but present indications are that these cells are far from being able to duplicate the performance of single units at the periphery. In single units of the cochlear nucleus, for example, following up to several hundred clicks per second has been observed [Kiang, unpublished observation]. The extent to which volleying (alternate firings of units) can result in following at rates higher than those of which any single unit is capable remains to be determined.

Electrical activity patterns recorded from human subjects can also be examined with a view to determining the degree of following. Figure 6 shows averaged human electroretinograms (ERG) in response to flashes presented at various repetition rates. A noteworthy feature of these data

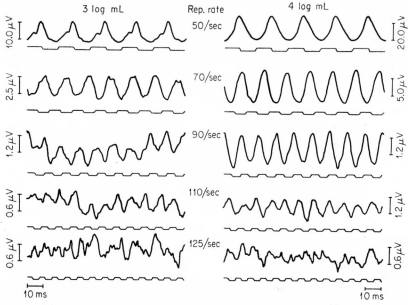

FIG. 6. Averaged human electroretinograms in response to repetitive flashes. The lower of each pair of traces represents the stimulus above which appears the corresponding averaged ERG. Under the conditions of this experiment, the subject reported that the test field appeared fused at a flash rate of 60 per sec for the 3 log mL luminance level and at 68 per sec for 4 log mL. Number of responses averaged for each luminance at the various repetition rates: 3 log mL —256 responses at 50 and 70 per sec, 512 at 90, 110, and 125 per sec; 4 log mL—256 responses at 50 per sec, 512 at all other flash rates. *Courtesy of L. A. Riggs. E. P. Johnson, and Eda B. Vidale.*

is that at repetition rates markedly in excess of the subject's psychophysically determined flicker fusion threshold (60 per sec at the lower luminance, 68 per sec at the higher one), the averaged ERG still follows the frequency of stimulus presentation. Thus, in agreement with data from other animals, electrical activity recorded from a peripherally located structure in humans indicates greater temporal resolution than that recorded from central structures [55]; furthermore, electrical responses from the periphery are also more stimulus-faithful than perceptual responses.

Similarly, electrocortical activity patterns recorded by means of scalp electrodes may also reflect greater temporal resolution than is apparent in the behavioral responses of human subjects. Geisler [33] has observed stimulus-locked activity in auditory responses to repetitive clicks at rates up to about 100 per sec—rates at which the listener has long ceased to resolve the component stimuli in a train of clicks.

In addition to variations in duration and repetition rate, other types of stimulus modifications have been employed in the study of neural representation of temporal events. The role that transients play in the patterning of sensory stimuli, and thus in the flow of information from the environment, has long been recognized. Busnel [20], for instance, has shown that grasshoppers fail to react to acoustic signals if these signals do not contain fairly sharp "on" or "off" transients. In a similar vein, the effect of stimulus rise time on electrical response patterns has been examined by Goldstein and Kiang [37]. These investigators recorded peripheral and cortical responses of cats to bursts of sound having different rise times. Their data indicate that characteristic components of both peripherally and cortically recorded response patterns which are clearly identifiable for stimuli with rapid rise times become undetectable when the rise time of sound bursts is made sufficiently long; however, the critical value at which this disappearance occurs differs rather drastically for these two electrode sites. At the level of the auditory nerve, the earliest and most prominent neural response component (the so-called "N_1 response") is no longer seen with stimuli whose rise times exceed 5 msec, a value at which simultaneously recorded cortical responses are still clearly evident. Not until rise time is lengthened to about 100 msec do cortical responses become undetectable. The authors interpret their findings in terms of the degree of synchronization in the discharge and the wave forms of the activity of units that contribute to responses recorded by macroelectrodes.

Localizable representations. At several points during the preceding discussion on the nature of neural representation of stimulus variables, we have touched on the issue of "local signs" in the nervous system. Neuroanatomists and neurophysiologists have mapped the brain for a variety of organismic states and by a variety of criteria. These maps differ so markedly that the viewer often finds himself at a loss to decide whether the different explorers initially set out to survey the same territory. A striking documentation of this point emerges from the contrast between Woolsey's [76] recent mapping of the regions of the cat's cortex that respond to auditory stimuli (see Fig. 7) and the numerous auditory maps collected by Ades [1]. The fact that Woolsey's map shows so many auditorily responsive regions does not mean, except in the crudest sense, that they are functionally equivalent. And yet, how much virgin territory is there left for the other modalities? We probably need to get used to the idea that different sense modalities interpenetrate each other's spheres of influence to a much greater extent than is consistent with a neat filing system. Inhibitory phenomena may be effective in reducing this overlap to manageable proportions. Mechanisms of inhibition may also permit us to maintain properties of commensurability between the various modalities [73] at the same time as they provide for cross-filing of related bits of sensory information.

The electrical activity that can be recorded almost simultaneously from a number of different neural sites manifests both gross and subtle

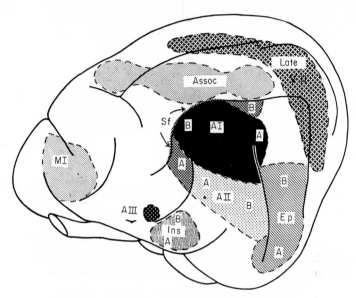

Fig. 7. Auditory response areas of cerebral cortex of cat. AI, auditory area I; AII, auditory area II; Ep, posterior ectosylvian area; Sf, suprasylvian fringe area; Ins, insular area; AIII, Tunturi's third area; Assoc. and MI, suprasylvian and precentral motor response areas; Late = area of late auditory responses in second visual area (VII). Reproduced from Woolsey [76].

changes in response patterns. Some data from Brazier [15], reproduced in Fig. 8, serve to illustrate this point. In addition to variations in neuro-electric activity encountered at different locations along classical afferent pathways, the widespread influences exerted by the brain stem reticular formation and by other neural systems, such as the limbic, on the modulation and integration of sensory inputs further complicate the analysis of the nature of neural representation of stimulus variables. The interaction between these nonspecific response systems (see Fig. 9) and modality-specific afferent pathways remains to be unraveled [68]. It can hardly be assumed to remain invariant under conditions of novel or monotonous stimulation, for various states of motivation and attention. From these and similar data, we must conclude that information about external events is cast in different neural "codes" at different locations. The specification of neurophysiological correlates of stimulus variables is thus confounded by

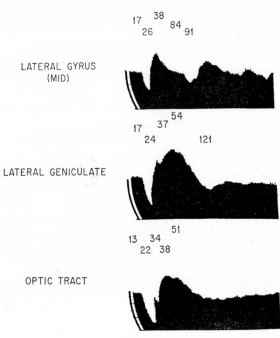

Fig. 8. Averaged responses to flash from three stations in the visual pathway of a cat; simultaneous recordings under moderate pentobarbital anesthesia with reference lead on the back of the neck. The numbers above each averaged response indicate (in milliseconds) on-set or peak latency of characteristic deflections in the particular wave form. Positivity of recording electrode with respect to reference electrode plotted in downward direction. Flash rate: 1 per 1.4 sec. Flash coincident with the first of the continuous series of pen deflections which are separated by intervals of 1 msec. Reproduced from Brazier [15, p. 700].

where in the nervous system one looks for them and it seems necessary to assume that behavior integrates and weights a set of neural patterns at different places and times in relation to the organism's expectancies, memory-storage, and required performance.[7]

[7] Views such as these are being accorded increasing recognition and emphasis; see, for example, Brindley's [18] recent book for a discussion of similar and related issues.

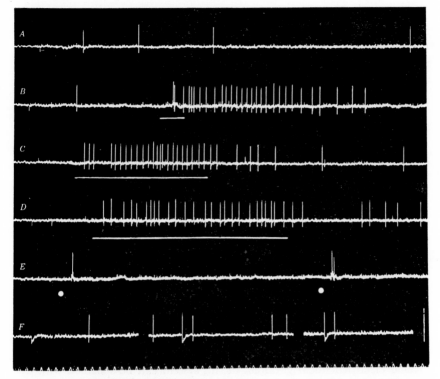

Fig. 9. Microelectrode recording from a single unit in the medial part of the pontine reticular formation of an unanesthetized cat in response to tactile, acoustic, and cortical stimulation. *A*, spontaneous discharge; *B*, tapping the ipsilateral forelimb; *C*, rubbing the animal's back; *D*, touching the cat's whiskers; *E*, hand claps; *F*, single shocks applied to the ipsilateral sensorimotor cortex. Delivery of stimuli indicated by white horizontal lines in *B,C,D*, dots in *E*, and artifacts that displace the record's base line in *F*. Time calibration at bottom of figure indicates 10-msec intervals.

This particular unit proved responsive to all test stimuli that were tried, although the pattern of spike activity is rather different for the different modalities. Reproduced from M. Palestini, G. F. Rossi, and A. Zanchetti [59].

PRELIMINARIES TO THE ASSESSMENT OF STATE VARIABLES

Studies of biological systems in terms of input-output relations have often invoked the familiar formulation: $R = f(O,S)$ where R stands for response variables, O for organismic or state-determined variables, and S for stimulus variables [75]. Great care has frequently been expended (particularly in the experimental psychology laboratory) on the specification and control of stimulus parameters. But too many researchers in this general area have tended to slight or ignore the other major class of independent variables in this equation—much of the psychological litera-

ture conveys the impression that the O in the formulation has been relegated to the status of a cipher. Admittedly, the temptation to consider
(or rather, *not* to consider) state variables in this fashion is great. The
problems inherent in the definition—not to mention those encountered in
attempts at experimental control—of state-determined variables in biological systems are in no sense trivial.

In contrast, in much of classical physics the state of a system that is
to be studied by input-output analysis can be dealt with fairly simply:
(1) The state of the system at the beginning of the experiment (at
$t = 0$) can be specified by a set of initial conditions; and (2) the previous history of the system (for $t < 0$) can, in the majority of instances,
be effectively ignored. (Thus prediction of future behavior depends little,
within certain limits of linearity, upon the past history of the system—in
this sense, the experimenter is dealing with a *tabula rasa*.) If the physical
system under study is a collection of more or less independent particles
(such as a gas), then the state of the system is most often given as a set
of distribution functions such as, for instance, the velocities of gas molecules. These distribution functions economically specify a set of state
variables whose nature gets progressively more complicated as the interaction between particles assumes greater importance.

Since a neuron may be considered as a complex physical system, we
should be able to predict its response, provided that the configuration of
critical electrochemical variables of this system can be specified with the
requisite accuracy. If we seek to predict the response not of a single
neuron, but of a sensory subsystem or of an entire nervous system, then
the specification of the previous history and of the initial state of this ensemble of closely and variably coupled neural components becomes a
formidable undertaking. Under these circumstances, we are forced to ask
ourselves whether we can discover certain short-cut methods whose
pragmatic purpose will be to improve our ability to predict response behavior. Descriptions in terms of such *quasi-state* variables may, for instance, serve to summarize a neuron's spontaneous activity, a distribution
function of thresholds for a neuronal population, or even an organism's
state of sleep or attention.

Many psychophysical experiments attempt to circumvent the specification of the subject's state by a combination of instructions and rewards designed to keep the subject in the same state, even though
identity of state across subjects remains an assumption. In electrophysiological experiments, a comparable dilemma is encountered with respect
to anesthesia: the attempt is made to maintain an animal at a given level
of anesthesia, the desired level usually being monitored by visual inspection of the animal's electrical activity. Similar situations obtain when
drugs other than anesthetics are administered, when gross physiological
changes such as sleep are admitted as variables in an experiment, or

when different levels of "unanesthesia" are to be specified in animals whose motivational state, for instance, is being manipulated.

In a sense, the old physiological paradigm of the two-shock experiment can be viewed as an attempt to get around some of these difficulties. The first or conditioning shock is intended to put a system into a given state, and the effects of the subsequent test shock are then interpreted in relation to this state. This approach has undoubtedly proved productive in the study of the behavior of an isolated peripheral nerve fiber that is no longer subject to the influences operative in the *in vivo* situation. However, the application of such a technique to more complexly connected neural components or systems ought to be accompanied by a more modest expectation of gains in prediction.

Electrophysiological descriptions of the state of a system can scarcely be more than summarizing measures. To some extent, these measures subsume an account of the functional neuroanatomy of the system. From this point of view, the nervous system of an animal that is attending to a particular sensory stimulus is, at least in part, differently "hooked up" from that of an animal that is either disinterested in its surroundings or that is attending to a stimulus of another sense modality. The plausibility of this position has been greatly enhanced by a number of recent findings. For instance, Hubel and others [45] report that, in the auditory cortex of unanesthetized and unrestrained cats, there are units that are brought into play only if the animal is paying attention to acoustic signals. These "attention" units failed to respond to typical laboratory stimuli (which were, nevertheless, adequate to elicit discharges from other cortical cells) unless there were overt behavioral manifestations that the subject was attending to the source of stimulation. On the other hand, a wealth of evidence attests to the fact that animals may cease to attend to environmental stimuli that once were effective in eliciting responses. On the physiological level, this phenomenon expresses itself in the form of sensory "habituation"—a term used to designate the progressive diminution in amplitude of evoked potentials as a result of the prolonged repetition of a given sensory stimulus. This effect is known to be reversible; a few paired presentations of the stimulus which is no longer effective and electric shock suffice to reinstate the previously extinguished evoked response [32]. Habituation has also been found to be a selective process in that its effect is confined to the particular stimulus that has been frequently repeated and does not extend to other or novel stimulation. Thus, while the evoked potentials in the cat's cochlear nucleus may be greatly reduced or even totally abolished during the course of repeated presentations of a given tonal stimulus, a different tone can elicit a normal evoked response [42]. Even a nonhabituated sensory stimulus may cease to elicit evoked responses during the time that an organism is focusing its attention upon another stimulus within a different sense modality. As

Hernández-Peón and his colleagues [43] have demonstrated, the presence of fish odors or of a mouse greatly reduced the response to a click recorded from the cat's cochlear nucleus so long as the cat was actively sniffing the odors or visually attentive to the mouse. Following the removal of the olfactory or visual stimulation, the click responses returned to their initial amplitude levels. Similar observations on a conscious human patient have recently been reported by Jouvet and Lapras [49]. In response to somesthetic stimulation of the face, the amplitude of the electrical activity recorded at the thalamus was greatly enhanced under instructions to pay close attention to the somesthetic stimuli and was markedly diminished when the subject's attention was drawn to other sense modalities. Incidentally, these various effects of attention and habituation are not found in anesthetized preparations.

Hence, a "wiring diagram" of *potential* connections is not necessarily the most meaningful description of a nervous system if we aim at predicting an organism's response to a sensory message. Rather, given a specific sensory task, we need to know whether the incoming neural signals will be admitted at all, and if so, to which central pathways other than the classical receiving areas they will be switched. The experimenter's instructions and the observer's expectations in typical psychophysical experiments are likely to influence these switching operations.[8]

The so-called "ongoing" or "spontaneous" electrical activity which is a property of nervous tissue has been much studied during the past few decades. Our theoretical understanding of the physiological mechanisms that underlie this phenomenon is still rudimentary and we know little of the ways in which existing background activity modulates stimulus-evoked neuroelectric events or is modulated by them. Nonetheless, ongoing activity may provide a useful index of a neuron's, or even of an organism's, state as sensory stimulation is reacted to selectively. In this context it merits our consideration.

In order to assess spontaneous activity in a quantitative manner, one usually needs to transform a time series of neuroelectric events into displays of quasi-state variables. Such a display represents a reduction of the original data and is usually more amenable to differential treatments and analytic investigation. In trying to ascertain whether a given parameter qualifies as a useful state variable, we may require answers to questions such as these: How stable is the display when data are obtained under

[8] Among other research findings that might be cited in support of these statements is some of the work recently reported from Soviet laboratories—Asratyan's [7] "trans-switching" experiments, wherein a given stimulus may simultaneously acquire two different signal meanings as a result of differential reinforcement procedures, or Anokhin's [6] treatment of the conditioned reflex as an integral behavioral act, especially his emphasis on the concept of "afferent synthesis" and on the role of anticipation in the formation of adaptive behavior.

identical experimental conditions? How sensitive is the display to important changes in the organism's (or neuron's) environment? How large a population of individuals can economically be described by a limited number of displays? In addition, we may ask whether a given display preserves information regarding temporal sequences, regarding simultaneous events in different parts of the brain, etc. In this connection, it is also desirable to be able to define the appropriate interval during which a given display of state variables does not change or, alternatively, the normal range of variation of such a display over a given time interval.

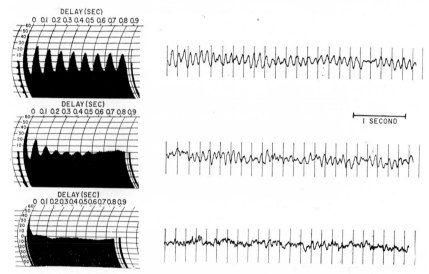

Fig. 10. Left: Autocorrelograms of 1-min samples of the EEG of three normal human subjects recorded from bipolar electrodes (right parietal to right occipital) on the scalp. Right: Samples of EEG ink tracings from these same subjects. Reproduced from Barlow, Brazier, and Rosenblith [10].

In the following paragraphs, we shall present several examples of such displays. Most of these displays have been derived from tape recordings of the EEG according to methods that have been described elsewhere [8, 11, 17, 64]. Similar methods are, of course, applicable to the description of patterns of autonomic function, biochemical activity, and the like.

As is well known, EEG recordings from normal human subjects show considerable variation one from another. If one uses the amount of alpha activity in the EEG as a criterion, it appears that records from different individuals distribute themselves along a continuum of values—from those manifesting the presence of clear-cut periodic components to those that appear totally devoid of any rhythmic component within the alpha range. The records in Fig. 10 were selected to illustrate this point. On the

DELAY IN MILLISECONDS

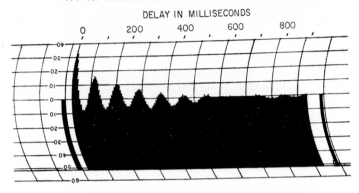

DELAY IN MILLISECONDS

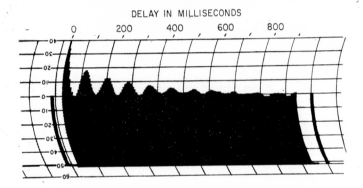

DELAY IN MILLISECONDS

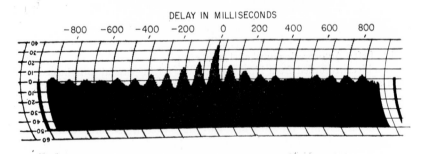

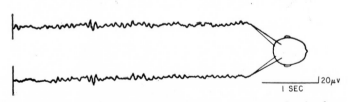

FIG. 11. Autocorrelograms and cross-correlogram for a 1-min simultaneous left and right parietooccipital EEG recording from (left) a normal human subject [11], and (right) a patient with a tumor of the right cerebral hemisphere [12]. For each individual, the first two displays represent the autocorrelograms of the EEG from the left and right sides of the head,

DELAY IN MILLISECONDS

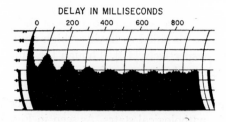

DELAY IN MILLISECONDS

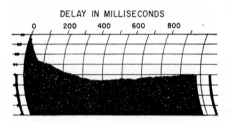

DELAY IN MILLISECONDS

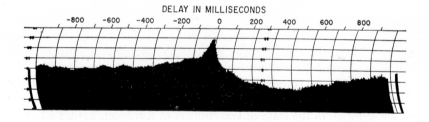

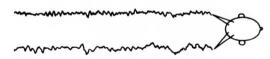

respectively, while the cross-correlation of the activity from the two hemispheres is depicted in the third display. A portion of the inked trace of each subject's EEG, showing electrode placement on the scalp, is reproduced at the bottom.

For the normal subject, the autocorrelograms for the two sides are quite similar and the cross-correlogram is symmetrical about the point of zero delay. In contrast, the autocorrelograms of the patient with a unilateral brain lesion are quite dissimilar and his cross-correlogram exhibits marked asymmetry with respect to the point of zero delay.

basis of either visual inspection of ink-written records or, more quantitatively, on the basis of the autocorrelograms of their EEG, the three subjects can at least be classified as having "high alpha," "medium alpha,"
and "no alpha," respectively [10]. Though the functional significance of
such a classificatory scheme across individuals remains to be established,
striking differences in the autocorrelograms of the EEG recorded from
comparable locations on the two sides of a subject's skull seem to accompany certain pathological states. As seen in Fig. 11, a high degree of
symmetry characterizes the cross-correlogram of the activity on the two
sides of a normal subject [11], whereas the cross-correlogram for a patient with a localized brain tumor manifests marked asymmetry [12].
While much of this information can be detected by the trained electro-
encephalographer in the ink-written EEG, the correlograms constitute
more objective displays of these data and thus make them more susceptible to experimental manipulation.

Repeated correlograms of the EEG in a given individual show a high
degree of stability, both short-term and relatively long-term, provided
precautions are taken to ensure careful control of experimental conditions
[10]. It is also worth noting that the basic EEG time series from which
the correlogram is to be computed must be of sufficient length, and yet
not so long that it becomes difficult for a subject to maintain himself in a
given state in the absence of external stimulation. Experience has shown
that intervals of the order of one to several minutes seem to yield the
most stable and repeatable correlogram displays. The use of longer intervals is advisable only if special measures can be taken to maintain the
subject in a given state. Recent evidence [64] indicates that subjects will
exhibit changes in state-variable displays (either correlograms or parametric displays of derived measures of alpha activity) when isolated from
auditory and visual stimulation for periods of approximately ten minutes.

The different types of state-variable displays are, as one would hope,
rather sensitive to the state of wakefulness of a subject. Figure 12 shows
how a medium-alpha autocorrelogram in the awake state becomes converted into a no-alpha correlogram when the subject is asleep. It further
demonstrates significant changes in the averaged evoked response to
randomly delivered flashes in the two conditions: during sleep, the wave
form of the early components is simpler, and the so-called "sensory afterdischarges" are absent [9]. These comments regarding evoked responses
to photic stimulation may be generalized when we refer to the results of
Fig. 5, where cortical responses to clicks are depicted for a cat in anesthetized and unanesthetized states. In addition to the difference in the
upper limit of following previously alluded to, changes in the wave form
of the evoked response in the two conditions are readily apparent. From
what we presently know of the greater lability of the later (as compared

to the initial) components of evoked responses, it seems not unreasonable to predict that changes in physiological state, as well as alterations in more psychological variables, are likely to affect these components substantially. Finally, it is useful to show that the administration of a drug, such as an anesthetic, alters a display that seeks to represent time patterns

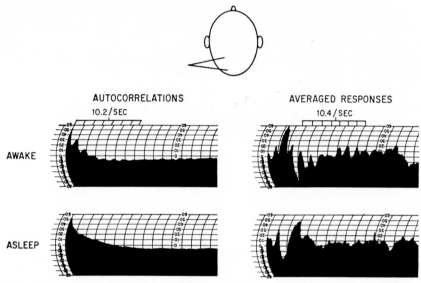

Fig. 12. Autocorrelograms and averaged evoked responses to aperiodic flashing from a normal human subject while awake and during natural sleep. Four-minute recordings from bipolar (left parietal to left occipital) scalp electrodes. Mean interval between successive flashes, approximately 1.1 sec. The autocorrelogram of the waking subject manifests a 10.2 per sec rhythm of moderate persistence, but no such rhythmic activity can be discerned in his autocorrelogram when the subject is asleep. Similarly, the averaged record shows a rhythmic afterdischarge with a frequency of 10.4 per sec as a part of the response in the waking state while no such sensory afterdischarge appears in the sleeping state. In addition, the wave form of the initial components of the averaged responses differs in the two states. Approximately 220 responses entered into the computation of each average. Reproduced from Barlow [9, p. 323].

of all-or-none spikes in even a single cortical neuron. Figure 13 shows how, in an extreme case, both the rate of firing and the distribution of interspike intervals are strongly affected—as is, of course, the poststimulus time histogram [34] that corresponds to the evoked response.

It is, however, appropriate to utter a caveat regarding these and other methods that aim at quantifying data on the electrical activity of the nervous system. The multivariate nature of the nervous system prevents one from taking too much stock in any given number or even in a computed curve. Somehow we must learn to derive quantities that character-

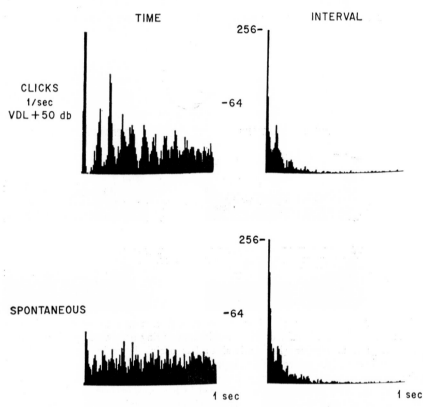

FIG. 13a. An extreme case of the effects of an increment in anesthesia upon the firing pattern of a single neuron in the auditory cortex of an anesthetized cat. The data have been processed in the following two forms: (1) poststimulus time histogram [34]—a histogram of the distribution of firing times relative to some fixed point in time; (2) interval histogram [34]—a histogram of the distribution of time intervals between two successive action potentials.

In the top half of Fig. 13a, these two types of analysis have been applied to the action potentials recorded following click stimulation. The lower half of Fig. 13a presents time and interval histograms of action potentials recorded in the absence of stimulation. For the stimulated condition, the poststimulus time histogram is computed with reference to the onset of the immediately preceding click, while for the nonstimulated (spontaneous) condition, a time marker occurring at intervals corresponding to the repetition rate of the click in the stimulated condition serves as the reference. *Courtesy of G. L. Gerstein.*

ize the essentials of neural activity in a fashion that is perhaps somewhat analogous to the dimensionless parameters of engineering systems. This point can be made more concrete. Farley and others [27] have shown

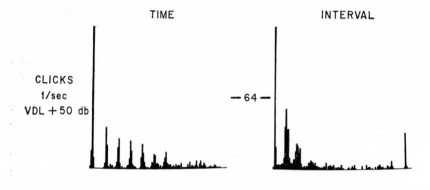

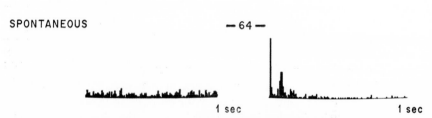

FIG. 13*b*. The effects of a small additional dose of anesthetic upon the displays *Courtesy of G. L. Gerstein.*

that there are individuals whose total alpha-activity profile when they are awake bears some resemblance to the profile of another individual while the latter is asleep. However, whenever a person falls asleep, there are systematic changes in his alpha-activity profile. In other words, we must learn to assess the significance of changes in state in relation to certain base lines and must refrain from attaching too much value to isolated pieces of numerical information.

TEMPORAL ASPECTS OF RESPONSES TO DISCRETE STIMULI

The last two decades have seen a renewed interest in the temporal aspects of man's sensory performance. Two factors may be identified as being primarily responsible for this revival of interest: the practical (often military) concern with man-machine systems of human engineering, and the information-theoretically inspired concept of human channel capacity. These developments complement our increased ability to analyze the temporal structure of neurophysiological response processes. It may well be that temporal response characteristics furnish clues that are highly relevant to the search for neurophysiological concomitants of sensory communication. At present, reaction time (RT) data are among the most sensitive indicants of sensory information-handling processes and deserve to be pursued by neurophysiologists in relation to stimulus, response, and state variables.

The over-all role of time and timing in behavior is, however, still too broad a topic to be considered in the light of contemporary neurophysiological knowledge. We shall, therefore, limit ourselves to a discussion of some temporal characteristics of responses to discrete stimuli. In so doing, we recognize that we structure the continuous variable *time* in terms of the more or less instantaneous occurrences of stereotyped events within both stimulus and response domains. Such a procedure, though admittedly arbitrary, permits us to infer and/or examine some of the properties of the sequence of electrical and behavioral events that intervene between stimulus and response. This sequence need not—indeed, must not—imply *post hoc, ergo propter hoc*. Nonetheless, its structure lends itself, in principle, to comparisons among a wide range of behavioral acts—from simple reflexes to what are now called "decision-making processes." This spectrum of integrated behaviors may cover a hundredfold range in time: the unconditioned reflex of the stapedius muscle in the middle ear occurs about 10 msec after the onset of an intense sound [31], while choice behavior that involves, for instance, the identification of one of a number of words in the presence of noise, may well occupy the greater part of a second [75].

The chain of event-classes that is intercalated between a stimulus and the relevant voluntary motor response may be enumerated in the following oversimplified list: Stimulus (S_i)[9] → Afferent events → Central sensory events → Central decision events → Central motor events → Efferent events → Motor response (R_j).[10] In the case of a simple reflex arc, the central elaboration is presumably short-circuited so that the reduced afferent-efferent path is traversed in much less time.

The above schema is vulnerable to a host of criticisms, most important among which is, perhaps, the contrast between this single one-way, series-connected channel and the actual nervous system with its multiplicity of inputs, of parallel pathways, of feedback loops (whose significance is perhaps greatest for extended patterns of stimulation), and of

---

[9] S_i is to be understood as referring to one of an ensemble of possible stimuli.

[10] R_j refers to one out of a repertory of possible responses.

spatial or temporal interaction mechanisms. Yet even this highly schematized view of the probable sequence of events permits us, at least, to distinguish those stages about which there exists some neurophysiological or behavioral information from those stages about which we are still totally in the dark. We naturally know most about the temporal characteristics of the more peripheral events in our S-R sequence and relatively little regarding those central links whose existence we postulate.[11]

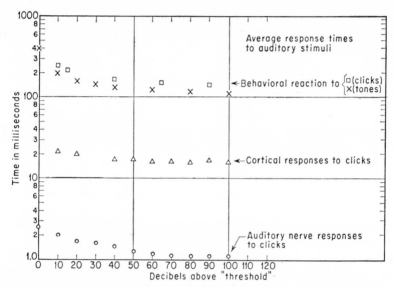

FIG. 14. Average response times to auditory stimuli. Top: Reaction time of a human observer in response to clicks and tones of various intensities. Middle: Latency of evoked cortical responses from the auditory area of a cat to repetitive clicks of various intensities. These latency values refer to time intervals that have elapsed between stimulus delivery and the peak of the initial surface-positive component of the evoked response. Bottom: Latency of neural responses from the cat's auditory nerve as a function of click intensity. Latency measured in terms of time intervening between delivery of stimulus and occurrence of the negative peak of the earliest neural event (N_1) in the auditory pathway.

To lend concreteness to some of our foregoing remarks, let us examine a simple reaction-time experiment in which a human observer presses a button in response to clicks of various intensity levels. The top part of Fig. 14 presents some data on this point that are in good agree-

[11] The available data from mature mammals (including man) on the latencies of afferent neural events prove to be quite similar for comparable physiological states. This similarity holds for neural events up to, and including, the so-called "surface-positive component" of the evoked potentials recorded from cortical receiving areas.

ment with comparable data reported by other investigators for either auditory or other sensory stimuli: Between aboslute threshold and the threshold for discomfort, RT decreases by at least 200 msec.[12] Over a comparable range of stimulus intensities, the latency of the evoked cortical response (i.e., to the peak of the surface-positive component) from the cat decreases by about 10 msec (see Fig. 14, center), while the latency of the earliest neural event (N_1) in the cat's auditory pathway decreases by approximately 2 msec (see Fig. 14, bottom). Thus, changes of latency with intensity on the afferent-sensory side constitute but a small fraction of the total change in reaction time of the motor response.

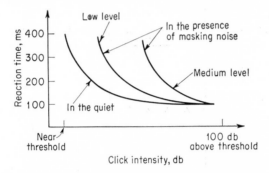

Fig. 15. Schematic graph of human reaction time to a masked acoustic stimulus. The curves depict mean reaction time to clicks as a function of stimulus intensity for clicks presented either in the quiet or in the presence of a thermal masking noise. Reaction-time data for two intensity levels of the masking noise are illustrated. After data by Thompson [74].

When we examine RT's to clicks in the presence of a given thermal noise, we find that the RT to a click that is barely detectable (just above the masked threshold) is comparable to the RT to a click near absolute threshold. As the click emerges from the background noise, the RT eventually decreases to the value of the RT observed in the quiet (see Fig. 15). From our knowledge of neural responses to masked clicks in the cat, we can again say that the corresponding changes in latency seen on the afferent-sensory side account for only a small percentage of the increases in RT that are observed as a consequence of the masking noise.

[12] Changes in the latency of the onset of the human electromyogram (EMG) as a function of stimulus intensity parallel those of the motor response; to a first approximation, we can say that (1) the interval between the onset of the EMG and the finger movement is of the order of 40 msec and (2) this interval is not sensitive to changes in stimulus intensity [4].

Several investigators [21, 44, 47] have studied the dependence of disjunctive reaction time upon the number of equiprobable alternatives to be discriminated. Their results are concordant in the sense that over a certain range a linear relation obtains between RT and the number of bits per stimulus presentation. Figure 16 underlines the striking parallelism between findings in audition and vision.[13] Although these experiments on human subjects were not accompanied by electrophysiological recordings, there is no reason to assume that a given stimulus would

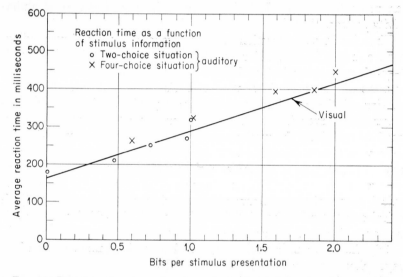

Fig. 16. Reaction time as a function of stimulus information. The straight line represents the best fit to data obtained by Hyman [47] from one of his subjects in response to visual stimulation. The circles and crosses represent reaction-time data obtained by Albert [3] from one of his subjects in response to auditory stimuli; here, the stimulus set was composed of either two or four elements. Reproduced from Rosenblith [65, p. 490].

manifest a variable afferent delay time depending upon the probability of its occurrence.

Other data, such as those obtained by Davis [22, 23] on reaction times to two successive stimuli, reinforce the rational assumption that important changes in RT reflect information-processing operations in the central links of our schematic chain. These operations seem to consume

[13] This behavior is, however, not independent of the particular response that is required. For example, if the ensemble of stimuli to be discriminated consists of speech sounds, and if the criterion response is the repetition of the sound just presented, then RT is, to a first approximation, independent of the size of the ensemble [24, 69].

the largest portion of the total RT and they also seem to contribute the largest fraction of the variance in RT in a given experimental situation. This view is further supported by the way in which state variables, independent of stimulus or response variables, influence RT. For instance, the effects exerted upon RT by the introduction of a forewarning signal, as well as by the interval between the warning signal and the stimulus proper [51], lend themselves to such an interpretation, as do Fuster's [30] findings on the effect of reticular stimulation in the monkey upon RT. In this connection, we should also mention the attempts that have been made to correlate RT (including variability of RT) and alpha-activity patterns [52].

Thus far in our discussion of some temporal aspects of responding, we have mainly been considering the onset or peak latencies of the earliest—with respect to stimulus delivery—neural responses from the receiving areas of the cortex in relation to RT's that characterize the motor behavior of the well-instructed human organism. These evoked responses persist even in anesthetized preparations; they may thus be assumed to constitute the most stable contribution to those operations of the nervous system that are chiefly given over to information-processing tasks.[14] The latencies of the initial surface-positive, surface-negative complex are, of course, not the only aspects of these more or less specific cortical events that are temporally related to stimulus delivery. Such cortical events tend to be of ill-defined duration; in addition to the primary evoked response, they often include a series of aftereffects [15, 25, 28, 39] that have been variously related to such phenomena as afterimages, short-term memory, and conditionability.

There exist even less specific response activities with relatively long latencies, such as the galvanic skin response and the so-called "blocking" of the alpha rhythm. This latter phenomenon has been investigated fairly systematically in relation to stimulus intensity. Bernhard [13], who has perhaps covered the widest dynamic range, shows that over a luminance range of 5 log units, alpha blocking time decreases from approximately 565 msec to about 165 msec. In his studies, he also shows that alpha blockade occurs earlier in time than the onset of response-connected electromyographic activity—a finding with which other investigators are not in agreement [26, 58].

Now that it has become possible to record electrophysiological responses from behaving animals, including man, attention is being

[14] In view of the fact that animals have been shown to be able to make relatively simple sensory discriminations in the absence of cortical receiving areas, one cannot even consider the classical evoked potentials as necessary antecedents of sensory performance. They may, nevertheless, constitute key inputs that permit the normally functioning organism to make much finer discriminations or to accomplish crude ones more rapidly.

focused upon "late" events [16]. Russian investigators have, for instance, emphasized the electrical concomitants of the orienting reflex [71]. It should become increasingly possible to enhance selected components of the electrical response complex through the use of conditioning procedures. There are already clear indications that conditioning procedures can change timing relationships in the electrical activity simultaneously recorded from various sites in the nervous system [2]. This approach to tracing the elements of a temporal sequence might well be supplemented by ablation studies. Although numerous ablation experiments in the past have shown relatively little impairment in the performance of simple tasks, these studies have seldom utilized temporal characteristics of responding although these are, in all likelihood, more sensitive indicants of performance deficits.

If one examines RT's to either single or multiple stimuli with a view to identifying the neural events that act as determiners of RT, one soon becomes aware of the lack of an appropriate model for such a search. We know that at the level of the organism, RT is a function of stimulus variables (such as intensity, size of stimulus ensemble, interstimulus interval, interstimulus discriminability[15]), of response variables (such as number of response alternatives and response probabilities, type of response activity), and of state variables. Since stimuli translate themselves into spatiotemporal patterns of neural activity (NSTP), it seems reasonable to postulate that RT's will be shorter when a stimulus activates or changes the state of more neurons or the more two NSTP's differ from one another. The study of such NSTP's in relation to RT's in behaving animals opens promising prospects for psychophysiologists.

CONCLUDING REMARKS

On the basis of experimental findings in the area of auditory and visual communication, as well as from a consideration of the manner in which sensory communication is transacted in language or in the less well-defined visual discourse, we are led to conclude that reliable response behavior depends primarily upon relational aspects of the physical variables that define a stimulus complex—rather than upon particular values of stimulus intensity or spectral composition, for instance. In this view of reliable communication, the importance, or even the desirability, of a direct, high-fidelity rendition of physical-stimulus variables within the nervous system becomes a matter of subsidiary interest. Far greater

[15] Numerous researchers have emphasized that RT is one of the most sensitive indexes of discriminability. For instance, RT continues to decrease for increasing differences in pitch even when these frequency differences have become sufficiently large to be identified correctly on 100 per cent of the trials [67].

significance attaches to concepts such as receptive fields, formants, spatial or color contrast, intensity gradients, and other relational descriptions of complex stimulus patterns. As we have previously mentioned, a variety of complex stimulus patterns may yield equivalent response behaviors; perceptual phenomena such as size or shape or color constancies point to the pervasiveness of such many-to-one relations. Although the neurophysiological correlates of such constancy phenomena remain to be elaborated, some recent findings from the frog's visual system [54] are suggestive on this score.

The formulation of a program of research designed to uncover those neuroelectric events that are meaningfully related to the sensory performance of organisms becomes thus the logical next step. The desire to commit ourselves to such a program does not automatically endow us with the ability to specify the relevant experimental design that will yield these data. At best, it may help us to formulate partial strategies such as the following:

1. Electrophysiological experimentation on a given species should preferably be conducted within the framework of the kind of sensory tasks that its environment naturally provides.

2. The demonstration of isolated phenomena, no matter how striking or convincing, is not a satisfactory substitute for systematic explorations of stimulus, response, or organismic variables. Parametric relationships should be determined over appreciable ranges of stimulus values. Other factors to be evaluated in establishing such relations include response modifications produced by the interaction of two or more stimulus dimensions or by variations in the background against which a given stimulus is presented.

3. Whenever possible, it seems advisable to obtain simultaneous measures of sensory performance and concomitant neuroelectric activity within the same organism. This approach is far more likely to yield comparable and correlative psychological and neurophysiological data; it also ensures a certain stability of state that now seems indispensable for the formulation of coherent S-R_ψ and S-R_ϕ relationships.

4. Regardless of the particular S-R_ϕ relations under study, there is little reason to assume that we have discovered neural substrates of the organism's ability to handle sensory information so long as we merely examine neuroelectric events (R_ϕ) that occupy only a small fraction of the total time required by the organism for the actual processing (R_ψ). Any reasonable account must include descriptions of significant neuroelectric events over the entire interval between stimulus delivery and occurrence of R_ψ.

The preceding remarks are not to be construed as implying that most of the data extant in the area of sensory neurophysiology are either useless or incorrect. Our aim has been to point out some of the limitations of knowledge that is based solely upon these data, and to point to currently available opportunities for gaining more realistic appraisals of concomitant neuroelectric and behavioral events during the process of sensory communication.

REFERENCES

1. Ades, H. W. Central auditory mechanisms. In J. Field, H. W. Magoun, & V. E. Hall (Eds.), *Handbook of physiology.* Vol. I. Sect. 1. *Neurophysiology.* Washington: American Physiological Society, 1959. Pp. 585–613.

2. Adey, W. R., Dunlop, C. W., & Hendrix, C. E. Hippocampal slow waves: distribution and phase relationships in the course of approach learning. *AMA Arch. Neurol.,* 1960, **3**, 74–90.

3. Albert, A. E. Analysis of variance in reaction time experiments. Unpublished B.S. thesis, M.I.T., Dept. of Math., 1956.

4. Allen, J., & Sashin, D. The latency of the human electromyogram in relation to reaction time. *Quart. Progr. Rep.,* M.I.T., Research Laboratory of Electronics, July, 1960, 240–242.

5. Amassian, V. E., Berlin, L., Macy, J., Jr., & Walter, H. J. Simultaneous recordings of the activities of several individual cortical neurons. *Trans. N. Y. Acad. Sci.,* 1959, **21** (Ser. II), 395–405.

6. Anokhin, P. K. New conception on the physiological architecture of the conditioned reflex. In *Symposium on brain mechanisms and learning, Montevideo.* Springfield, Ill.: Charles C Thomas. In press.

7. Asratyan, E. A. The initiation and localization of cortical inhibition in elements of the conditioned reflex arc. Paper read at the Pavlovian Conference on Higher Nervous Activity, sponsored by the N.Y. Acad. of Sci. and the Acad. of Med. Sci. of the U.S.S.R. New York, October, 1960.

8. Barlow, J. S. Autocorrelation and crosscorrelation analysis in electroencephalography. *IRE Trans. med. Electronics,* 1959, **ME-6**, 179–183.

9. Barlow, J. S. Rhythmic activity induced by photic stimulation in relation to intrinsic alpha activity of the brain in man. *EEG clin. Neurophysiol.,* 1960, **12**, 317–326.

10. Barlow, J. S., Brazier, M. A. B., & Rosenblith, W. A. The application of autocorrelation analysis to electroencephalography. *Proceedings First National Biophysics Conference,* Columbus, Ohio, Mar. 4–6, 1957. New Haven, Conn.: Yale Univer. Press, 1959. Pp. 622–626.

11. Barlow, J. S., & Brown, R. M. *An analog correlator system for brain potentials,* Tech. Report No. 300, M.I.T., Research Laboratory of Electronics, July 14, 1955.

12. Barlow, J. S., & Freeman, M. Z. Comparison of EEG activity recorded from homologous locations on the scalp by means of autocorrelation and

crosscorrelation analysis. *Quart. Progr. Rep.*, M.I.T., Research Laboratory of Electronics, July, 1959, 173–181.

13. Bernhard, C. G. Contributions to the neurophysiology of the optic pathway. *Acta Physiol. Scand.*, 1940, **1**, Suppl. 1, 1–94.

14. Bishop, G. H. Natural history of the nerve impulse. *Physiol. Revs.*, 1956, **36**, 376–399.

15. Brazier, M. A. B. A study of the late response to flash in the cortex of the cat. *Acta Physiol. Pharmacol. Neerlandica*, 1957, 6, 692–714.

16. Brazier, M. A. B. (Ed.) *The central nervous system and behavior.* Transactions of the First Conference. New York: Josiah Macy, Jr. Foundation, 1958.

17. Brazier, M. A. B. Some uses of computers in experimental neurology. *Exp. Neurol.*, 1960, **2**, 123–143.

18. Brindley, G. S. *Physiology of the retina and the visual pathway.* London: E. J. Arnold, 1960.

19. Bullock, T. H. Neuron doctrine and electrophysiology. *Science*, 1959, **129**, 997–1002.

20. Busnel, R. G. Étude de l'un des caractères physiques essentiels des signaux acoustiques réactogènes artificiels sur les orthoptères et d'autres groupes d'insectes. *Insectes Sociaux*, 1956, **3**, 11–16.

21. Crossman, E. R. F. W., & Szafran, J. Changes with age in the speed of information-intake and discrimination. *Experientia Supplementum IV*, 1956, 128–135.

22. Davis, R. The limits of the "psychological refractory period." *Quart. J. exp. Psychol.*, 1956, **8**, 24–38.

23. Davis, R. The human operator as a single channel information system. *Quart. J. exp. Psychol.*, 1957, **9**, 119–129.

24. Dichter, M. Reaction time to consonant-vowel syllables in ensembles of various sizes. *Quart. Progr. Rep.*, M.I.T., Research Laboratory of Electronics, July, 1960, 220–221.

25. Doty, R. W. Potentials evoked in cat cerebral cortex by diffuse and by punctiform photic stimuli. *J. Neurophysiol.*, 1958, **21**, 437–464.

26. Durup, G., & Fessard, A. L'électroencéphalogramme de l'homme. Observations psycho-physiologiques relatives à l'action des stimuli visuels et auditifs. *L'Année psychologique*, 1935, **36**, 1–32.

27. Farley, B. G., Frishkopf, L. S., Clark, W. A., Jr., & Gilmore, J. T. *Computer techniques for the study of patterns in the electroencephalogram*, Tech. Report No. 337, M.I.T., Research Laboratory of Electronics, and Tech. Report No. 165, M.I.T., Lincoln Laboratory, Nov. 6, 1957.

28. Fleming, T. C., & Evarts, E. V. Multiple response to photic stimulation in cats. *Amer. J. Physiol.* 1959, **197**, 1233–1236.

29. Frishkopf, L. S., & Rosenblith, W. A. Fluctuations in neural thresholds. In H. P. Yockey, R. L. Platzman, & H. Quastler (Eds.), *Symposium on information theory in biology.* New York: Pergamon, 1958. Pp. 153–168.

30. Fuster, J. M. Effects of stimulation of brain stem on tachistoscopic perception. *Science,* 1958, **127,** 150.

31. Galambos, R., & Rupert, A. Action of the middle ear muscles in normal cats. *J. acoust. Soc. Amer.,* 1959, **31,** 349–355.

32. Galambos, R., Sheatz, G., & Vernier, V. G. Electrophysiological correlates of a conditioned response in cats. *Science,* 1956, **123,** 376–377.

33. Geisler, C. D. Electrical responses to acoustic clicks from human scalp. *Quart. Progr. Rep.,* M.I.T., Research Laboratory of Electronics, April, 1960, 137–143.

34. Gerstein, G. L. Analysis of firing patterns in single neurons. *Science,* 1960, **131,** 1811–1812.

35. Goldstein, M. H., Jr. Effects of "overlapping" for cortical responses. *Quart. Progr. Rep.,* M.I.T., Research Laboratory of Electronics, October, 1959, 165–170.

36. Goldstein, M. H., Jr. A statistical model for interpreting neuroelectric responses. *Information and Control,* 1960, **3,** 1–17.

37. Goldstein, M. H., Jr., & Kiang, N. Y-S. Synchrony of neural activity in electric responses evoked by transient acoustic stimuli. *J. acoust. Soc. Amer.,* 1958, **30,** 107–114.

38. Goldstein, M. H., Jr., Kiang, N. Y-S., & Brown, R. M. Responses of the auditory cortex to repetitive acoustic stimuli. *J. acoust. Soc. Amer.,* 1959, **31,** 356–364.

39. Grüsser, O.-J., & Grützner, A. Neurophysiologische Grundlagen der periodischen Nachbildphasen nach kurzen Lichtblitzen. *v. Graefes Arch. Ophthalmol.,* 1958, **160,** 65–93.

40. Guillemin, E. A. *Introductory circuit theory.* New York: Wiley, 1953.

41. Hartline, H. K. Receptor mechanisms and the integration of sensory information in the eye. *Revs. mod. Phys.,* 1959, **31,** 515–523.

42. Hernández-Péon, R., & Scherrer, H. "Habituation" to acoustic stimuli in cochlear nucleus. *Fed. Proc.,* 1955, **14,** 71. (Abstract)

43. Hernández-Péon, R., Scherrer, H., & Jouvet, M. Modification of electric activity in cochlear nucleus during "attention" in unanesthetized cats. *Science,* 1956, **123,** 331–332.

44. Hick, W. E. On the rate of gain of information. *Quart. J. exp. Psychol.,* 1952, **4,** 11–26.

45. Hubel, D. H., Henson, C. O., Rupert, A., & Galambos, R. "Attention" units in the auditory cortex. *Science,* 1959, **129,** 1279–1280.

46. Hughes, J. R., & Rosenblith, W. A. Electrophysiological evidence for auditory sensitization. *J. acoust. Soc. Amer.,* 1957, **29,** 275–280.

47. Hyman, R. Stimulus information as a determinant of reaction time. *J. exp. Psychol.* 1953, **45,** 188–196.

48. John, E. R., & Killam, K. F. Electrophysiological correlates of avoidance conditioning in the cat. *J. Pharmacol. exp. Ther.,* 1959, **125,** 252–274.

49. Jouvet, M., & Lapras, C. Variations des réponses électriques somesthésiques au niveau du thalamus chez l'homme au cours de l'attention. *C. R. soc. Biol.,* 1959, **153,** 98–101.

50. Jung, R., Creutzfeldt, O., & Grüsser, O-J. The microphysiology of cortical neurones: its significance for sensory and cerebral functions. *German med. Mon.,* 1958, **3,** 269–276.

51. Klemmer, E. T. Time uncertainty in simple reaction time. *J. exp. Psychol.,* 1956, **51,** 179–184.

52. Lansing, R. W. Relation of brain and tremor rhythms to visual reaction time. *EEG clin. Neurophysiol.,* 1957, **9,** 497–504.

53. Lashley, K. S. Integrative functions of the cerebral cortex. *Physiol. Revs.,* 1933, **13,** 1–43.

54. Lettvin, J. Y., Maturana, H. R., McCulloch, W. S., & Pitts, W. H. What the frog's eye tells the frog's brain. *Proc. IRE,* 1959, **47,** 1940–1951.

55. Lindsley, D. B. The reticular system and perceptual discrimination. In H. H. Jasper, L. D. Proctor, R. S. Knighton, W. C. Noshay, & R. T. Costello (Eds.), *Reticular formation of the brain.* Boston: Little, Brown, 1958. Pp. 513–534.

56. Meikle, T. H., & Sechzer, J. A. Interocular transfer of brightness discrimination in "split-brain" cats. *Science,* 1960, **131,** 734–735.

57. Miller, G. A. The magical number seven, plus or minus two: some limits on our capacity for processing information. *Psychol. Rev.,* 1956, **63,** 81–97.

58. Monnier, M. Retinal, cortical and motor responses to photic stimulation in man. *J. Neurophysiol.,* 1952, **15,** 469–486.

59. Palestini, M., Rossi, G. F., & Zanchetti, A. An electrophysiological analysis of pontine reticular regions showing different anatomical organization. *Arch. Ital. Biol.,* 1957, **95,** 97–109.

60. Peake, W. T. *An analytical study of electric responses at the periphery of the auditory system,* Tech. Report No. 365, M.I.T., Research Laboratory of Electronics, March, 1960.

61. Peake, W. T., Goldstein, M. H., Jr., & Kiang, N. Y-S. "Steady-state" auditory nerve potentials for different stimulus repetition rates. *J. acoust. Soc. Amer.,* 1959, **31,** 123. (Abstract)

62. Rose, J. E., & Mountcastle, V. B. Activity of single neurons in the tactile thalamic region of the cat in response to a transient peripheral stimulus. *Johns Hopkins Hosp. Bull.,* 1954, **94,** 238–282.

63. Rosenblith, W. A. Some electrical responses from the auditory nervous system. In *Proceedings of the Symposium on Information Networks.* Brooklyn, N.Y.: Polytechnic Institute of Brooklyn, 1954. Pp. 223–247.

64. Rosenblith, W. A., and Members of the Communications Biophysics Group of the M.I.T., Research Laboratory of Electronics. *Processing neuroelectric data.* Cambridge, Mass.: The Technology Press of M.I.T., 1959.

65. Rosenblith, W. A. Sensory performance of organisms. *Revs. mod. Phys.,* 1959, **31,** 485–491.

66. Rosenblith, W. A. Some quantifiable aspects of the electrical activity of the nervous system (with emphasis upon responses to sensory stimuli). *Revs. mod. Phys.,* 1959, **31,** 532–545.

67. Rosenblith, W. A., & Stevens, K. N. On the DL for frequency. *J. acoust. Soc. Amer.*, 1953, **25**, 980–985.

68. Rossi, G. F., & Zanchetti, A. The brain stem reticular formation: anatomy and physiology. *Arch. Ital. Biol.*, 1957, **95**, 199–435.

69. Saslow, M. G. Reaction time to consonant-vowel syllables in ensembles of various sizes. *Quart. Progr. Rep.*, M.I.T., Research Laboratory of Electronics, July, 1958, 143–144.

70. Sholl, D. A. *The organization of the cerebral cortex.* New York: Wiley, 1956.

71. Sokolov, E. N. Neuronal models and the orienting reflex. In M. A. B. Brazier (Ed.), *The central nervous system and behavior.* Transactions of the Third Conference. New York: Josiah Macy, Jr. Foundation, 1960. Pp. 187–276.

72. Stevens, S. S. On the psychophysical law. *Psychol. Rev.*, 1957, **64**, 153–181.

73. Stevens, S. S. Cross-modality validation of subjective scales for loudness, vibration, and electric shock. *J. exp. Psychol.*, 1959, **57**, 201–209.

74. Thompson, W., Jr. Human reaction time to a masked acoustic stimulus. *Quart. Progr. Rep.*, M.I.T., Research Laboratory of Electronics, July, 1958, 185–186.

75. Woodworth, R. S., & Schlossberg, H. *Experimental psychology.* New York: Holt, 1954.

76. Woolsey, C. N. Organization of cortical auditory system: a review and a synthesis. In G. L. Rasmussen & W. F. Windle (Eds.), *Neural mechanisms of the auditory and vestibular systems.* Springfield, Ill.: Charles C Thomas, 1960. Pp. 165–180.

SENSORY PROCESSES AND THEIR RELATION TO BEHAVIOR: STUDIES ON THE SENSE OF TASTE AS A MODEL S-R SYSTEM

CARL PFAFFMANN

Walter S. Hunter Laboratory of Psychology

Brown University

Introduction 380
Electrophysiology of Taste and the Mechanism of Discrimination 384
　Receptor potentials 384
　Gustatory afferent nerve discharges 385
　Afferent pattern and taste qualities 389
　Cutaneous modalities 391
　Other senses and quality 393
　Central control of receptors 394
The Behavioral Consequences of Gustatory Stimulation 395
　Reinforcing functions of stimuli 395
　The afferent discharge and behavior 396
　Responses to sugar and saccharin 399
　Biological basis of taste reactions 403
　Hedonic responses 403
　Physiological mechanisms in reinforcement 408
Summary 410
References 411

INTRODUCTION

Psychology as a formal scientific discipline dates its beginnings from 1873, when Wilhelm Wundt founded the laboratory of psychology at Leipzig. In the immediately preceding period, great advances had been made in the study of sensation and the sense organs by the psychological physiologists in the parent discipline of physiology. The names of Helmholtz, Müller, and von Frey are cited as often in the history of physiology as in the history of psychological science [9]. With psychology defined as the science of consciousness, sensation was firmly grounded as one of the

380

basic "conscious contents" of the introspectively known mental life. Hence it was natural that a goodly portion of the experimental work in the "new psychology" focused upon the study of sensory processes. To have questioned how the study of sensory processes might have relevance for psychology would have seemed incomprehensible to the psychologists of that generation. To them the study of sensation and of psychology were almost synonymous.

Philosophers since ancient times had assigned a significant role to the senses. Aristotle's doctrine of the *tabula rasa,* the classic formulation of the associationist and empiricist view, pictured the mind as blank until inscribed by sensory experience. The British empiricist John Locke and his successors based their system of psychology upon the view that there are no innate ideas, that we have no knowledge except that which comes by way of the senses. Condillac, the French follower of Locke and Hume, conceived that a statue need only be endowed with organs of sense to be brought to life and thus come to possess "the most complex and sophisticated thoughts or 'movements of the soul,' the most elaborate play of the imagination, the most subtle scientific speculation" [7].

The detailed study of sensory processes utilizes a number of techniques—physical, chemical, anatomical, physiological, as well as psychophysical—which bridge the different scientific disciplines. Two major questions have dominated researches upon the senses through the years, that of sensory quantity and that of sensory quality. The quantity problem concerns the nature of the relation between sensory magnitude and stimulus intensity, epitomized in the well-known Weber-Fechner law. The magnitude of sensation is said to increase arithmetically as the stimulus intensity increases logarithmically. This generalization is largely approximate, for there are systematic divergences from it at the upper and lower intensity limits of the stimulus scale. Actually it is open to criticism on several counts when stated in the above form. Further, new methods of psychophysical scaling suggest that the relation between sensation magnitude and stimulus may be more properly a power rather than a logarithmic function [9, 83]. But we shall not discuss this problem in any detail.

We plan to concentrate upon the other major problem, that of sensation quality. This likewise was the subject of another classical formulation, the doctrine of specific nerve energies enunciated by Johannes Müller. "Sensation consists in the sensorium's receiving through the medium of the nerves, and as a result of the action of an external cause, a knowledge of certain qualities or conditions, not of external bodies, but of the nerves of sense themselves" [9]. Regardless of the mode of stimulation, the sensation is always specific to the particular sense organ, sensory nerve, and associated central neural structures being stimulated. The eye, however stimulated, gives rise to sensations of light; the ear, to sensations of sound; taste buds, sensations of taste.

The further extensions of the doctrine of specific nerve energies to account for the different sensation qualities within a single sensory modality was a logical next step, taken by Helmholtz when he formulated his place theory of hearing. Pitch was attributed to the activation of a specific region of the basilar membrane of the inner ear. Individual nerve fibers arising from these specific locations were stimulated and gave rise to the unique tonal quality of pitch. *Pitch,* then, was dependent upon *which* nerve fiber was activated. A perusal of the modern developments in auditory research will show that this is an important cornerstone of certain theoretical formulations today [88, 91]. In the less complex senses, like the cutaneous or gustatory senses, von Frey and his school propounded the notion of modalities within each of these senses. Skin sensitivity was said to consist of warm, cold, touch, and pain. Taste was said to consist of the four basic modalities, salt, sour, bitter, and sweet. Each modality was thought to have its unique set of receptors. Quality depended upon which of these receptors was activated and complex sensations resulted from mixtures or blends of the primary sensory processes.

It is to be noted that the early psychological observations and experiments yielded much data that are still valid. The punctate character of skin sensitivity and the differing distributions of touch, warm, cold, and pain spots can be readily demonstrated in the laboratory. The regional differences in the sensitivity of the tongue to the four basic tastes is also well established. But the theory of the mechanism underlying such patterns of sensitivity was and still is a much-debated subject.

Theories of sensory function have nearly always proved to be theories about mechanism, of anatomical structure and physiological function. In the classic period of sensory psychophysics, little direct physiological evidence was available. The techniques had not yet been developed for a direct study of the receptor processes. The unique feature of the modern period in studying sensory processes is the great reliance upon electrophysiological methods.

In 1928, Adrian's book *The basis of sensation* [1] heralded the modern era. The subject of inquiry was not sensation itself but the functions of the receptor organs, and the method was electrophysiological. The development of the electronic vacuum tube, together with appropriate amplifying circuits and recording instruments, made it possible to study directly the activity of sense organs and sensory nerves. Since 1928, of course, advances in techniques and instrumentation have been so dramatic that the recording of electrical activity—in the sense organs, peripheral nerves, central nervous system, and effector organs— has made it possible to probe not only the physical basis of sensation and perception, but the physical mechanisms of many processes in the nervous system which underlie behavior as a whole.

In this paper we shall discuss the sense of taste—less for its own sake than as a model sensory system. Taste is relatively simple; indeed it is often classed among the lower or "other" senses. Its anatomical substrate, the taste bud—though it is a specialized receptor organ—does not have the anatomical complexity of the eye or ear, with their many accessory structures. The nerves to the taste buds are readily accessible for recording after appropriate surgery. The single fibers in the taste nerves make direct contact with one or more receptor cells in the taste bud, so that only one junction intervenes between nerve fiber and sense cell. The range of sensory qualities mediated by taste is relatively restricted, typically exemplified by such terms as *salty, sour, bitter,* and *sweet,* and these are qualitative differences which are readily perceptible to the observer. The afferent code for sensory quality, therefore, should be directly amenable to study [65].

But in addition to this classical sensory function, the sense of taste is distinguished by its important role in the control of feeding responses and preference or avoidance behavior—without the requirement of prior conditioning or learning. For example, sucrose and a number of other taste stimuli are accepted and ingested in great quantity, whereas others like quinine will be rejected or avoided. These strong positive and negative reactions appear to result directly from the taste stimuli themselves. Furthermore, these stimuli can serve to motivate the acquisition of instrumental responses leading to ingestion of the stimulus in question. In short, taste stimuli can act as reinforcers. We shall discuss the correlations that can be drawn between certain features of the taste afferent-nerve discharge and the behavior controlled thereby. Thus we shall consider sensory processes from a somewhat broader base than that of sensory psychophysiology alone. In this discussion, we shall attempt to relate the specific phenomena of the sense of taste to the broad question of sensory stimuli and their role in reinforcement and in the control of behavior generally.[1,2]

[1] The experiments herein reported were supported in part by projects and grants from the Office of Naval Research, National Science Foundation, and the General Foods Corporation.

[2] The original draft of this chapter was prepared in 1957 and contained an early formulation of two ideas that subsequently were elaborated in two separate papers, *The afferent code for sensory quality,* published in *The American Psychologist* in 1959, and *The pleasures of sensation,* published in the *Psychological Review* in 1960. By permission, the latter is incorporated almost in its entirety in the second section, *The Behavioral Consequences of Gustatory Stimulation,* of the present chapter. The first section *Electrophysiology of Taste and the Mechanism of Discrimination,* has been brought up to date since the original draft.

ELECTROPHYSIOLOGY OF TASTE AND THE MECHANISM OF DIS-CRIMINATION

Electrophysiological observations may be made at a number of points in the sensory neural chain; at the receptor organ, afferent nerve, sensory nuclei of the spinal cord or brain stem, thalamus, and cerebral cortex. At each level, the particular problem being investigated may vary, but essentially the method depends upon the fact that every cell in the nervous system is polarized with a difference of potential across the cell membrane. Stimulation or excitation usually entails depolarization of the membrane and hence a change in the electrical potential to be recorded in or near the active cell. Since the outside of most cells is positive and the inside negative, the change upon excitation is typically an increase in negativity at the active site. But the electrical change in receptor cells as compared with that in the afferent nerve fibers may have quite different properties.

There appear to be two basic kinds of electrical processes in cells. One is a graded response, i.e., graded in amount, depending upon the strength of the stimulus. The second is the "all-or-none" discharge of the membrane which occurs when the stimulus has reached some threshold value. Below threshold there is no conducted response—only a local graded response which increases with increase in the stimulus strength. At some critical threshold value, the graded local response triggers off the all-or-none impulse, which is then conducted down the nerve fiber by a self-regenerative process. The all-or-none response shows no further increase in size, though the stimulus may be increased many times [85].

Receptor potentials. The graded response appears to be related to the excitation process, especially in sense organs, postsynaptic neurons, or effector organs, as well as in the nerve fiber itself. The all-or-none impulse is characteristic of conducting systems, the long dendrites or axons which stretch over distance between sense organ and central nervous system and effector. The electrical responses of a number of sense organs have been studied directly. In the more complex organs like the ear and the eye, the receptor potential may be complex, consisting of several components which arise from different parts of the sense organ. Not all of these are necessarily neural in origin. In other instances, e.g., the Pacinian tactile corpuscle, the graded response originates in the fine terminations of the sensory fiber within the corpuscle. In other cases, these graded responses appear to arise in specialized receptor cells. There is increasing evidence that the initial step in sensory stimulation entails such a graded depolarization of the receptor cell or specialized receptor ending, which appears to act as a *generator potential,* i.e., it generates the spike discharge in the afferent nerve fiber leading from the receptor.

Whether all receptors produce a generator potential as a preliminary step leading to excitation of the afferent nerve remains to be established [28].

Evidence for a graded receptor potential in the gustatory sense cells has been provided by Kimura and Beidler [40], who inserted micropipette electrodes into the taste buds and were able to record potential changes that were graded in amount with the concentration of the taste solution bathing the taste bud. In the afferent nerve, however, an increase in the intensity of the solution leads to an increase in the frequency of impulse discharge. Another variable, namely, number of fibers firing,

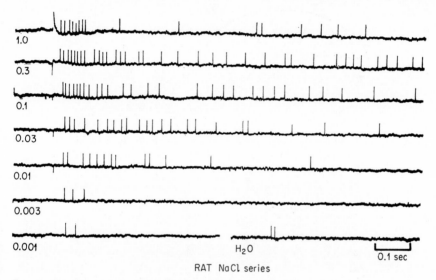

FIG. 1. Response of a single NaCl sensitive element from the rat. This element also responded to HCl and KCl. Responses to quinine and sucrose were insignificant. After data by Pfaffmann, 1955.

will also be found to increase with the strength of the stimulus. Thus, in the afferent nerve trunk, both frequency of impulse discharge and number of fibers active are correlated with increase in stimulus intensity [62, 63].

Gustatory afferent nerve discharges.   Figure 1 shows a typical series of oscillograph tracings obtained from a *single* nerve fiber when different concentrations of sodium chloride are applied to the tongue of the rat. The upward deflections or "spikes" signal the passage of each impulse past the recording electrodes. With the stronger stimuli there is a higher frequency of discharge. Threshold for this fiber lies at approximately 0.003 M, which is the minimum concentration required to stimulate the ending associated with this fiber. Other fibers will show similar behavior, but may possess higher thresholds. The tongue therefore contains a population of taste receptors with thresholds of differing values.

Actually, the sensory nerve is a cable, made up of many different fibers. Each is connected with one or more receptor cells so that a general measure of over-all taste sensitivity may be obtained by recording from the intact nerve. This discharge consists of activity in many fibers which are associated with endings sensitive to different chemicals and to different levels of concentration. The single-fiber recordings of Fig. 1 were obtained only after the nerve cable had been dissected down to a strand

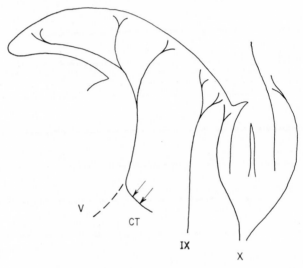

Fig. 2. Diagram of the peripheral nerve supply to the tongue. V, trigeminal nerve; IX, glossopharyngeal n.; X, vagus n.; CT, chorda tympani n. Arrows show the placement of the recording electrodes. After data by Pfaffmann, 1957.

containing one functional nerve. Sometimes the same effect may be achieved by the use of microelectrodes which consist of fine needles or micropipettes.

The nerve fibers subserving taste travel from the mouth region in three nerves: the lingual, glossopharyngeal, and vagus nerves. These all contain touch, temperature, pressure, and pain fibers, as well as those concerned with taste. From the anterior tongue, the taste fibers branch from the lingual nerve to form the chorda tympani nerve. Here it is possible to record almost exclusively from taste nerve fibers. This nerve is exposed by appropriate surgery in the anesthetized animal and placed on the electrodes leading to the recording apparatus.

A block diagram of the apparatus together with sample records is shown in Fig. 3. The nerve is shown schematically placed upon the recording electrodes leading to the preamplifier. The preparation and preamplifier are shown enclosed in a screened shielded cage in order to exclude stray electrical artifacts [64]. The preamplifier output leads to the cathode ray oscillograph (CRO), which yields a typical multifiber asynchronous discharge, as shown by the upper tracing. The audio-monitoring system is in parallel with the CRO. The CRO response in such a preparation is difficult to use analytically, and an integrating circuit converts the signal into the more convenient form shown in the

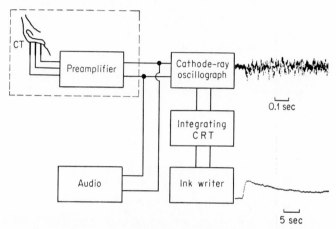

Fig. 3. Diagram of recording method. The two tracings on the right show sample records. After data by Pfaffmann, 1957.

lower trace. The integrator time constant can be adjusted to give an accurate portrayal of the envelope of activity in the nerve discharge. A quantitative measure of activity is obtained from the magnitude of deflection for each stimulus. The curves in Fig. 4 are based on such measurements in the rat for quinine, hydrochloric acid, sodium chloride, and sucrose solutions. The basic taste stimuli can be arranged in order of thresholds from low to high as follows: quinine, hydrochloric acid, sodium chloride, sucrose. In this animal, as in man, quinine is effective in relatively low concentrations. Sugar, at the other end of the scale, requires relatively high concentrations and yields only a slight response. The electrolytes lie in an intermediate position along the abscissa. Their discharges are of significant magnitude.

The integrator method was used originally by Beidler [5, 6] in studies on the physicochemical mechanisms of taste stimulation. Comparisons of a series of inorganic salts show that the cation is the more important determinant of stimulation by salts than the anion. Furthermore, the response to electrolytes is of such a nature that the chemical processes of stimulation appear to depend upon adsorbtion of the ions or molecules upon the receptor surface. The process seems to resemble the binding of ions by polyelectrolytes as in an ion exchange column. Electrophysiological measures also show that the effectiveness of acids as stimuli is not simply related to pH or to total acid combining power. These findings are in agreement with classical psychophysical observations which show that organic acids are more stimulating than would be predicted by pH alone. Liljestrand [46] showed a number of years ago that the pH of an organic

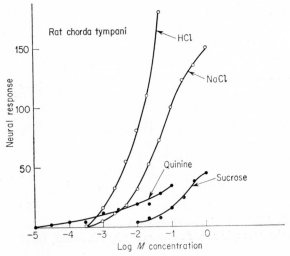

Fig. 4. Magnitude of integrator deflections to stimuli of different concentrations in the rat. Neural response magnitude in arbitrary units.

acid and salt buffer system could be radically altered, but that the sourness would remain. All such findings suggest that the effectiveness of different acids mimics, in principle, the adsorbtion of acids upon certain protein surfaces. Thus an adsorbtion process seems to be a critical first step for taste stimulation [6]. A similar mechanism appears to hold for the nonelectrolytes, but in this case the spatial arrangement or configuration of the molecule also plays an important role. Thus the relative sweetness of D and L forms of glucose is different and in some instances, such as asparagine, the D form is sweet and the L form tasteless. A number of other evidences point to a specific sensitivity for certain molecular groups or configurations in sweet and bitter sensitivity [57].

Afferent pattern and taste qualities. The integration manner of representation is an over-all measure and does not show that the animal can distinguish one substance from another. Actually, an animal like the rat will avoid quinine, HCl, and KCl but will show a preference for NaCl

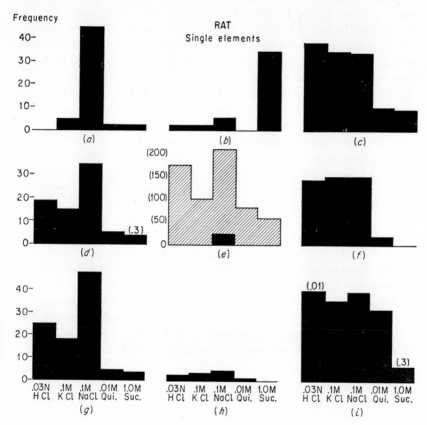

Fig. 5. Bar graphs summarizing the frequencies of response during the first second of discharge to the standard taste solutions. The responses of nine different single-fiber preparations, *a* to *i*, are shown. A cross-hatched bar graph is superimposed on the graph of element *e* to show the relative magnitudes of the integrator responses for the same test solutions. Figures in parentheses give the concentration values of test stimuli that differed from those indicated on the abscissa for elements *d* and *i*. After data by Pfaffmann, 1955.

and sucrose. Hence, there must be some differential characteristic of the sensory nerve message that is not shown in the total nerve record.

To determine how the animal can distinguish among different chemicals, i.e., make a discrimination, requires the single-fiber analysis. Figure 5 shows the response of nine single-fiber preparations to the following five standard molar solutions; .03 HCl, .1 M NaCl, .1 M KCl, .01 quinine hydrochloride, and 1.0 sucrose.

The bar graph shows the magnitude of response in each of the single-fiber preparations in impulses per second of discharge. The central cross-hatched bar graph shows the relative magnitude of response to these same solutions in the integrated response of the whole nerve. It is apparent that the individual fibers do not have exactly the same pattern as does the total nerve, although it must contain (be the sum of) the sensitivities of all the individual fibers of which it is composed. Individual fibers may have quite different "spectra" of activity. Furthermore, it is apparent that many single afferent taste fibers respond to several if not all of the basic taste stimuli of classical theory. Thus, although the peripheral taste receptors are differentially sensitive to different chemicals, they are not uniquely specific to each of the basic four tastes. Whereas fiber a in the figure does appear specific to NaCl and b appears specific to sugar, all the remaining units show a mixed or overlapping pattern. The microelectrode studies in which the recording electrode was placed directly in the individual sensory cells of the taste bud show that the receptor cell itself may have a similar distribution of sensitivity [40]. Thus the spectrum of sensitivity shown in a single afferent nerve fiber does not result merely from a multiple branching of fibers among several specific receptor cells. The individual receptor cell may possess a multiplicity of sites reactive to different chemicals or classes of chemicals.

Although the specific results shown in Fig. 5 are based on studies of taste sensitivity in the rat, studies of taste in other species (rabbits, hamsters, cats, and monkeys) were found to follow the same principles [17, 23, 62, 63, 99]. Some tendency for greater specificity may be found for units in the data on the monkey, but this organism does possess many "broadly tuned" sensory neural units as well.

It should be apparent that these results do not support the classical view of the four basic tastes with four basic receptor mechanisms for salt, sour, sweet, and bitter. Indeed, in certain species, water alone is capable of eliciting a significant discharge. The addition of a low concentration of sodium chloride in these instances may lead to a *decrease* in neural activity [47]. Thus, the sensory stimulus may either modulate or reduce ongoing activity as well as initiate the discharge of impulses in some fibers to provide discriminable information as to the state of the receptor surface. Cohen, Hagiwara, and Zotterman [17] have also elucidated the pattern concept as the basis for gustatory quality in a recent publication. Frings [25] has suggested that salt, sour, sweet, and bitter be considered as salient phenomenal qualities or *nodal points* in the taste spectrum rather than the pure tastes of the basic receptor organs. If we may generalize beyond our data to the case of man—assuming that the same thing holds true—there appear to be many combinations of sensitivity so that stimulation by different chemicals leads to different *afferent input patterns. It is upon such patterns that discrimination or, more subjectively, the perception of different sensory qualities depends.*

Cutaneous modalities. Evidence from other senses makes it clear that the same principles may be applicable to them as well. According to classical theory, cutaneous sensitivity was composed of different modalities—light touch, deep pressure, warm, cold, and pain. The well-established punctate distribution of the skin sensitivity has already been mentioned. This finding—coupled with the fact that morphologically different kinds of receptor endings could be found in the skin by histological methods—led to the view that the different skin modalities depended upon such anatomically distinct types of ending. Much of the early research on the skin was devoted to the search for the specific receptor for each particular modality. And, although the correlation between free nerve endings and pain and between nerve endings around hairs and touch seemed reasonable, these were based on indirect evidence. The attempted correlation between structure and function for warm and cold was much less convincing, if not actually negative in outcome [90].

A number of dissenting voices had been raised against these simple correspondences. In the classical period Goldscheider argued that pain resulted from excessive stimulation of any sensory nerve. At a later period, Nafe [58] argued for a quantitative theory of feeling; differences in the pattern of activity in the sensory nerves from the skin and subcutaneous blood vessels were said to determine sensory quality. Most recently Weddell and his co-workers [90] have argued vehemently against the classical specificity view on a number of counts. They maintain that many of the so-called "types" of cutaneous receptor are the results of histological artifact. Furthermore, when morphological differences are to be found, all gradations between one type and another may be observed and any classification of receptors by morphology is highly arbitrary. Weddell and his group have relied primarily upon methylene blue vital-staining methods in order to avoid histological artifacts. They regard tactile spots as high points of sensitivity often caused by clustering of a number of nerve endings, not by the presence of a single receptor. The normal skin is innervated in a multiplicity of ways by a plexus of nerve fibers. Indeed, contrary to the common view, it is suggested that when a skin region is supplied by only one fiber without overlapping supply from other nerve twigs, then the skin is hypersensitive, with the characteristic overreaction and poor localization often seen in traumatized skin. The so-called "protopathic sensitivity" is thought to result from a paucity of overlapping innervation. In a good many human skin areas, no specialized receptors can be found at all, only free nerve endings, yet in such areas, psychophysical measurements showed that the full range of cutaneous qualities could be experienced. This work has convincingly demonstrated that the one-to-one correlation of cutaneous quality with anatomical receptor type cannot be maintained.

Electrophysiological recordings from the afferent nerves have shown that nerve fiber types cannot be assigned specific roles in sensory quality. The classical studies of Erlanger and Gasser [22] showed that sensory nerve fibers were clustered into groups of different diameters and hence different conduction rates. The larger fibers conducted more rapidly,

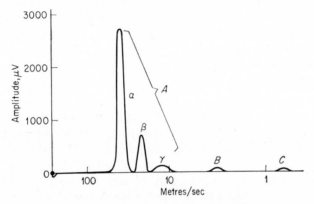

Fig. 6. Compound action potential showing different potential elevations and hence fiber groups in frog sciatic nerve. The graph has been constructed from records of the compound action potentials recorded at a point some distance from the site of stimulation. In mammalian nerves the rates of conduction are faster than those of the frog's nerve. From E. G. Walsh. *Physiology of the nervous system.* New York: Longmans, 1957.

the smaller more slowly. But the distribution of sizes and velocities appeared to show discontinuities so that the compound action potential measured at some distance from the point of stimulation was composed of a series of elevations (see Fig. 6). These elevations reflected the clustering of fibers with different diameters in the mixed sensory nerves. Much effort was expended in attempting to correlate specific elevations with the several skin modalities. Without reviewing this detailed experimentation, it can be said that no such simple correlation could be maintained. Although certain tactile and muscle afferent endings tend to be associated with fibers of large diameter, all other cutaneous sensory modalities seem to be mediated by fibers throughout the medium to slow conduction range.

Furthermore, when individual fiber discharges are studied in the mixed sensory nerves of the skin of animals, a picture not unlike that just described for taste seems to emerge. Receptors are clearly differential, yet the sensitivity they display cannot adequately be encompassed by the classical modalities. The adequate stimulus of many receptor neural units overlap or fall into two or more of the phenomenological classes. Some pressure receptors in the cat's tongue, for example, may also be activated by cooling [38]. Table 1 from another study [55] shows that there are several different kinds of pressure, temperature, and nociceptive sensory ending.

TABLE 1

Type	Fiber diameter, μ	Receptive field
Touch/phasic	8–14	1–2 spots
Pressure/tonic	3–5	spotlike
Large nociceptive	8–11	4–5 mm²
Small nociceptive	3–5.5	2–4 mm²
Wide-receptive	2–5	1,500–4,000 mm²
Cold	1.5–3	spotlike
Hair	6–12	100–500 mm²
Subcutaneous	6–10	—
Scratch	8–10	below 150 mm²
Unmyelinated	—	—

SOURCE: Maruhashi, et al. [55].

The classification of receptors suggested by these data does not have an isomorphic correspondence with sensory quality as experienced. Rather these endings may be better described by quantitative differences in such parameters as area, time of onset and offset of discharge, and thresholds to different stimuli, different quality, etc. Some of the receptors appear to be highly specific and punctate, others may be diffuse in area and very general in their response. It would appear that the pattern of activity within a matrix of differentially sensitive receptors provides the basis for qualitative discriminations. The classical modalities are not necessarily primary in the physiological sense; they may be only the more familiar qualities which can be aroused from the sensory surface.

Other senses and quality.   Although taste and touch are lower senses and thus may be expected to display less specificity than the higher senses of vision and hearing, there is evidence that the general principles just elaborated may be relevant for them as well. The selective sensitivity among the individual primary auditory fibers is very broad. The nerve fibers arising in the basal turn of the cochlea respond to tones of any audible frequency; only those arising in the upper part are restricted, in this case, to low-frequency tones [84]. Further, it has been suggested that the temporal patterning of the discharge—especially at the low frequencies—provides the basis for pitch discrimination [91]. In the case of vision, it has been suggested that different frequencies in the third-order afferent fibers from the retina may signal different spectral events at the periphery [27]. There is as yet no evidence or indication as to how such "frequency codes" are differentiated by the central receiving mechanisms.

In any case, it seems apparent that much more attention must be paid to the role of the patterning of input in the afferent channels. In the case of gustation, the frequency of firing in the individual nerve fibers appears to have significance for quality to the extent that this indicates the relative amount of activity in particular fibers *in relation* to the total sensory nerve population available. It is not simply the activity in any one nerve fiber that is important. Rather it is the accompanying activity in other parallel afferent fibers, the *pattern* of activity, that provides the basis for discrimination.

This answer to Müller's problem implies and points up a changing orientation in the relation of physiological fact and theory to psychology. The search for answers to many psychological questions has often followed a simple-minded reductionist strategy of looking for physiological entities isomorphic with psychological categories. In sensory psychology, this is tantamount to placing the sensations and sensory qualities at the finger tips, the retina, or tongue, as the case might be. Physiology thus phenomenalized is a pseudo physiology, and is not in accord either with the facts of psychology or physiology.

Central control of receptors. Before turning to a consideration of the behavioral significances of the gustatory sensory input, one further development should be mentioned; that is the increasing evidence of a feedback between the sensory systems and other parts of the central nervous system [49, 54]. Psychological studies, of course, have yielded data that could be readily explained by some change in the receptor sensitivity consequent upon stimulation itself or other changes in the state of the organism. Although the important kinesthetic feedback to the central nervous system has long been known and believed to be of great signficance for many psychological functions, the new evidence shows that the feedback plays not only upon the CNS, but through the CNS back again to the very receptor itself [43]. The recent findings of efferent neural pathways to the ear and the empirical demonstration of a modulation of sensitivity by discharges over this efferent bundle are relevant here [26]. The indication that olfactory sensitivity may be enhanced by efferent discharges over the sympathetic nerves to the nasal mucosa [87] are of similar import. In the case of olfaction, such evidence might be relevant to the reported changes in sensitivity in psychophysical experiments induced by changes in hormonal balance [44]. Nevertheless, the generality of such relations is still to be clarified. Behavioral evidence suggestive of receptor sensitivity changes have not been substantiated by direct studies in every case. No changes in the gustatory sensitivity following changes in physiological balance of the blood stream could be detected, in spite of dramatic changes in preference behavior [16, 34, 66, 69]. But further studies of the gustatory system in this context are warranted.

THE BEHAVIORAL CONSEQUENCES OF GUSTATORY STIMULATION

All that has been discussed up to this point might be subsumed under the general heading of cognitive function. The classical doctrine of specific nerve energies was directed to the question of how information concerning the state of affairs at the receptor surface was transmitted to and through the CNS to give rise to sensations or to make discrimination possible. In this case, the emphasis is upon the informational content of the sensory input, and the major effort in sensory psychophysiology up to the present has been directed almost exclusively to this problem.

Reinforcing functions of stimuli. The other concept we wish to include concerns functions of the stimulus other than discrimination per se. As many behavior theorists have pointed out, a stimulus may have many different functions; one of the most important is *reinforcement*. Certain stimuli, by virtue of their presentation, tend to make the probability of a response more or less likely upon some subsequent occasion. Reinforcement as a stimulus function has important consequences for the senory control of behavior.

The primary reinforcing function of stimuli has long been recognized for such negative reinforcers as electric shock or stimuli of high intensity which also elicit "defense" reaction or reflexes. Other stimuli related to such biological activities as eating, drinking, or sexual activity are well known as positive primary reinforcers. Yet the particular aspect of the stimulus and response which serves as reinforcement is still open to debate—as between need reduction or drive reduction or some direct stimulus instigation of consummatory behavior, for example. And certain other stimuli, not directly related to eating and drinking, appear to be capable of serving as primary positive reinforcers. Two examples are stimulus change (or novelty) and stimulus onset, such as of dim light for the rat. Both appear to have positively rewarding effects [33, 41]. Yet these effects have been emphasized only recently and their nature is not yet clear.

The afferent discharge and behavior. From the point of view of behavior, the basic response to taste solutions is either one of acceptance or rejection. Thus, the classical manifold or four tastes (salt, sour, bitter, and sweet) may be reduced to two behavioral classes: acceptance and rejection. We have used a typical two-bottle Richter-type preference situation to study such behavior in different species [3, 15, 64]. Certain substances may be accepted at low, but rejected at the higher concentrations. This is so for NaCl in the rat where the well-known preference-

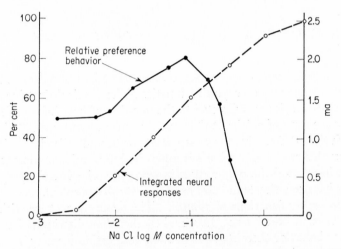

Fig. 7. Composite graph showing the neural response in the chorda tympani nerve of the rat, for sodium chloride (right ordinate) and the relative preference for the same concentrations observed in preference tests. Percentage preference score computed from $S_1/S_1 + H_2O$ where S_1 equals cubic centimeter intake of taste stimulus and H_2O is cubic centimeter intake of water. Reproduced from C. Pfaffmann in *Flavor research and food acceptance*. New York: Reinhold, 1958.

aversion response can be demonstrated to be a function of concentration as shown in Fig. 7. The solid line shows relative preference behavior

$$\frac{\text{cc intake taste solution}}{\text{cc intake taste} + \text{cc intake } H_2O}$$

Most acceptable solutions, including sugar, will follow this pattern when ingestion measures are used. Figure 7 also shows the neural response in the rat chorda tympani nerve to the same salt solutions. The broken line shows the integrated neural responses as a percentage of the maximum response observed. This curve is based upon the increment in discharge from a background of low activity following a water rinse with both transient and steady state values included. The curve for steady state level of response is very similar except at the low end. Recent studies have suggested [20, 98] that in the normal behaving animal, the taste receptors would be bathed in saliva which for the rat would be slightly below or nearly at the isotonic point equivalent to 0.9 per cent NaCl (.13 M). Hence, there would be a significant discharge at rest which would be increased by hypertonic solutions but decreased by hypotonic solutions. Water would reduce the level of discharge most of all. This appears to be the case when direct recordings are made from the chorda tympani under appropriate conditions. It is theorized that the rat drinks hypotonic [20] solutions as "diluted water" because hypotonic saline solutions reduce the resting level to a lesser degree than does water. The reduction in activity is inversely proportional to the concentration of saline up to the isotonic point where no change occurs. The animal is said to drink hypotonic saline in lieu of water but in greater volume in order to get an effect equivalent to that of water. Thus the parallel between the rising limb of the response curve and the electrophysiological response as determined from the water baseline may be only an apparent one. Further research is needed to show how these two functions, the behavioral and electrophysiological, are related in this particular instance. The fact that the peak preference and inversion of the curve are around the isotonic value implies that some factor related to water balance has become operative.

Indeed Stellar, Hyman, and Samet [82] have shown that the salinity of the gastric contents does affect the salt preference. Strong salt solutions intubated directly into the stomach depress the drinking of the more concentrated salt solutions. On the other hand, this is not the only stop factor; in the same study, animals with an esophageal fistula showed the preference for hypotonic solutions and aversions for hypertonic ones, even though the solutions never reached the stomach. Taste factors alone appear capable of eliciting the typical salt preference-aversion function. Thus the "stop" may indicate a change in "sign" of the afferent input merely as a consequence of its increasing intensity. Perhaps there is a central-neural switching when the intensity of the afferent salt discharge reaches a critical value. Most intense sensory stimuli have aversive effects.

The relation of behavior to sensory afferent discharge for some of the other basic taste stimuli is shown in Fig. 8. The upper figure shows the preference-response curves for sugar, acid, and quinine, as well as salt. We show here only the intake above 50 per cent for salt and sugar, but at higher concentrations, the curves fall below the 50 per cent value. The responses for acid and quinine are both aversions; no preference is shown. Note in the lower curves that the absolute magnitudes of neural response are quite different for the electrolytes as compared with the nonelectrolytes. The behavioral response to quinine is quite definite and appears before there is a clear signal greater than the noise for the nerve response. Here the behavioral indicator is the more sensitive. In an analogous way, the response to sucrose behaviorally is clear and definite, yet the neural

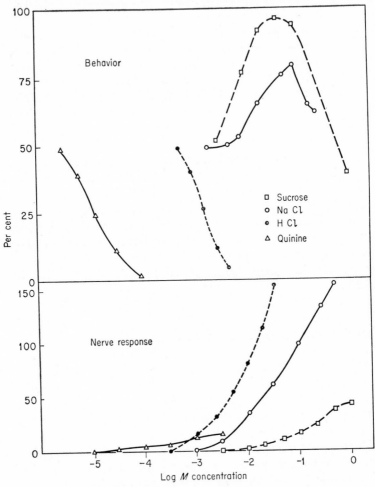

Fig. 8. Composite graph of behavioral and afferent neural responses in the rat. Upper figure shows the preference-aversion responses as percentage intake as a function of stimulus concentration. Lower figure shows neural responses in arbitrary units.

response is disappointingly small. Intrinsic differences in the magnitude of the neural response, due in part to fiber size, etc., show that sheer size of electrical signal itself cannot be correlated with behavioral effect. On the other hand, the range of effective stimulus-concentration values in the two sets of determinations for each stimulus show good agreement. The exact form or position of the preference-aversion curves along the abscissa may be shifted, depending upon such factors as order of presentation of stimuli, degree of hunger or physiological need, and amount of experience with the taste stimuli. It is the general nature of the relations between sensory input and behavior that is shown in Fig. 8.

Responses to sugar and saccharin. The behavioral response to sugar solutions has been studied rather extensively and it now seems possible to give an account of the "start" and "stop" factors in relation to sensory input. The preference curve just shown is based on ingestion of sugar over a 24-hr or longer period. Ingestion is a rising function of concentration to a peak preference when the typical inflection occurs and intake declines. This relation is found also in the single-stimulus method. McCleary [52] was one of the first to show that the intake of sugar solution is limited by an osmotic postingestion factor. Others have shown similar effects of gastric factors by studying the effects of intubation upon intake [45, 56, 77, 82]. However, the relative frequency of choice in the brief-exposure preference method does not show the inflection [95]. Here there appears to be a linear relation between the level of acceptability and logarithm of concentration. A study of the rate of bar pressing as a function of concentration of sucrose solution used as the reinforcement showed that, in a continuous schedule, rate increased for the weaker concentrations but showed an inversion at the higher value [30]. On a periodic schedule, however, the rate of bar press was found to be linear with the log of the concentration. The latter schedule provides relatively little drinking per response. But bar-press rate also can be depressed by intragastric injections [77].

The relations between bar pressing on the two schedules and the preference-ingestion data of Richter and Campbell [70] are shown in Fig. 9, together with the electrophysiological response curve for the rat [32]. Note that the inversion point in the two-bottle preference test is close to the inversion point of the continuous reinforcement schedule. Both points lie close to the top of the electrophysiological sensory function. On the periodic schedule, rate rises as the sensory function increases. The fact that there is no inversion where the amount ingested is small appears to implicate the postingestion factor as a primary stop mechanism [18, 76]. Such a formulation would be consistent with Young's statement that "sugar solutions are basically hedonically positive for the rat as compared with salt which is first positive but then negative" [94].

Studies which compared the effect of two different sugars (glucose and sucrose) on consummatory behavior, choice response, and rate of bar press likewise point to the importance of postingestive factors. Isohedonic solutions (equally accepted concentration in short comparative tests) were not consumed in equal amount when presented singly for longer periods. The glucose solutions were consumed in lesser volume than their isohedonically matched sucrose solutions, and the cumulative mean intake of both sugars was linearly related to osmotic pressure for the longer periods [76]. In the Skinner box, the concentration of these two sugars which give equal rate of response on an aperiodic schedule (i.e., have equal reinforcing value) correspond to the isohedonic con-

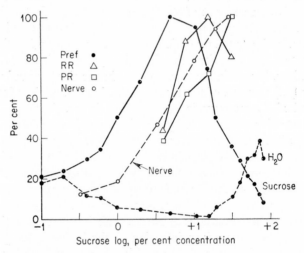

Fig. 9. Composite graph showing the neural response to sucrose and the behavioral measures obtained by three different procedures in the rat. *Pref* is the typical 2-bottle 24-hr ingestion preference method. Both the sucrose and water intakes are shown as smoothed curves, based on data by Richter and Campbell. *RR* is the rate of bar pressing during a test period for a small drop of sucrose on a regular reinforcement schedule. *PR* is the same for a periodic reinforcement schedule. Both after data by Guttman, 1953. Values have been adjusted to yield maximum values of ordinates of each original curve equal to 100.

centrations [76, 93]. Guttman [31] previously showed that the equal reinforcing solutions correspond to the equally sweet concentrations found in psychophysical experiments [12, 53].

With Hagstrom, we have also compared the relative efficacy of sucrose and glucose as gustatory stimuli for the rat, using the electrophysiological recording method [32]. This could be done even though the magnitude of response to sugar is relatively small. Figure 10 shows the relative responses to the two sugars, and Fig. 11 shows the comparison

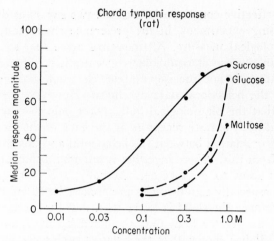

Fig. 10. Integrator-response magnitudes to three sugars for the rat chorda tympani nerve. Ordinate is relative magnitude, 100 equals the response to 0.01 M NaCl. After data by Hagstrom and Pfaffmann, 1959.

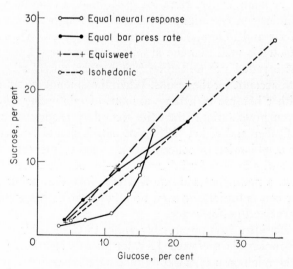

Fig. 11. Equal response concentrations of glucose and sucrose for electrophysiological measures, equal bar-press rates, equisweet solutions and isohedonic solutions. After data by Hagstrom and Pfaffmann, 1959.

of the equi-effective concentrations of the two sugars as determined in the barpressing experiment, in the preference choice test, and by the electrophysiological measure. All measures agree that sucrose is more effective than glucose of equimolar concentration, although the quantitative relation is not precise, for the electrophysiological data are curvilinear, the behavioral data are linear. However, it should be remembered that the physiological data reflect only the chorda tympani response and not the taste receptors at the back of the mouth. Perhaps the curvilinear relation between the behavioral and physiological measures arises from this. Where ingestion is minimal, behavior and sensory effectiveness seem to go together. Actually, the postingestion factor seems to be especially significant in preferences based on ingestion. The glucose-preference threshold is lower than that for sucrose, and the intake of glucose greater than that predicted by the sensory measures. Soulairac [79] has shown that the relative preference for sugars in a typical two-bottle preference test is correlated with their relative rates of absorption from the gastrointestinal tract.

Experiments utilizing other learning situations have been concerned with the action of sugar or saccharin as reinforcers [39, 73, 74, 78, 96, 97]. There is ample evidence that the sweet taste is rewarding, whether it is nutritive or nonnutritive. Here too, performance is an increasing function of stimulus concentration, where conditions appear to maximize the sensory effects and minimize the postingestion factor. When amount or temporal factor is such that the absolute amount or volume of stimulus or nutrient ingested per unit time is low, then purely stimulus factors seem best to account for the results. When the amount consumed per unit is large, either because of a large amount of reinforcing agent or short time between presentations, then the secondary postingestive factors intrude. As Collier and Siskel [18] point out, it should be possible—with the proper combination of concentration, volume, interval between reinforcement, and number of reinforcements—to obtain a monotonic stimulus function, a nonmonotonic function with inversion points at different volumes or concentrations or even no relation at all between amount of reinforcement and performance.

These considerations presumably apply to Campbell's measurements of the just-noticeable preferred JNP for sucrose solutions [14]. He determined the minimal concentration increment necessary to produce a 75 per cent preference for the stronger of a pair of sucrose solutions in a two-bottle preference situation. Stronger solutions required a larger concentration increment than did the weak ones, and the plot of JNP against stimulus concentration showed a U-shaped function reminiscent of the more familiar Weber intensity-discrimination functions. The resemblance may be due only in part to the properties of the sensory input because, as we have just suggested, preference is the composite of sensory as well as postingestion factors. The osmotic effects of the stronger sugar solutions might be particularly strong. This situation contrasts with the JNR functions for the noxious stimuli, where the stimulus itself may be more directly the source of the reinforcement, uncomplicated by secondary factors [13].

Thus we see that sensory stimulation of the mouth receptors, especially of taste, has a direct relevance for the control of ingestive behavior and the instrumental responses which lead to ingestion. Although a number of investigators have provided evidence that the mouth receptors may be bypassed and that learning can still take place, all such evidence shows that such learning is less effective than when stimulation of the mouth receptors is included [19, 56]. Nearly all workers, whatever their theoretical predilections, have shown the importance of stimulation and sensory contact—some would say "sensory satisfaction"—in the reinforcement process. Indeed, as Bindra [8, p. 134] concludes in his recent monograph on motivation, "Whatever the interpretation, it seems clear that, up to a certain point, an increase in sensory stimulation is a positive reinforcer."

Biological basis of taste reactions. The fact that certain taste stimuli control ingestion directly appears to be biologically determined. Frings [24] has pointed out that nearly all organisms accept sugar solutions. There are exceptions—perhaps related to certain aspects of metabolic or other biochemical divergences—among the species. Cats cannot taste or discriminate sugar solutions [15, 63] and birds [67] do not appear to show sucrose preferences, but these examples are remarkable largely for their divergence from what otherwise appears to be a general rule. Further, there is no convincing evidence that the "sweet tooth," where it does exist, depends upon the concomitant nourishment. The drinking of nonnutritive saccharin solutions under prolonged exposure to them shows no sign of extinction such as might be expected if the preference for saccharin or sweet were acquired by past association with nourishment [73]. Here we have "sweet for sweet's sake."

We have been able to show that a bitter aversive stimulus can be made more acceptable *only temporarily* when it is paired with the alleviation of thirst in early infancy [89]. Newborn guinea pigs were raised on a normally avoided solution of sucrose octaacetate (SOA) as the only source of water for a 3-week period. At an older age these organisms showed the usual rejection of SOA. Gustatory stimuli, therefore, appear to be biologically determined as the instigator of consummatory or avoidance responses and as primary positive or negative reinforcing stimuli.

Hedonic responses. So far, we have discussed the mechanisms of a variety of behaviors which appear to be under the control of sensory stimulation *qua* "sensory stimulation." We have not discussed the question of the affective or hedonic aspects of sensory stimulation—the pleasure of sensation, so to speak. To do so we should now like to turn to other kinds of data derived from studies of man.

Of all the applied psychophysical fields, none has made greater use of the affective or hedonic rating-scale methods, along with purely sensory testing procedures, than has the field of flavor technology. In a series of carefully controlled tests the U.S. Army Quartermaster Food Acceptance Laboratory [68], using a nine-point hedonic rating scale, has been able to predict with good reliability the actual choices of food and the acceptance of menus on the part of soldiers in the field. These tests frankly ask such ratings as the following:

> Like extremely
> Like very much
> Indifferent
> Dislike very much

In this case the hedonic ratings are not determined solely by stimulus properties of food, for other studies by the group have documented the important role played by familiarity and past experience. Nonetheless, the frankly hedonic rating initiated by the sensory stimulation is a good predictor of actual acceptance and ingestion.

We have been impressed by the apparent similarity of our rat preference curves to those of hedonic value obtained many years ago by Engel [21]. In those experiments, subjects were asked to rate different intensities of taste stimuli as either pleasant, unpleasant, or indifferent. The data can be treated in a number of ways, but in Fig. 12 we see the ratings of four different taste modalities expressed as a percentage of pleasant ratings minus the percentage of unpleasant ratings for a group of seven observers, using summed ratings of all observers. The abscissa is proportional to the concentrations adjusted for each of the different stimulus solutions. Note that sugar begins at a slightly unpleasant value and rises with concentration to reach a plateau. Sour, bitter, and salt all start from indifference, rise to a peak, and then fall off to unpleasantness. Sweet is predominantly pleasant, bitter predominantly unpleasant, with salt and sour intermediate.

In Fig. 13, we have plotted the animal preference curve and the hedonic rating by Engel's subject for sodium chloride solutions by concentration. The hedonic ratings here were computed simply as the percentage of the total ratings that are pleasant. Except for position along the abscissa, the two curves show a striking similarity. Beebe-Center [4] earlier called attention to these same relations and compared the animal preference responses with hedonic ratings. Actually, the more recent analysis of the postingestive factors that control the intake of sucrose solutions has done much to clarify the discrepancy between Engel's hedonic curve for sugar and the rat's preference for sugar. The sucrose hedonic curve does not turn down at the higher concentration (see Fig. 12). As noted earlier, rate of bar pressing on a periodic schedule and frequency of choice in the brief-exposure test are likewise monotonically related to concentration. Thus hedonic rating and reinforcement bear the same relation to stimulus concentration.

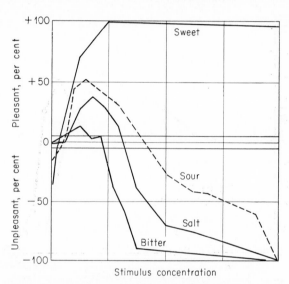

Fig. 12. The preponderance of "pleasant" or "unpleasant" judgments in relation to the concentration of taste solution. Ordinate gives per cent "pleasant" minus per cent "unpleasant." The abscissa is proportional to concentration, the full length of the base line standing for 40 per cent cane sugar, 1.12 per cent tartaric acid, 10 per cent NaCl and 0.004 per cent quinine sulphate (by weight). After data by Engel, 1928. Reproduced in Woodworth, R. S. *Experimental psychology*. New York: Holt, 1938.

In the preference-aversion curves for other substances, the stop mechanism may be sensory (gustatory) in origin or may arise from other than postingestive effects. If the taste of strong salt solutions is aversive per se, then we might expect that, regardless of reinforcement schedule, response will fall off above the optimal salt concentration in a manner resembling the fall-off in Engel's curves. The same might hold for saccharin which has a bitter sensory component at the higher concentrations. Further study of these effects is needed.

We have been emphasizing stimulus properties as prime determinants
of the hedonic effect, but let us hastily point out that specific training
and experience may make some unpleasant odors and tastes acceptable
or even preferred. We are reminded here of the whisky drinker's development so aptly described by Brown [11].

Straight whiskey, when first ingested, typically effects rather violent defense reactions. Because of this, the novice drinker usually begins with sweet
liqueurs, "pink ladies," and wines, and slowly works his way through a series

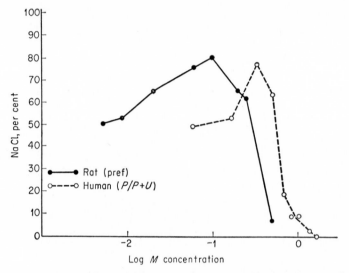

Fig. 13. Comparison of animal preference and hedonic ratings of
man in response to sodium chloride solutions. From *Flavor research*
"neutral spirits" becomes indeed psychologically neutral.)

of beverages characterized by the gradual disappearance of cola and ginger
ale additives. Finally, only plain water or even nothing need be mixed with
the raw product. To the hardened drinker, straight whiskey does not taste
bad—*not bad at all!* (It is thus that a product euphemistically labelled
"neutral spirits" becomes indeed psychologically neutral.)

Although this description appeared in defense of a drive-reduction
formulation of behavior and learning, the mere fact that drive reduction
was supported and buttressed by the use of sweet and pleasant stimuli
seems to have been overlooked. There is no convincing evidence that the
primary relation between hedonic tone and sensory stimulation is entirely
acquired. Indeed, quite the converse seems to be true.

The relation of sensory stimulation to hedonic process has been noted
by earlier workers. Sherrington [75] noted that the stimulation of con-

tact receptors, as contrasted with distance receptors, is characterized by strong affective tone and that the contact receptors stand in very close relation to consummatory responses. Stimulation of the touch receptors of the lips and touch and taste in the mouth initiates reflex movements that precede the act of swallowing. Troland [86] spoke of three classes of stimulus reception: nociception, beneception, and neutroception. The principal nociceptor system was pain, but other examples were hunger, thirst, the taste of bitter, strong salts and acids, and certain foul or repugnant odors, etc. In the beneceptor class were the sense organs mediating erotic behavior, the taste of sugar, and certain odors. Vision, hearing, touch, and proprioception were relegated to neutroception. Although Troland's criterion was that of biological utility, Young [92] pointed to the high correlation between pleasantness and beneception, unpleasantness and nociception. He also notes that there is a frequent correlation between pleasantness and approach, and unpleasantness and avoidance. Further, he points out that the affective responses to simple colors and tones are much weaker than those evoked by odors, tastes, and cutaneous or organic stimuli.

In his work on palatability, Young espouses a clearly hedonistic theory of reinforcement in which the affective process is regarded as a postulate, an intervening construct [94]. The reactions of animals to taste solutions can only be described when reference is made to their positive or negative hedonic effects. Thus sugar solutions are hedonically positive and the level of acceptability is directly proportional to the logarithm of the concentration. Salt, on the other hand, does not show this one-to-one correspondence with sensory intensity. Low concentrations of salt are said to be hedonically positive for the rat but at high concentrations are hedonically negative. Such terminology often appears simply to rename approach or avoidance behavior with hedonistic synonyms. We all know what we mean when we say in laboratory jargon that the rat likes sugar; we know he will take it in preference to water, he may press a bar for it, he may take it when it is adulterated with something he does not like, such as quinine. But such usage does not necessarily indicate the primacy of the hedonic process; we must have further experimental study of acceptance and rejection and of their relation to hedonic or affective processes.

Thus it is abundantly clear that instigation of consummatory response or of rejection, reinforcement of instrumental response, and hedonic effect are all closely related and that reproducible stimulus functions can be demonstrated for each. A definitive choice as to which of these is primary cannot yet be made. I would like to propose that sensory stimulation per se, together with its ensuing central neural events, be considered as a prime determinant in the chain of events culminating in acceptance behavior, reinforcement, and hedonic effect. The further study of such stimulus functions and their analysis, particularly at the physiological level, is a problem that merits the highest priority.

Physiological mechanisms in reinforcement. I should like to add a word or two about possible physiological mechanisms in the reinforcing and hedonic functions of stimuli. The studies of cranial self-stimulation [10, 59, 60] show that the reward and punishment systems within the brain itself, but particularly the reward systems, have been found to depend in large measure upon the limbic system. In classical neuroanatomy, this was known as the rhinencephalon or "smell brain," but its relation to

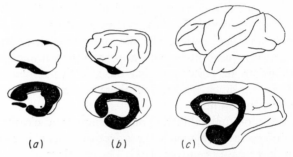

(a)   (b)   (c)

Fig. 14. Lateral and medial surfaces of brains of rabbit a, cat b, and monkey c, drawn roughly to scale. The drawings illustrate that the limbic lobe, represented in black, forms a common denominator in the brains of all animals. After data by MacLean, 1954.

olfaction seems less and less particular. The limbic lobe, including the hippocampus, completely surrounds the hilus of the hemisphere. Its various subcortical cell stations include the amygdala, septal nuclei, the hypothalamus, anterior thalamic nuclei, etc. The limbic lobe of the rabbit, cat, and monkey is shown in black in Fig. 14. The limbic lobe appears to form a common denominator in the brains of all mammals.

Its constancy of gross and microscopic structure throughout the phylogeny of the mammal contrasts strikingly with the mushrooming neopallium which surrounds it. . . . Papez theorized that the experimental evidence also points to the limbic lobe as a cortical common denominator for a variety of emotional and viscerosomatic reactions in the mammal [50].

There is increasing evidence of a sensory viscerosomatic influx into the limbic system. In pathological involvements, particularly of the temporal lobe, discharges in this part of the brain may be associated with a wide variety of auras involving all the body senses as well as a great number of feeling and emotional states. Among the more purely sensory auras are crude olfactory sensations, alimentary symptoms including taste, thirst, hunger, nausea, and somatic sensations ranging from pains to paresthesia. Prolonged rhythmic responses were observed in the pyriform area from olfactory, gustatory, and painful stimulation by MacLean, Horwitz and Robinson [51]. They note that all three of these senses accent the quality and intensity of a stimulus rather than its spatial relationships.

We do not wish to imply that this system is essentially one for viscero-somatic sensation, for it is also implicated in a variety of complex effects such as the Klüver-Bucy syndrome [42], memory losses [61], the lowering of rage thresholds in some cases or increased docility after ablation in others [2, 29, 72, 80], and a variety of cranial self-stimulation effects [10, 59]. The details of these relations are beyond the scope of the present discourse. What we wish to emphasize is that there are significant sensory inputs into this system which may relate to the hedonic and reinforcing features of stimulation as compared with the purely cognitive or arousal functions. This is not to be confused with the reticular activating system which has been the concern of much neurophysiological research in recent years. The reticular system is particularly involved in arousing or alerting the organism upon sensory and other types of stimulation.

Most sense organs appear to have at least two central neural pathways. One is the discrete projection system which passes through the well-known primary projection pathways via the thalamic sensory relays to the cerebral cortex; a second is the nonspecific path by way of the reticular activating system with diffuse projections to the cortex and other neural structures. The reticular system receives inputs from all modalities, i.e., it is multimodal and intramodal. The classical projection systems may be said to mediate primarily the discriminative sensory functions; the nonspecific system to mediate physiological and behavioral arousal [54].

The many ramifications of the nonspecific sensory system are the concern of much ongoing research. Lindsley [48], Schlosberg [71], and others have suggested its relation to emotion and Lindsley and his coworkers have been studying its further relevance for perception. Hebb [36, 37] has also linked the arousal system to reinforcement. Changes in level of activation are thought to be reinforcing, per se, depending upon the prevailing level at the time of stimulation. Thus, in the sensory isolation experiments, "subjects experienced great swings of motivation, which alternated between periods of apathy and intense desires to get back to a normal environment." Hebb concludes, "clearly man's motivation is a function of his exteroceptive stimulation." However, we should like to distinguish between arousal and reinforcement of this kind.

Sprague, Chambers, Stellar, Liu, and Robson [81] have made some interesting studies of chronic animals with extensive lesions in the lateral lemniscal, primary sensory pathways. Their lemniscal animals, i.e., the sensorially restricted animals, displayed little affect in any situation, except, perhaps the most extreme. They flex and tend to pull away from a pinch, but do not attack or show any autonomic response. They showed little or no aversive reaction to an ether cone, although they lacrimated and sneezed. Prior to the operation they solicited petting and responded to it well; afterward, they gave no reaction to petting.

These observations suggest that the affective response to sensory stimuli might be mediated by a system other than the diffuse arousal system, which, it might be noted, already seems to have been over-worked theoretically by psychologists. We would like to call to mind the "thalamic syndrome," described by Head and Holmes [35]. Lesions in the region of the thalamus are characterized by "over-reaction," by excessive affectivity, for both pleasurable as well as painful sensations. This is pathology characterized by the affective modification of sensation. Although the *syndrome thalamique* is well known to clinical neurologists, its exact mechanism is still not clear. For our purposes, it is sufficient to note that in this condition, the basic hedonic responses to sensory stimulation, some of the pleasures of sensation as well as the displeasures, can be unmasked. In short, we are suggesting that the affective con-sequences of sensory stimulation are mediated by processes that depend upon the primary projection systems and their ramifications in thalamic and old-brain neural connections. Obviously much work is required to place these speculations upon a more solid foundation.

SUMMARY

The historical background of sensory psychology was briefly sketched from the "sensationalist" empirical philosophy and early sensory physi-ology to the dramatic developments in electrophysiology of the senses in the 1920s. The application of electronic instrumentation to the study of receptor processes gave a major impetus to this field of inquiry and psychologists joined physiologists in an interdisciplinary effort.

Theories of sensory function have been and are largely theories of physiological mechanism and the new method permitted the direct study of mechanism. A review of the electrophysiological studies of the sense of taste showed that the classical formulation of the doctrine of specific nerve energies required recasting to encompass new evidence to the effect that, although the end organs are differentially sensitive, they do not fall into rigidly specific categories. Two or more of the primary taste stimuli were found to activate the same sensory-neural units to varying degrees. A mechanism of discrimination was proposed which depended upon a *pattern* of activity in a number of parallel sensory input channels. Evidence was presented from the cutaneous and other senses to show that similar principles were applicable to them as well.

It was further shown that the classical approach to sensory psychology emphasized almost exclusively the cognitive and informational function of stimuli and receptor processes. Yet stimuli mediated by the sense organs have a number of other important behavioral functions, one of the most important of these being that of reinforcement. Gustatory stimuli particularly have important reinforcing properties. By the combination of psychophysiological studies of receptor function and studies utilizing preference or other behavioral techniques, it was possible to analyze certain of the "stop" and "start" factors in behavior. For example, when adequate account was taken of secondary postingestive factors, it was shown that the preference for such stimuli as sucrose was directly proportional to the magnitude of the sensory input. In other cases, e.g., NaCl, the behavior appeared to be a duplex function of stimulus intensity, first positive at the low and then negative at the higher intensities. Further studies of this sort should make it possible to analyze the relative contributions of sensory stimulation to the control of behavior in general, and so to broaden the scope of sensory psychophysiology beyond its classical concern with cognitive or discriminative processes. The significance for psychological science of the study of sensory functions in the years ahead may depend as much upon the study of these behaviorally significant relevances as upon the more classical problems of the quantity and quality of sensory discrimination.

REFERENCES

1. Adrian, E. D. *The basis of sensation.* New York: Norton, 1928.
2. Bard, P., & Mountcastle, V. B. Some forebrain mechanisms involved in expression of rage with special reference to suppression of angry behavior. *ARNMD,* 1947, **27,** 362–404.
3. Bare, J. K. The specific hunger for sodium chloride in normal and adrenalectomized white rats. *J. comp. physiol. Psychol.,* 1949, **42,** 242–253.
4. Beebe-Center, J. G. Feeling and emotion. In H. Helson (Ed.), *Theoretical foundations of psychology.* New York: Van Nostrand, 1951. Pp. 254–317.
5. Beidler, L. M. Properties of chemoreceptors of tongue of rat. *J. Neurophysiol.,* 1953, **16,** 595–607.
6. Beidler, L. M. A theory of taste stimulation. *J. gen. Physiol.,* 1954, **38,** 133–139.
7. Berlin, I. *The age of enlightenment.* Boston: Houghton Mifflin, 1956.
8. Bindra, D. *Motivation, a systematic re-interpretation.* New York: Ronald, 1959.

9. Boring, E. G. *A history of experimental psychology.* New York: Apple-ton-Century-Crofts, 1950.

10. Brady, J. V. Temporal and emotional factors related to electrical self-stimulation of the limbic system. In H. H. Jasper, L. D. Proctor, R. S. Knighton, W. C. Noshay, & R. T. Costello (Eds.), *Reticular formation of the brain.* Boston: Little, Brown, 1958. Pp. 689–704.

11. Brown, J. S. Pleasure-seeking behavior and the drive-reduction hypothesis. *Psychol. Rev.,* 1955, **62,** 169–179.

12. Cameron, A. T. *The taste sense and the relative sweetness of sugars and other substances.* Sugar Research Foundation Scientific Report Series, No. 9, 1947. Pp. 1–72.

13. Campbell, B. A. Auditory and aversion thresholds of rats for bands of noise. *Science,* 1957, **125,** 596–597.

14. Campbell, B. A. Absolute and relative sucrose preference thresholds for hungry and satiated rats. *J. comp. physiol. Psychol.,* 1958, **51,** 795–800.

15. Carpenter, J. A. Species differences in taste preferences. *J. comp. physiol. Psychol.,* 1956, **49,** 139–144.

16. Carr, W. J. The effect of adrenalectomy upon the NaCl taste threshold in rat. *J. comp. physiol. Psychol.,* 1950, **43,** 377–380.

17. Cohen, M. J., Hagiwara, S., & Zotterman, Y. The response spectrum of taste fibers in the cat: a single fiber analysis. *Acta. Physiol. Scand.,* 1955, **33,** 316–332.

18. Collier, G., & Siskel, M., Jr. Performance as a joint function of amount of reinforcement and inter-reinforcement interval. *J. exp. Psychol.,* 1959, **57,** 115–120.

19. Coppock, H. W., & Chambers, R. M. Reinforcement of position preference by automatic intravenous injection of glucose. *J. comp. physiol. Psychol.,* 1954, **47,** 355–357.

20. Deutsch, J. A., & Jones, A. D. Diluted water: an explanation of the rat's preference for saline. *J. comp. physiol. Psychol.,* 1960, **53,** 122–127.

21. Engel, R. Experimentelle Untersuchungen über die Abhängigkeit der Lust und Unlust von der Reizstarke beim Geschmacksinn. *Arch. ges. Psychol.,* 1928, **64,** 1–36.

22. Erlanger, J., & Gasser, H. S. *Electrical signs of nervous activity.* Philadelphia: Univer. of Penn. Press., 1937.

23. Fishman, I. Y. Single fiber gustatory impulses in rat and hamster. *J. cell. comp. Physiol.,* 1957, **49,** 319–334.

24. Frings, H. Biological backgrounds of the "sweet tooth." *Turtox News,* 1946, **24,** No. 8.

25. Frings, H. A contribution to the comparative physiology of contact chemoreception. *J. comp. physiol. Psychol.,* 1948, **41,** 25–34.

26. Galambos, R. Suppression of auditory nerve activity by stimulation of efferent fibers to cochlea. *J. Neurophysiol.,* 1956, **19,** 424–437.

27. Granit, R. *Receptors and sensory perception.* New Haven, Conn.: Yale Univer. Press, 1955.

28. Gray, J. A. B. Initiation of impulses at receptors. In *Handbook of Physiology.* Vol. I, Sect. 1. Baltimore, Md.: Williams & Wilkins, 1959. Pp. 123–145.

29. Green, J. D. The rhinencephalon and behavior. In Ciba Foundation symposium. *Neurological basis of behavior.* Boston: Little, Brown, 1958. Pp. 222–235.

30. Guttman, N. Operant conditioning, extinction and periodic reinforcement in relation to concentration of sucrose used as reinforcing agent. *J. exp. Psychol.,* 1953, **46,** 213–224.

31. Guttman, N. Equal reinforcement values for sucrose and glucose solutions compared with equal sweetness values. *J. comp. physiol. Psychol.,* 1954, **47,** 358–361.

32. Hagstrom, E. C., & Pfaffmann, C. The relative taste effectiveness of different sugars for the rat. *J. comp. physiol. Psychol.,* 1959, **52,** 259–262.

33. Harlow, H. F. Motivation as a factor in the acquisition of new responses. In M. R. Jones (Ed.), *Current theory and research in motivation.* Lincoln, Neb.: Univer. of Neb. Press, 1953. Pp. 24–49.

34. Harriman, A. E., & MacLeod, R. B. Discriminative thresholds of salt for normal and adrenalectomized rats. *Amer. J. Psychol.,* 1953, **66,** 465–471.

35. Head, H., & Holmes, G. Sensory disturbances from cerebral lesions. *Brain,* 1911, **34,** 102–254.

36. Hebb, D. O. Alice in wonderland or psychology among the biological sciences. In H. F. Harlow & C. N. Woolsey (Eds.), *Biological and biochemical bases of behavior.* Madison, Wis.: Univer. of Wis. Press, 1958. Pp. 451–467.

37. Hebb, D. O. *A textbook of psychology.* Philadelphia: Saunders, 1958.

38. Hensel, H., & Zotterman, Y. The response of mechanoreceptors to thermal stimulation. *J. Physiol.,* 1951, **115,** 16–24.

39. Hughes, L. H. Saccharine reinforcement in a T maze. *J. comp. physiol. Psychol.,* 1957, **50,** 431–435.

40. Kimura, K., & Beidler, L. M. Microelectrode study of taste bud of the rat. *Amer. J. Physiol.,* 1956, **187,** 610.

41. Kling, J. W., Horowitz, L., & Delhagen, J. E. Light as a positive reinforcer for rat responding. *Psychol. Rep.,* 1956, **2,** 337–340.

42. Klüver, H. The "temporal lobe syndrome" produced by bilateral ablations. In Ciba Foundation symposium. *Neurological basis of behavior.* Boston: Little, Brown, 1958. Pp. 175–186.

43. Kuffler, S. W., & Hunt, C. C. The mammalian small-nerve fibers: a system for efferent nervous regulation of muscle-spindle discharge. *Res. Publ. Ass. nerv. ment. Dis.,* 1952, **30,** 24–47.

44. LeMagnen, J. Variations specifiques des seuils olfactifs chez l'homme sous actions androgene et oestrogene. *C. R. Acad. Sci.,* 1949, **228,** 947–948.

45. LeMagnen, J. Le rôle de la réceptivité gustative au chlorure de sodium dans le méchanisme de régulation de la prise d'eau chez le rat blanc. *J. Physiol. Path. Gen.,* 1955, **47,** 405–418.

46. Liljestrand, G. Uber den Schwellenwert des sauren Geschmacks. *Arch. neerl. Physiol.,* 1922, **7,** 532–537.

47. Liljestrand, G., & Zotterman, Y. The water taste in mammals. *Acta Physiol. Scand.,* 1954, **32,** 291–303.

48. Lindsley, D. B. Emotion. In S. S. Stevens (Ed.), *Handbook of experimental psychology.* New York: Wiley, 1951. Chap. 14.

49. Lindsley, D. B. Physiological psychology. *Annu. Rev. Psychol.,* 1956, **7,** 323–348.

50. MacLean, P. D. The limbic system and its hippocampal formation in animals and their possible application to man. *J. Neurosurg.,* 1954, **11,** 29–44.

51. MacLean, P. D., Horwitz, N. H., & Robinson, F. Olfactory-like responses in pyriform area to non-olfactory stimulation. *Yale J. Biol. Med.,* 1952, **25,** 159–172.

52. McCleary, R. A. Taste and post ingestion factors in specific hunger behavior. *J. comp. physiol. Psychol.,* 1953, **46,** 411–421.

53. MacLeod, S. A construction and attempted validation of sensory sweetness scales. *J. exp. Psychol.,* 1952, **44,** 316–323.

54. Magoun, H. W. *The waking brain.* Springfield, Ill.: Charles C Thomas, 1958.

55. Maruhashi, J., Mizuguchi, K., & Tasaki, I. Action currents in single afferent nerve fibers elicited by stimulation of the skin of the toad and the cat. *J. Physiol.,* 1952, **117,** 129–151.

56. Miller, N. E. Experiments on motivation. *Science,* 1957, **126,** 1271–1278.

57. Moncrieff, R. W. *The chemical senses.* (2nd ed.) New York: Wiley, 1951.

58. Nafe, J. P. The pressure, pain and temperature sense. In C. Murchison (Ed.), *Handbook of general experimental psychology.* Worcester, Mass.: Clark Univer. Press, 1934. Chap. 20.

59. Olds, J. Self-stimulation of the brain. *Science,* 1958, **127,** 315–324.

60. Olds, J. S., & Milner, P. Positive reinforcement produced by electrical stimulation of septal area and other regions of the rat brain. *J. comp. physiol. Psychol.,* 1954, **47,** 419–427.

61. Penfield, W. The role of the temporal cortex in recall of past experience and interpretation of the present. In Ciba Foundation symposium. *Neurological basis of behavior.,* Boston: Little, Brown, 1958. Pp. 149–174.

62. Pfaffmann, C. Gustatory afferent impulses. *J. cell. comp. Physiol.,* 1941, **17,** 243–258.

63. Pfaffmann, C. Gustatory nerve impulses in rat, cat, and rabbit. *J. Neurophysiol.,* 1955, **18,** 429–440.

64. Pfaffmann, C. Taste mechanisms in preference behavior. *Amer. J. clin. Nutr.,* 1957, **5,** 142–147.

65. Pfaffmann, C. The afferent code for sensory quality. *Amer. Psychologist,* 1959, **14,** 226–232.

66. Pfaffmann, C., & Bare, J. K. Gustatory nerve discharges in normal and adrenalectomized rats. *J. comp. physiol. Psychol.,* 1950, **43,** 320–324.

67. Pick, H., & Kare, M. Certain aspects of taste preference in chickens and calves. Paper read at Eastern Psychol. Ass., Atlantic City, N.J., April, 1959.

68. Pilgrim, F. J. The components of food acceptance and their measurement. *Amer. J. clin. Nutr.*, 1957, **5**, 142–147.

69. Richter, C. P. Total self-regulatory functions in animals and human beings. In *The Harvey lectures*. Springfield, Ill.: Charles C Thomas, 1942. Pp. 63–103.

70. Richter, C. P., & Campbell, K. H. Taste thresholds and taste preferences of rats for five common sugars. *J. Nutr.* 1940, **20**, 31–46.

71. Schlosberg, H. Three dimensions of emotion. *Psychol. Rev.*, 1954, **61**, 81–88.

72. Schreiner, L., & Kling, A. Behavioral change following rhinencephalic injury in the cat. *J. Neurophysiol.*, 1953, **16**, 643–659.

73. Sheffield, F. D., & Roby, T. B. Reward value of a non-nutritive sweet taste. *J. comp. physiol. Psychol.*, 1950, **43**, 471–481.

74. Sheffield, F. D., Roby, T. B., & Campbell, B. A. Drive reduction versus consummatory behavior as determinants of reinforcement. *J. comp. physiol. Psychol.*, 1954, **47**, 349–354.

75. Sherrington, C. *The integrative action of the nervous system.* New Haven, Conn.: Yale Univer. Press, 1948.

76. Shuford, E. H., Jr. Palatability and osmotic pressure of glucose and sucrose solutions as determinants of intake. *J. comp. physiol. Psychol.*, 1959, **52**, 150–153.

77. Smith, M., & Duffy, M. The effects of intragastric injection of various substances on subsequent bar pressing. *J. comp. physiol. Psychol.*, 1955, **48**, 387–391.

78. Smith, M., & Duffy, M. Evidence for a dual reinforcing effect of sugar. *J. comp. physiol. Psychol.*, 1957, **50**, 242–247.

79. Soulairac, A. La physiologie d'un comportement: l'appétit glucidique et sa régulation neuro-endocrinienne chez les rongeurs. *Bull. Biol.*, 1947, **81**, 273–432.

80. Spiegel, E., Miller, H., & Oppenheimer, J. Forebrain and rage reactions. *J. Neurophysiol.*, 1940, **3**, 538–548.

81. Sprague, J. M., Chambers, W., Stellar, E., Liu, C. N., & Robson, K. Chronic reticular and lemniscal lesions in cats. *Fed. Proc.*, 1958, **17**, 155.

82. Stellar, E., Hyman, R., & Samet, S. Gastric factors controlling water- and salt-solution-drinking. *J. comp. physiol. Psychol.*, 1954, **47**, 220–226.

83. Stevens, S. S. On the psychophysical law. *Psychol. Rev.*, 1957, **64**, 153–181.

84. Tasaki, I. Nerve impulses in individual auditory nerve fibers of guinea pigs. *J. Neurophysiol.*, 1954, **17**, 97–122.

85. Tasaki, I. Conduction of the nerve impulse. In *Handbook of physiology*. Vol. I, Sect. 1. Baltimore, Md.: Williams & Wilkins, 1959. Pp. 75–121.

86. Troland, L. T. *The fundamentals of human motivation.* New York: Van Nostrand, 1928.

87. Tucker, D., & Beidler, L. M. Autonomic nervous system influence on olfactory receptors. *Amer. J. Physiol.*, 1956, **187**, 637.

88. Von Békésy, G., & Rosenblith, W. A. The mechanical properties of the ear. In S. S. Stevens (Ed.), *Handbook of experimental psychology*. New York: Wiley, 1951. Pp. 1075–1115.

89. Warren, R. P., & Pfaffmann, C. Early experience and taste aversion. *J. comp. physiol. Psychol.*, 1958, **52**, 263–266.

90. Weddell, G., Somesthesis and the chemical senses. *Annu. Rev. Psychol.*, 1955, **6**, 119–136.

91. Wever, E. G. *Theory of hearing*. New York: Wiley, 1949.

92. Young, P. T. *Motivation of behavior*. New York: Wiley, 1936.

93. Young, P. T. Psychologic factors regulating the feeding process. *Amer. J. clin. Nutr.*, 1957, **5**, 154–161.

94. Young, P. T. The role of affective processes in learning and motivation. *Psychol. Rev.*, 1959, **66**, 104–125.

95. Young, P. T., & Greene, J. T. Quantity of food ingested as a measure of relative acceptability. *J. comp. physiol. Psychol.*, 1953, **46**, 288–294.

96. Young, P. T., & Shuford, E. H., Jr. Intensity, duration, and repetition of hedonic processes as related to acquisition of motives. *J. comp. physiol. Psychol.*, 1954, **47**, 298–305.

97. Young, P. T., & Shuford, E. H., Jr. Quantitative control of motivation through sucrose solutions of different concentrations. *J. comp. physiol. Psychol.*, 1955, **48**, 114–118.

98. Zotterman, Y. Species differences in the water taste. *Acta Physiol. Scand.*, 1956, **37**, 60–70.

99. Zotterman, Y. Afferent taste impulses in the monkey. Personal communication. 1960.

SOME INTERRELATIONS AMONG PHYSICS, PHYSIOLOGY, AND PSYCHOLOGY IN THE STUDY OF VISION

FLOYD RATLIFF
The Rockefeller Institute

Introduction 418
The Nature of Light 419
   Concepts Based Primarily upon Direct Visual Observations 420
      Rectilinear propagation with a finite velocity 420
      Reflection and refraction 422
      Dispersion 422
      Interference and diffraction 423
      Polarization 425
      The ultimate dimensions of light in early stages of the wave theory . . 425
   Quantitative Visual Photometry 426
   The Development of Physical Measures of Light 428
The Transmission and Integration of Neural Activity in the Visual System . 432
   The Nerve Impulse 432
      Animal electricity 433
      The action potential 434
      The electrical activity of single neurons 436
   The Activity of the Optic Nerve 437
      The responses of single visual elements 437
      The integration of neural activity in the retina 446
Some Behavioral Aspects of Vision 457
   The Science of Behavior 458
   Some Fundamental Behavioral Concepts 460
      The response 461
      Drive and reinforcement 461
      The stimulus control of behavior 462
   Some Behavioral Studies of Visual Processes 463
      Brightness discrimination 464
      Simultaneous brightness contrast 466
      The absolute visual threshold 469
      Dark adaptation 471
      Spectral sensitivity 471

Discussion   473

   The Meaning of Objectivity   474

   Measurement   475

References   477

INTRODUCTION

Sensory phenomena occupy a unique and important position in many a conception of science and epistemology. Consider, for example, this brief quotation from one well-known view [27]:

> Science is the attempt to make the chaotic diversity of our sense-experience correspond to a logically uniform system of thought. . . . The sense-experiences are the given subject matter . . .

Although philosophers and scientists alike may find much to criticize in the details of this particular view of science—or of any other, for that matter—most will agree with the general notion contained therein that it is our observations of various phenomena and our observations of the interrelations among these phenomena which form the starting point of all scientific research. Any conception of science or any theory of knowledge would be incomplete if it did not contain some account of the manner in which we make these observations and of the processes underlying them. In our attempts to attain such an account, we are led across many of the traditional boundaries of scientific disciplines. Psychology is brought into close relation with other sciences, especially with physics and physiology. But with the growing complexity of each of these sciences, and with the attendant specialization within each of them, the interrelations among them are often obscured.

It is the purpose of this paper to illuminate some of these interrelations by examining the development and present status of some of the fundamental concepts in each of these three scientific domains, particularly in their relation to the study of vision.[1]

In the study of vision a very large number of apparently disparate problems are encountered. For example, such diverse topics as the molecular basis of visual excitation and social influences upon conceptions of beauty in art are both properly a part of visual research. But it would be impractical, as well as presumptuous, to undertake an encyclopedic examination of every aspect of vision so broadly defined and of every known relation to vision of the three disciplines under consideration. Therefore, we shall consider only a few aspects of the follow-

[1] The preparation of this manuscript was supported, in part, by a research grant from the National Institute of Neurological Diseases and Blindness, U.S. Public Health Service, and by contract with the U.S. Office of Naval Research.

ing representative problems from physics, physiology, and psychology: (1) the nature of light and its place in the whole spectrum of radiant energy; (2) the manner and mechanism of the transmission and integration of activity in the nervous system; and (3) the behavioral factors involved in the formation of a discrimination. When examined separately, these might seem to be unrelated, but many interrelations may be seen among them (and among the disciplines which claim them) when they are regarded not only as separate problems worthy of investigation in themselves, but also as components of a more complex problem: how animals see. Let us examine each of these three general problems in turn, both in their relation to their respective disciplines, and—especially—in their relation to the study of vision. (In keeping with the purpose of this volume we shall treat physiological problems in somewhat greater detail than the others.)

THE NATURE OF LIGHT

A study of the development of the theory of light reveals that nearly all of its major concepts were originally based upon naïve *visual observations*. Indeed, it must have been the visual appearance of various substantial objects that first led to the concept of something as unsubstantial as light. For we do not see light as a distinct entity; we see objects of various colors and brightnesses. Some objects (a very hot piece of iron, the sun, and many others) can be seen simply by looking at them; they are self-luminous. Because they are visible even when examined alone, we say that they *emit* light which reaches our eyes. Other objects (cold iron, persons, pencils, etc.) can ordinarily be seen only when in the presence of a luminous object. Since we are thus enabled to see these otherwise invisible objects, we say that they are illuminated by the luminous ones and that they *reflect* light to our eyes [71].

Such concepts seem almost trivial, but they certainly are not. Indeed, in many ancient theories of vision it was believed that something emanated from the eye and rendered objects visible, much in the manner in which objects are made sensible to touch by the act of reaching out and placing our hands upon them. The simple but extremely important idea that we see by means of the light emitted from some objects and reflected from others came to the fore because it was the only conception which seemed consistent with *all* visual observations of luminous and nonluminous objects placed in various relations to one another. Furthermore, the concepts of rectilinear propagation with a finite velocity, reflection and refraction, dispersion, interference, and polarization—all so important in our present-day theory of light—were based upon similar simple and direct visual observations of the patterns of brightness produced when luminous and illuminated objects were placed in certain relationships to one another. But in spite of the productivity of direct visual observations, the development of the physical theory of light has been marked by deliberate and generally successful attempts to make the theory independent of all *specific* sensory phenomena.

Let us look at some of the various kinds of visual observations upon which several important concepts in our present theory of light were originally based. We shall then consider why it has seemed necessary to shift the theory to other foundations, how this was accomplished, and some of the consequences of this maneuver for the study of vision itself.

Concepts Based Primarily upon Direct Visual Observations

Rectilinear propagation with a finite velocity. We have long believed that light travels in straight lines. We *see* rectilinear propagation quite directly in a smoky or dusty atmosphere when the sun passes behind a mountain or cloud and we see the straight "rays of light" emanating from the sun. The necessary conditions for this phenomenon are a luminous object (the sun), a more or less opaque object (cloud or mountain), and objects to be illuminated or not illuminated as the case may be (the dust or smoke particles).

In the laboratory, the pinhole camera, with its well-known universal focus and perfect rendition of perspective, provides a simple and convincing demonstration of the rectilinear propagation of light. If we form an image of a luminous object with such a camera, we find that any point on the luminous object, the corresponding point on its image, and the pinhole aperture all fall on a straight line. (This and similar simple systems for observing the path of light by eye give no evidence that the light spreads outside the region defined by the straight lines drawn in this manner.) That the light actually proceeds outward from the luminous object may be shown by cutting a ray at any point by an opaque object; the light is always occluded in a straight line beyond the point where the ray is cut. These simple observations, of course, lead us to believe that the light travels along these straight lines, and the conclusion that light is propagated from one place to another immediately raises the problem of the velocity of its propagation—a problem which can be solved by simple *visual* observations.

To determine a velocity, a distance and a transit time must be measured. Galileo[2] attempted (unsuccessfully) to determine the velocity of light by stationing two observers some distance apart and measuring the

---

[2] For an excellent detailed history of physical optics, see Mach [71]; for a brief account see Strong [89]. A survey of many of the early theories of vision may be found in Polyak's treatise on the retina [75]. For a comprehensive history of psychological studies of sensory processes, see Boring [15].

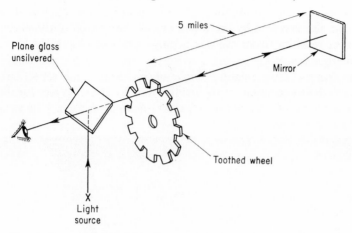

5 miles

Plane glass
unsilvered

Mirror

Toothed wheel

X
Light
source

Fig. 1. Fizeau's method for determining the velocity of light. Light
from the source X falls on an unsilvered plane glass. That which
is reflected passes through an aperture in the toothed wheel to a
mirror about five miles away, and is reflected back through the
aperture in the wheel, and some is transmitted through the plane
glass to the eye of the observer. (Only the optical axes of the system
are shown. The necessary lenses have been omitted to simplify the
sketch.) If the wheel is rotated, the teeth and apertures are alternately in the light path. At a certain high speed of rotation the
light from the source cannot be seen. The "pulse" of light which
passes through an aperture to the mirror is occluded on its return
by a tooth of the wheel which, in the meantime, has moved into
the light path. At a slightly higher speed of rotation, however, the
next aperture moves into the light path in time to permit the
pulse of light to return to the eye. At a still higher speed of
rotation, the image is eclipsed again by the second tooth, and so
on. The speed of rotation which results in the first eclipse of the
image viewed by the observer is determined. The distance from the
wheel to the mirror and back and the time for an aperture to be
replaced by the next tooth gives the velocity of light. A significant
improvement in this method was made later by Foucault who arranged conditions so that a *displacement* of the image was observed. This method had the advantage that a displacement of an
image may be observed with more precision than can the maximal
eclipse of an image.

time required for a light signal to be sent from one to the other and back
again. This method was essentially correct, and it differs little in principle
from the method used by Fizeau at about the middle of the nineteenth
century in the first successful terrestrial measurement of the velocity of
light (see Fig. 1). Note that in Fizeau's method the essential observation
is the determination of conditions under which an image, *seen directly by
the observer,* appears maximally dark.

Reflection and refraction. The properties of reflection and refraction were also revealed by the direct visual observation of the patterns of brightness resulting from various arrangements of objects such as those illustrated in Fig. 2.

The simple laws relating angle of incidence and reflection were known in their entirety as early as 1100 A.D. In 1611, Kepler furnished a complete survey of all cases of refraction from air into glass by means of

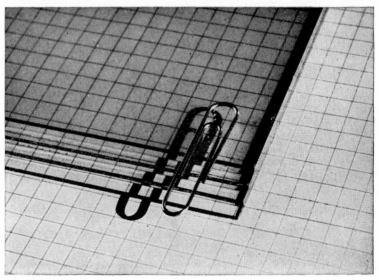

Fig. 2. Refraction. The shadow of the paper clip cast through all four of the plates of glass is displaced to the right more than one division of the graph paper under the plates as compared with that portion of the shadow cast directly upon the paper. By means of an arrangement no more complex than this, the laws of refraction were determined. Note that the essential observation is of the location of the edge of a shadow, i.e., the transition from a bright to a dark area in the pattern of brightness *seen* by the observer. Concepts of wavelength, interference, polarization, etc., were all originally based upon such simple, direct visual observations.

an experimental arrangement similar to the one illustrated. (The correct quantitative form of the law is due to Snell.) Note again the beautiful simplicity of these arrangements. All that is required is a luminous object, an opaque object, a reflecting or refracting material, and a screen illuminated by the reflected or refracted light. The fundamental observation is of the locations of the edges of shadows—that is, the locations on the screen of transitions from one level of brightness to another. The observation is made directly by eye.

Dispersion. A particularly interesting and important case of refraction may be seen directly if a glass prism is placed in a beam of sunlight illuminating a screen. The illuminated area on the screen is deviated and becomes much longer but no wider than without the prism; it also takes on the colors of the rainbow. Newton correctly associated this dispersion with different refractive indexes and illustrated clearly that the refractive index measured is not the same for all light, but depends upon the spectral color of light used. Passing some of the dispersed light through a second prism, moreover, indicates that the refractive index determined with a given color of light obtained in this manner is constant. Again the ex-

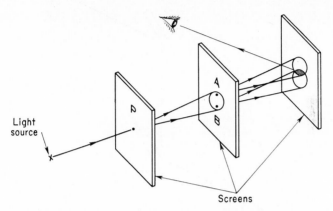

Light source

Screens

FIG. 3. Young's interference experiment. (Highly schematic.) Light from the source X passes through the pinhole P in the first screen and illuminates a second screen in which there are two small apertures, A and B. Light passing through these apertures illuminates a third screen. Where the patches of illumination overlap on the third screen, light and dark bands are seen. Evidently one light beam *interferes* with the other, for no such bands are seen when first one and then the other of the apertures A and B are occluded. Both the deviation from simple rectilinear propagation and the interference of one beam with the other, seen under these conditions, can be adequately described by the mathematics of wave motion. Note that here, as in the preceding illustrations, the essential observation is of the patterns of brightness *seen* directly by eye.

perimental arrangement is extremely simple, as in the examples cited above. And the principal data are derived from *direct visual observations* of various patterns of brightness and color.

Interference and diffraction. Early investigators believed that one light beam in no way interfered with another, but the proper experimental arrangement—again involving direct visual observation—shows that this is not the case. At the same time, it reveals the periodic nature of light.

In Young's experiment (see Fig. 3), light from a source is passed through a small aperture and allowed to fall on an opaque screen in which there are two small apertures some distance apart. The light which passes through these two apertures falls upon another screen. It is clear that the light does not follow a single straight path from the source, because (if the two apertures are fairly close together) the light from each one slightly overlaps that from the other. Where they overlap, dark and light bands are seen. The dark bands are evidently due to interference of

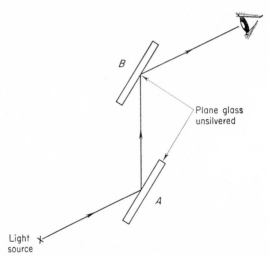

FIG. 4. Polarization: the experiment of Malus. Some of the light from the source X is reflected by the unsilvered glass A to the unsilvered glass B, where some is reflected to the observer's eye. If the glass B is held at the same angle with respect to the axis AB of the beam of light incident upon it, but is rotated about this axis so that the light is reflected from it in a plane perpendicular to the plane of the sketch, a remarkable change in brightness occurs. When viewed from this direction, the source appears much darker than before. (The effect depends critically upon the angles of incidence of the light on the two glass plates.) Note that the fundamental observation is of the *brightness* of the object viewed directly by the observer.

one beam with the other, for no such effects are seen if first one and then the other of the two apertures is occluded. Similar light and dark bands are also seen if the light from a single pinhole passes by an obstacle. It was believed that both of these effects were the outcome of some periodic feature of the light along its path, for the locus of the maxima and minima of brightness could be shown to be related to the lengths of various paths of light from points at the source to points on the screen. Again, as in the preceding examples, the experiment culminates in a direct visual observation of the relative brightness of various points on the screen.

Polarization. In the experiment of Malus shown in Fig. 4, an asymmetry of light rays is seen by direct visual observation of light reflected by surfaces—first in a symmetrical orientation with respect to one another, then in an asymmetrical relation. Although the length of the light path remains constant, the brightness of the illumination is found to diminish progressively as the asymmetry of the orientation of the reflecting surfaces increases, and to increase again as they become more symmetrically positioned. Although the two reflecting surfaces always remain at the same angles with respect to the axis of the light beam, we have the peculiar situation in which Malus's second reflector, when turned about this axis, reflects in one position and not in another. Such experiments led us to believe that light has properties of a transverse wave. Note that the fundamental observation is of a maximum and a minimum in the brightness seen directly by the observer.

The ultimate dimensions of light in early stages of the wave theory. The observations described above are typical of the many hundreds of similar ones which eventually led to the development of the classical wave theory of light. And it is important to remember that—although we sometimes say that we see certain patterns of brightness and darkness because of the wave nature of light—the fact is that we say that light has a wave nature because we see certain patterns of brightness and darkness. In other words, the observations precede the concepts.

The point we wish to emphasize here is that the essential observations which led to the classical conception of light were all *visual* observations. Light could only be measured by eye, and the critical measures were nearly always of the locus of some feature of the brightness of an illuminated object seen directly by the observer—points of maximal and minimal brightness as in an interference pattern, or a transition from one level of brightness to another as at the edge of a shadow. These locations were, of course, measured in terms of their distances from other points; occasionally, as in the determination of velocity, the time of occurrence of certain events was significant. In other words, the ultimate dimensions of light, in these early observations, were a curious mixture of two "objective" quantitative dimensions, length and time, and a "subjective" qualitative dimension, brightness.

This latter dimension, brightness, was quite unsatisfactory for a number of obvious reasons. For one thing, there are many pitfalls in the direct observation of brightness. If we cover one eye for a few minutes, we find that a luminous object now appears much brighter to the eye that has been covered than to the other eye. Or if we look at a bright object for a short time, we find that now it and other objects appear less bright than before. *It is evident that when there are no methods of measuring light independently of the eye, the properties of the observer and the properties of the light observed may be confounded.*

However, the early students of light were well aware of such dangers, and did their utmost to minimize them. For example, in most of the early experiments cited above, the principal measurements (such as determinations of the loci of maxima and minima, or the loci of transitions from one level of brightness to another) were based on relative brightness. Such measures change but little with changes in the sensitivity of the eye. Thus, by various ingenious methods of visual photometry, they were able to make light measurements which were—to a considerable extent—independent of changes in the sensitivity of the eye. Let us examine these methods and their limitations.

Quantitative Visual Photometry

One of the most serious shortcomings of direct visual observations of brightness is that they are qualitative rather than quantitative. Indeed, quantitative determinations of visual brightness that are sufficiently precise for scientific purposes are extremely difficult—if not impossible—to make. Lambert and others who developed quantitative visual measures of light recognized these difficulties. By using the eye as a null instrument in the comparison of an unknown brightness with a standard brightness, they were able to circumvent many, but not all, of the limitations imposed by the peculiar properties of the visual system. These brightnesses were balanced, so to speak, by adding or removing identical standard unit sources. Consequently, the fundamental concepts of photometry are not based upon estimates of absolute magnitudes of brightness, but rather upon an analysis of the manipulations of sources and objects which result in a comparison object and an unknown object appearing equally bright. The three fundamental principles of photometry—(1) that the illuminance increases in proportion to the number of identical sources which illuminate a surface; (2) that the illuminance varies inversely as the square of the distance of a source from the surface illuminated; and (3) that the illuminance varies as the cosine of the angle of incidence of the light reaching the surface—all were derived from determinations of certain conditions under which two differently illuminated surfaces appear equally bright (see Fig. 5). Since visual photometry is based on a null method, it is—to a certain extent—independent of the absolute level of the brightness observed during the measurement.

Such photometric observations differ little, in principle, from the use of unit weights and balancing scales. In neither case is there any simple relation between the quantities determined and the sensations experienced. Of course, everyday experience tells us that two 1-lb weights usually feel heavier than one, or that two apparently identical light sources usually make an object appear brighter than when illuminated by either one alone. But we do not say that two 1-lb weights feel twice as heavy as a 1-lb weight, nor do we say that the object illuminated by two sources appears twice as bright as when illuminated by one. Indeed, there is no reason to expect to find a simple relation between the numbers that we

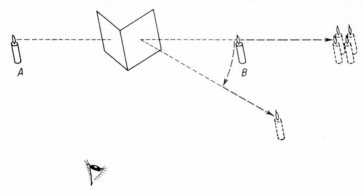

Fig. 5. An illustration of the principles of visual photometry. A sheet of opaque paper is folded so as to provide two plane reflecting surfaces which can be independently illuminated. Viewed from the position indicated, the two visible surfaces of the paper appear equally bright when the two identical unit sources A and B are placed equidistant from these surfaces and at the same angles with respect to them. If the source B is moved farther away from the surface it illuminates, but without changing its angular position with respect to the plane of that surface, then additional unit sources are required to make the surface that B illuminates appear as bright as the surface illuminated by A. If the source B is moved so that its rays fall perpendicularly upon the surface it illuminates, then that surface will appear brighter than the one illuminated obliquely by A; and B must be moved farther away to make the two surfaces appear equally bright. Note that the *difference* in brightness is not measured; the laws of visual photometry are based upon the determination of various conditions of illumination, such as the ones illustrated, under which two comparison surfaces appear *equally* bright.

might assign to the brightness experienced and the visual photometric determination of the illumination on the object being viewed. Visual photometry does not measure the quantity of brightness experienced by the observer; the eye merely serves as a null instrument.

In spite of the fact that the null method of visual photometry provided a relatively successful means of making quantitative measures of light, it was doomed to fail in one very important respect. Light must be visible to be measured by visual photometry. Quite early in the study of light, there was considerable evidence that some light was not visible, and that the eye was a selective detector of that which was visible. For example, Newton had noted as early as 1704 that certain spectral colors " . . . affect the senses more strongly than all the rest together . . . " This observation was substantiated by Fraunhofer (in 1815), who, while studying the problem of color correction in lenses, had made some quantitative photometric measures of various parts of the solar spectrum. In general, his results were in agreement with the earlier but less precise observations made by Newton and others: the middle range of visible wavelengths in the solar spectrum appeared brighter than either the shorter or the longer wavelengths.

However, such observations taken alone were not sufficient to justify the conclusion that the eye is a selective detector of light. (An alternative interpretation could be that there is merely less light to begin with at the two ends of the solar spectrum.) But these and other observations, such as Purkinje's finding that the spectral sensitivity of the eye was not constant, were sufficient to raise doubts as to the efficacy of the eye as an essential part of an instrument for the measurement of light. Furthermore, physical optics was still in the awkward position of having to utilize a specific sense system in the measurement of light. Light was still, in part, a visual concept—it could not be completely specified in physical terms. Nonvisual measures of light were sorely needed, but they were not developed until attention was turned to the study of some of the nonvisual properties of light.

The Development of Physical Measures of Light

Luminous objects are often hot. They are not only hot to the direct touch; they also *radiate* heat. This radiation seems to obey some of the laws of reflection and refraction found for visible light. For example, when we form a very small visual image of an intense source, we also concentrate the heat from the source. (This, the principle of the burning glass, has been known for ages.) Studies of such radiant thermal properties of luminous objects led to some of the most important developments in the study of light. Of particular interest at this point in the discussion is the finding that nonvisible radiation, with properties much like visible radiation, is often emitted from luminous objects.

In 1800, the British astronomer Herschel, while studying the distribution of radiant heat in light by placing very sensitive thermometers along the solar spectrum, found considerable heat beyond the red end of the visible spectrum. This was, of course, the discovery of what we now know as the infrared portion of the spectrum. He found also that this radiation had at least one other property in common with visible light:

it obeyed Snell's law of refraction. The following year, J. W. Ritter, while studying the blackening of silver chloride by different portions of the spectrum, found that the action was strongest beyond the violet end of the visible spectrum—in what is now know as the ultraviolet region.

These two observations established definitely and clearly that radiation from luminous objects was not confined to visible wavelengths. Was this radiation the same as visible radiation? At the time of his discovery Herschel thought not. He believed radiant heat to be something different from light. Gradually, however, with improved techniques and more extensive studies—one notable one made some forty years later by Herschel's son—it became apparent that the only striking difference between visible and nonvisible radiation was visibility. The visual system was definitely a selective detector of radiant energy. But better physical methods of measuring light were still needed, for the direct thermometric method of Herschel had many limitations. Other techniques, particularly the changes in electrical properties of heated metals, proved to be superior.

One such method utilizes the thermoelectric current generated when the junction of two metals, a thermocouple, is heated. A series of such junctions, a thermopile, is even more efficient. Another instrument, the bolometer, developed by Langley in the 1880s, uses as a measure of heat the change in the resistance of a metal strip. A pair of identical metal strips, blackened to increase their absorption, is used to form the arms of a Wheatstone bridge. One of the strips is then exposed to light and the bridge is rebalanced to measure the change in resistance produced by the heating effect of the light. Such devices can be calibrated in terms of the amount of heat (which can be specified independently of its effects on the instrument) required to produce certain changes in electrical resistance. Once calibrated in this manner, they become instruments for the measurement of radiant energy. The development of these and other methods for the nonvisual measurement of light was a great achievement for physical optics. The physical conception of light was freed from its dependence upon vision and was brought into close relation with other physical concepts. The ultimate dimensions of light were now length, mass, and time; the visual concept of brightness was no longer required.

In addition, the study of thermal and other nonvisual properties of light led to a very important result for the study of vision itself. It was definitely established that the visual system was a selective detector of radiant energy, visible light being only a very small portion of a broad spectrum of radiant energy. Let us consider briefly the manner in which the theory of light was gradually incorporated into a more general physical theory. We shall then turn to a consideration of the role of a purely physical conception of light in the study of vision.

The thermodynamic concept of the "black body"—based upon Prevost's *law of exchange*, which was formulated in 1792—was of particular significance in bringing light into relation with other physical concepts. This law may be stated as follows: All objects continuously radiate heat energy; objects in a state of thermal equilibrium radiate the same amount of energy per second that they absorb from the radiations of surrounding objects. The validity of this law may be shown experimentally by placing objects in an enclosure from which practically no heat can escape. All the objects in the enclosure eventually reach and maintain the same temperature. We know that some objects (those with blackened surfaces) seem to absorb more heat than others (those with highly polished surfaces). Yet, since they too will come to thermal equilibrium, the emission of heat—as well as the absorption—must be correspondingly large for the blackened body and correspondingly small for the highly reflecting body. From such observations the concept of the black body was derived—a black body being one which absorbs *all* of the radiant energy incident upon it, and which is, consequently, a perfect radiator. While such bodies probably do not exist in nature, very close approximations to them may be constructed.

The study of black bodies and other radiators has been an important chapter in the history of physical optics. The relation of the emissivity of such black bodies to their absolute temperature (the Stefan-Boltzman law) was predicted theoretically, as was the relation of the emissive power, at various temperatures, of objects other than black bodies to the emissive power of black bodies at those temperatures (Kirchhoff's law). Many experimental observations verified these relations. It was found that the energy at every wavelength not only increases rapidly with the temperature of an emitting object, but also that the wavelength at which the maximum energy is emitted undergoes a shift toward shorter wavelengths with increasing temperature—as described by Wien's displacement law.[3]

However, attempts to formulate laws of the energy distribution throughout a continuous spectrum of black-body radiation, notably those of Rayleigh and Jeans, were only partially successful. Such failures, while disturbing, did not result at the time in an alteration of the wave theory of light. The mathematics of wave motion seemed to provide a descriptive system appropriate to practically all observations on radiant energy. Maxwell's summary of electromagnetic laws, and his precise and elegant formulation of a wave theory of electromagnetism (following

---

[3] The color change associated with this shift is the basis of the optical pyrometer, a precision instrument for the *visual* measurement of high temperatures. Long before the development of this instrument, blacksmiths used the luminosity and color of heated iron as an index of its malleability.

Faraday's experiments on light and magnetism, and subsequently verified by Hertz) had brought light into relation with other types of radiation far removed from the visible spectrum. Visible light was now regarded as a small portion of a very broad and continuous electromagnetic spectrum. And for a time it appeared that the electromagnetic theory of light was adequate, that it satisfactorily described all experimental results, or that it *could* do so if we would only wait for the proper insights into the matter.

But it is not easy to predict the course of science. The next important insights led instead to a radical revision of some of our concepts. Planck's successful derivation of a radiation formula for the distribution of energy in black-body radiation required a new constant, the implications of which were that the energy was corpuscular in nature. This and a number of observations on photoelectric effects could not be incorporated in the generally accepted wave theory. Owing to Einstein's interpretations in particular, the concept of the quantum—so important in modern physics—was developed.

Although this sketch of some of the developments in physical optics is both brief and incomplete, it is sufficient evidence for the point we wish to make. Physical optics has been freed from its dependence upon specific visual experiences.

In the modern theory of light, vision is of little importance except for its role in the historical development of the theory. Light has been brought into relation with other physical concepts, none of which is now dependent upon *specific* sense experiences. Indeed, it is now possible to measure the velocity of light, to observe diffraction, polarization, etc., by instrumental means which are independent of any specific sensory system, for we now have at our disposal a number of photothermal, photochemical, and photoelectric devices for both the detection and measurement of radiant energy.[4]

However, even though the maneuver of avoiding dependence upon specific sense experiences meets the usual criteria of objectivity, we must remember that it does not enable physics to avoid psychological problems altogether. The observer is still an essential part of any observational instrument he uses. Nevertheless, the shifting of the foundations of the theory from specific observations to observations which can be made via any sensory system was an extremely important maneuver, both for

---

[4] For a general survey of the principles of geometrical optics, see Hardy and Perrin [42]. For a survey of physical optics, see Jenkins and White [64]. For a more recent account at an advanced level, see Ditchburn's excellent treatise on physical optics [23]. In addition to its general treatment of physical optics Strong's book [89] contains a number of appendixes covering recent developments in each of several special fields.

physics and for other sciences utilizing physical concepts. In particular, the development of the present-day concept of radiant energy has enabled us to study vision in a noncircular way which was not possible before. It provides us with an independent variable whose specification does not depend (except in its historical origins) upon the properties of the particular sensory system being investigated.

In the study of visual processes there are two major classes of dependent variables, considering the problem very broadly. These are physiological variables and psychological variables. There are numerous suitable examples of each in the two general topics which we have chosen for discussion: (1) the transmission and integration of neural activity; and (2) behavioral factors involved in the formation of discriminations. Let us first examine some physiological dependent variables; later we shall turn to a consideration of behavioral variables.

THE TRANSMISSION AND INTEGRATION OF NEURAL ACTIVITY IN THE VISUAL SYSTEM

The optic nerve forms a "bottleneck" through which must pass all the information that the central nervous system receives from the retina. Consequently, the activity observed in this nerve may be expected to bear a close relation to the physical and chemical events which occur at the site of its generation in the retina and to the subsequent visual behavior which it initiates.

The most striking feature of the activity of the optic nerve—and of other nerves as well—is that it appears in the form of discrete pulses, each one very much like every other one. Variations in the external stimulus to the eye are signaled, not by changes in these pulses themselves, but by changes in their temporal pattern. But before undertaking a detailed examination of the activity of the optic nerve in response to stimulation of the eye by light, let us digress from the topic of vision and consider in some detail the principal unit of nervous action with which we shall be concerned in this section: the nerve impulse. As in the discussion of light, an effort will be made to trace briefly the development of the concept so that both its origin and present status may be more clearly understood.

The Nerve Impulse

The fundamental concepts of neurophysiology, like those of physical optics, were originally based upon relatively simple observations. As in the case of the transmission of light from one place to another, the propagation of activity along a nerve could not be seen directly. It could only be inferred from the relations among other events which were observable, such as the application of a stimulus to a sense organ and the subsequent movement of an animal. It is not surprising that early ideas of nerve conduction were based almost entirely upon the observation of simple immediate responses to stimuli, rather than upon observations of more complex animal behavior. Such reflexes were sufficiently simple so that the stimuli which initiated them could easily be specified. The resultant responses, too, were easily identifiable and followed the stimuli so closely in time that a causal relation between them could be envisaged. (Also, there was a tendency then—even as today—to attribute more complex behavior, where such simple relations between stimuli and responses could not be observed, to the autonomous action of the "soul" or "mind.")

From such crude beginnings, our present-day concept of nerve action has evolved. We now conceive of it as a complex made up of a large number of transient physical and chemical events. Basically, the activity of a single neuron appears to be a pulselike electrochemical process which is actively propagated along the slender axon of the nerve cell, and involves ion exchange between the inner and outer portions of the axon. For example, tracer studies have shown that when the giant axon of the squid is momentarily stimulated to action, there is a rapid inward movement of sodium and an outward movement of potassium, followed by a somewhat slower restoration to the original state of equilibrium [62]. (Basic to all these processes, of course, is a complex metabolic system [18].)

Of all these transient events which together are regarded as nerve action, the changes in electrical potential have been the most significant in the development of the concept of the nerve impulse and in the study of sensory neurophysiology. These electrical events alone clearly reveal that nerve action is composed of discrete propagated impulses. For this reason, we shall consider only the electrical aspects of nerve action in the present discussion of visual neurophysiology. But first let us trace the development of some of our present-day conceptions of the electrical signs of nervous activity.[5]

Animal electricity.   In the late 1700s, Galvani made two important neurophysiological observations. One was his experiment with metals and the other his experiment without metals. The first was a chance discovery. Preparatory to experiments on the effect of atmospheric electricity on contraction of frog muscle, frogs' legs had been suspended from an iron railing by copper hooks. Galvani noted what appeared to

---

[5] Some aspects of the history of the study of electrical signs of nervous activity are treated by Brazier [16]. For general surveys of more recent studies of the electrical aspects of nerve action, see Brink [17] and Lloyd [69].

be spontaneous activity in these preparations and attributed this to "animal electricity" being conducted by the metals. We know today—and Galvani's severest critic, Volta, knew then—that the activity probably resulted from stimulation by the current generated at the junction of dissimilar metals.

But Galvani's second experiment without metals could not be explained in a like manner. This experiment consisted of producing a muscular contraction by placing the nerve of a nerve-muscle preparation in contact with an injured portion of the muscle. Galvani believed the contraction to be due to the flow of animal electricity. Proof of this, however, awaited the development of sensitive instruments for the detection of electrical currents. In 1838, Matteucci, after Oersted's improvements of the galvanometer, was able to show that a difference of potential actually exists between the nerve and the injured portion of the muscle—the so-called "injury potential" or "resting potential." But these were measurements of more or less static conditions. The observation of a change in potential associated with the action of nerve and muscle was yet to come.

The action potential.   In 1843, in the first of his many papers on animal electricity, Du Bois Reymond described a variation in the resting potential of nerve when it was stimulated to action. The outside of the nerve became more negative with respect to the cut end of the nerve. This was an extremely important discovery. It was now possible to measure activity in the stimulated nerve itself, rather than having to infer such activity from the contraction of a muscle following the stimulation of the nerve. Furthermore, it eventually made possible the study of the activity of sensory nerves which are not directly attached to muscle. However, Du Bois Reymond's discovery was not sufficient by itself to establish the fact that the negative variation in potential was an aspect of the propagated nerve action inferred from other observations. As matters stood, observations had shown merely that both the negative variation in potential and the muscle contraction followed close after the stimulus to the nerve. They were not necessarily related in any other way. And it was nearly a quarter of a century before it was shown that they have another property in common. *The inferential nerve action and the negative variation are propagated with the same velocity.*

In the 1840s, however, the rate of propagation of nerve activity was generally regarded as instantaneous and immeasurable, or at least as traveling with the speed of light—which for all practical purposes could be regarded as instantaneous when only a few centimeters of distance were involved. But Helmholtz's brilliant experiment, reported in 1850, showed that the propagation of nervous activity was neither instantaneous nor immeasurable. Rather, it traveled with a finite and surprisingly slow velocity, a velocity so slow that it could be measured with the instruments of a century ago (and with the ingenuity of a Helmholtz).

Helmholtz's successful measurement of the velocity of nerve conduction followed soon after he had turned to physiology for experimental proof of his newly formulated conception of the conservation of energy. The nerve-muscle preparation was well suited for his purposes. The muscle could be almost completely isolated from outside sources of energy and caused to do work and to generate heat merely by stimulating the slender nerve leading to it. While working with such preparations, he conceived his simple method for the determination of the conduction velocity of nerve. Of course, Helmholtz did not observe the velocity of a visible thing moving along the nerve. Using Pouillet's ballistic galvanometer, he measured the time which elapsed between the application of a stimulus to the nerve and the appearance of a muscle contraction. The difference between the stimulus-response times observed using two different points of stimulation some distance apart on the nerve gave the conduction time between these two points. By this method, the time calculated did not include the time taken for the activity to be transmitted across the nerve-muscle junction, nor the time of the muscle contraction; it was the time of nervous conduction alone. Despite the crudity of the instrumentation, in comparison with the complex electronic instruments of today, Helmholtz's measurements are still regarded as essentially correct.

As we pointed out above, no propagated changes along the length of the nerve during conduction were observed. It was not until 1866 that Bernstein, by means of a similar technique, demonstrated that the negative variation in potential was propagated along the nerve with the same velocity as the conduction velocity measured by Helmholtz. The two appeared to be closely related; the wave of negativity sweeping along the nerve came to be regarded as a measurable aspect of the previously purely inferential nerve activity. Such propagated changes in potential in active nerve fibers, the so-called "action potentials," are the principal dependent variables in modern sensory electrophysiology.

It must be remembered, however, that the action potentials observed in these early investigations were not those of single neurons; they were *compound* action potentials recorded from the whole nerve trunk, which is composed of many neurons. The analysis of the exact nature of the contributions of the individual nerve fibers to this compound potential awaited the development of more sensitive instruments for measuring electrical phenomena. Such instruments were not to be available for many years.

In the meantime, two very important observations on the fundamental character of nervous activity were made. In 1899, Gotch and Burch found that a nerve, after being stimulated to action, cannot be excited again immediately, no matter how strong the stimulus. For a brief period, the nerve is absolutely refractory. The refractoriness gradually lessens, however, and the nerve soon regains its original excitability. This evidence of an excitability cycle, coupled with the already abundant evidence that the propagated potential was transient, firmly established the fact that nerve action is not continuous in time—it is pulselike.

Indirect evidence that the activity of the whole nerve is not continuously graded in size was obtained by Lucas in 1909. He found that the contraction of a muscle did not increase in a smoothly graded manner as the stimulus to its nerve was gradually increased. Rather, the contraction increased by discrete steps. From this observation, Lucas inferred that the increasing stimulus excited additional fibers of the nerve trunk, and that, when once excited, they responded maximally. An increase in the stimulus would not affect the muscle until it was sufficient to excite another nerve fiber, the response of which would then result in another steplike increase in the muscle contraction. These and other observations were leading neurophysiologists to the conclusion that nerve action consists of the propagation of discrete pulses of activity, of approximately constant duration and magnitude, in the individual neurons. Let us now turn to the evidence which gave direct and conclusive support to these concepts.

The electrical activity of single neurons. The analysis of the electrical activity of *single* neural elements was made possible by improved instrumentation. The use of the vacuum tube in electrophysiological instruments [29, 34] made possible the amplification and recording of extremely small potential changes in nerve that had gone unnoticed in studies with less sensitive instruments. And the cathode ray oscilloscope [33] provided electrophysiology with an essentially inertia-less recording device which follows quite faithfully the potential changes impressed upon it. (Use of this instrument enabled Erlanger and Gasser [28] to make their classic and important studies of the compound nature of the action potential in nerve.)

Advances in neurophysiology do not depend upon improved instrumentation alone, however. The isolation and study of single neural elements in nerve trunks, while greatly facilitated by vacuum-tube amplification, depended primarily upon a simple and ingenious technique of microdissection developed by Adrian and Bronk [1]. Their measurements of the activity of individual neurons showed directly and conclusively, for the first time, that the action potentials of single neurons are discrete "pulses" of approximately uniform magnitude and duration (see Fig. 6). The magnitudes of these potentials are independent of the strength of stimulus; they depend upon the local state of the axon at the time the action potentials are conducted. If a nerve fiber responds at all, it responds with action potentials of nearly uniform size.

These improved instruments and techniques were not only of considerable significance in the study of nerve action, they also opened up a whole new field of sensory neurophysiology. For, although early studies of the massive discharge of action potentials in whole nerves yielded much important information about the neurophysiology of sensory systems

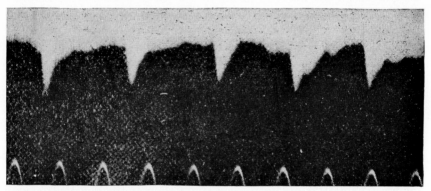

FIG. 6. Records of action potentials in single fibers of the phrenic nerve (rabbit). Vacuum-tube amplification. Records obtained by means of capillary electrometer. Potential changes are signaled by vertical deflection of the shadow. Time marked in .01 sec. Successive transverse cuts were made in the nerve bundle until only a single fiber remained active. These are the first records of single nerve fiber activity obtained by microdissection. From Adrian and Bronk [1].

(e.g., the early work of Adrian and Matthews on the optic nerve [2, 3, 4]), detailed quantitative analysis awaited the development of instruments and techniques for the study of units of activity in single neural elements. Such analyses have provided us with a wealth of knowledge about how information is transmitted from peripheral sense organs to the central nervous system. Let us examine some of these neurophysiological studies of optic nerve activity and see how they are related to certain psychological observations.

The Activity of the Optic Nerve

The responses of single visual elements. By means of an exquisite technique of microdissection, Hartline was able to isolate and study the activity of single optic nerve fibers in both the invertebrate [50] and the vertebrate eye [44]. The use of microelectrodes by Granit and Svaetichin

[41] and also by Wilska [96] soon provided an important additional technique for the study of retinal physiology.[6]

In the human retina the activity from nearly 130 million rods and cones converges on approximately 1 million optic nerve fibers. In the eyes of other vertebrates the degree of convergence is similar. Evidently, the activity in any one of these optic nerve fibers, with the possible exception of those arising in the fovea, is influenced by the activity of a large number of receptors. Because of this, it is difficult to relate the activity in a single optic nerve fiber directly to the properties of the individual retinal receptors. However, in the eye of the horseshoe crab, *Limulus,* activity can only be elicited in an optic nerve fiber by stimulating the particular receptor unit (ommatidium) from which that fiber arises. We shall consider some of the observations on this less complicated invertebrate eye first, for they provide us with information about the properties of single receptor units and serve to illustrate some of the fundamental relations and principles of visual neurophysiology.

In a typical experiment, an eye of the horseshoe crab, *Limulus,* is excised with a few millimeters of the attached optic nerve. A small bundle of fibers is dissected from the nerve and placed upon recording electrodes leading to the input of an amplifying system. The dissection of this bundle is continued until only a regular succession of uniform action potentials is obtained upon stimulation of the eye, that is, until only a single active fiber remains in contact with the electrodes. These uniform potential fluctuations are typical of the activity in sensory nerves. Changes in the stimulation of the receptors from which they arise are signaled only by changes in the frequency of the discharge of action potentials. Ordinarily there are no significant changes in the amplitude of the potential fluctuations. Their occurrence or nonoccurrence and the time intervals between them when they do occur appear to be the *only* variables available for the transmission of information over greatly elongated nerve fibers. (But see Bishop on local graded responses [10].)

One of the most striking relations seen in the study of single optic nerve fibers isolated in this manner is the one between the frequency of

[6] Various aspects of the structure and physiology of the retina have been reviewed in detail or treated extensively in monographs by specialists in each of the several fields concerned. Particularly noteworthy are four books which have appeared recently: Polyak's monumental work on the vertebrate visual system [75], published posthumously; Granit's Silliman lectures on receptor processes [40]; Dartnall's account of the visual pigments [22]; and the translation into English of the second volume of LeGrand's work on physiological optics [68]. See also Granit's earlier treatise on the retina [38]. Important review articles, both old and new, include the reviews of biochemistry of vision by Hecht [58] and, more recently, by Wald [92, 93]; the reviews of the electrophysiology of vision by Hartline [46, 48] and by Riggs [85]; the review of the role of quantum fluctuations in vision by Pirenne [74]; and the review of the physiology of the compound eye by Wulff [98].

discharge of action potentials and the intensity of the stimulus (see Fig. 7). Similarly, in human vision one of the most striking relations is the one between intensity and the brightness perceived. But the response of a single element, like perceived brightness, is not determined solely by the intensity of the immediate stimulus. Equally important are the effects which we interpret as a reflection of a change in the physiological state of the system, such as depletion or restoration of photosensitive materials (see Fig. 8). While it is true that the changes in brightness which result from either stimulus changes or changes in the physiological state of the observer are among the most striking features of vision,

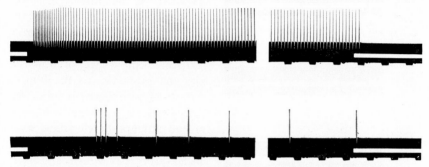

FIG. 7. Oscillograms of action potentials of a single optic nerve fiber of *Limulus*, in response to prolonged illumination of the eye. For the top record the intensity of the stimulating light was ten thousand times that used for the bottom record. The signal of exposure to light blackens out the white line above time marks. Each record interrupted for approximately 7 sec. Time marked in .2 sec. Deflections of the upper black edge are the amplified action potential spikes of a single active fiber in a bundle dissected from the rest of the optic nerve and slung across electrodes connected to the input of a vacuum-tube amplifier. From Hartline, Wagner, and MacNichol [56].

few of the fundamental concepts of visual psychophysics are based upon the measurement of such brightness changes per se. We are forced to turn to other kinds of measures because of the difficulties in making quantitative determinations of the magnitudes of these brightness changes. Psychophysical measurements of spectral sensitivity, thresholds, dark adaptation, etc., are based almost entirely upon determinations of stimulus conditions which produce some constant effect.[7] In neuro-

[7] The nearly identical natures of the methods of visual photometry and of visual psychophysics should be noted. In each case the eye is used as a null instrument. (Strangely enough, one of the shortcomings of visual photometry—the fact that it often confounds the properties of the visual system with the properties of light—does not interfere with its use in measuring the properties of the eye, now that we can measure light by other methods.) The intimate relation between photometry and psychophysics is further evidenced by the fact that "Weber's law" was discovered by the photometrist Bouguer, while making photometric measurements, nearly a century before Weber discovered it.

physiology, however, both the variations in the neural response accompanying stimulus or other changes and stimulus conditions which yield constant neural responses may be measured equally well. At first we shall consider only the latter measure because of its formal similarity to conventional psychophysical measures.

A comparison of the stimulus conditions which yield constant responses in experiments with single optic nerve fibers and in human psychophysical experiments shows that many properties of whole visual systems may be but manifestations of the properties of the sense cells. For there are many similarities between the properties of single receptor units in the relatively simple eye of *Limulus* and the properties of the human eye as revealed by such measures. This becomes particularly evident in the attempt to elucidate some of the fundamental properties of each—properties which are likely to be found in any photosensitive system. For example, Fig. 9 shows the relative energies at various wavelengths required to produce a certain constant effect in the receptor unit and an analogous constant effect in the human eye. We see that both are selective detectors of radiant energy and that under these particular conditions the spectral sensitivity of the human eye is very much like the spectral sensitivity of a single receptor unit in the eye of *Limulus*.

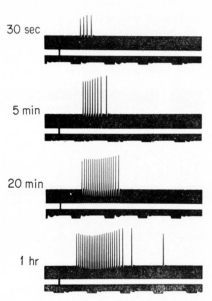

Fɪɢ. 8. Dark adaptation of a single receptor unit. Bursts of impulses in an optic nerve fiber (*Limulus*) in response to a test flash (.01 sec, fixed intensity) thrown upon the eye at the times indicated following an adapting exposure. Signal of flash appears in white line above time marker. Time marked in .2 sec. From Hartline [46].

Such spectral sensitivity curves are, no doubt, determined primarily by the absorption properties of the photopigments in these eyes.

In many photochemical systems, it matters little when the light is absorbed. For example, in the camera a dim illumination with a long exposure may be as effective in producing a latent image on the film as is an intense illumination at a short exposure. This, of course, is an illustration of the reciprocity law of Bunsen and Roscoe, which states that the photochemical effect of a flash of light depends only upon its energy

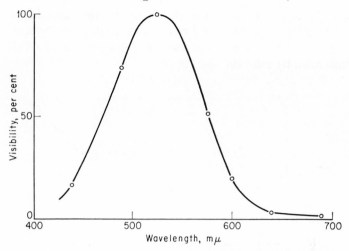

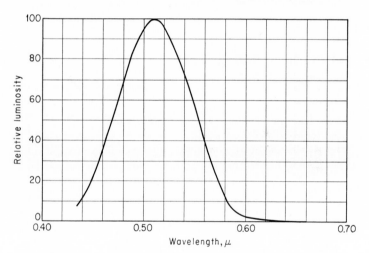

Fɪɢ. 9. Visibility curve for a single receptor unit of the *Limulus* eye (upper graph) and a dim vision luminosity curve for the human eye (lower graph). In each case the reciprocal of the intensity necessary to produce a specified response at each of the various wavelengths was determined and plotted as ordinate. (In both graphs the maximum value obtained was set equal to 100.) Single receptor data obtained by Graham and Hartline [35]; figure from the review by Hartline [46]. Human data from Wright [97]. For similar electrophysiological results obtained from the vertebrate retina see Fig. 26.

(intensity × duration). In both the single receptor and in the human eye, we find that this reciprocal relation between intensity and duration holds up to a critical time; to produce a given constant effect the energy of a flash must be constant (see Fig. 10).

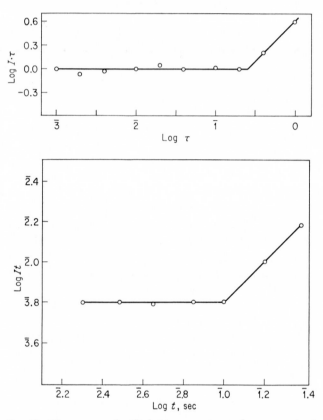

Fig. 10. The energy of a flash necessary to produce a constant response as a function of the duration of the flash. Upper graph, single photoreceptor unit of the *Limulus* eye. Hartline [43]. Lower graph, human eye. From Long [70]. To obtain this result in the human, it is necessary to use small areas of stimulation, as was shown in the early work of Graham and Margaria [36].

At very low energy levels, as in the determination of an absolute threshold, an energy fluctuation of only a few quanta is believed to be significant in determining a visual response. In the human eye (and in the single receptor unit), there is no clearly defined threshold of response. Apparently identical stimuli near threshold may be seen (or may elicit activity in the optic nerve) on one occasion and not on the next. The nature of this uncertainty is such that it has been interpreted as being due to very small fluctuations in the number of quanta contained in the stimulus. Although there are alternative interpretations, there are two lines of evidence which lend strong support to this particular interpretation.

1. Physical measurements establish that the amount of light reaching the photoreceptors in a near-threshold flash is quite small—so small that only a few quanta are involved.

2. Plots of the relative frequencies with which flashes of various intensities are seen (or with which they produce some constant response in the optic nerve preparation) closely resemble the Poisson distributions which give the probability that the flashes will deliver at least a certain small number of quanta (see Fig. 11).

There are many other similarities between the human visual system and single receptor units. For example, the course of the slow recovery of sensitivity in the dark by a single receptor after various conditions of light adaptation is very much like the familiar dark-adaptation curves obtained from the human eye under similar stimulus conditions. (See Fig. 12.) The similarity is greatest under conditions of dim illumination where the duplex nature of the human retina is not manifest. These recovery curves are, undoubtedly, in part a reflection of the breakdown and regeneration of photochemical substances within the individual receptors themselves.

These parallels just illustrated are quite remarkable, especially in view of the facts that (1) they not only involve widely separated species and (2) in the *Limulus* experiments the activity of a single axon arising from a single ommatidium comprising but a few cells is observed, while in the human psychological experiments the response measured is the product of the activity of billions of cells. It is probable that the parallels appear because, in each case, events are observed that are largely determined, or at least limited, by certain fundamental physical and chemical properties common to the individual receptors in both these eyes. But in both cases the experiments have been carefully designed so as to reveal these receptor properties: the illumination was confined to single receptors or to small retinal areas; it was of short duration and was often monochromatic; and its spatial configuration was usually quite simple.

When we turn to the more complex stimulus conditions under which the eye normally functions—i.e., the illumination of large retinal areas, long durations, mixtures of wavelengths, more complex spatial configurations, etc.—these simple dependencies on the physical and chemical properties of the individual receptors are obscured. But as they are obscured, the processes of neural integration in the retina are revealed.

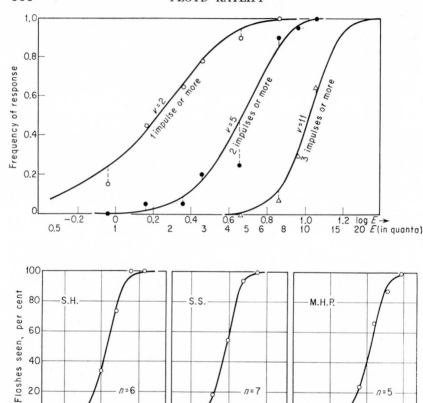

Fɪɢ. 11. Visual thresholds for single receptor unit of *Limulus* (upper graph) and for the human eye (lower graph). The intensity control of the apparatus which delivers the flash of light to the eye is, in each case, set at various fixed low values plotted as the abscissae of each graph. In the single optic nerve fiber experiment, the relative frequencies of occurrence of one or more, two or more, and three or more impulses per flash are plotted as ordinates. In the human psychophysical experiments the percentages of flashes seen are plotted as ordinates. Each curve is from a different subject. In each graph the experimental data are plotted by symbols; the solid lines are theoretical curves calculated on the basis that there are fluctuations in the number of quanta per flash, and that the ordinate gives the probability that a flash contains the number of quanta indicated near each curve. The human curves should be compared with the "two-impulse" and "three-impulse" curves for the single photoreceptor. Single photoreceptor curves from unpublished data obtained by Hartline, Milne, and Wagman [53], for abstract, see [52]; human psychophysical data from Hecht, Schlaer, and Pirenne [60].

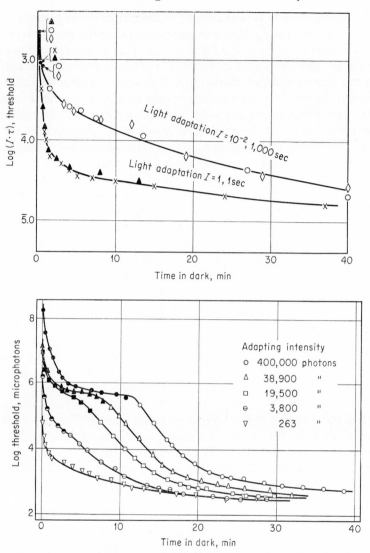

FIG. 12. Dark adaptation following various intensities of light adaptation. Upper graph: single receptor unit of *Limulus;* lower graph: human eye. In each graph the intensity to produce a constant (threshold) response is shown on the ordinate; the time in dark following exposure to light is shown on the abscissa. Single photoreceptor data from Hartline and McDonald [51]; human psychophysical data from Hecht, Haig, and Chase [59].

The integration of neural activity in the retina. The neural mechanisms of the retina are more than mere devices for the passive transmission of information about the temporal and spatial pattern of illumination on the receptor mosaic. Certain significant features are selected from the immense detail there, enhanced at the expense of other less significant features, and only then transmitted to the central nervous system. Just as the artist often seeks to avoid the "danger in becoming engrossed in accuracy at the expense of significance" [94], so does the eye sacrifice accuracy about information of little consequence in order to enhance that which is most significant to the organism.

What are the most significant features of an organism's visual environment? It is quite evident that both wavelength and intensity per se, the important stimulus variables in the studies of photoreceptor properties cited above, are of much less significance in the perception of objects than is certain information derived from relations among various aspects of the pattern of illumination. In the case of the human, this may be illustrated quite easily. The apparent colors of natural objects may be altered radically simply by wearing tinted sunglasses—yet the objects themselves are recognized without the slightest difficulty. Spectral color may be removed altogether—as in black-and-white still photography, movies, or television—and if the artistry is good enough—as in many oriental paintings done entirely in black ink on a white background— the absence of color is hardly noticed. Furthermore, the intensity may be changed over an extremely wide range. For example, a tremendous intensity change of several log units occurs between full noon and twilight, but the perception of objects is not significantly affected. Of course, under most of these different conditions of illumination, the ratios of the intensities remain invariant. But even the intensity relations themselves—as well as their absolute levels—may be radically altered, as in negatives or silhouettes, and many objects thus portrayed can still be recognized without difficulty.

Under all these various conditions, the one invariant visual feature of an object seems to be the loci of transitions from one color to another or from one intensity to another. As long as these loci are indicated, even if only by thin lines, as in a line drawing or a cartoon, the most significant information is retained. Thus these contours and their configurations, whether produced by color or intensity differences or both, and whether the differences are in one relation or another, seem to contain much of the essential information which enables us to recognize objects and to distinguish one object from another.

How is information about such contours abstracted from the information in the retinal image and transmitted by the optic nerve? In addition to the simple and direct signaling of intensity levels on the various receptors in the retinal mosaic (see Fig. 7), the interplay of excitatory and inhibitory influences over the myriad interconnections in the retina serves this purpose. Two important consequences of this integrative activity are (1) the enhancement of differences in neural activity from differently illuminated regions of the retina, and (2) the enhancement of neural responses to temporal changes in intensity. Inhibitory interaction, in particular, plays an important role in both cases.

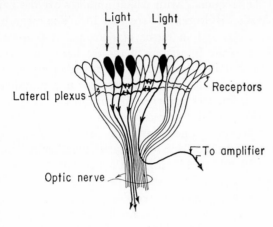

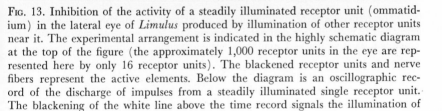

Fig. 13. Inhibition of the activity of a steadily illuminated receptor unit (ommatidium) in the lateral eye of *Limulus* produced by illumination of other receptor units near it. The experimental arrangement is indicated in the highly schematic diagram at the top of the figure (the approximately 1,000 receptor units in the eye are represented here by only 16 receptor units). The blackened receptor units and nerve fibers represent the active elements. Below the diagram is an oscillographic record of the discharge of impulses from a steadily illuminated single receptor unit. The blackening of the white line above the time record signals the illumination of neighboring receptor units. Time in .2 sec. From Ratliff, Miller, and Hartline [81]; see also the earlier report by Hartline, Wagner, and Ratliff [57].

In the lateral eye of *Limulus* the neural interaction is purely inhibitory [49]; nature has kindly provided us with a unique neural system in which we can study inhibitory interaction without the added complication of the excitatory influences found in many retinas. Let us examine it in some detail before considering the neural interaction in the more complex eyes of vertebrates.

The inhibitory influences in the eye of *Limulus* appear to be mediated by an extensive plexus of lateral interconnections immediately behind the receptors [57]. This network is somewhat analogous to the network of lateral interconnections (horizontal cells and amacrine cells) in the verteb́rate eye and may quite properly be called a retina [72, 73, 81]. The inhibitory effect, mediated by this network, may be summarized briefly [57]. The ability of a receptor unit to discharge nerve impulses in an axon arising from it is reduced by illuminating other receptor units in its neighborhood: the threshold to light is raised, the number of impulses discharged in response to a suprathreshold flash of light is diminished, and the frequency with which impulses are discharged during steady illumination is decreased (see Fig. 13). The magnitude of the inhibitory effect—measured in terms of decrease in frequency of impulses—depends upon the frequency of the discharge of impulses from neighboring receptor units, the number of neighboring receptor units responding, and their distance from the receptor unit inhibited.

The inhibitory influences are exerted mutually among neighboring receptor units. When activity is recorded from two optic nerve fibers coming from two receptor units nearby one another, the frequency of discharge of each when they are illuminated together is generally less than when each is illuminated by itself—the magnitude of the inhibition of each one depending linearly on the frequency of response of the other, once a threshold has been reached (see Fig. 14). Thus the frequency of response of each is the resultant of the excitation from its respective light stimulus and the inhibition exerted on it by the other. When several receptors are illuminated simultaneously, their influences on any one of the group are found to combine in a simple additive manner—if the effects of their mutual inhibition, which depends strongly on their spatial separation, are taken into account.[8]

[8] The responses to steady illumination of a group of n receptor units that inhibit one another mutually are described quantitatively by a set of n simultaneous linear equations, each with $n - 1$ inhibitory terms combined by simple addition:

$$r_p = e_p - \sum_{j=1}^{n} K_{p,j}(r_j - r^0_{p,j})$$

$$p = 1, 2, \ldots n$$

The response (r) of a particular receptor unit p is to be measured by the frequency of discharge of impulses in its axon. This response is determined by the excitation (e) supplied by the external stimulus to the receptor diminished by whatever inhibitory influences may be exerted on the receptor by other neighboring receptors. (The excitation of a given receptor is to be measured by its response when it is illuminated by itself, thus lumping together the physical parameters of the stimulus and the characteristics of the photoexcitatory mechanism of the receptor.) In each equation the magnitude of the inhibitory influence is given by the last term, written in accordance with the experimental findings as a simple linear expression. The "threshold" frequency that must be exceeded before a receptor can exert any inhibition is represented by r^0. It and the "inhibitory coefficient," K, in each equation are labeled to identify the direction of the action: $r^0_{p,j}$ is the frequency of receptor j at which it begins to inhibit p; $K_{p,j}$ is the coefficient

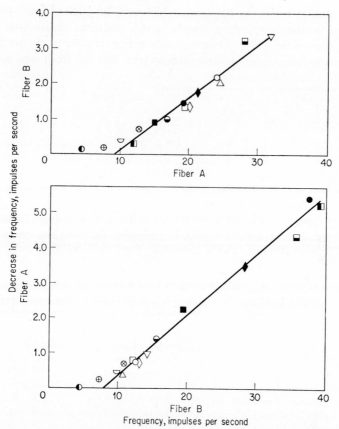

Fig. 14. Graphs showing mutual inhibition of two receptor units 1 mm apart in the eye of *Limulus*. The different points were obtained by using various intensities of illumination on receptor units *A* and *B* in various combinations. The data for points designated by the same symbol were obtained simultaneously. From Hartline and Ratliff [54].

Clearly, the diminution of the inhibitory influences with increasing separation of the receptor units involved introduces a topographic factor that must give to the inhibitory interaction its special significance in retinal function. On the basis of this diminution with distance, one can

---

of the inhibitory action of receptor *j* on receptor *p*. With increasing separation between the elements involved the thresholds of action increase and the inhibitory coefficients decrease. (See Hartline and Ratliff [54] and [55] and Ratliff and Hartline [80] for further details and for restrictions on the range of these equations.) For a theoretical formulation of inhibitory interaction based on psychophysical experiments see Fry [32].

predict, qualitatively, the responses which will be elicited from particular receptor units by various simple spatial patterns of illumination of the receptor mosaic. For example, when additional receptors are illuminated in the vicinity of an interacting pair too far from one receptor

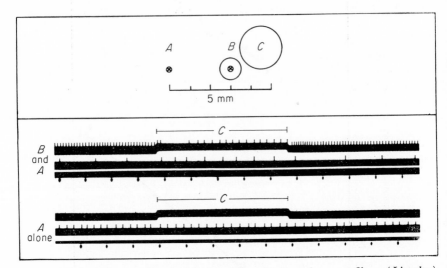

Fig. 15. Oscillograms of the electrical activity of two optic nerve fibers (*Limulus*) showing inhibition and disinhibition. In each record the lower oscillographic trace records the discharge of impulses from receptor unit *A*, stimulated by a small spot of light 0.1 mm in diameter confined to its facet. The upper trace records the activity of receptor unit *B*, located 3 mm from *A*, stimulated by a spot of light 1 mm in diameter, centered on the facet of *B* but also illuminating about ten receptor units in addition to *B*. A third spot of light, *C*, 2 mm in diameter was directed onto a region of the eye centered 1.5 mm from *B* and 4.5 mm from *A*, as shown in the sketch. Exposure of *C* is signaled by the upward offset of the upper trace. Lower record: activity of *A* in the absence of illumination on *B*, showing that illumination of *C* had no appreciable effect under this condition. Upper record: activity of *A* and *B* together, showing (1) inhibition of *A* (compare with lower record) resulting from activity of *B*, and (2) the effect of illumination of *C*, causing a drop in the frequency of discharge of *B* and, concomitantly, an increase in the frequency of discharge of *A*, as *A* was partially released from the inhibition exerted by *B*. Time marked in .2 sec. The black band above the time marks is the signal of illumination of *A* and *B*: thin when *A* was illuminated alone; thick when *A* and *B* were both illuminated. From Hartline and Ratliff [54].

unit to affect it directly, but near enough to the second to inhibit it, the frequency of discharge of the first would be expected to increase as it is partially released from the inhibition exerted on it by the second. This *disinhibition* is what was found (see Fig. 15).

In addition, significant contrast effects may be expected to occur at or near the boundaries of differently illuminated areas. Receptor units near the boundary between a dimly illuminated region and a brightly illuminated region of the retina will be subject to inhibitory influences from other receptor units located within each of these regions—receptor units far from the boundary will be inhibited only by their immediate neighbors in the same field of illumination. Thus a unit within the dimly illuminated region but near this boundary will be inhibited not only by dimly illuminated neighbors, but also by brightly illuminated ones. The total inhibition exerted on it will therefore be greater than that exerted upon other dimly illuminated elements that are farther from the boundary. Consequently, its frequency of response will be less than theirs. Similarly, a unit within (but near the boundary of) the brightly illuminated field will have a higher frequency of discharge than other equally illuminated units located well within the bright field but subject to stronger inhibition since their immediate neighbors are also brightly illuminated. Thus, at the expense of the distortion of information about the absolute intensity of the light falling on each receptor, the information about transitions from one level of illumination to another will be enhanced by the process of mutual inhibition among the receptor units. Experiments bear out these theoretical predictions (see Fig. 16). But we must remember that this is a relatively simple eye. The integration of neural activity in the vertebrate eye is much more complex.

One of the most striking features of the functional organization of the vertebrate retina is its pronounced sensitivity to change. It is primarily a dynamic rather than a static system. Hartline [44] found that, although some of the fibers of the vertebrate optic nerve respond with a steady discharge of impulses to steady illumination of the eye (much like the simpler eye of *Limulus* just described), the majority are completely silent during such illumination. But they respond vigorously with a burst of impulses when the illumination is turned on, and again when it is turned off. Even more surprising are those fibers whose only response is to the cessation of illumination, and even this response is suppressed upon reillumination. (See Fig. 17 for oscillograms of the two latter response types.)

Although these are the responses of single fibers of the optic nerve, they are not simple manifestations of the activity of single receptors. Each fiber can be excited to action by stimulation of any of a large number of receptors with which it has anatomical connections. The dimensions of this receptive field are undoubtedly limited by those anatomical connections. However, the field varies greatly within these limits, depending upon the intensity of the spot used to map it, for the sensitivity is not uniform over the whole field [47]. Furthermore, a given region of the retina does not belong exclusively to any one receptive field; there is considerable overlap. (We do not know whether a given

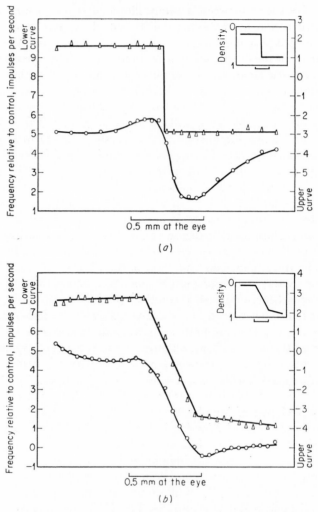

Fig. 16. The discharge of impulses from a single receptor unit in the eye of *Limulus* in response to simple patterns of illumination. A "step" pattern of intensity (*a*) and a gradient between two levels of intensity (*b*) were provided by projecting the demagnified images of photographic plates on the surface of the eye. In each figure the small insert shows the relative density (along the length of the plate used) as measured, prior to the experiment, by means of a photomultiplier tube in the image plane where the eye was to be placed; the density of the plate was uniform across its entire width at every point.

In each experiment a "control" frequency of discharge was determined by illuminating the test receptor alone with a receptor may contribute to the excitation of more than one optic nerve fiber or whether those serving each fiber are merely interspersed with one another.) This picture of the vertebrate retina is further complicated by Kuffler's findings [67] that in the cat the response types are labile; their nature depends in part upon the background illumination.

Even in this great diversity and lability of response, effects have been seen which, it seems to us, can only be ascribed to inhibitory influences. For example, Hartline [45] found that in the eye of the frog, an "off" response elicited in a single fiber by illuminating one group of receptors may be inhibited by illuminating another group of adjacent receptors in the same receptive field. Barlow [7] has observed a similar inhibitory effect using stimuli outside the receptive field. And Kuffler [67] has shown that in the eye of the cat, as a general rule, the peripheral and central areas of receptive fields are functionally antagonistic. And when two such areas within the receptive field interact, the responses of both through their common path become modified [see also 8, 39]. Thus, in the vertebrate eye—as in the invertebrate—we find physiological mechanisms which may enhance information about intensity differences at the expense of information about the absolute levels of intensity.

There are a number of well-known contrast phenomena in human vision, such as Mach's bands (see Fig. 16), brightness contrast (see Fig.

---

small spot of light of constant intensity. The upper curve in each figure (scale of ordinate on the right) shows the frequency of the discharge of impulses from the same test receptor relative to this control frequency, when it *alone* was illuminated by whatever part of the pattern of illumination fell upon it as that pattern was moved across the eye. (The plate was moved in successive small steps so that, in effect, the test receptor "scanned" stepwise across the image.) The light was occluded from all the other receptors so that they would exert no inhibition on the test receptor.

The lower curve in each figure (scale of ordinate on the left) shows the frequency of discharge from the same test receptor relative to the control frequency, when light was not occluded from the other receptors. Many receptors were stimulated simultaneously by whatever portions of the pattern of illumination fell upon them as the pattern was moved across the eye. The effects of their inhibitory influences on the test receptor are evident. (Only the *forms,* not the absolute values of the two curves in each figure are to be compared; the change from one condition to the other could not be made quickly enough to permit a direct comparison.)

Note the resemblance in (*a*) to border contrast and in (*b*) to Mach's bands in human vision. From Ratliff and Hartline [80].

18), and color contrast, which presaged some of the physiological evidence of inhibitory interaction described above. In addition to retinal
inhibitory interaction, to which these effects are usually ascribed, similar interaction probably occurs at higher levels of the visual system as
shown, for example, by Asher's binocular experiments [5]. In all of
these phenomena, the information about *differences* in retinal illumina-

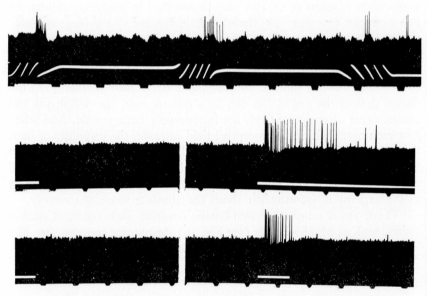

Fɪɢ. 17. Records of impulses discharged in single optic nerve fibers of the vertebrate eye (frog). Upper record: responses to movement of a small spot of light on
the retina. The diagonal white lines signal the movement, each being equivalent to
7 μ on the retina. This fiber was one which responded to both the onset and
cessation of illumination. Lower records: discharge of impulses in a nerve fiber
which responded to the cessation of illumination. In these two records the illumination is signalled by the blackening of the white line above the time marks. The
full response of this fiber to cessation of illumination (upper record of the pair)
is abruptly cut short by reillumination (lower record of the pair). In all records
time is marked in .2 sec. Records from Hartline [46].

tion is preserved and enhanced at the expense of the accuracy of the
less significant information about the absolute values of the intensity and
wavelength of that illumination. Indeed, many of these effects have
long been used by artists for this very purpose. Some of Seurat's drawings and paintings, in particular, contain fine examples of the accentua-
tion of contours by means of simultaneous brightness contrast and color
contrast [84].

   In the vertebrate eye, information about contours can also be transmitted and accentuated by those systems which respond vigorously to

changes in the level of illumination. It can be seen that they would be stimulated by the image of an object moving in the visual field, or by similar changes resulting when the eye scans a visual scene. In the human, such scanning occurs continually on a small scale, for our eyes are never completely immobile—even when we attempt to fixate steadily on a stationary object [83]. Such motions maintain the perception of contours. This was shown by experiments in which an optical system was arranged so as to counteract these movements [25, 86] and provide a stationary image on the retina (see Fig. 19).

In all such experiments, the contours and discontinuities in the stabilized retinal image gradually faded from view and the visual field where the image had appeared took on a homogeneous appearance— even though the image was physically unchanged on the retina. The results are not artifacts due to the necessary attachments to the eye, for doubling the normal motions of the retinal image by inserting a Dove prism in the viewing path maintains vision [86] and moving or flickering the stabilized image by various means causes it to reappear [19, 66]. Furthermore, stationary retinal images produced without attachments to the eye [24, 77] also gradually disappear from view. It seems probable that such disappearances of stabilized

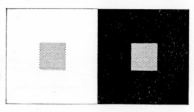

Fig. 18. Simultaneous brightness contrast. The two gray squares in this figure are identical, although the one on the black background appears much brighter than the one on the light background. An inhibitory mechanism similar to that described in the text may underly this and other similar contrast phenomena. Compare with Figs. 13, 16, and 22.

images are due to the inactivation of neural mechanisms (which respond to changes in illumination) rather than to photochemical adaptation, for the appearance of a moving image—superimposed upon the same part of the retina as a stationary image which has disappeared—is often unchanged.

The complex "on-off" and "off" responses observed in neurons of the vertebrate retina have been ascribed by Hartline [44] and Granit [38] to the excitatory and inhibitory interactions of retinal structures interposed between these neurons and the photoreceptors, rather than to special properties of the photoreceptors themselves. The reasons for this interpretation are many. As mentioned above, the principal ones are that (1) these transient responses elicited by illuminating one group of receptors may be greatly modified by illuminating other receptors nearby [45, 7]; and (2) depending on the locus of illumination and the level of background illumination [67] and state of adaptation [8], a particular fiber may exhibit a variety of responses. Furthermore, it has been possible to synthesize on-off and off responses in individual fibers of the *Limulus* optic nerve by pitting excitatory and inhibitory influences against one another [82]. These latter experiments lend additional support to the view that on-off and off responses are the result of the interplay of excitatory and inhibitory influences by showing that the experimental

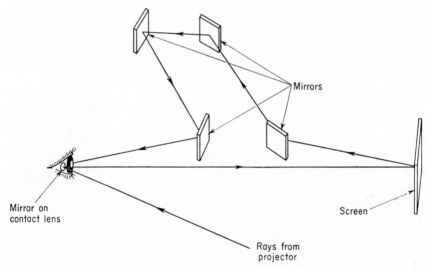

FIG. 19. Diagram of a method for providing a motionless image on the retina even though the eye makes small motions. The mirror on the contact lens fitted to the eye is used as a part of a projection system. An image projected on a screen by this system is viewed by a path which is twice as long as the path from the eye mirror to the screen. This compensates for the fact that a beam of light reflected from a mirror turns through twice the angle of rotation of the mirror; thus the retinal image is stationary with respect to the retina. Images viewed in this manner gradually lose contrast and eventually fade out altogether. These results lend support to the idea that motion of the retinal image serves to activate retinal elements which respond principally to changes in intensity (see Fig. 17). Redrawn after Riggs, Ratliff, Cornsweet, and Cornsweet [86]. See also [25, 63, 76, 90].

manipulation of these influences can, indeed, yield such transient responses. It would appear that inhibitory interaction is an essential component of both the static retinal mechanisms which serve to enhance information about *spatial* differences in the retinal image and the dynamic mechanisms which serve to enhance information about *temporal* changes.

It is evident, from these few examples, that the optic nerve—even in some relatively simple eyes—does not consist of a collection of "private lines" to transmit information about the radiant energy falling on each receptor. The pattern of activity in the optic nerve is by no means a direct copy of the pattern of radiant energy incident on the retina. Certain kinds of information about the stimulus pattern are enhanced at the expense of other kinds of less significant information.

As we have seen, some of the consequences of such integrative processes in the retina are clearly manifested in our visual experience. Indeed, every mechanism involved in the retinal process of photoreception and in the generation, transmission, and integration of optic nerve activity leaves some imprint of its character on vision. While some of these mechanisms play a greater and some a lesser role, a full understanding of the dependence of vision on retinal processes is not to be found in any one of them, but in the combined contributions of all.

However, even though we can relate many of these processes to certain aspects of visual experience, we cannot hope to find, in the retina and optic nerve, similar physiological correlates with *all* visual experience. For what we see is not determined solely by the immediate retinal events. The information transmitted to the central nervous system by the optic nerve is further integrated with information from other sense organs and with "stored" information obtained previously.

SOME BEHAVIORAL ASPECTS OF VISION

It has been convenient in the preceding sections to speak of seeing, sense experience, etc., in a common-sense manner. The use of such familiar terms from the vernacular makes for ease of discourse. But when discussing these phenomena as the subject matter of a science, it is important to remember that our ordinary language is an imprecise social instrument and that its familiarity and superb utility may sometimes lead to carelessness in its scientific use. Indeed, many of the difficulties of earlier introspective psychology arose because investigators were not always careful to dissociate, in so far as possible, problems of language and problems of sensation. In studies of the senses of lower animals, the true nature of sensory phenomena is less apt to be obscured by language. If anything, the lack of a common language for communication between experimenter and subject brings the problems into sharper focus and leads to a better understanding of them.

Let us examine, first of all, some fundamental assumptions and concepts in the science of animal behavior. We shall then turn to a consideration of a few specific examples of the application of contemporary behavioral science to the study of vision and the relation of these examples to some of the physiological observations discussed earlier.

The Science of Behavior

The objective science of behavior has a rather curious history. In brief, it began as a subsidiary of biological science, became more or less independent, and finally merged with—and almost completely swallowed up—the field of scientific psychology. Treatments of these and other historical aspects of psychology are readily available elsewhere.[9] For this reason, we shall confine our remarks to a few comments on the logical necessity called behaviorism.

The behavioristic approach to psychology has not been foisted upon us by behaviorism, by operationism, or by any other particular school of thought or ism. It is the subject matter of psychology itself which dictates this point of view. And this has been recognized again and again by different investigators with different backgrounds and with different interests and goals. Let us illustrate this with five short examples.

Almost two and a half centuries ago Berkeley wrote in *An essay towards a new theory of vision:*

It is evident that, when the mind perceives any idea not immediately and of itself, it must be by the means of some other idea. Thus, for instance, the passions which are in the mind of another are of themselves to me invisible. I may nevertheless perceive them by sight; though not immediately, yet by means of the colours they produce in the countenance. We often see shame or fear in the looks of a man, by perceiving the changes of his countenance to red or pale.

One hundred years ago the Russian neurophysiologist I. M. Sechenov wrote in his *Reflexes of the brain:*[10]

All the endless diversity of the external manifestations of the brain can finally be regarded as one phenomenon—that of muscular movement. Be it a child laughing at the sight of a toy, or Garibaldi smiling when he is prosecuted for his excessive love of his fatherland, a girl trembling at the first thought of love, or Newton enunciating universal laws and writing them on paper—everywhere the final manifestation is muscular movement.

Remember, this was in 1863. The temper of the times then is well illustrated by the fact that the St. Petersburg Censorial Committee condemned the book and banned its sale because of the materialistic point

---

[9] There are no comprehensive studies devoted exclusively to the origin and development of present-day behavior science; however, a considerable amount of relevant material may be found in Boring's *History of experimental psychology* [14].

[10] Quoted in Babkin's biography of Pavlov [6]. Copyright 1949 by the University of Chicago. Reproduced by permission of the University of Chicago Press.

of view. The committee even recommended that court action be taken against Sechenov. Discussing psychology Sechenov said:[11]

The new psychology will have as its basis, in place of the philosophizings whispered by the deceitful voice of consciousness, positive facts or points of departure that can be verified at any time by experiment. . . .

In England, about twenty years later, one of Darwin's followers, G. J. Romanes, wrote in *Animal intelligence:*

In our objective analysis of other or foreign minds . . . all our knowledge of their operations is derived, as it were, through the medium of ambassadors—these ambassadors being the activities of the organism. . . .

He also noted that:

When viewed from their objective side the most elaborate powers of reasoning, or the most comprehensive of judgments is seen to be nothing more than a case of exceedingly refined discrimination . . . between stimuli of an enormously complex character—while the most far-sighted of actions, adjusted to meet the most remote contingencies of stimulation, is nothing more than a neuromuscular adjustment to the circumstances presented by the environment.

And here, written some thirty years later, is a more familiar quotation from John B. Watson, who is generally given credit for the founding of a formal school of behaviorism in America with his publication of a short article entitled *Psychology as the behaviorist views it* [95]:

Psychology as the behaviorist views it is a purely objective branch of natural science. Its theoretical goal is the prediction and control of behavior. Introspection forms no essential part of its methods nor is the scientific value of its data dependent upon the readiness with which they lend themselves to interpretation in terms of consciousness.

This point of view has been accepted by many who would not regard themselves, or be regarded by anyone else, as behaviorists. This quotation from Frenkel-Brunswick [30], who recently wrote in defense of some current psychoanalytic concepts, is a good example of this fact:

There is no alternative but to be behavioristic in any psychological endeavor; neither the so-called "subjective phantasies" in which psychoanalysis is interested, nor "introspective" events of any kind in others, can be constituted except from the manifest physical observation of organisms.

The simple fact is that there has never been a real choice in the matter, nor is there yet. Our only source of knowledge about other minds is in the overt behavior or in the physiological processes of those

[11] Quoted in Frolov's biography of Pavlov [31]. Copyright 1937 by Kegan Paul, Trench, Trubner and Co., Ltd. Reproduced by permission of Routledge and Kegan Paul, Ltd.

organisms in which the mental processes are said to occur. And in this one restricted sense, behaviorism amounts to nothing more than mere acceptance of the inevitable.

In a larger sense, however, the behavioristic movement in psychology has amounted to a great deal more than this. Indeed, the important feature of this movement was not behaviorism per se—it was, instead, the introduction and widespread use of a productive methodology. And this was accomplished by means of a slow evolutionary process rather than by a sudden revolution. If one examines the work of various zoologists, physiologists, and psychologists such as Morgan, Loeb, Lubbock, Jennings, Thorndike, Sechenov, Pavlov, Yerkes, and Watson, it is seen that there was a gradual development over a period of several decades of rigorous experimental methods for the study of animal behavior. Wherever appropriate, existing methods and concepts from other natural sciences were freely applied to studies of behavior. Whenever necessary, new experimental methods were developed and new concepts formulated. And it is our view that it was the introduction and application of these experimental methods—rather than the innumerable polemics about what was or was not the proper subject matter of psychology—which was responsible for the considerable progress made in the study of human and animal behavior during the past century.

Some Fundamental Behavioral Concepts

In his essay *Is Shakespeare dead?*, Mark Twain described the reconstruction of a magnificent brontosaur skeleton for display in a museum. Only nine of the original bones were available, but with the aid of 600 barrels of plaster of Paris—and a great deal of imagination—this apparently serious limitation was easily overcome. So it is, sometimes, with theoretical formulations in science. Fact and fancy are combined to form a truly magnificent creation in which the uninitiated may find it difficult to distinguish real bone from plaster of Paris. For this reason, we would like to present here—as in the preceding sections—a brief nontheoretical account of some fundamental concepts. It will be our principal aim to show how various significant aspects of behavior may be measured and expressed in quantitative terms. This elementary account, we believe, may provide a sufficient background for those unfamiliar with behavioral studies to understand fully the experiments on vision to be described later.[12]

[12] For a general introduction to the science of behavior, see Keller and Schoenfeld [65]. An older but somewhat more detailed account of learning and conditioning is the survey by Hilgard and Marquis [61]. For an example of a recent systematic account of modern behavior science, see Spence [88].

The response. Because it is complex and almost continuous, the behavior of an animal is exceedingly difficult to describe in its entirety. To make the task easier, and to provide a descriptive system amenable to a quantitative treatment, we resort to various arbitrary schemes for analyzing the behavior into simple units. The units are commonly designated as *responses*. Most often a response is defined as that behavior which brings the animal to a certain point in space, or which results in some specified movement of an object. For example, entrance into an alley of a maze, the movement of a lever, picking up a certain object, etc., may each be called a response. Responses are seldom, if ever, defined by an exact description of the movements involved. (In fact, two entirely different patterns of muscular movement which have the same consequences may often be treated as identical response units.) Furthermore, even though the word "response" connotes the existence of a stimulus, responses are usually defined independently of the stimulus conditions which elicit them. Indeed, in many cases the stimulus is unknown.

The quantitative description of responses often superficially resembles the description of nerve activity outlined in the preceding section. Common measures include latency of response, frequency, temporal patterning, relative numbers of responses in different situations, etc. Occasionally, some aspect of the magnitude or vigor of individual responses is measured. All such measures are physicalistic.

Drive and reinforcement. Animals are seldom completely inactive. Usually there is a great deal of behavior to observe, whether one deliberately does something to activate the animal or not. But in most experiments it is desirable to bring the animal's behavior under experimental control and to elicit a particular pattern of behavior. The old adage "You can lead a horse to water, but you can't make him drink," is not to be interpreted literally. In fact, after a few hours of deprivation, he will not only drink—if given free rein—he will lead you to the water hole. Similarly, in many experiments deprivation of materials essential for the bodily maintenance of the animal is the key to control of his behavior. The animal deprived of food or water usually becomes quite active and we say that a *drive* has been established. (Of course, other kinds of deprivation may be equally effective, or may become so under proper conditions.) Actually, however, concepts of drive and motivation are rather complex, and exact measurement of the magnitude of a drive in any particular case is not a simple matter. But in the sensory experiments to be discussed here—where drive itself is not the subject of investigation—simple measures, such as hours of deprivation or loss of body weight due to deprivation, are adequate to ensure that a nearly constant drive level is being maintained.

Once such a drive has been established, the synthesis of a behavior pattern may then be accomplished by *reinforcement* of certain responses. Simply stated, reinforcement consists of giving the animal some (usually a small amount) of the food or water which has been withheld from him whenever he makes the desired response. Obvious quantitative measures of significance include the time of reinforcement relative to the time of occurrence of the response, time between successive reinforcements, and amount of reinforcement. These reinforced responses are, in general, retained in the animal's repertory, and those which are not reinforced are either lost or overshadowed by the others.

Fortunately, animals in a state of deprivation are often so active that the desired response (e.g., reaching the goal box in a maze) may appear with little coaxing. If not, responses are usually sufficiently variable so that, by reinforcing those which most closely approximate the one desired, the behavior may gradually be shaped into whatever form one chooses. Once the desired behavior pattern has been established, it may then be maintained, extinguished, and reestablished at will by proper control of deprivation and reinforcement.

The stimulus control of behavior. It is quite easy to bring an animal's behavior under control of stimuli other than those found in the reinforcing agent itself. This is accomplished by arranging conditions so that an appropriate response in the presence of these stimuli leads to reinforcement. Suppose, for example, that two alleys of a maze are differently illuminated, and food is placed only at the end of the darker alley. Eventually, animals placed in the maze may come to choose consistently the dark alley, even when the positions of the alleys are randomly interchanged. Similarly, in situations where a brief response is repeated again and again, as in operant conditioning, the responses might be reinforced only when they occur in the presence of a certain stimulus. Under such conditions, the responses may eventually occur with much higher relative frequency in the presence of the stimulus than in its absence. It is such differential responding in the presence of various stimuli which leads us to say that an animal "sees" a light, or "hears" a sound, or otherwise senses a stimulus. Indeed, the very word "stimulus" connotes the existence of a response, and some purists even insist that stimuli can only be defined in terms of the behavioral responses which they elicit. But the usual common-sense approach is to apply the term at first rather loosely to any and all objects and events in the animal's environment, and later, on the basis of specific behavioral observations, to classify stimuli further according to their observed effectiveness in the control of behavior. For example, we may describe visual stimuli quite rigorously in purely physical terms prior to any behavioral observations and then, on the basis of such observations, further denote these stimuli as subthreshold, suprathreshold, etc.[13] The words used are less important than a clear understanding of their defining operations.

In a very general way, this brief account shows how a pattern of behavior may be established and maintained by the technique of deprivation and reinforcement, and how this behavior may then be utilized as a quantitative dependent variable in the study of the animal's sensory processes. Let us now examine in some detail a few specific examples of the more rigorous application of such techniques to the study of vision.

Some Behavioral Studies of Visual Processes

Human psychological studies in vision are relatively simple in principle. A subject is instructed to observe a visual stimulus and report on what he sees. Usually the observation is limited to one or two aspects of the stimulus, and a simple "yes" or "no" answer suffices for the report. From these reports, and from physical measures of the stimuli which elicit them, the experimenter can ascertain the smallest detectable stimulus value (absolute threshold), the smallest detectable stimulus change (difference threshold), values of stimuli which appear equal (points of subjective equality), and other similar information. Simple verbal instructions and verbal reports usually suffice in such experiments. Indeed, the verbal instructions to the subject on where to sit, what to look at, how to report, when and how much he will be paid, etc., are so efficient and so easy to give that we tend to forget what a complex process the acquisition of a common language by the experimenter and subject has been and how important this language is in such an experiment. This is forcibly brought to our attention, however, as soon as we undertake similar experiments with infrahuman subjects.

We must give instructions to the animal just as we do to the human, but without recourse to a common language. A method of animal psychophysics, developed by Ratliff and Blough for the study of visual processes [79] and which was subsequently modified and improved by Blough [11, 12, 13], retains the basic simplicity of human psychophysics. Instructions are given the animal by means of differential reinforcement of two responses under varying stimulus conditions, and the animal's responses constitute the report.

The method utilizes certain techniques developed by B. F. Skinner and his co-workers in the study of animal behavior [87]. These particular

---

[13] In the studies of the fluctuations of visual responses attributed to quantum fluctuations in the stimulus, one finds a curious compound of two kinds of stimulus definition. Physical measures establish only that the number of quanta reaching the retina is small and variable; the specification of the average number which actually stimulate the eye is based on the responses of the subject or the responses of the physiological preparation, as the case may be (see Fig. 11).

techniques were chosen because they permit the use of responses which can be clearly specified, rapidly repeated, and elicited at a high rate with infrequent reinforcements. In the experiments to be described, a pigeon is trained to peck on either of two adjacent microswitches mounted in the wall of the animal chamber. These responses, by means of a simple switching circuit, automatically control a varying visual stimulus in a manner similar to Békésy's automatic method of human audiometry [9] and Craik and Vernon's automatic method of human visual psychophysics [20]. The animal's responses are reinforced in such a way that, when a discrimination has been learned, they restrict the stimulus to a narrow range of values. Such an arrangement results in a self-regulating system: the animal's responses control the stimulus, which in turn controls the animal's responses. The state of equilibrium which is reached may be utilized as a measure of the animal's sensory capacities, for they are the principal unknown components of the whole arrangement.

Brightness discrimination. An adaptation of this general method was made for the study of visual processes in the pigeon (see Fig. 20). In this experiment, one response closed switch A and decreased the intensity of a spot of light, the other response closed switch B and increased the intensity. The schedule of reinforcement was adjusted to keep the combined frequency of occurrence of the two responses at a constant high level. For this purpose, a variable-interval schedule was used. Only a small percentage of the responses was reinforced, and the time interval between these reinforcements was varied at random between certain limits. About equal numbers of reinforcements were given for each of the two responses. The effect of such a schedule is a uniform rate of responding over periods of many hours. (This has the advantage that continuous measurements may be made. Also, variations in the uniform rate indicate the presence of extraneous stimuli, apparatus failure, and other difficulties.)

Once a uniform rate of responding was reached, reinforcement was made contingent upon the intensity of the variable stimulus. Response A was reinforced only when the intensity of this variable stimulus was *greater* than that of a comparison stimulus set at some fixed intensity. And response B was reinforced only when the intensity of this variable stimulus was *less* than the comparison stimulus. Such differential reinforcement soon brings about differential responding to stimulus intensities below and above the intensity of the comparison stimulus. After sufficient training, an animal would be expected to give response A at practically all stimulus intensities greater than the comparison stimulus, and response B at practically all intensities less than the comparison stimulus, since these are the only responses which are directly reinforced.

If the discrimination were perfect, the variable stimulus would never differ from the comparison stimulus. An infinitesimal increase would result in response *A*, which would decrease the intensity of the variable stimulus; as soon as it dropped below the comparison stimulus by an infinitesimal amount, response *B* would be made and the intensity of the stimulus would be increased, and so on. (Various techniques, which need

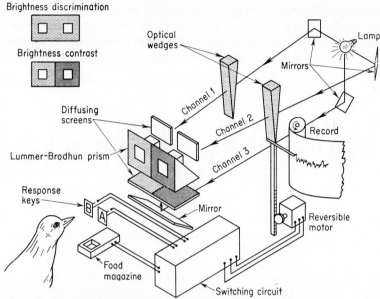

FIG. 20. Schema of apparatus for measuring brightness discrimination in the pigeon. Light from three illuminated screens are combined, by means of a double Lummer-Brodhun prism, to form patterns of illumination such as those shown in the insert. Channel 1 provides a spot of light of some fixed intensity. Channel 2 provides a similar spot whose intensity can be adjusted by the pigeon by pecking on the two response keys *A* and *B*. Channel 3, entering the prism from below, provides a surround of any desired pattern and intensity. To simplify the sketch a number of optical components have been omitted [78, 79].

not be described here, were employed to prevent indiscriminate response alternation.)

Of course, a real animal never makes a perfect discrimination. Figure 21 shows the actual performance of a pigeon while being trained to "match" two spots of light in intensity by this procedure. Responding is more or less random at first. Then the effects of the differential reinforcement begin to appear. The fluctuations of the variable stimulus become smaller, and they depart less and less from the comparison stimulus. However, a stable performance is reached, with a considerable

amount of fluctuation still occurring about the comparison stimulus—
even though the rate of the stimulus change is relatively slow with respect
to the rate of the animal's responses. The minimum amplitude of
these oscillations may be regarded as a measure of the difference
threshold, for within this range the responses are not significantly controlled by the stimulus. The mean value of the stimulus oscillations is the
point at which responses A and B are equally probable; it is analogous
to the point of subjective equality in human psychophysics.

It is likely that the two responses are never determined by the
stimulus alone. There are many factors which result in nonindependence of successive responses. For example, if several reinforcements

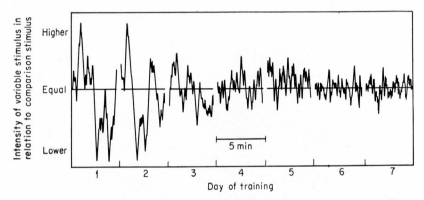

Fig. 21. The acquisition of an intensity discrimination in the pigeon. Five-
minute samples of records obtained during 1-hr sessions on each of 7 successive
days. See text for method; note that it is similar to the null method of visual
photometry illustrated in Fig. 5 [78, 79].

in a row by chance followed the same response, the relative probability
of that response might be raised temporarily. Such occurrences might be
expected to increase the extent of stimulus fluctuations. However, they
should not affect the mean value in the long run, for most variables
such as deprivation and schedule of reinforcement probably affect
both responses about equally. Such shortcomings of this method have
their parallels in human psychophysics as has been shown by Verplanck,
Collier, and Cotton [91].

Simultaneous brightness contrast. Pigeons were trained on the
simple intensity discrimination described above until it appeared that
there would be no further improvement in their performance. Then
each bird was tested during brief periods in which a bright surround
was placed around one of the stimulus spots, while the area around the
other spot remained dark. No reinforcement was given during the test
periods. Such measurements could be made only a few times because the

birds soon learned that no reinforcement accompanied the presentation of the surround and stopped responding whenever it appeared.

In human vision, such a pattern of illumination makes the spot with the bright surround appear much darker than the comparison spot, as was illustrated in Fig. 18. Evidently the effect is similar in the case of the pigeon, for it immediately readjusts the intensity of the variable spot (see Fig. 22) much as a human subject does using the same apparatus. Such contrast effects, in both the human and the pigeon, bear a striking formal similarity to the neural inhibitory effects described in the preceding section.

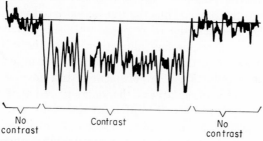

No contrast   Contrast   No contrast

FIG. 22. Simultaneous contrast in the pigeon. The pigeon "matched" two spots of light in intensity as in Fig. 21. Then a bright surround was placed around one of them, resulting in a stimulus configuration similar to that shown in Fig. 18. Under these conditions, the intensity of the variable stimulus was adjusted to a lower intensity by the pigeon. When the bright surround was removed, the intensity of the variable spot was increased until it physically matched the comparison stimulus. These results are interpretable in terms of a neural inhibitory mechanism such as the one found in *Limulus* (see Fig. 13) [78, 79].

It is evident that in any complex discrimination a great deal of care must be taken to ensure that irrelevant properties of the stimulus and irrelevant aspects of the animal's behavior do not significantly affect the results. And to be absolutely certain that the contrast effect described above is not spurious, a number of factors will eventually have to be explored systematically. In particular, the above method—as applied in the contrast experiment—encounters a number of problems which result mainly from the fact that the animals are trained under one set of stimulus conditions and tested under another. We shall consider three related categories of such problems: (1) extinction of the response in the test situation; (2) effects of the novelty of the test stimulus; and (3) difficulty in determining the effective stimulus variables.

In many psychophysical experiments, it is not possible to specify in advance what ideal limit the discrimination should approach. Such was the case in the contrast experiment. It is the subject, not the experimenter, who must decide (on the basis of his previous training) which of the two responses to make. Reinforcement cannot be made contingent upon the physical intensities of the stimuli as they can in the simple matching of the two stimuli required in the training period. The usual solution to this problem, and the one used in this experiment, is to develop some discrimination by reinforcing proper responses during the training period, and then to make measurements without reinforcement during the test periods—trusting that the discrimination will carry over from one to the other. Thus the test period is actually an extinction period, and the animal's rate of response gradually decreases—in fact, the animal may stop responding altogether. Thus the advantages of a steady rate are lost, and the time available for measurements is limited.

The abrupt introduction of a conspicuous and novel stimulus into a routine situation also often affects the ongoing response pattern. The effect varies considerably with different situations and animals; in the pigeon "freezing" is one typical reaction to such radical changes. Smaller changes may produce cooing, wing flapping, and pacing about the cage—any one of which will result in a slower rate of responding. This effect was observed in the contrast experiment. The introduction of the bright surround around one of the spots caused the rate of responding on both switches to decrease somewhat. It is evident in Fig. 22 that this decrease in response rate interfered with accurate measurement of the surround's effect. The variability of the adjustment was much greater, primarily because of this decrease in the rate of responding. However, the mean value of the adjustment was approximately constant throughout the test period, even though the rate of responding first decreased and then gradually increased later on.

A human subject may be told to pay attention to any desired aspect of a stimulus situation and to respond to that aspect alone. An animal is told to "pay attention" by means of differential reinforcement. But it must be assumed that the animal may discriminate any environmental change that is differentially related to reinforcement. Unfortunately, the experimenter may have one stimulus variable in mind when he sets up reinforcement contingencies, and, though the animal may seem to learn on the basis of this variable, subsequent tests may show it to be responding to some other aspect of the situation. In the present experiments, for example, the intensity of one stimulus spot relative to its background brightness (rather than the relative intensities of the two spots) could have been a controlling relation. But such a spurious discrimination based on the relationship of spot to background can be broken by changing the background over a wide range of intensities during training, so that reinforcement will be contingent only on the relative intensities of the two spots. Techniques of this sort must always be devised when dealing with complex stimuli in order to ensure that the proper stimulus variables are controlling the behavior.

The absolute visual threshold. Some experiments by Blough [11, 12], measuring the absolute threshold of vision, exemplify practical solutions to all three types of problems just discussed. They avoid a novel testing situation, they make possible continuous reinforcement, and they reduce stimulus variables to a minimum.

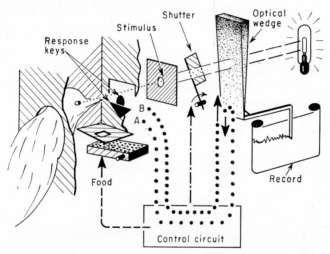

Fɪɢ. 23. Schema of apparatus for measuring absolute visual threshold in the pigeon. See text. From Blough [13].

Only the threshold is measured, but the measurements are made under conditions so that they map out more complex functions, such as dark-adaptation curves and spectral-sensitivity curves. A single stimulus varying in intensity is used, and the animal is required to make two distinct responses to it (see Fig. 23). Response *A* causes the intensity of the stimulus to decrease; response *B* causes it to increase. Of course, the threshold intensity is not known in advance, and reinforcement cannot be made directly contingent upon any finite value of the stimulus, as it was in training an animal to match two stimuli. But Blough has solved this problem in a simple, yet very effective, way. Only response *B* is directly reinforced, and this only when the stimulus is occasionally occluded by a shutter. Since the animal cannot discriminate between the stimulus which is physically occluded from view and the one which is

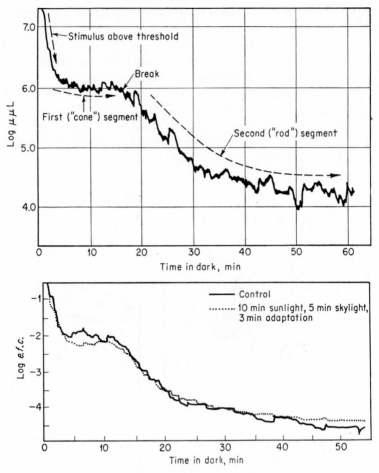

FIG. 24 Dark adaptation in the pigeon (upper graph) and in the human (lower graph). The behavioral measure of dark adaptation in the pigeon was obtained by means of the techniques outlined in the text. Data from Blough [11]. The human data were obtained earlier by Craik and Vernon [20], whose method also utilized a continuously varying stimulus. Note the similarity of the results, with regard to both the general form and the variability of the two curves. Compare also with the human and single nerve fiber curves in Fig. 12.

merely below his threshold of vision, he makes response B in both cases, that is, whenever the stimulus disappears for any reason. The end result of this arrangement is that the pigeon's responses keep the stimulus oscillating about his absolute threshold [9, 20]. Indeed, the inability to discriminate between a dim light and total darkness is precisely what is meant by the term *below threshold* [13].

Dark adaptation. If a schedule of reinforcement which generates a fairly steady rate of responding is used, the temporal course of threshold changes—as in dark adaptation—can be followed in essentially the same manner as in Craik and Vernon's study of human dark adaptation [20]. The results of such experiments are shown in Figs. 24 and 25. Compare these with the electrophysiological results and also with the human psychophysical results illustrated in Fig. 12.

Spectral sensitivity. Blough has measured the spectral sensitivity of the pigeon by means of a slight modification of the above method [12]. Dark-adaptation curves were obtained using various narrow bands of wavelengths. Spectral-sensitivity curves were then obtained from these

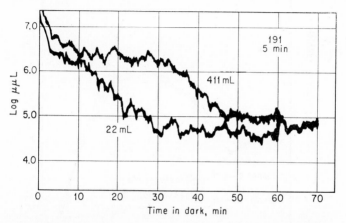

Fig. 25. Behavioral measures of dark adaptation in the pigeon following two different intensities of light adaptation. Curves obtained by means of the techniques outlined in the text. From Blough [11]. Compare with Fig. 12.

data by plotting the threshold values from initial and final portions of the curves. These yielded, respectively, photopic and scotopic luminosity functions. The results are similar to those obtained in electrophysiological investigations in which the responses of retinal ganglion cells in the eye of the pigeon were recorded (see Fig. 26). Compare the scotopic portions of these results with the spectral sensitivity of the human and with that of a single visual receptor element shown in Fig. 9. The parallels are striking.

It is important to note that the observations in the animal experiments we have described do not differ, in principle, from those in human psychophysical experiments. In each case the fundamental observations are of stimuli, and the responses of the subject—human or infrahuman —to these stimuli. (However, we must not overlook the great differences between the methods of controlling the subject's behavior in the two situations.) Similarly, our statements in our ordinary language—like those in our scientific language—about sense experiences, consciousness, etc., that take place in others are statements about what people *do* in

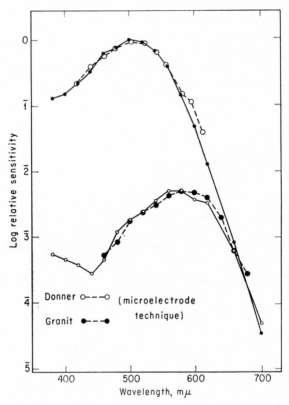

Fig. 26. Scotopic and photopic spectral sensitivity in the pigeon. The behavioral curves (solid lines) are in correct relation to one another. The microelectrode curves (dashed lines) were fitted separately by eye. Compare with Fig. 9. Figure from Blough [12]. Behavioral data obtained by Blough; electrophysiological data from Donner [26] and Granit [37].

various situations. But recognition of these facts, if we keep them in proper perspective, does not constitute a rejection of consciousness nor of any other mentalistic concept. Such recognition is merely a first step toward an understanding of the nature of these concepts. Unfortunately, mentalistic concepts were ostentatiously rejected by some early behaviorists. Coupled with their rejection was the implicit suggestion that such concepts are based on phenomena not amenable to an objective treatment. These attitudes actually gave support to the notion that we can, if we choose, undertake a scientific study of consciousness, sensations, etc., by some means other than observations of behavior or its underlying physiological mechanisms. No such alternative procedures exist at present.

DISCUSSION

There is a common notion that certain unique problems are encountered when we attempt to bridge the gaps between physics and physiology or between physiology and psychology. However, the fact of the matter is that the whole issue of the interrelations among the several disciplines poses no special or unique scientific problems. The study of relations among phenomena which cut across the boundaries of traditional disciplines does not differ, in principle, from the study of relations among phenomena within a single discipline. For example, problems and concepts of various "hybrid" sciences, such as biophysics, biochemistry, psychophysiology, are neither bizarre nor unique. They resemble the problems and concepts of the "pure" sciences themselves.

To a certain extent, such similarities in problems and in concepts are a reflection of the fact that the boundaries of the various disciplines are somewhat arbitrary to begin with—often two independent disciplines may deal with the same phenomena. But the principal basis for these similarities throughout *all* of science is not that the various disciplines deal with the same or similar phenomena, but rather that they all utilize certain similar basic procedures. All scientific problems and all fundamental scientific concepts, from whatever discipline, have their origins in *observations* of various phenomena—and all such observations, regardless of the special instrumentation or techniques which may be involved, are made by human observers via one of their sense organs. This fact in itself might seem trivial, since—except for those few fortunate individuals who claim to be endowed with extrasensory perception—we have no alternative procedures. But it is not trivial, for it means that all scientific disciplines are placed on an equal footing, and that they are all confronted with certain identical fundamental problems at the very outset. One such problem is how to avoid confounding the properties of the thing observed with the properties of the observer—the problem of *objectivity*. Another is how to analyze complex phenomena into units to which we can assign numbers—the problem of *measurement*.

In general, these problems are solved in a similar manner by all disciplines, and it is these similar solutions which—more than any other single factor—enable us to relate apparently disparate disciplines to one another. Let us examine each of these problems briefly, and then turn finally to a consideration of their significance in the interrelations among disciplines.

The Meaning of Objectivity

Science supposedly treats public things and events external to the mind of the individual observer. Yet science is also supposedly based directly on our private, individual sense experiences. This apparent paradox has not gone unnoticed by philosophers; whole philosophies have been built around this one dilemma. But the practical escape from this dilemma seems to be the same, whether one subscribes to a philosophy of realism or idealism—or to neither. There are certain procedures which we commonly use to satisfy ourselves that things exist independently of specific observations and specific observers. In general, these procedures are to check the observations made via one sensory system against those made via another, and to verify the observations made by one individual by comparing them with those made by other individuals.[14] That is to say, we resort to a form of skepticism or systematic doubt regarding specific sense perceptions, as did Shakespeare's Macbeth when he asked—

> Is this a dagger which I see before me,
> The handle toward my hand? Come, let me clutch thee.
> I have thee not, and yet I see thee still.
> Art thou not, fatal vision, sensible
> To feeling as to sight? or art thou but
> A dagger of the mind, a false creation,
> Proceeding from the heat-oppressed brain?

And we extend this doubt to the observations made by other persons, as when Macbeth, after "seeing" Banquo's ghost, asked—

> Can such things be,
> And overcome us like a summer's cloud,
> Without our special wonder? You make me strange
> Even to the disposition that I owe,
> When now I think you can behold such sights
> And keep the natural ruby of your cheeks,
> When mine is blanch'd with fear.

And Ross, who had seen nothing, replied:

> What sights, my lord?

However, in our nonscientific life we seldom go all the way with such procedures. There are many things of which we are aware through a single sense system, e.g., rainbows, stars, etc., but which we accept as real. Indeed, in everyday life we formulate a great many concepts which

[14] This, of course, offers no escape from the philosopher's "egocentric predicament."

are based on observations made via one or a few of our senses. And we may even accept one individual's dreams or hallucinations as divine revelation. The objectivity of science goes a great deal farther than does common-sense objectivity. An attempt is made to base *all* our scientific concepts upon observations which can potentially be made via *any* sense system and by *any* observer. Now any *one* of such observations is neither more nor less subjective—or objective—than is any other single sense observation. Nor is any one observation any more or less private—or public—than is any other.[15] But by basing our concepts on observations which either are made—or can potentially be made—via more than one sensory system and by more than one observer, the concepts transcend the peculiarities of particular senses and particular observers. Thus—in this restricted sense—the concepts we formulate are objective and public. We have, of course, no procedures for the complete dissociation of observer and object observed, nor do we have any procedures by which two persons can observe exactly the same thing.

Measurement

Although measurement does not necessarily involve the use of numbers, one of its major aims is usually to assign numbers to natural phenomena in some systematic way. But, as Dantzig [21] says in his discussion of the evolution of the number concept, it *appears* that "the harmony of the universe knows only one musical form—the *legato;* while the symphony of number knows only its opposite—the *staccato.*"[16]

How, then, are we able to assign *discrete,* unique real numbers to *continuous* natural phenomena? The difficulties are not as great as they might seem on the surface. Indeed, on the mathematical side of the problem, we have the assurance of mathematicians [21] that there really is no contradiction between the concept of a point and a linear continuum, but that according to the Dedekind-Cantor axiom: "It is possible to assign to *any* point on a line a unique real number, and, conversely, *any* real number can be represented in a unique manner by a point on the line."[16] In other words, our number system is actually

[15] "My toothache" is the classic example of a private phenomenon, but the fact of the matter is that my toothache which I feel when my tooth is abscessed is, strictly speaking, no more private than is "my light," which I see when I turn on a lamp. One important difference between the two cases is that visual stimuli—even though for different observers they are never identical—are often highly correlated because they often have a common external source of energy. Pain stimuli for two observers, on the other hand, are seldom derived from a common external source of energy, and thus are less often correlated. This is one essential difference between what we commonly call "public" phenomena and "private" phenomena.

[16] From Dantzig [21]. Copyright 1930 and 1933 by The Macmillan Co. Reproduced by permission of The Macmillan Co.

continuous, and in this respect it offers no theoretical limit to our methods of measurement. This, however, does not solve the empirical problem of how to go about the process of assigning numbers to the phenomena we observe. Fortunately, the procedure is quite easy if there are natural fluctuations of one kind or another in the phenomena being observed—such as the cyclical disappearance and reappearance of the sun (which has long provided us with a convenient unit of time), and the marked repeated changes in electrical potential in nerve axons (which only recently have provided us with convenient units of nerve activity). But the problem is not so simple if something we wish to measure is not markedly cyclical or if there are no abrupt changes in its character to serve as natural divisions. In such cases we circumvent this difficulty by comparing the phenomenon with a scale consisting of artificial units of similar phenomena. We have seen how the early photometrists did this by the use of arbitrary units of light. There is, of course, a very large number of such units in current use—all so familiar that they require no further discussion here.

Although some of the many methods of measurement now in use are quite complex and may require elaborate instrumental aids, the fact remains that—no matter how many refinements or instrumental aids we add—the procedures remain fundamentally the same. We make quantitative measurements by assigning numbers to naturally occurring cycles or fluctuations in phenomena or else we create—by some artifice—a scale of arbitrary units of similar phenomena to which numbers may be assigned and which may be compared with the phenomena to be measured.

We wish to emphasize that objective and quantitative methods of observation are not the exclusive property of any one discipline. In the particular areas that we have considered, physics, physiology, and psychology are all equally objective and all use basically similar methods of measurement: the only striking differences among these three disciplines at the observational level are the differences in the units of mensuration employed.

Now what is the significance of these simple facts with respect to the interrelationships among these disciplines? First of all, they enable us to place in better perspective one problem which has plagued philosophy for centuries and which always appears in one guise or another whenever an attempt is made to relate psychology to the biological and physical sciences: the problem of the interrelation of the so-called "mental" and "material" universes.

The physical concept of radiant energy, the physiological concept of the nerve impulse, and other physical and physiological concepts, are— as we have seen—based on relatively simple observations of natural phenomena. It is on the basis of similar observations that we are led to say that a person or animal sees, or hears, or is conscious. In other words, our *scientific* concepts of mental events and our *scientific* concepts of material events are all derived from a common matrix of experimental observations and are all formulated in a similar manner. There is no essential difference in their fundamental natures. Consequently, there are no special problems in relating one to the other. Or at least, there are no problems which are not also encountered in relating material concepts to one another or mental concepts to one another.

While equal objectivity in observation places the various disciplines on the same basis in this one respect, the similarity among the several disciplines extends also to their methods of mensuration, and this similarity provides the basis for an additional strong bond among them. For, even though the units of mensuration employed by the various disciplines may be quite different in some respects, they have one thing in common: they are, by their very nature, all denumerable. Consequently, the phenomena measured in terms of any of these units are all amenable to description and treatment in terms of a common logical system: mathematics. And this is particularly important, for the slender threads of interrelation among the various disciplines are seldom evident in the mere congeries of raw experimental data; they are most often revealed by some mathematical analysis of those data.

Of course, objectivity and quantitative measurement are not absolutely necessary at all times and in all aspects of science. Indeed, as we have attempted to show, it is a historical fact that many major concepts stem from originally nonobjective and nonquantitative observations. Undoubtedly, this will often occur in newly developing areas of science. But it is clear that all such concepts have been abandoned as soon as they could be replaced by more rigorously formulated ones.

What course the future development of interrelations among sciences will take, it is impossible to know. But this much is evident—there are no natural boundaries between the several sciences. Those boundaries which do exist are man made—and they are maintained primarily for pedagogical purposes and for administrative convenience rather than for any valid scientific reasons. The study of natural phenomena need not be constrained by such barriers.

REFERENCES

1. Adrian, E. D., & Bronk, D. W. The discharge of impulses in motor nerve fibres. *J. Physiol.*, 1928, **66**, 81–101.
2. Adrian, E. D., & Matthews, R. The action of light on the eye. Part I. The discharge of impulses in the optic nerve and its relation to the electric change in the retina. *J. Physiol.*, 1927, **63**, 378–414.

3. Adrian, E. D., & Matthews, R. The action of light on the eye. Part II. The processes involved in retinal excitation. *J. Physiol.*, 1927, **64**, 279–301.

4. Adrian, E. D., & Matthews, R. The action of light on the eye. Part III. The interaction of retinal neurones. *J. Physiol.*, 1928, **65**, 273–298.

5. Asher, H. The suppression theory. *Br. orthopt. J.*, 1953, **10**, 23–31.

6. Babkin, B. P. *Pavlov.* Chicago: Univer. of Chicago Press, 1949.

7. Barlow, H. B. Summation and inhibition in the frog's retina. *J. Physiol.*, 1953, **119**, 69–88.

8. Barlow, H. B., FitzHugh, R., & Kuffler, S. W. Change of organization in the receptive fields of the cat's retina during dark adaptation. *J. Physiol.*, 1957, **137**, 338–354.

9. Békésy, G. von. A new audiometer. *Acta Otolaryngol.*, 1947, **35**, 411–422.

10. Bishop, G. H. Natural history of the nerve impulse. *Physiol. Rev.*, 1956, **36**, 376–399.

11. Blough, D. S. Dark adaptation in the pigeon. *J. comp. physiol. Psychol.*, 1956, **49**, 425–430.

12. Blough, D. S. Spectral sensitivity in the pigeon. *J. opt. Soc. Amer.*, 1957, **47**, 827–833.

13. Blough, D. S. A method for obtaining psychophysical thresholds from the pigeon. *J. exp. Anal. Behav.*, 1958, **1**, 31–44.

14. Boring, E. G. *A history of experimental psychology.* New York: Appleton-Century-Crofts, 1929.

15. Boring, E. G. *Sensation and perception in the history of experimental psychology.* New York: Appleton-Century-Crofts, 1942.

16. Brazier, M. A. B. *The electrical activity of the nervous system.* New York: Macmillan, 1951.

17. Brink, F., Jr. Excitation in the neuron. Synaptic mechanisms. In S. S. Stevens (Ed.), *Handbook of experimental psychology.* New York: Wiley, 1951. Pp. 50–120.

18. Brink, F., Jr., Bronk, D. W., Carlson, F. D., & Connelly, C. M., The oxygen uptake of active axons. *Cold Spring Harbor Symposia on quant. Biol.*, 1952, **17**, 53–67.

19. Cornsweet, T. N. Determination of the stimuli for involuntary drifts and saccadic eye movements. *J. opt. Soc. Amer.*, 1956, **46**, 987–993.

20. Craik, K. J. W., & Vernon, M. D. The nature of dark adaptation. Part I. Evidence as to the locus of the process. *Br. J. Psychol.*, 1941, **32**, 62–81.

21. Dantzig, T. *Number, the language of science.* (2nd. ed. rev.) New York: Macmillan, 1937.

22. Dartnall, H. J. A. *The visual pigments.* New York: Wiley, 1957.

23. Ditchburn, R. W. *Light.* New York: Interscience, 1953.

24. Ditchburn, R. W., Fender, D. H., Mayne, Stella, & Pritchard, R. M. A stabilized retinal image of the iris. *Proc. Phys. Soc.*, B., 1956, **LXIX**, 1165.

25. Ditchburn, R. W., & Ginsborg, B. L. Vision with a stabilized retinal image. *Nature,* 1952, **170,** 36.

26. Donner, K. O. The spectral sensitivity of the pigeon's retinal elements. *J. Physiol.,* 1953, **122,** 524–537.

27. Einstein, A. Considerations concerning the fundaments of theoretical physics. *Science,* 1940, **91,** 487–492.

28. Erlanger, J., & Gasser, H. S. The compound nature of the action current of nerve as disclosed by the cathode ray oscillograph. *Amer. J. Physiol.,* 1924, **70,** 624–666.

29. Forbes, A., & Thacher, C. Amplification of action currents with the electron tube in recording with the string galvanometer. *Amer. J. Physiol.,* 1920, **52,** 409–471.

30. Frenkel-Brunswick, E. Meaning of psychoanalytic concepts and confirmation of psychoanalytic theories. *Scient. Mon.* 1954, **79,** 293–300.

31. Frolov, Y. P. *Pavlov and his school.* London: Routledge and Kegan Paul, 1938.

32. Fry, G. A. Mechanisms subserving simultaneous brightness contrast. *Amer. J. Optom.* and *Arch. Amer. Acad. Optom.,* 1948, **25,** 162–178.

33. Gasser, H. S., & Erlanger, J. A study of the action currents of nerve with the cathode ray oscillograph. *Amer. J. Physiol.,* 1922, **62,** 496–524.

34. Gasser, H. S., & Newcomer, H. S. Physiological action currents in the phrenic nerve: an application of the thermionic vacuum tube to nerve physiology. *Amer. J. Physiol.,* 1921, **57,** 1–26.

35. Graham, C. H., & Hartline, H. K. The response of single visual sense cells to lights of different wavelengths. *J. gen. Physiol.,* 1935, **18,** 917–931.

36. Graham, C. H., & Margaria, R. Area and the intensity-time relation in the peripheral retina. *Amer. J. Physiol.,* 1935, **113,** 299–305.

37. Granit, R. The photopic spectrum of the pigeon. *Acta Physiol. Scand.,* 1942, **4,** 118–123.

38. Granit, R. *Sensory mechanisms of the retina.* London: Oxford Univer. Press, 1947.

39. Granit, R. Aspects of excitation and inhibition in the retina. *Proc. Roy. Soc., B.,* 1952, **140,** 191–198.

40. Granit, R. *Receptors and sensory perception.* New Haven, Conn.: Yale Univer. Press, 1955.

41. Granit, R., & Svaetichin, G. Principles and technique of the electro-physiological analysis of colour reception with the aid of microelectrodes. *Upsala läkaref. förh.,* 1939, **65,** 161–177.

42. Hardy, A. C., & Perrin, F. H. *The principles of optics.* New York: McGraw-Hill, 1932.

43. Hartline, H. K. Intensity and duration in the excitation of single photoreceptor units. *J. cell. comp. Physiol.,* 1934, **5,** 229–247.

44. Hartline, H. K. The response of single optic nerve fibers of the vertebrate eye to illumination of the retina. *Amer. J. Physiol.,* 1938, **121,** 400–415.

45. Hartline, H. K. Excitation and inhibition of the "off" response in vertebrate optic nerve fibers. *Amer. J. Physiol.,* 1939, **126,** 527. (Abstract)

46. Hartline, H. K. The nerve messages in the fibres of the visual pathway. *J. opt. Soc. Amer.*, 1940, **30**, 239–247.

47. Hartline, H. K. The receptive fields of optic nerve fibers. *Amer. J. Physiol.*, 1940, **130**, 690–699.

48. Hartline, H. K. The neural mechanisms of vision. In *The Harvey lectures.* Ser. XXXVII. Springfield, Ill.: Charles C Thomas, 1941–42. Pp. 39–68.

49. Hartline, H. K. Inhibition of activity of visual receptors by illuminating nearby retinal elements in the *Limulus* eye. *Fed. Proc.*, 1949, **8**, 69. (Abstract)

50. Hartline, H. K., & Graham, C. H. Nerve impulses from single receptors in the eye. *J. cell. comp. Physiol.*, 1932, **1**, 277–295.

51. Hartline, H. K., & McDonald, P. R. Light and dark adaptation of single photoreceptor elements in the eye of *Limulus*. *J. cell. comp. Physiol.*, 1947, **30**, 225–253.

52. Hartline, H. K., Milne, L. J., & Wagman, I. H. Fluctuation of response of single visual sense cells. *Fed. Proc.*, 1947, **6**, 124. (Abstract)

53. Hartline, H. K., Milne, L. J., & Wagman, I. H. Personal communication.

54. Hartline, H. K., & Ratliff, F. Inhibitory interaction of receptor units in the eye of *Limulus*. *J. gen. Physiol.*, 1957, **40**, 357–376.

55. Hartline, H. K., & Ratliff, F. Spatial summation of inhibitory influences in the eye of *Limulus*, and the mutual interaction of receptor units. *J. gen. Physiol.*, 1958, **41**, 1049–1066.

56. Hartline, H. K., Wagner, H. G., & MacNichol, E. F. The peripheral origin of nervous activity in the visual system. *Cold Spring Harbor Symposia on quant. Biol.*, 1952, **17**, 125–141.

57. Hartline, H. K., Wagner, H. G., & Ratliff, F. Inhibition in the eye of *Limulus*. *J. gen. Physiol.*, 1956, **39**, 651–673.

58. Hecht, S. Rods, cones, and the chemical basis of vision. *Physiol. Rev.*, 1937, **17**, 239–290.

59. Hecht, S., Haig, C., & Chase, A. M. The influence of light adaptation on subsequent dark adaptation of the eye. *J. gen. Physiol.*, 1937, **20**, 831–850.

60. Hecht, S., Schlaer, S., & Pirenne, M. H. Energy, quanta and vision. *J. gen. Physiol.*, 1942, **25**, 819–840.

61. Hilgard, E. R., & Marquis, D. G. Conditioning and learning. New York: Appleton-Century-Crofts, 1940.

62. Hodgkin, A. L., & Huxley, A. F. Movement of sodium and potassium ions during nervous activity. *Cold Spring Harbor Symposia on quant. Biol.*, 1952, **17**, 43–52.

63. Iarbus, A. L. The perception of an image fixed with respect to the retina. *Biophysics.*, 1957, **2**, 683–691.

64. Jenkins, F. A., & White, H. E. *Fundamentals of optics.* New York: McGraw-Hill, 1950.

65. Keller, F. S., & Schoenfeld, W. N. *Principles of psychology.* New York: Appleton-Century-Crofts, 1950.

66. Krauskopf, J. Effect of retinal image motion on contrast thresholds for maintained vision. *J. opt. Soc. Amer.*, 1957, **47**, 740–744.
67. Kuffler, S. W. Discharge patterns and functional organization of mammalian retina. *J. Neurophysiol.*, 1953, **16**, 37–68.
68. Le Grand, Y. *Light, color and vision.* New York: Wiley, 1957.
69. Lloyd, D. P. C. Electrical properties of nerve and muscle, and Functional properties of neurons. In J. F. Fulton (Ed.), *Howell's textbook of physiology.* Philadelphia: Saunders, 1947. Pp. 7–30; 96–120.
70. Long, G. E. The effect of duration of onset and cessation of light flash on the intensity-time relation in the peripheral retina. *J. opt. Soc. Amer.*, 1951, **41**, 743–747.
71. Mach, E. *The principles of physical optics.* New York: Dover, 1956. (Republication of the English translation first published in 1926)
72. Miller, W. H. Morphology of the ommatidia of the compound eye of *Limulus. J. biophys. biochem. Cytol.* 1957, **3**, 421–428.
73. Miller, W. H. Fine structure of some invertebrate photoreceptors. *Ann. N.Y. Acad. Sci.*, 1958, **74**, 204–209.
74. Pirenne, M. H. Physiological mechanisms of vision and the quantum nature of light. *Biol. Rev.*, 1956, **31**, 194–241.
75. Polyak, S. *The vertebrate visual system.* Chicago: Univer. of Chicago Press, 1957.
76. Ratliff, F. The role of physiological nystagmus in monocular acuity. *J. exp. Psychol.*, 1952, **43**, 163–172.
77. Ratliff, F. A stationary retinal image requiring no attachments to the eye. *J. opt. Soc. Amer.*, 1958, **48**, 274–275.
78. Ratliff, F. Simultaneous contrast in the pigeon. (Unpublished research)
79. Ratliff, F., & Blough, D. S. *Behavioral studies of visual processes in the pigeon,* Tech. Report, U.S. Navy, Off. Nav. Res., 1954. (Contract N5 ori-07663, Proj. NR 140-072.)
80. Ratliff, F., & Hartline, H. K. The responses of Limulus optic nerve fibers to patterns of illumination on the receptor mosaic. *J. gen. Physiol.*, 1959, **42**, 1241–1255.
81. Ratliff, F., Miller, W. H., & Hartline, H. K. Neural interaction in the eye and the integration of receptor activity. *Ann. N.Y. Acad. Sci.*, 1958, **74**, 210–222.
82. Ratliff, F., & Mueller, C. G. Synthesis of "on-off" and "off" responses in a visual-neural system. *Science*, 1957, **126**, No. 3278, 840–841.
83. Ratliff, F., & Riggs, L. A. Involuntary motions of the eye during monocular fixation. *J. exp. Psychol.*, 1950, **40**, 687–701.
84. Rich, D. C. *Seurat and the evolution of "La Grande Jatte."* Chicago: Univer. of Chicago Press, 1935.
85. Riggs, L. A. Electrical phenomena in vision. In A. Hollaender (Ed.), *Radiation biology.* Vol. III. *Visible and near-visible light.* New York: McGraw-Hill, 1956. Pp. 581–619.
86. Riggs, L. A., Ratliff, F., Cornsweet, J. C., & Cornsweet, T. The disappearance of steadily fixated test objects. *J. opt. Soc. Amer.*, 1953, **43**, 495–501.

87. Skinner, B. F. *The behavior of organisms.* New York: Appleton-Century-Crofts, 1938.
88. Spence, K. W. *Behavior theory and conditioning.* New Haven, Conn: Yale Univer. Press, 1956.
89. Strong, J. *Concepts of classical optics.* San Francisco: Freeman, 1958.
90. Toraldo di Francia, G. Basic research in the field of vision. Instituto Nazionale di Ottica, TSR. No. 1, Arcetri-Firenza, 1954.
91. Verplanck, W. S., Collier, G. H., & Cotton, J. W. Non-independence of successive responses in measurements of visual threshold. *J. exp. Psychol.,* 1952, **44,** 273–282.
92. Wald, G. The biochemistry of vision. *Ann. Rev. Biochem.,* 1953, **22,** 497–526.
93. Wald, G. The molecular basis of visual excitation. *Amer. Scient.,* 1954, **42,** 73–95.
94. Warner, L. *The enduring art of Japan.* Cambridge, Mass: Harvard Univer. Press, 1952.
95. Watson, J. B. Psychology as the behaviorist views it. *Psychol. Rev.,* 1913, **20,** 158–177.
96. Wilska, A. Aktionspotentialentladungen einzelner Netzhautelemente des Frosches. *Acta Soc. med. Fenn. 'Duodecium' A.,* 1939, **12,** 50–62.
97. Wright, W. D. *Researches on normal and defective color vision.* St. Louis, Mo.: Mosby, 1947.
98. Wulff, V. J. Physiology of the compound eye. *Physiol. Rev.,* 1956, **36,** 145–163.

NOTES ON SOME INTERRELATIONS OF SENSORY PSYCHOLOGY, PERCEPTION, AND BEHAVIOR

C. H. GRAHAM
Department of Psychology
Columbia University

AND

PHILBURN RATOOSH
Department of Psychology
University of California

Introduction 483
    Types of stimulus-response relations in sensory and perceptual experiments 484
    Descriptive terminology and sensory dimensions. 484
    Relations of sensation and perception: some implications of an experiment 485
    Formal properties of psychophysical measurement 485
    Rational accounts of process in sensory experiments versus scaling . . 485
Types of Stimulus-response Relations in Sensory Psychology and Perception . 485
    The experiment involving introspective reports 485
    The psychophysical experiment 487
    Absolute judgments 488
    Thresholds and perceptual functions 492
    A symbolic formulation. 493
Descriptive and Explanatory Terminology: Sensory Dimensions 497
Relations of Sensation and Perception: Some Implications of an Experiment. 499
    What are the relations between sensation and perception? 499
    Experiments on visual duration 500
    The duration threshold 502
Formal Properties of Psychophysical Measurement 503
Rational Accounts of Sensory Relations 505
Summary 510
References. 512

INTRODUCTION

This chapter[1] will take up, in a free-ranging way, several topics in the field of sensory psychology[2] and related areas.[3] The discussion will

[1] The preparation of this manuscript was supported in part by a contract between the U.S. Office of Naval Research and Columbia University. Reproduction in whole or in part is permitted for any purpose of the United States Government.

[2] Behavioristic descriptions of perception and sensation appeared early in the

deal with the topical headings which are introduced and, to some extent, characterized in the paragraphs immediately below.

Types of stimulus-response relations in sensory and perceptual experiments. This topic is concerned with the specification and formulation of what subjects do in sensory and perceptual experiments and with the implications of the description for a more complete treatment of behavior. What, for example, may one say about a frequently encountered type of treatment, one that describes many topics of psychology in terms of behavior but considers sensation and perception in a context of phenomenological description? Often in the latter case lip service is paid to the idea that experiments of sensation and perception do indeed involve behavior, and that appropriate translation terms are to be understood for their linkage to other areas of psychology. What kinds of behavior are exhibited in the experiments on sensation and perception is rarely explicated. (We do not feel that a sufficient description is given by the statement that sensation and perception manifest discrimination.) What is needed, we think, is a specification of the kinds of stimulus-response functions that characterize experiments in these areas. Our discussion will be concerned with this topic.

One type of function, the absolute judgment or estimate, is at present a major focus of interest and is receiving considerable attention from Stevens [46, 47], for example. In general it may be less important than some other types of behavior function discussed here, but the interest that it now evokes causes us to treat it with special attention and to present some aspects of the topic that are not always considered.

Descriptive terminology and sensory dimensions. The discussion of the second topic provides an example of how certain psychological dimensions or attributes may be specified in a stimulus-response psychology. In a word, we here deal with the problem of translation of terms from a phenomenological or mentalistic psychology to a behavioristic one. As an example of such translation, we consider words from the study of color vision. What, we ask, does such a translation involve?

---

systematic development of an objective psychology. Hunter's paper [27] may be taken as an important example.

[3] Much of the discussion in the first two sections is taken directly from Graham [13]. The third section involves direct quotations from Graham [12]. Permission to quote the material on descriptive terminology and sensory dimensions has been received from the American Psychological Association, and permission to quote material on relations of sensation and perception has been received from the National Academy of Science, National Research Council. (The discussion on descriptive terminology and sensory dimensions appeared also in the chapter on color theory by C. H. Graham in Vol. I of *Psychology: a study of a science* and in [13]. Permission has been received from the *Journal of general physiology* to reproduce Figs. 1, 4, 5, and 6.)

Relations of sensation and perception: some implications of an experiment. Many psychologists who take the position that the field of perception is a basic area of psychology may exhibit unclear opinions about the field of sensation. It is, they may say, a specialized aspect of psychology, or if not that, then an area of physiology. Our analysis raises objections against this "double-standard" approach and concludes that the two topics do, in fact, constitute a single subject matter. In order to emphasize the latter point and to show the interrelations of phenomena across conventionally conceived boundaries, we present an analysis of a type of perceptual experiment, one that is concerned with the duration threshold. We consider the nature of its roots in sensory phenomena together with a discussion of errors in interpretation that may occur when the essential unity of all aspects of the duration problem, sensory and perceptual, is not understood.

Formal properties of psychophysical measurement. The view often has been taken that measurement in psychology is impossible or illusory or at least not fundamental. This objection is discussed, and it is concluded that *no* measurement is fundamental in the sense of Campbell.

Rational accounts of process in sensory experiments versus scaling. Psychologists have emphasized, through the years, the importance of establishing sensory and psychophysical scales. As contrasted with this historical trend, the areas of vision (see Graham [14], for example, on color vision) and more recently conditioning (see Hull [26]; Estes [5]; Bush and Mosteller [3]) present several examples of a different type of quantitative treatment, the rational account. Our discussion of our fifth topic indicates how one such rational account, directed to an area that has received great attention from the point of view of scaling, may provide analyses and results that have advantages over those obtainable from the scaling approach. It is not stated that scaling or the search for scales may not provide useful results; it is, however, said that for certain purposes of theoretical analysis, etc., the rational account may often exhibit greater scope in its testable implications. The example discussed is concerned with some data of intensity discrimination that could serve as a basis for Fechnerian scaling. However, an entirely different sort of treatment is described and some of its implications are developed.

TYPES OF STIMULUS-RESPONSE RELATIONS IN SENSORY PSYCHOLOGY AND PERCEPTION

Various types of behavior are encountered in experiments on sensation and perception.

The experiment involving introspective reports. Consider first the type of situation that applies to the experiment dealing with introspective reports of sensations or perceptions evoked by particular objects or events involving the objects. Concretely, the question arises: What do we have to do in this situation to get a subject to give us a phenomenal or introspective report in the presence of certain objects that we supply?

Proper procedure in such a situation demands, of course, that we instruct the subject to give us a phenomenal or introspective report and that we supply the appropriate objects in their appropriate relations. The consequent behavior on the part of the subject will be the emission of a sequence of words—words that are, we presume, functions of the subject's past history of reinforcements (by parents and other persons) in a sequence of discriminative trainings as discussed, for example, by Skinner [42]. These verbal responses are often said to be descriptive of stimuli. In situations such as the one described, the experimenter hears such words given by the subject as *moving, color, short, white, object, large, red, duration, size, movement, intensity, texture,* and a whole gamut of expressions that apply to the character of the stimuli. Since these words were conditioned in response to aspects of stimuli that are now present, they are appropriate responses, both to the subject and the similarly conditioned experimenter. In all of this, the place of the instruction stimuli in restricting the possible number of responses given by the subject remains to be understood. How do the experimenter's instructions control the subject's behavior so that he responds within limited categories of behavior to restricted categories of stimuli? To say, for example, that the instructions provide the necessary "sets" is not very informative.

It would be of considerable interest to compare a subject's behavior under instructions to introspect or give a phenomenal description with behavior under instructions to describe objects. Certainly the subject may manifest different behaviors as exemplified in the "subjective" attitude and the "objective" attitude. To what extent differences are apparent in his behavior is a question on which not very many relevant data exist at present. While the problem should not deter us, it may have later implications for a behavioristic account of perception.

In experiments of the sort under consideration—that is, experiments on phenomenal appearances or introspective reports—it is true that the instructions used do not greatly restrict responses. The latter may exhibit a great many degrees of freedom—that is, many different words may be spoken. In addition, neither stimuli nor responses are usually measured in the observations on phenomenal appearances or introspection.

The problem of analyzing and classifying the responses in an experiment of this type is, of course, one of the major problems of psychology. However, the problem of analysis and classification of responses does not involve accepting them as understandable conversation, but is one of formulating their uniformities and rules in a system where they are taken as behavior. This sort of analysis provides the anomaly that conversation is not viewed as such, but is considered in terms of other words or symbols—that is, scientific description that formulates the rules of the subject's conversation. We deal here, of course, with the problem, discussed by Bergmann and Spence [1], of the subject's language and the experimenter's metalanguage. On this point they say:

. . . the empiricist scientist should realize that his behavior, symbolic or otherwise, does not lie on the same methodological level as the responses of his subjects, and consequently that he should not in reporting the latter use any mentalistic terms which have not been introduced from a physicalistic meaning basis. This latter fact may also be expressed by saying that all his terms should be behavioristically defined . . . the last point can be stated in the following way: In studying his subjects, including their symbolic responses (object language), the behavior scientist himself uses a different language (pragmatic metalanguage).

The psychophysical experiment. Let us now turn to another type of experiment, one that, as contrasted with the experiment on introspection, shows measurement of both stimuli and responses as well as considerable restriction of both. Of course, this type of experiment is scientifically at a somewhat higher level of development than the introspective experiment, due to the fact that in the past its permissible stimuli and responses have been isolated and measured in one way or another. In this situation the type of relevant procedural question is: What do we have to do to get a subject to say, with a certain degree of probability, "I see a light," or its converse, "I don't see a light"? The subject, in the course of any single stimulus presentation, can only give one of the two possible responses (or under appropriate conditions, their equivalents, "Yes" or "No").

This type of experiment is the classical psychophysical experiment. It turns out, in this situation, that luminance must be manipulated, and we can plot some measure of response—for example, its probability of occurrence—against some appropriate function of luminance. This procedure has been followed in Fig. 1.

This figure gives the psychophysical data of three subjects for an experiment on quantum requirements at threshold by Hecht, Shlaer, and Pirenne [22]. Such a function is a stimulus-response relation that shows how a measure of response varies with a controlling stimulus variable. From such a relation it is possible to obtain a new datum, a value of the stimulus variable that corresponds to a given probability of response occurrence—for example, the 50 per cent value. This new and extremely important datum is familiarly known to us as a threshold.

The two categories of the experiment that have been discussed, the phenomenal report and the psychophysical, lie at the extremes of an array of psychological experimentation, the array being ordered on the basis of degree of stimulus and response restriction. The introspective experiment involves relatively unrestricted stimuli and responses, while the psychophysical experiment usually involves a high degree of restriction in both.

Absolute judgments. Other types of experiments take up positions between the extremes of such a continuum. One may have in mind particularly the type of experiment involving absolute judgments, estimates, or naming behavior. This type of experiment deals with the relation between environmental stimulus variables, often measurable in some theoretical numbering system taken, for example, from physics, and large families of variable responses. This is the sort of experiment that involves

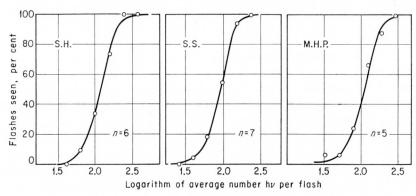

FIG. 1. Frequency of seeing functions obtained by Hecht, Shlaer, and Pirenne [22].

such procedural questions as: What do we have to do to make a subject say "I see five dots," or "This is red," or "This has a value of three on a scale of 1 to 5"? The response given in this experiment is one that has developed during the subject's life history in the presence of objects. Naming a color and giving a numerical estimate of brightness are examples of such responses.

Figure 2 gives a set of hypothetical curves for color naming in the spectrum. Each curve gives, as a function of wavelength, the frequency of occurrence of the response that applies to the curve.[4]

A number of undesirable ways of talking about the results of the experiment on absolute judgments hinge on this problem. Here one may mention two examples. First there is the device—harmless enough if we

[4] The curves of Fig. 2 were not drawn on the basis of data. They were constructed on the basis of "reasonable guesses" relating to other kinds of color discrimination. Since this paper was written, Aleeza C. Beare, working at Columbia University, has made experimental determinations of color-naming functions at two levels of luminance. The functions are, in fact, quite similar to the hypothetical ones shown in Fig. 2.

keep in mind what is being done—that has sometimes been used to imply response continuity. This is the device of assuming a response continuum as the correlate of physical dimensions of the stimulus, as when we say that orange (rather than the wavelengths that evoke the response "Orange") is next to red in the spectrum (rather than the wavelengths that evoke the response "Red"). Secondly, there is the procedure of treating numerical estimates as if they were numerical data. For example, the word "ten" emitted by a subject in an experiment on estimated brightness may be treated, erroneously, we think, as if it were the quantified outcome of a measuring operation. The symbol for response (accepted by the experimenter as a number) is added to the list of other numbers of the same sort, and the experimenter says that an average response is finally computed. No independent operations of measurement have been applied under these circumstances to the subject's responses.

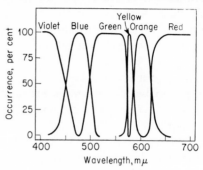

FIG. 2. Hypothetical curves for frequency of occurrence of color names in the spectrum.

In any case, it should be pointed out that we can theoretically derive critical values—threshold values—from certain types of experiments on absolute judgments. For example, we can find, on the average, how many dots are required for the response "Five." We can also find out how many are required for the responses "Four," "Three," "Two," "One," etc. Similarly, in the case of estimates of brightness, one can find the value of luminance that is on the average correlated with the response "Ten," for example. We do *not* find what the average response is for the same luminance.

As contrasted with the method of constant stimuli with two categories, where only two responses can be elicited no matter what the value of the discriminative stimulus, the method of absolute judgment allows for the production of a great number of responses. For example, in the naming of a color, one response gives way to another response at many places in the visual spectrum. In a word, the subject gives many names to the appropriate respective wavelength bands.

Figure 3 gives some data on verbal estimates of brightness,[5] a topic

---

[5] Note also, for example, the reports by Richardson [40] and Helson [23] on estimates of hue, brightness, and saturation and the reports by Stevens [46] on the estimates of loudness. For criticisms of estimates in vision, see Smith [44] and Guild [17]; for criticism of estimates of loudness, see Garner [7].

studied by Stevens and Galanter [47]. The data were obtained as an exercise by Harris Ripps and Aleeza Beare, to whom we are indebted. They were not extensive enough to give smooth frequency distributions of different number names and so we have exceeded permissible limits and smoothed them more to fit our fancy than to fit data. Nevertheless, they represent clearly enough two kinds of treatment of data.

The first way, in Fig. 3a, involves the averaging of the presumed quantities that are represented by the verbal responses. The second method, in Fig. 3b, involves the specification of the stimulus conditions required to produce a given response. The latter procedure is in line with the one employed for the data on color naming. The verbal response applying to each distribution is indicated in quotation marks.

The averaging, as in curve a, of the presumed quantities specified by the verbal responses may be, from the point of view of behavior specification, an undesirable way to deal with the data. For example, there seems to be nothing more intrinsically quantitative in the responses involved in brightness estimates than there is in the responses of color naming.

What we do have in both cases is a specification of stimulus conditions which, given certain instances of instruction, provide us with frequency distributions of various response occurrences. The number of frequency distributions is, of course, determined by the number of responses given by or allowed to the subject.

Another less important objection may be registered against the method of averaging estimates by treating responses as though they were quantities. Such a procedure, it may be argued, seems to regard the responding person as a reporter and observer rather than as a subject. He is treated as if he makes private measurements and then reports them. It would, in our estimation, be preferable to regard the subject as a responding organism whose experimental data are verbal responses which may be measured or operated on *by* the experimenter. He (the subject) should not be regarded as a communicator of private measurements. From our viewpoint, the quantitative significance of the responses given by the subject constitutes a problem that has to be explained rather than information that has been obtained.

It might be thought that our analysis leads to a blind alley in the treatment of number estimates within a context of quantitative description. Carried to no farther domain that that of scaling, this conclusion would indeed be correct. But a new domain of analysis develops if one regards the problem as requiring theoretical and experimental answers. In particular, one might like answers to the question: How does the language behavior of estimates correlate with other measurable variables? A context is required, based on empirical data and theoretical ideas, that

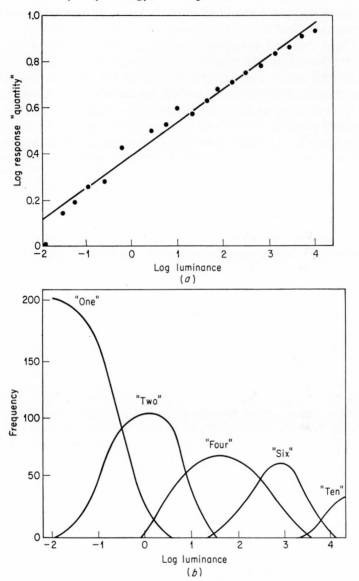

Fig. 3*a*. Average estimates (i.e., average log response "quantities") of brightness for various levels of luminance.

Fig. 3*b*. The frequency distributions of log luminance for the responses "One," "Two," etc. Both curves involve computations on the same experimental data.

will allow us to understand what the behavioral bases and correlates of estimates may be.[6]

Thresholds and perceptual functions. The concept of threshold,[7] i.e., a critical value of stimulus corresponding to a given response criterion, need not be elaborated here; it is an old and pervasive principle of psychology. Nevertheless, it will not be out of place to point out that, by virtue of this quantity, it is possible to treat as a single datum the outcome embodied in a total psychophysical function and so derive what might be called a perceptual function—that is, a function obtained from a sequence of experiments concerned with finding thresholds under many different conditions. Such experiments pose such procedural questions as the following: What do we have to do to get a subject to say, "This light is brighter than that one," under conditions where we systematically vary the standard light?

Figure 4 shows such a sequence of psychophysical curves obtained by Mueller [35] in a determination of the just-discriminable increment in luminance at various luminance levels. Each curve gives a threshold ΔL, the critical value of ΔL taken as corresponding to the 50 per cent response occurrence.

In a further extension of the data, we determine how the second-order datum, the threshold ΔL, varies with changes in the standard light. The function obtained in these circumstances shows how determined

---

[6] This footnote is written three years after the original text. During this interval Stevens and his collaborators have performed a considerable number of experiments. Included among the most recent is a report by J. C. Stevens, J. D. Mack, and S. S. Stevens on the matching of sensations in seven continua by force of handgrip (*J. exper. Psychol.*, 1960, **59**, 60–67). The subjects produced forces on a hand dynamometer to match various levels of sensory intensity including brightness of a light. The results were found to be highly consistent and to be in accord with expectations based on power-function formulations. In these experiments the matching stimuli across sensory systems is an interesting result that may prove useful and important. A further aspect of the experiments is taken to demonstrate the similarity of estimating data and matching-to-handgrip data. The argument may carry a degree of conviction, but we shall be readier to accept estimates as numerical data when further analysis discloses more about the private behavior components of the estimates. Stevens, Mack, and Stevens seem also to be aware of the need to analyze the estimating and matching behaviors involved in their experiments, particularly in terms of subjects' experiences with objects that produce the stimulating energies. In a word, they are concerned with "stimulus errors."

[7] Perhaps the term *perceptual function* is not wholly desirable. It might be, for example, that *critical-value function* would be more appropriate. One difficulty with the term *perceptual function* lies in the fact that it seems to convey to some persons the idea that it is concerned with perception, while the term *psychophysical function* is concerned with sensation. This characterization is, of course, completely wrong. We shall maintain that sensation and perception are operationally congruent domains, each involving both types of function.

values of ΔL (each one based on a psychophysical function) vary with the luminance of the standard light.

Figure 4 represents such a function. It is the curve for Mueller's threshold values of ΔL as a function of the background luminance to which ΔL is added. Such a function, which we may term a *perceptual*

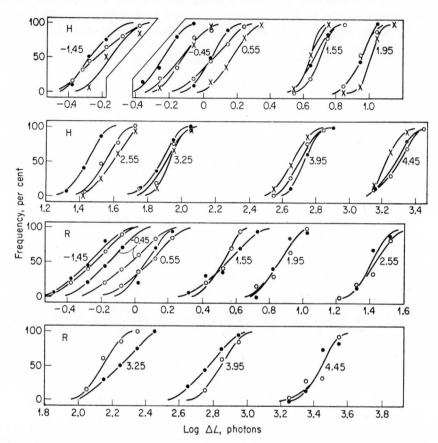

Fig. 4. Frequency of seeing curves obtained by Mueller [35] for brightness-discrimination thresholds at various luminance levels.

function, shows how a critical value of stimulus, the threshold, varies as a function of a controlling variable.

A symbolic formulation. It is of interest to examine the present analysis in terms of a symbolic formulation that has been used by Graham [8, 9, 11, 13] to specify some classifications of relations among stimulus, response, and conditions of the subject. Specifically, the variables of the present analysis must be examined to see if they can be described as special cases of the general relation

$$R = f(a,b,c \ldots n \ldots t \ldots x,y,z) \tag{1}$$

This relation expresses the assumption of a behavioristic program: response is a function of certain specifiable variables. In particular, the first letters of the alphabet a, b, c . . . refer to properly specified aspects of stimuli; the last letters x, y, z to properly specified conditions of

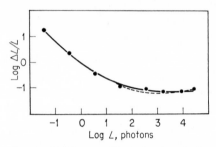

FIG. 5. Brightness-discrimination ratios at various luminance levels based on the data of Mueller [35] at the 50 per cent frequency in the curves of Fig. 4.

the subject (physiological and inferred, including the effects of instruction stimuli); R, to response; n, to number of presentations; and t, to time. The terms are not always independent of each other.[8]

It is important to realize that x, y, and z may be, among other things, the consequences of past stimulation.

[8] Guilford [19], in his description of modern psychophysics, gives a modified account of Graham's formulation [8, 9, 12, 13]. Guilford's account differs from Graham's in the sense that Guilford takes R, response, to be an unobservable varible (e.g., loudness) antecedent to a judgment, J. For Graham, R refers to a behavioral response, e.g., a movement of part or all of the organism.

Ogle [36], in discussing the theory of stereoscopic vision, makes reference to Graham's formulation [11] and makes this statement concerning experiments in stereoscopic vision: "On the basis of the behavioristic assumption that the subjective depth response can be described as a function of certain specifiable variables, the data obtained in experiments delineating stereoscopic can be expressed by $D = f(\eta \ldots Q)$," where η is the disparity in the ocular images of the two eyes of any two objects in space and Q is a complex of structural variables.

No criticism is leveled against Ogle's formulations of variables in stereoscopic vision. Some objection may, however, be raised against the confusion in interpretation that may arise when Graham's formulation is referred to in connection with the idea that a *subjective* depth response may be described as a function of certain specifiable variables. No confusion could occur if the word "subjective" were eliminated.

The stimulus-response data of a psychophysical experiment can be represented, at least for the cases of the methods of constant stimuli and limits, by the equation

$$R = F(a, x_1) \tag{2}$$

This equation is a special case of Eq. (1): response is a function of an aspect a of the stimulus, with x_1, the effect of instructions, explicitly specified as constant. The same sort of analysis can be applied to the data of absolute judgments.

(It must be admitted parenthetically that to a considerable extent the discussion here presented depends for its validity on the choice of the methods of constant stimuli and limits, both with extensive series of observations. When the method of adjustment is used, response measurement becomes difficult.)

A combination of psychophysical experiments provides the data for a perceptual function as in

$$a_c = (b, x_1, R_1) \tag{3}$$

Here a critical aspect of stimulus a_c is represented as a function of another aspect of stimulus b. In this case x_1, the effect of instruction, and R_1, the criterion response, are maintained constant. In other experiments, a could be determined as a function of such variables as n, t, or y.

Equations (1), (2), and (3) and similar ones give a convenient classificatory account of the types of relations found in the psychophysical experiment. What about the relations of the experiment on phenomenal appearances? Is there a distinction between the data of the introspective and psychophysical experiments? Certainly there seems to be in two respects. First, both the stimuli and responses of the introspective experiment are relatively unrestricted. They depend for their occurrences upon the behavior of a subject who is responding and being stimulated in many different ways. Secondly, neither stimuli nor responses are measured in the introspective experiment, and so a quantitative description of stimulus-response dependence is impossible. While it is true that stimuli and responses are presumably related from a rigorous mathematical point of view, the statement has little utility in the absence of knowledge of the specific relation. Nevertheless, we can use the reports of such an experiment at a conversational level to provide us with hypotheses to be tested in the more formalized psychophysical experiment. We may also examine the reports themselves with a view to analyzing them in the context of a descriptive or explanatory system of language.

It is to be hoped that we shall not long remain ignorant of what the subject is doing in the introspective experiment and, in fact, in any circumstance in which he talks.

The question has been asked whether or not the instruction-stimulus variables in Eq. (1) are to be understood as mensurable or susceptible to mathematical representation in any way comparable to the stimulus-aspect terms, or even to various physiological-state variables of a sort for which mathematical representation may be conceived. How, it is asked, may instruction stimuli be put into Eq. (1) so that one may still end up with a mathematical statement?

It is obvious that, at present, there is no measurable state due to instruction stimuli comparable, for example, to the concentration of visual purple as it is measured by reflection from the back of the eye in the technique used by Rushton [41]. The latter example gives an outstanding example of the direct measurement of a condition of the subject.

The conditions of the organism established by instructions are not now directly measurable but some of their effects are. An example of this kind of dependence is given in a paper by Smith and Wilson [43] who studied frequency of hearing an 800-cps tone for various signal-to-noise levels. The authors showed that two sets of instructions, one telling the subject to be conservative and the other to be liberal in reporting the presence of a tone, had an effect on the position and shape of the frequency of hearing curves. The curve for liberal instructions assumed a position generally above the curve for conservative instructions and at lower values of signal-to-noise.

The results are described in terms of a formulation which considers the subject's attitude toward reporting. The effect of attitude is to move a cut-off line along a dimension of intensity effect. A signal falling above this line is reported; one falling below the line is not reported. Under the terms of the formulation, the percentage of reports under conservative instructions increases in a manner different from the percentage of reports under liberal instructions.

It may be objected that the parameter that establishes the intensity effect above the conservative cutoff and the intensity effect above the liberal cutoff are essentially critical aspects of stimuli. Of course, these "condition" parameters are not independent of stimulus values, but this is, in fact, in accord with possibilities implicit in Eq. (1), where it is stated that the variables are not necessarily independent of each other. In this connection, it is worth pointing out that in the absence of a more fundamental treatment—such as might be provided by a direct measure of instructional effects—the variation of certain parameters of the experimental curves may provide a useful and appropriate method for measuring or specifying quantitative contributions of instructions. Presumably, this type of specification can be a rather general one and could apply in many circumstances. Another method that might be suggested would concern some sort of appropriate scaling of instruction stimuli. Values properly introduced into the rational formulation might have useful consequences. No doubt, other possibilities of formulating contributions of instructions may become available.

DESCRIPTIVE AND EXPLANATORY TERMINOLOGY: SENSORY DIMENSIONS

The stimulus-response relations of the sensory and perceptual experiment have often been classified and described in terms of psychological, sensory, or perceptual dimensions. Among the frequently discussed dimensions are those to which the terms *brightness, hue, duration,* etc., have been applied. In some contexts these terms may be taken as analogous to or interchangeable with attributes of sensation. In other contexts they are taken to be psychological correlates of aspects of stimuli. In any case, it seems clear that psychologists require terms of this sort to specify and classify the types of behavior involved in discrimination experiments. Our problem concerns the formal significance for behavior of terms of this sort. In considering the meanings of these words in an objective psychology, we shall here deal with certain examples taken, for illustrative purposes, from the field of color vision. In this area it might conceivably be possible to get along without such words as "color," "brightness," "saturation," or "hue," provided that we could specify the end terms of a given discrimination. Experience, however, shows that, even if we could always (as we cannot) express uniquely the energy relations that correlate with a given response (and vice versa), the use of such terms would be cumbersome. For this reason we shall here consider the roles of such words as "hue," "saturation," "brightness," "color," and "chromaticness." We shall not argue the question of whether these names are labels, intervening variables, or hypothetical constructs. The applicable terms will probably be chosen on the basis of the theorist's attitude.

Consider, first, the use of the term *hue.* This term is to be understood as either a label for or as an inferred effect (behavioral, physiological, or mathematico-representational) in the following stimulus-response sequence: (1) instructions to a subject who has had a past history with the vocabulary represented in the instructions, (2) the presentation of radiant energy to the subject, and (3) the subject's responses. It turns out, as a matter of empirical fact, that wavelength is the most important variable in (2) for hue discrimination.

The dependence of hue discrimination on wavelength may have been established early in such observations as the ordering of stimuli by a person when he is instructed to arrange colors on the basis of hue. The subject is said to discriminate differences in hue when he gives one response (for example, a hue name) to a radiant flux of one narrow wavelength band and another response to flux of a different wavelength. Another type of correlated observation involves the subject's giving one response ("No, there is no difference in hue") to a small difference between wavelengths of a pair of stimuli, and another response ("Yes, there is a difference in hue") to a larger difference. The threshold wavelength difference is evaluated at the appropriate frequency of occurrence of the two responses.

It will be observed that the word "hue" comes into play at least twice in the sequence of instructions, stimulus, and response. It occurs as part of the instructions, as in the statement "Arrange these colors on the basis of hue," and it is the term for the inferred effect relating stimulus and response, or the label for the relation.

The word "hue" used in the instructions (and reacted to by the subject) is analytically a different word from the word applied to the discrimination. The difference in the two is comparable to the difference discussed by Bergmann and Spence [1] when they contrast the social language of the subject and the experimenter with the metalanguage of the experimenter as a scientist. Possibly, the difference could be specified by the use of subscripts, as in hue_i and hue_d where the former word represents the term in the instructions, and the latter the term applied to the discrimination. The former term controls a subject's activity; it tells him what to do; it may imply little or no theoretical context. The latter term involves whatever meanings may be attached to it by its ramifying empirical and theoretical connections. Thus, for example, it may imply an elaborate context of physiological mechanisms.

Considerations comparable to those holding for the word "hue" exist with respect to the term *saturation*. The term represents the inferred effect or relational label holding between such a stimulus variable as colorimetric purity and differential responses that exist when a subject is instructed to order colors on the basis of, for example, "paleness of color."

Differences in brightness may be discriminated by processes analogous to those holding for hue discrimination. The subject, under instructions to arrange stimuli according to brightness or to indicate brightness differences, gives different responses (for example, the words "dim" and "bright") to different luminances, or he may differentially signal a difference between luminances. Such discriminations are said to be brightness discriminations. The word "brightness" appears in the double sense characteristic of the word "hue."

The term *color* represents a generic type of discrimination based on a combination of wavelength, colorimetric purity, and luminance. The subject, properly instructed, can respond by naming different colors or with such differential responses as "Same color," or "Different."

The term *chromaticness* is of considerable interest, based as it is on a very definite type of representational theory: the chromaticity diagram. Chromaticness theoretically represents a generic type of discrimination based on a combination of wavelength and a quantity called excitation purity. It thus may be taken to be a combination of hue and saturation, with brightness removed from consideration. As a concept, it is based on a highly abstract mathematical representation, and its correlated responses have not as yet been carefully considered.

The words "sensation" and "perception" themselves require some discussion. The words do not in themselves refer to an inferred effect (as has been the case with the words previously discussed). They are class names for all such variables. Presumably, they are to be understood as the classes of all relations conventionally subsumed under the words "sensation" and "perception." (We shall not here go into the problem of formal bases for this subsumption.) In any case, we should not expect to hypothesize about a generic process of perception as we might about a specific component process such as hue, brightness, etc.

This discussion of representative terms in the field of color, some being taken directly from an older psychology, will probably show that the latter terms can be used in the vocabulary of a behavior science. Whether they will serve there more suitably than new terms is an open question. Would it be better, for example, to speak of wavelength discrimination rather than hue? On this problem, at least one thing may be said: Comparable aspects of wavelength discrimination show different dependencies on wavelength as functions of other variables. Put in another way, hue varies with other factors than wavelength. The difficulty posed by this fact can be surmounted, but possibly only at the cost of some terminological cumbersomeness.

RELATIONS OF SENSATION AND PERCEPTION: SOME IMPLICATIONS OF AN EXPERIMENT

What are the relations between sensation and perception? A useful answer to this question is given by people who say that the basic sensory problem in perception is the analysis of cues.

First, consider the analysis of cues from the point of view of the psychophysicist. A cue variable is specified when experiment shows the stimulus conditions that are required for a given response. Can it be shown, we may ask, that one specified stimulus cue is more elementary than another for the production of a given class of response? The answer to this question is, of course, a theoretical one. The subject does not give the answer; it is the experimenter's and theorist's statement that gives a basis for making the judgment. It often happens when the account is available that we are no longer interested in the question because we have something better, a relation.

The interpretation as to elementary products of analysis that holds for the psychophysicist holds also, but in more specific detail, for the psychophysiologist. His specification of cues is similar to that of the psychophysicist; it is only in terms of theoretical physiological considerations (augmented when need be by experimental physiological observations on preparations) that he gives a process account for the intact organism. Judgments as to what is elementary have no significance for other than classificatory purposes. Finally, it should be mentioned that the situation as regards sensation in an earlier day was no different from the one that holds in the case of analytic elements today. Titchener [48], for example, did not claim that sensations were observed. They resulted, he said, from logical analysis, i.e., theory, applied to perception.

This discussion of elements indicates that operationally and with respect to experimental procedures and outcomes the presumed differences between sensory discrimination and perceptual discrimination are meaningless. It is, however, a fact that within the general body of perceptual relations, different theoretical representational schemes exist, involving different levels and numbers of subrepresentations. In a word, different kinds and degrees of theory are interspersed among the modal subject matters of perception. These theories are parts of what will eventually become an inclusive network of relations that describe and explain the field of perception. Included in these connecting relations are some that, due to historical factors, have received the term *sensory*. The continued use of the term can be justified only as a matter of convenience, not of substance.

One may at this point make a plea concerning the general study of perception. Specifically, it is this: Since sensory theory is an integral part of perceptual theory, then let us hope that the future will see the integration of subject matters and theory within the same array of connections. To disregard the so-called "sensory" in a consideration of perception can only be done at the cost of relevant information.

Experiments on visual duration.   To indicate the connections that may exist between a presumably perceptual determination and its sensory implications, let us consider the following question, well known to workers on the span of attention: How many words can be recognized in a flash of light lasting 0.001 sec? Under these circumstances it will be found that a certain number of words can be recognized *if* the luminance of flash is great enough; if it is not, no words will be seen. There is evidence to show that the energy required to provide a given effect in these circumstances (reading of a given number of words) is, up to the limit of a critical duration t_c, in accordance with the Bunsen-Roscoe law, $Lt = c$, where L is luminance; t, time; and c, a constant characteristic of the criterion effect. This type of result would be expected to hold in the case at hand when it is a necessary condition that each sensory receptor of the stimulus pattern contribute its action to the over-all activity involved in recognizing words. The limiting unit of action is an increase or decrease in the photolytic effect in the sense cell, and to this the Bunsen-Roscoe law applies nearly exactly [16, 20]. This type of result has been shown to hold specifically for the perceptual performance involved in the span of attention. Hunter and Sigler [28] have shown that, for the correct report of number of dots not exceeding eight, the law applies up to approximately the limits of critical duration; thereafter, the relation $L = c' = c/t_c$ applies up to a duration of about 1 sec. Beyond the critical duration (and up to about 1 sec) the maximum number of dots correctly identified exceeds eight.

It is probably unnecessary to go into the details of the significance of the critical duration. It can be understood in terms of a hypothetical, probably idealized, experiment on reaction time. The subject is told to respond immediately when he sees a flash of light. The time between onset of light and reaction is measured. Flashes of light are presented to the subject in varying durations and luminances. It is found experimentally that, up to a critical duration, light of short duration (with luminance constant) and low luminance (with duration constant) gives a short reaction time. Beyond the critical duration, reaction time varies only with luminance. The relationship is such that, for a given wavelength composition of light and within a critical duration, the Bunsen-Roscoe law holds for a given reaction time. Above the critical duration, $L = c'$.

What is the meaning of the critical duration in an experiment of this kind? We shall consider this question in connection with a light longer than critical duration (i.e., longer than about 0.01 sec, depending on the area of the stimulus), say, 0.05 sec. During this duration the subject, who has been instructed to respond to a light as rapidly as he can, either sees the initial part of the flash or not, depending on luminance. If he sees the initial part of the flash, he presses a key; thereafter any light entering the eye during the stimulus duration is wasted so far as seeing goes. Thus the critical event that triggers the subject's response takes place considerably before the light has stopped shining. Under these circumstances, it is meaningless to talk about stimulus duration as influencing reaction time when the subject reacts to the initial onset of light.

Determinations relating to the critical duration might be used to elucidate important information about the effects of visual stimulation, for example, the nature of behavior (given in the span of attention experiment) to stimuli exposed for medium durations (0.05 to about 0.5 sec) as contrasted with responses given to stimuli of durations shorter than 0.05 sec. Behavior of the first type is called estimating behavior; behavior of the second type is called subitizing [31]. Presumably the reaction of the subject to initial triggering events is represented in his subitizing reactions to short flashes. Under these conditions, a subject can correctly identify the number of dots up to a limit of six to eight; this datum was formerly called the span of attention. The event that is sufficient to provide a span of attention does not provide a correct estimate of more than six to eight dots. Estimations applicable to more than six to eight dots may require counting behavior. The events that provide such responses do not occur immediately after the initial effects of light, and it is obvious that critical events involving counting, verbalizing, etc., take place long after the beginning of the flash. Under these circumstances, the number of correct responses for large numbers is limited only by such a factor as the time required to count large numbers in the presence of illumination that continues for a long time. The events controlling the response, of course, take place far beyond the critical duration.

The duration threshold. A methodological problem related to the preceding discussion arises in connection with experiments on the duration threshold.

An experiment on the duration threshold may involve a procedure such as the following: An exposure device is used to present stimuli such as words, figures, etc., for known durations (at a constant luminance) immediately following a preexposure luminance. The experimenter sets the shortest exposure duration to be used and presents a word in the form of a flash. The subject looks at the illuminated surface of the screen during the preexposure period and attempts to pronounce the name of the word that appears on the screen during the exposure interval. If the subject cannot pronounce it, the exposure duration is then changed to a new and longer value and the same word presented again. The subject is tested at longer and longer durations until an exposure is reached where the word is reported correctly. This value of exposure is taken to be the duration threshold. The threshold may be treated as a function of a number of variables. Howes and Solomon [25], for example, studied it as a function of word probability and McGinnies, Comer, and Lacey [33] as a function of word length and word frequency.

Many, though not all, experiments on the duration threshold involve as their shortest durations rather long exposures in the vicinity of 0.01 sec, which itself is near the critical duration. However, the shortest duration available in a given experiment has no implications for the argument about to be presented. The essential thing is that as duration increases beyond the critical duration, one enters a temporal domain in which increasing duration has no effect in determining a response to light onset. Repeated exposures at increasing duration beyond the critical duration simply mean increase in the number n of the same effective exposures. In a word, the increasing duration does not change the stimulus for a given initial event. For durations greater than critical, $L = c'$. If a presumed threshold is found at the end of a series of increasing durations, the duration taken as threshold, the last duration of the series, is, in fact, an artifact. In this type of experiment and for durations between about 0.01 and 1.0 sec, the number of flashes n (irrespective of the changes in duration) is an inverse measure of probability of seeing. In such an experiment, the theoretically appropriate threshold to determine is the luminance threshold.

If, in a different type of experiment, the relevant consideration is estimation behavior, where responses to more than six to eight dots are examined, a different story would be expected to apply; durations beyond critical duration *would* have significant effects on performance; the number of dots correctly identified would increase with t. [For additional considerations relating to duration thresholds, see the experiment by Goldiamond and Hawkins (*J. exp. Psychol.*, 1958, **56**, pp. 457, 463), who were able to simulate duration-threshold data without stimuli.]

Those considerations which, in the present situation, apply to duration and luminance factors imply the need to understand the sensory laws that limit perceptual discriminations. It is obvious in the present instance that no clear idea of perceptual processes can be gained independently of a full appreciation of sensory effects. "Operationally and with respect to experimental procedures and outcomes the presumed differences between a sensory discrimination and perceptual discrimination are meaningless." (See Graham [12].)

FORMAL PROPERTIES OF PSYCHOPHYSICAL MEASUREMENT

In 1932, a committee of distinguished scientists of the British Association for the Advancement of Science was appointed to consider whether quantitative estimates of sensory events are possible. In 1938, the committee's report contained disagreements, and a request was made for reappointment to consider whether the views expressed could be reconciled. In 1939, in a final report, it was concluded that agreement was impossible, and separate answers were published representing various views.

Those physicists who gave a negative answer to the question whether quantitative estimates of sensory events are possible agreed that whatever else sensory psychologists might be doing, they do not, properly speaking, make measurements.

A principal objection to the use of the term *measurement* in psychology was that psychological measurement is not *fundamental* measurement in Campbell's sense of the term [17]. A fundamental measurement, according to Campbell, is a measurement that, *inter alia,* does not depend on the measurement of any other magnitude. The measurement of length, mass, and time are often given as examples. As Bergmann and Spence express it, fundamental scales require operations exclusively within a dimension. "Manipulations within a dimension do not involve utilization of any of the empirical laws which connect it with other dimensions. The manipulations, for instance, by which we compare the lengths of yardsticks and build their operational sum . . . lie entirely within the dimension of length" [1]. "The operation of measuring length depends upon judgements of the contiguity of parts of lines, which is a relation instinctively perceived" [4].

It was more than a hundred years ago that Bessel's investigations of errors in measuring stellar transits—a "fundamental" measurement of time—showed clearly that use of these measurements must involve consideration of psychological properties of the observer.

As Menger [34] points out, measurements in empirical science are classes of ordered pairs, in which one element represents the operation and conditions of making the measurement and the other element the numerical value obtained. Now conditions of making measurements are never pure; they involve the use of instruments whose construction is based on elaborate theory. That is, the result of any measurement includes the complexities of the measuring operation, so that no measurement can be simple or fundamental in the sense of being independent of other measurements. For example, the ordinary operation of measuring length involves consideration of the properties of thermal expansion of the ruler; this, in turn, requires measurement and control of temperature; and this necessitates a thermometer and theory of heat.

The motivation of the fundamentalists seems clear. It is to find an impregnable bedrock as a foundation on which empirical science is to be erected. The recognition that there is no such foundation need not lead to pessimism—science has lived without it up to now.

The operations required in psychophysical measurement involve, in addition, the conditions of the subject. Instruction stimuli are designed to put the subject into a standard condition in the same way that control of temperature and pressure standardizes conditions of many kinds of physical measurement.

Types of measurement can be classified into scales by a consideration of the numerical values of the ordered pairs defined above. We can categorize by means of the group of transformations with respect to which the set of numerical values remain invariant. See Stevens [46] for a discussion of a classification of scales.

RATIONAL ACCOUNTS OF SENSORY RELATIONS

A scale may be thought of as a mathematical representation of a relationship, determined by the class of the scale, with specifiable magnitudes of identifiable phenomena.[9] The empirical scale may be established on the basis of relatively direct recognition of an appropriate representation, or, at the other extreme, the choice of the relation may depend upon the development of a sequence of descriptions or subrepresentations. We may refer to the first type of representation as "empirical" while the second type may be called "rational" or "theoretical." We do not imply that the two differ in kind. Any differentiation between the two types on other grounds than number of subrepresentations in the representational chain is probably not justifiable.

Some psychologists with a positivistic bent seem to imply that the theorist should always strive for a minimum number of subrepresentations. Against this position it may be argued that, whereas one should not multiply hypotheses, neither should one disregard known or tested subrelations in a given descriptive representation.

The establishment of a scale of intensity of sensation would seem to involve the establishment of a mathematical relation for specifiable measured intensities of sensation. It can be shown that the concept of intensity of sensation is formally unnecessary if observations are restricted to the variables that must be used to define intensity of sensation. In such cases, emphasis may be on representations that refer to such variables as frequency of occurrence of contrasting discriminative responses, photochemical processes, etc.

The area of vision displays less extensive use of empirical scales of intensity of sensation than some other areas of sensory psychology. Such scales have played, even recently, an unaccented if not negligible role in systematizing the general area of visual brightness discrimination. In general, little emphasis has been placed on the concept of sensation as a function of stimulation; rather, hypotheses have been advanced in terms of subrepresentations concerning biological processes or behavior principles.

As an example of a rational account that involves a chain of sub-

[9] The basic content of this section was originally prepared by C. H. Graham for presentation at the International Congress of Psychology in 1957. It was not given then but was on a program at the December, 1958, meeting of the American Association for the Advancement of Science.

representations in the area of vision, we shall discuss some research on visual brightness discrimination. The discussion has direct relevance to the subject of intensity of sensation, for it concerns data obtained in the great tradition of the Weber experiment. The account may be significant on another score. It may indicate that, whereas scales of intensity of sensation may be developed by direct-ratio scaling methods, in many cases analysis of the differential threshold as a function of various stimulus variables may tell us far more about the underlying sensory mechanisms. On this score we agree with the statement by Bergmann and Spence [1]; " . . . disguise of interesting results as a search for scales cannot possibly be to the advantage of psychophysics." In what follows we are clearly not interested in scaling; we are interested in explicating, by example, some aspects of an analysis by rational formulation. Finally, and in connection with this account, we raise the interesting question: What may be the fate of a still useful but incorrect rational account?

Recent work has served to indicate some important quantitative characteristics of brightness discrimination in vision [2, 15, 24, 32, 39]. The analysis and basic experiment of Graham and Kemp started from a formulation by Hecht [21] founded on the equation

$$\frac{dx}{dt} = k_1L(a - x)^m - k_2x^n$$

where x is the product of photolysis, $a - x$ the concentration of sensitive material, and L the luminance. According to this equation, the rate of photolysis is represented as a difference between a forward reaction involving light and a back reaction not involving light. Extended to brightness discrimination, the formulation presumes that after a few minutes in the light, the rate of formation of x is brought to a stationary state. When the flash ΔL stimulates the eye under these circumstances, an increase in photolysis occurs, a constant increment providing the basis for discrimination.

It turns out in an experiment of this sort that the duration of ΔL and the relative sizes of the fields are important parameters. Certain considerations applying to the Bunsen-Roscoe law respecting the reciprocal effects of time and luminance indicate that the product of duration of exposure t and ΔL should be a constant up to the limits of a duration t_c. Beyond this critical duration, ΔL is equal to another constant. The finally developed equations for brightness discrimination are

$$\frac{\Delta L \cdot t}{L} = c\left[1 + \frac{1}{(KL)^{1/2}}\right]^2$$

for durations of exposure less than t_c and

$$\frac{\Delta L \cdot t_c}{L} = c \left[1 + \frac{1}{(KL)^{\frac{1}{2}}} \right]^2$$

for durations equal to or greater than t_c.

The factors we have just considered mean that brightness discrimination data, for which $\log \Delta L/L$ is plotted against $\log L$, constitute a family of curves spread along the ordinate axis in such a way that duration of ΔL is a parameter. This expectation is in fact the case, as may be seen in Fig. 6. The position of each curve depends on the value of t associated with it.

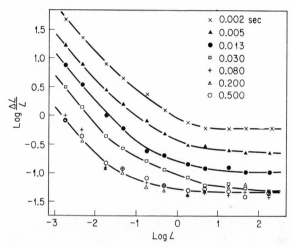

Fig. 6. The relation between $\Delta L/L$ and L for various durations of ΔL [15].

The critical duration is another parameter that determines the particular form of the dispersal of curves on the axes of ordinates and abscissae. It is required that t_c be estimated from the data, and this can be done by an appropriate plot of $\log (\Delta L \cdot t)$ against $\log t$, as shown in Fig. 7. t_c is read from each graph as the value of t at the sharp elbow of each curve. Its relation to prevailing luminance is representable by the equation given by Keller and is determined by a plot of $\log t_c$, found from the preceding graph, against L as in Fig. 8. The data are represented by the equation

$$t_c = t_o L^{-n}$$

where n is approximately 0.12 and t_o a scale constant. When this relation is introduced into the original formulation, it gives us part of the answer to a question that has caused considerable controversy for many years:

Do brightness discrimination curves rise at high luminances or are they flat?

It can be shown that, under these experimental conditions, if the equivalent of t_c, that is $t_o L^{-.12}$, be substituted in the brightness-discrimination equation for durations greater than or equal to t_c, then all curves

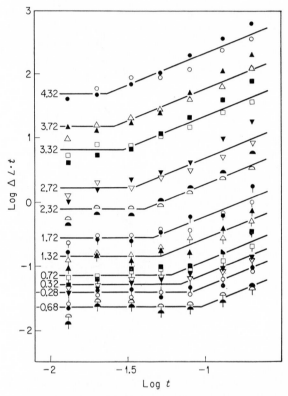

FIG. 7. The relation between ΔL and L for various values of L. Horizontal lines represent the equation $\Delta L \cdot t = c$; inclined lines, $\Delta L = c'$. The number beside each curve is the logarithm of the background luminance [32].

are flat at the high luminances as predicted. If the correction is not stated explicitly and the role of critical duration not evaluated, then the curves do in fact rise. These expectations are represented in the theoretical curves in Fig. 9. For durations greater than critical duration, a plot of log $\Delta L/L$ against log L gives a curve that rises at high luminances. For the same conditions, a plot of log $\Delta L/L^{1.12}$ against log L gives a curve that remains flat.

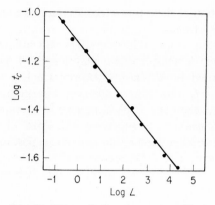

FIG. 8. The relation between critical duration (t_c) and background luminance (L) [32].

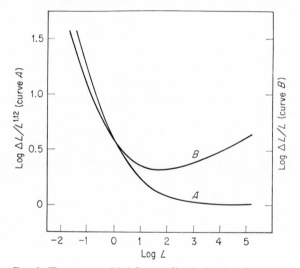

FIG. 9. Two types of brightness-discrimination functions for durations of exposure exceeding critical duration. In curve A log $\Delta L/L^{1.12}$ is plotted against log L. Curve B represents the variations of log L for the same conditions. All values are in arbitrary units [32].

Whether the curve rises at high luminances even for durations smaller than t_c has been shown to depend also on the relative sizes of the two fields. When the test field is similar in size to the adapting field, then even with durations smaller than t_c the curve rises at high luminances. When the test field is much smaller than the adapting field and the duration of exposure smaller than t_c, then the curve remains flat.

Thus a consideration of these two variables resolves a seeming discrepancy between two types of data.

It is obvious that many other variables will influence brightness-discrimination curves. A notable one is wavelength of light. An absorption factor as represented by luminosity theoretically sets the position of the curves on the log L axis. Since, however, the photometric units of L involve luminosity, the cone ("high-intensity") sections of curves for all wavelengths are theoretically superimposed. Area of adapting field for fixed test field is another factor that influences position of the intensity-discrimination curve. For different areas the curves are parallel on the ordinate axis, the curve for the smallest area being displaced to high values of $\Delta L/L$.

It cannot be maintained that the original Hecht formulation is correct. Some recent discussions of new or previously unconsidered data relating particularly to the visual cycle and to quantum factors [35, 38, 41, 49] indicate that some of the subrepresentations of the original account are not correct. Interesting modifications of the original account have been presented by Jahn [29, 30]. It should be observed that the principle involved in this discussion concerning the value of the rational account does not depend for its validity on the correctness or incorrectness of the Hecht theory. The fact, however, that we recognize the original formulation as being certainly incomplete and probably incorrect has interesting significance in the present context, where we have used it as an example of a rational account that specifies testable implications and provides a framework for their structuring. The fact that now we say that the account is incorrect seems to modify a judgment previously held concerning its value.

The fact is, however, that the formulation is still useful. It represents experimental results over a considerable range of governing variables. In addition, it also contains enough useful theoretical ideas so that a wise scientist will be wary about rejecting it completely until a better account comes along. Finally, the formulation has the temporary virtue of encompassing more than a single *ad hoc* relation. In a word, the example given here is by no means the first to be used with recognition of weaknesses and the need for caution. Few hypotheses are correct beyond a restricted domain, and it may be better to use one that represents a considerable degree of testable thought than to start anew at a first evidence of failure. Sometimes it is better to patch than to build anew. Sometimes the reverse is true.

SUMMARY

This chapter discusses four topics that are important in a consideration of the interrelations of sensory psychology and related fields. The point of view taken is one of emphasizing the behavioral aspects of sensory discrimination. The topics are introduced and characterized in the introductory section of this paper.

1. The first topic deals with the types of stimulus-response relations that apply to the following forms of behavior: (*a*) introspective or phenomenological descriptions, (*b*) psychophysical discriminations, (*c*) absolute judgments, and (*d*) thresholds and perceptual functions.

In the case of experiments involving introspective or phenomenological description, neither stimulus nor response is usually quantitative. Only *b* and *d* usually involve measured aspects of both stimulus and response. Special attention is paid in the case of the absolute judgment to numerical estimates of brightness. Two ways of specifying the results of this type of experiment are described, and the quantitative and psychological implications of both are discussed. It is suggested that the numerical character of brightness estimates is to be specified by further analysis; it is not to be taken for granted as representing a measured quantity any more than are, for example, the verbal responses involved in color naming.

The nature of a threshold is examined. The threshold is a single critical value derived from a psychophysical curve. Because of its existence, the data of a whole curve may be represented by a single value. When several thresholds are determined as a function of a controlling variable, we obtain a perceptual (or critical-value) curve.

A symbolic formulation treats response as a function of stimulus aspects, time, and conditions of the subject. This formulation has been discussed previously in other articles [8, 9, 11, 13]. It provides a context for classifying various types of sensory and perceptual experiments. It is pointed out that influences due to conditions of the subject, e.g., as exhibited by instructions, may be specified in a number of ways. One important way involves noting how psychophysical functions vary with conditions of the subject.

2. The second topic considers how psychological dimensions or attributes may be described in a stimulus-response psychology. The terms *hue, brightness,* and *saturation,* taken from color vision, are analyzed and their formal characteristics specified. The terms are found to represent inferred variables in a stimulus-response relation or to be labels for such relations. The meaning of the class terms *sensation* and *perception* are also considered.

3. The third topic deals with relations of sensation and perception. On various bases it is stated that the use of the word "sensory" as different from "perceptual" can be justified only as a matter of convenience, not of content. Various aspects of experiments on visual duration are described to show that the duration threshold, often taken to represent a measure of perceptual discrimination, is to be understood

in terms of data that are often thought of as sensory. Perceptual and sensory data lie within a single coextensive domain.

4. The fourth topic deals with the nature of measurement in general and psychophysical measurement in particular. We argue that all measurement involves considerations of dimensions other than those being measured, and hence that no measurement is fundamental in Campbell's sense of the term. We believe also that instruction stimuli to a human subject (or a training procedure for an animal) play the same role in standardizing conditions of measurement as the control of temperature and pressure in many kinds of physical measurement.

5. The final topic deals with rational accounts as contrasted with psychological scaling. We believe that workers in the field of psychophysics have often been excessively preoccupied with the problem of psychological scales; much of the subject matter of the field is, we feel, more advantageously treated in other contexts. An example of rational description and theory is presented for the classical case of brightness discrimination. It is concluded from the discussion that the rational treatment of this selected case has many useful outcomes, even though it may need modification or replacement. The question of what one does when a rational account is found to be inadequate (even though it continues to predict data quantitatively) is considered. It is concluded that the advantages of a given rational account are not rejected until a better account is developed.

REFERENCES

1. Bergmann, G., & Spence, K. W. The logic of psychophysical measurement. *Psychol. Rev.*, 1944, **51**, 1–24.
2. Biersdorf, W. R. Critical duration in visual brightness discrimination for retinal areas of various sizes. *J. opt. Soc. Amer.*, 1955, **45**, 920–925.
3. Bush, R. R., & Mosteller, F. *Stochastic models for learning.* New York: Wiley, 1955.
4. Campbell, N. R. *An account of the principles of measurement and calculation.* London: Longmans, 1928.
5. Estes, W. K. The statistical approach to learning theory. In S. Koch (Ed.), *Psychology: a study of a science.* Vol. 2. New York: McGraw-Hill, 1959. Pp. 380–491.
6. Ferguson, A. (Ch.), Quantitative estimates of sensory events. *Advancement Sci.*, 1940, **1**, 321–333. (Final report of the Committee)
7. Garner, W. R. Advantages of the discriminability criterion for a loudness scale. *J. acoust. Soc. Amer.*, 1958, **30**, 1005–1012.
8. Graham, C. H. Psychophysics and behavior. *J. gen. Psychol.*, 1934, **10**, 299–310.
9. Graham, C. H. Behavior, perception and the psychophysical methods. *Psychol. Rev.*, 1950, **57**, 108–120.

10. Graham, C. H. Visual perception. In S. S. Stevens (Ed.), *Handbook of experimental psychology.* New York: Wiley, 1951. Pp. 868–920.
11. Graham, C. H. Behavior and the psychophysical methods: an analysis of some recent experiments. *Psychol. Rev.,* 1952, **59,** 62–70.
12. Graham, C. H. Form perception and sensory processes. In J. W. Wulfeck & J. H. Taylor (Eds.), *Form discrimination as related to military problems.* Washington: National Academy of Sciences, National Research Council, 1957.
13. Graham, C. H. Sensation and perception in an objective psychology. *Psychol. Rev.,* 1958, **65,** 65–76.
14. Graham, C. H. Color theory. In S. Koch (Ed.), *Psychology: a study of a science.* Vol. 1. New York: McGraw-Hill, 1959. Pp. 145–287.
15. Graham, C. H., & Kemp, E. H. Brightness discrimination as a function of the duration of the increment in intensity. *J. gen. Physiol.,* 1938, **21,** 635–650.
16. Graham, C. H., & Margaria, R. Area and the intensity-time relation in the peripheral retina. *Amer. J. Physiol.,* 1935, **113,** 299–305.
17. Guild, J. Discussion of the paper by Richardson [40, pp. 114–116].
18. Guild, J. In denial of the measurability of sensation intensity. In A. Ferguson (Ch.), *Advancement Sci.,* 1940, **1,** App. IV, 344–347.
19. Guilford, J. P. *Psychometric methods.* New York: McGraw-Hill, 1954.
20. Hartline, H. K. Intensity and duration in the excitation of single photoreceptor units. *J. cell. comp. Physiol.,* 1934, **5,** 229–347.
21. Hecht, S. A theory of visual intensity discrimination. *J. gen. Physiol.,* 1935, **18,** 767–789.
22. Hecht, S., Shlaer, S., & Pirenne, M. H. Energy, quanta, and vision. *J. gen. Physiol.,* 1942, **25,** 819–840.
23. Helson, H. Fundamental problems in color vision. I. *J. exp. Psychol.,* 1938, **23,** 439–476.
24. Herrick, R. M. Foveal luminance discrimination as a function of the duration of the decrement or increment in luminance. *J. comp. physiol. Psychol.,* 1956, **49,** 437–443.
25. Howes, D. H., & Solomon, R. L. Visual duration threshold as a function of word-probability. *J. exp. Psychol.,* 1951, **41,** 401–410.
26. Hull, C. L. *Principles of behavior.* New York: Appleton-Century, 1943.
27. Hunter, W. S. The subject's report. *Psychol. Rev.,* 1925, **32,** 153–170.
28. Hunter, W. S., & Sigler, M. The span of visual discrimination as a function of time and intensity of stimulation. *J. exp. Psychol.,* 1940, **26,** 160–179.
29. Jahn, T. L. Brightness discrimination and visual acuity as functions of intensity. *J. opt. Soc. Amer.,* 1946, **36,** 83–85.
30. Jahn, T. L. Kinetics of visual dark adaptation. *J. opt. Soc. Amer.,* 1946, **36,** 659–665.
31. Kaufman, E. L., Lord, M. W., Reese, T. W., & Volkmann, J. The discrimination of visual number. *Amer. J. Psychol.,* 1949, **62,** 498–525.
32. Keller, M. The relation between the critical duration and intensity in brightness discrimination. *J. exp. Psychol.,* 1941, **28,** 407–418.

33. McGinnies, E., Comer, P. B., & Lacey, O. L. Visual-recognition thresholds as a function of word length and word frequency. *J. exp. Psychol.*, 1952, **44**, 65–69.

34. Menger, K. Mensuration and other mathematical connections of observable material. In C. W. Churchman & P. Ratoosh (Eds.), *Measurement: definitions and theories.* New York: Wiley, 1959.

35. Mueller, C. G. Frequency of seeing functions for intensity discrimination at various levels of adapting intensity. *J. gen. Physiol.*, 1951, **32**, 463–474.

36. Ogle, K. N. Theory of stereoscopic vision. In S. Koch (Ed.), *Psychology: study of a science.* Vol. 1. New York: McGraw-Hill, 1959. Pp. 362–394.

37. Pirenne, M. H., & Marriott, F. H. C. Absolute threshold and frequency of seeing curves. *J. opt. Soc. Amer.*, 1955, **45**, 909–912.

38. Pirenne, M. H., & Marriott, F. H. C. The quantum theory of light and the psycho-physiology of vision. In S. Koch (Ed.), *Psychology: a study of a science.* Vol. 1. New York: McGraw-Hill, 1959. Pp. 380–491.

39. Ratoosh, P., & Graham, C. H. Areal effects in foveal brightness discrimination. *J. exp. Psychol.*, 1951, **42**, 367–375.

40. Richardson, L. F. The measurability of sensations of hue, brightness or saturation. In *Report of a joint discussion on vision* (held on June 3, 1932, at the Imperial College of Science by the Physical and Optical Societies). London: London Physical Society, 1932. Pp. 112–114.

41. Rushton, W. A. H. The cone pigments of the human fovea in colour blind and normal. In *Visual problems of colour.* Vol. I. (National Physical Laboratory, Symposium No. 8.) London: H. M. Stationery Office, 1958. Pp. 71–101.

42. Skinner, B. F. The operational analysis of psychological terms. *Psychol. Rev.*, 1945, **52**, 270–277.

43. Smith, M., & Wilson, E. A. A model of the auditory threshold and its application to the problem of the multiple observer. *Psychol. Monogr.*, 1953, **67**, 1–35.

44. Smith, T. The quantitative estimation of the sensation of colour. *Br. J. Psychol.*, 1929–30, **20**, 362–364.

45. Stevens, S. S. Mathematics, measurement, and psychophysics. In S. S. Stevens (Ed.), *Handbook of experimental psychology.* New York: Wiley, 1951. Pp. 1–49.

46. Stevens, S. S. The direct estimation of sensory magnitudes: loudness. *Amer. J. Psychol.*, 1956, **69**, 1–25.

47. Stevens, S. S., & Galanter, E. H. Ratio scales and category scales for a dozen perceptual continua. *J. exp. Psychol.*, 1957, **54**, 377–411.

48. Titchener, E. B. *A textbook of psychology.* New York: Macmillan, 1919.

49. Wald, G. On the mechanism of the visual threshold and visual adaptation. *Science*, 1954, **119**, 887–892.

PERCEPTUAL EXPERIENCE: AN ANALYSIS OF ITS RELATIONS TO THE EXTERNAL WORLD THROUGH INTERNAL PROCESSINGS

KARL ZENER* AND MERCEDES GAFFRON†
Department of Psychology
Duke University

Introduction 516
Experiential Events and the Scientific Status of Experiential Properties 517
  The common and differential roles of experience in psychology and in physics. 518
  The special significance of experience for the science of psychology . . 520
A Phase Analysis of Perceiving 523
  Major components of the perceptual-behavioral event 523
  Arbitrariness of selection of any phase as the natural starting point of analysis. 523
  Differentiation between the world of objects or events and the medium world 524
  The world of object-events (Phase 1). 525
  The medium world (Phases X, 2). 526
  Classical cognitive formulation of perception. 528
  Interaction phases and transmission phases; "the" independent variable and contingent conditions 529
  Receptor processes (Phase 3) 530
  The central processes (Phases 4a, 4c, 4e) 532
  The effector process (Phase 5) 536
  The medium world (Phase 6) 536
  The world of object-events (Phases 7, 1'). 537
Interrelations among Phases. 537
The Scientific Status of the Concept of Behavior; Multiple Meanings of Behavior 538
Multiple Meanings of "O Perceives X". 542
Some Implications of the Phase Analysis and of the Discrimination of Specific Meanings of Perceiving for Research in Perception 549

* Pp. 516–562; 608–614.
† Pp. 562–608.

Experiential Report in Relation to the Requirements of Scientific Objectivity . 552
 Cognitive versus phenomenal report: physics versus psychology .   .   . 552
 Reformulated criterion of objectivity 554
Experiential Report: Methodological Comments 556
Phenomenal Properties and Perceptual Organizations 562
 Typical Constellations of Phenomenal Properties in Spontaneous Perceptual
  Reorganizations 564
  "Reversal" as qualitative reorganization 569
  Texture versus brightness organizations 570
  Figure-ground reversal as qualitative reorganization 572
  Qualitative reorganizations, physiological processings, and differential
   behavioral consequences 572
 Anisotropies in Spatial Relationships.   573
  The method of changed picture orientation 573
  Inversions 574
  Right-left reversals 593
 Survey and Perceptual Organization 602
  The "causal" descending diagonal 605
  Experiential anisotropy of eye movements 606
  Effects of looking behavior in actual situations 607
Concluding Statement 608
References.   615

INTRODUCTION

The task undertaken in this essay was an analysis and classification of the facts and relationships generally grouped under the rubric of perception. This was to involve a mapping of the patterns of relationships in terms of relative coherence as contrasted with their overlap with other subfields of psychology or even with certain bordering disciplines. It became immediately evident that the conceptual termini of such relationships were so heterogeneous in character and so ambiguous with respect to their memberships in different scientific language systems as to preclude any precise topographical plotting of lawful relationships. The problem is enhanced by the current lack of concern with determination of ranges of generalization of established relationships, by a lack of clarity as to the experimenters' actual foci of interest, and by a difficulty in distinguishing between systematic and empirical variables. And this has been the case not only in the formulation of problems of perception, but also in explicit decisions in the selection of experimental variables and in theoretical interpretation of experimental findings.

Thus, grouping of relationships would be unduly arbitrary. A precondition for the proposed task of mapping has seemed, therefore, a conceptual analysis of perception based on a more explicit discrimination of its phases and their interrelationships in functioning. Perceptual events cannot profitably be separated from their behavioral context in the interaction or transaction between organism and environment. The analysis of phases, therefore, covers in skeletal form the whole perceptual-behavioral-event sequence, but with more intensive treatment of the afferent phases of the cycle. Such a discrimination should permit clearer identification of foci of theoretical interest, as distinguished from the sheerly empirical experimental variables.

It has not seemed profitable to attempt any explicit definition of the range of problems covered by the single term "perception." Any formal delimitation would inevitably be arbitrary. It has seemed more useful to recognize at the outset that the term has covered a multiplicity of relationships, each representing different foci of interest in the total process. For the present purpose, at least four general kinds of relationships may be discriminated. One set is that between direct experience and its causal conditions or its behavioral consequences (*experiential* relationships). Another set is that between the cognitive, categorizing, or inferential acts and their determinants or behavioral consequences (*cognitive* relationships). A third set is that between differences in stimulus conditions and differential behavior (perceptual *discrimination*). A fourth set is that between a specified form of behavior and its external stimulating or releasing conditions (perception as *behavior control*).

One focus of theoretical interest in the perceptual process which has lately been grossly neglected is experience—as distinguished from behavior and cognition. In the present article we have chosen to concentrate upon the experiential aspect of perceptual functioning, in the hope of some clarification of its relationships to the external world perceived and to internal processes mediating the perception.

Since in communicating about experience there is no adequate verbal substitute for its actual occurrence, we have unconventionally introduced concrete stimulus materials in the form of pictures as an integral part of the presentation. This should permit us to communicate to the reader our own experiential differentiations as stated in verbal phenomenal descriptions by evoking in him corresponding direct experiences through his own perception of the same situations.

EXPERIENTIAL EVENTS AND THE SCIENTIFIC STATUS OF EXPERIENTIAL PROPERTIES

Before proceeding to the phase analysis of perception we want to examine the scientific status of experience as the property of the perceptual process upon which we have chosen to focus. It certainly is not relatable in any simple fashion to any one phase; therefore, we will postpone until the following section the discussion of this relationship. Experience may be conceptualized as one kind of behavior, but this is unsatisfactory because of the highly ambiguous character of the concept of behavior itself (see below, pp. 538 ff.). Also this purely verbal device tends to obscure significant distinctions. Since not all "behavioral" events have experiential properties, let us designate events which do have them as *experiential events.*

In the more typical human perceptual activities the property referred to as experiential, or phenomenal, or conscious—or less appropriately indicated by the nouns "awareness," "consciousness," "experience"—is an integral and significant property of the events. It is not here assumed that this experiential property is a substantive reality separable from the total process of organism-environment interaction (as is perhaps implied by the usage of the nouns).

Here we wish to examine the reasons why this aspect of reality will play such a central role in our present analysis. The discussion may appear to some readers as naïve or boringly obvious. Explicit treatment of the issues involved, however, has seemed necessary before proceeding to the phase analysis since previous discussions have often tended to beg the major issues or treat them cavalierly, although different positions on these issues have radical differential consequences for the study not only of perception, but of the whole of psychology. The level on which the examination is developed reflects our dominant concern with its implications for present *research in perception.* The central role of experience is required by considerations both of an epistemological and of an empirical, even a quasi-ontological, nature. Let us first examine the former.

That the individual scientist's own experience constitutes his most immediate, direct, subjectively most certain acquaintance with reality is scarcely open to serious question. That upon occasion it may mislead him with respect to objective properties of reality is also evident. Nevertheless, the experience of each individual may safely be accepted as *his* most certain starting point for *his* empirical knowledge. "Objective," public, scientific knowledge presupposes individual knowledge.

The common and differential roles of experience in psychology and in physics. Our primary concern is the special status of experience of the individual for the psychology of perception, rather than its status for scientific knowledge in general. It is frequently asserted that all the sciences, from physics to psychology, are in an identical situation epistemologically in that they all are equally dependent on reports of direct experience for their basic data. Because of this position, it is desirable to examine the reasons for asserting a special significance of experience for perception and, more generally, for the science of psychology. Titchener stated that the same experiences (of time, space, mass) are the subject matter of psychology and physics, but are approached from different points of view; that "there can be no essential difference between the raw materials of physics and the raw materials of psychology" [58, pp. 6 ff.]. Pratt has contended that the world of experience may be subdivided into sectors, each of primary concern to individual sciences [52, pp. 27 ff.]. Köhler has argued, "So far, direct experience has been shown to be the raw material of both physics and psychology" [41a, p. 29]. The "physicist and the psychologist are once more in exactly the same situation. It does not matter at all whether I call myself a physicist or a psychologist when I observe a galvanometer. In both cases my observation is directed toward the same objective experience" [41a, p. 29].

In this situation, both the physicist and the psychologist are actually concerned with the objective alignment of pointer and mark, not with their visually experienced alignments, except derivatively. Except in a psychophysical experiment, the primary focus of both is the magnitude of that property of the physical system which he is measuring and which is *indicated* by the alignment. Although both proceed from an experiential, perceptual, observational act, the actual report is generally a cognitive, not a phenomenal, one; both remain basically indifferent to the particular experiential character of the perception, provided sufficient accuracy is attained in estimating the objective state of affairs.

This is likely to be generally quite satisfactory for the physicist, since the perceptual situation in pointer readings is one in which variations in phenomenal character are slight, both qualitatively and quantitatively, and it is functionally very flexible in that it can be connected via a physical instrument with a great variety of physical situations. This is so for the physicist since the security of his inference to the aspects of reality in which he is primarily interested rests upon his adequate knowledge of the structure of his instrument, of the physical laws governing its operation, its calibration, and the character of the connection of the instrument with the relevant physical events. Furthermore, this is all knowledge which it has taken centuries to achieve. It tends to be forgotten (except in actual experimental practice) that such crass control observations—as to whether electrical contacts are tight or whether leaks in a vacuum system exist—are as crucial in interpreting the meaning of a pointer reading as is the reading itself.

The experimenting physicist's concern with experiential aspects of his perceptions is to standardize the effects of their ubiquitous intrusion into his observations. He designs his observational situations to maximally reduce the richness and variety of phenomenal experiences. He uses them in their simplest form as a necessary epistemological tool; but he maximally frees himself from any effects they might exert upon the formation of his concepts and the development of his hypotheses. He does not normally take experience as an essential property of the natural system of events he is investigating, however integrally it may be related to his own observational system. It does not constitute the focus of his scientific thinking. In situations in which the psychologist is interested in recording or measuring some physical property of the organism's "behavior," the same considerations as to irrelevance of the experiential aspects of instrument reading apply. *The difference lies in the fact that practically always the particular experiential character is irrelevant for the physicist—but in many significant situations it is central for the psychologist.*

The physical scientist's lack of interest in the specific qualities of his observation base is stressed here. At the present time, it is heuristically more important to shift the emphasis in discussions of this problem from the assertion of a common, indispensable epistemological role of experience in physics and in psychology to an insistence upon the enormous differences in the detailed character of this role in the two sciences. The later empirical sections of this article provide illustrative evidence of this assertion.

The special significance of experience for the science of psychology. Epistemologically, the role of experience in psychology is most complicated and its empirical significance is enormously more vital. In part this stems from practical considerations. In psychological experimentation the identification of many properties of objective situations of which psychological events are a function may be directly made by—often can be made only by—a particular perceptual (cognitive) act. Often it is much more complex and differentiated than the simple reading of pointer on a scale—the ethologist's identification of a behavioral act as a social stimulus, for instance. Such a perceptual act substitutes, in effect, for the contact of the physicist's observational instrument with the property of the system it is measuring and the controlled conversion of energies within the instrument, as well as for the physicist's own perceptual act. However, for equivalent certainty it requires a knowledge of the cognitive process equivalent to the physicist's knowledge of the instrument; this, of course, does not presently exist. Nevertheless, the analyses of the perceptual act of observation and the act of reporting on experience both lie within the province of psychology. Thus psychology's interest in the epistemological role of experience and its responsibility for analysis of the acts of perception and of report are greater than is the case in any other science.

The major—but strangely most neglected—reason for psychology's focal concern with experience is, however, more empirical and ontological. We will later consider the confusion introduced by the use of the ambiguous systematic word "behavior" to designate the entire realm of psychological events. Here we will examine briefly, without precommitment as to its relation to the concept of behavior, the status of experiential events within the science of psychology.

We have defined experiential events as events which have, among other properties, an experiential or phenomenal character. Our problem is not how much of the reality with which psychology might profitably concern itself *may* be nonexperiential. Certainly a great deal is. Rather the task is to examine the extent to which experiential events themselves, including their phenomenal properties, are a fundamental subject matter of psychology. (An interesting but secondary task would be to determine the character of the limitations which are imposed on any study of the nonexperiential properties of experiential events by a complete rejection, implicit or explicit, of their experiential character.)

Full acceptance of a focal concern with experiential events implies, however, far-reaching reorientation of conceptual thinking and research effort. It would certainly require development of a much more adequate descriptive terminology; a more adequate analysis of the perceptual processes of observation and the linguistic processes of report required to achieve sufficient scientific objectivity; and finally, a much more detailed determination of the role played by experiential properties in the causal context of the "behavioral" aspects of organism-environment interaction. That this would also require a more searching analysis of the descriptive and conceptual properties of the "behavioral" phases of the interaction than has been customary is evident.

It is clear that these requirements are arduous. On strong grounds, their fulfillment has been adjudged scientifically impractical; this is common knowledge to all who are aware of the history of psychology in this country. However, first things should come first; arduousness is not itself a valid reason for regarding any significant task as unachievable. Commitment to a task as forbidding as the one just outlined can be justified only in terms of its great potential value. Let us briefly consider the basic reasons for undertaking it.

Trying to develop a detailed brief for the value of the fullest possible understanding of the character and conditions of human experience would be embarrassing, nearly demeaning. It would be embarrassing in part because to me the necessity of such an argument is scarcely understandable. However, we do not need to document here the effectiveness of the behavioristic revolution in radically transforming our psychological thinking through the effort at exclusive utilization of strictly nonexperiential terms (for corroboration see Hebb [30]). It is sufficient to indicate that although the dogmatism of the behavioristic denial of the scientific usability of experience in psychology has waned—as the earlier volumes of this project have demonstrated—other presentations in this and succeeding volumes will doubtless show that the pragmatic effects of the doctrine have in fact persisted almost undiminished. And intellectually the inertia of the implicit is often far greater than that of the explicit. In the face of this situation, it is not sufficient to point out, almost defensively, that to neglect experience is to ignore one possible access to events, that two approaches are quantitatively better than one [41b, p. 6]. This implies that, in some sense, either is partially adequate. It is our contention that the purely nonexperiential approach is inadequate for many problems in psychology, in particular for those of perception.

The most primitive and fundamental reason for the study of experiential events remains the most compelling—the personal conviction of humans, probably including most psychologists, that direct experience occurs and is in some sense a real, integral, and most significant property of the total perceptual-behavioral event. As a responsible psychologist, is it possible to repudiate this personal conviction or regard it as scientifically irrelevant? Or even the conviction that activity of other humans possesses a somewhat comparable experiential property, however indeterminate its specific character? Experiential events *are* clearly of fundamental significance and value for human beings; for this reason alone, they should constitute the subject matter of the science of psychology. The invitation and challenge to scientific understanding of these events in *all* their properties, including the characteristic experiential properties, is not to be lightly denied on the basis of scientific ineligibility (if such a category in such a context is even admissible) without the fullest exploration of the possibility of developing concepts appropriate to their specific character and indigenous methods of inquiry appropriate to these properties.

Understanding experiential events clearly requires the capacity for adequate characterization of their experiential properties. It is not possible to characterize adequately experiential events by using terms which are cleanly stripped of any direct experiential reference, i.e., by terms referring only to the nonexperiential properties of such events. Thus it is not *technically* possible to characterize in radically nonphenomenal terms the perceiving of a colorful and fragrant flower; the wearing noise of traffic; the movement of a melody; the uneven ground on which one walks; the careening approach of a truck out of control; a patterned, textured terrain viewed from an airplane; the multimodally experienced woods on an autumnal walk; the upturned trusting face of a young child; the pain of a toothache; resistances to an act of courage, of self-determination; the joy, the suffering of another person; the painful fact of noncommunication; the charm of a human gesture or expression, painted or real.

The development of partially adequate nonexperiential indicators for such events would always depend upon their prior identification on a phenomenal basis. The fundamental concern would ultimately remain the understanding of those experiential properties.

If, for the behaving, experiencing individual and for the psychologist as scientist, the phenomenal properties of events are actual, real, they must inescapably be treated as central, as intrinsic in any significant analysis of the process of perception.

A PHASE ANALYSIS OF PERCEIVING

That current theoretical discussions frequently blur over critical distinctions is evident. Our immediate task is to discriminate among the many stages or phases of the perceptual event the minimum number required for unambiguous characterization of functional relationships at the level of specificity desirable in contemporary research. This is undertaken illustratively in terms of a theoretically neutral specification of the essential phases of one representative class of perceptions, the visual perception of and reaction to a distant external object, event, or situation.

Major components of the perceptual-behavioral event. An analysis of the process of perception must start by indicating the actual events and event properties to be analyzed. Human perception of external objects and situations occurs in a context of ongoing interaction between an organism and its environment. The classic statement of this basic fact still remains that of Dewey [15]. Our analysis accepts as fundamental the following components: the experiencing, behaving organism-person and its internal mediating processes; the external environments (the immediately surrounding medium of energy flux and the generally more remote one of external objects and events); a process of changing relationships between these two major components of the situation during the course of the ongoing perceptual interaction itself. It is the peculiar role of experience—the experiential properties of the perceptual interaction—which we wish to emphasize.

Arbitrariness of selection of any phase as the natural starting point of analysis. Since perceptual processes occur typically in a context of an ongoing interaction between organism and environment, full understanding of the events at any instant in any phase of the perceptual process would normally necessitate reference to "remote" conditions beyond the phase. Actually most perceptual generalizations state relationships between the properties of nonconsecutive phases with minimal characterization of the intervening phases. A basic conviction underlying the present analysis is that much is to be gained by clarification of the detailed interrelationships among the different phases. The intent is to increase explicit awareness of the extents and ways in which the in-direct relationships are dependent upon sets of specifiable *contingent conditions* in the intervening phases.

Embedding of the perceptual process in an ongoing behavioral context means that selection of any particular phase as a natural starting point of an analysis is arbitrary, or at least contextually determined. Purely heuristic considerations of ease of communication dictate the device here adopted of starting with the external object and of labeling the phases numerically. This presents an easier analogy with experimental procedures and also is most congruent, paradoxically, with traditional cognitive and physiological formulations with which we will later take issue. Only the sequence and the pattern of interrelationships are to be taken seriously.

Differentiation between the world of objects or events and the medium world.   What is perceived in the perception of distant objects is ordinarily taken to be some object or event segregated in space and time (an apple, a gesture, a melody), or a relationship, or a situation. Their existence and specification in space or time does not generally de-pend upon their being the object of a perceptual process, but upon the external conditions which determine their segregation as actual units. It is these object or event units that *humans* perceive, behave with refer-ence to, remember, and—as experimenters for the most part—control in experimental situations [39]. On the other hand, whether all mammals —for instance, cats—behave characteristically toward physical *objects* rather than toward gaps or volumes in space is questioned by M. Gaffron. Clearly most of the external world, at least spatially considered, is not occupied by physical objects but rather consists of objectless "empty" space, filled, not with objects but with energy fluxes of enormous com-plexity and fluidity. These energies are not ordinarily considered as being perceived, but rather as mediating the perceptions of distant objects. Nevertheless, the energy fluxes are real. Not only are they indispensable for the perception of distant objects, but in many instances have molar properties isomorphically related to them. Furthermore, it is this energy flux of electromagnetic, thermal, chemical, mechanical energies in which the organism is directly environed and through which it moves.

Let us refer to this subdivision of the external world as the "medium world" and the aggregation of more segregated objects and events as the "object-event-world." The existence of whirlpools and whirlwinds shows that such a distinction is a rough, not a sharp, one. Nevertheless it is important for several reasons. Although it is the realities of the object-event-world toward which on the whole we behave, perception of objects is mediated through energies of the medium world, and this *indirectness of contact* constitutes one of the basic problems of perception. It is extraordinary that the distinction between these two external subworlds has taken so long to acquire adequate theoretical sharpness, and it has yet to attain consistent observance.

Brief historical reference to the lack of sharp discrimination between these two subworlds may illustrate the remarkable persistence of confusion. Titchener conspicuously failed to bring his treatment of perception into relation with the external world of stimulus objects, considering chiefly interrelations at the level of stimulation [58]. Watson oscillated in his usage of the term "stimulus" without consistent conceptual differentiation between the stimulus situation defined generally in common-sense language and the stimulus proper (external energy flux) defined in purely physical-chemical terms [62]. Hull stated his basic postulates in terms of the latter, yet in actual experimentation the event controlled (by which the response was consistently elicited) was the object source producing the stimulus energy. And, in his basic summary diagram and his glossary of conceptual interrelations [34, pp. 383, 407], he does not distinguish between stimuli and stimulus objects (although he does so casually in an earlier diagram [34, p. 33]. Koffka [39, pp. 79ff., 98] discriminated between distal and proximal stimuli, discussing even the role of the properties of the medium for stimulus transmission, and so did Brunswik [10]. Theoretical formulation of all perceptual constancy problems requires this distinction. Yet there has remained a remarkable lack of precision of detail in these terminological distinctions. Even the term *proximal stimulus* in vision is ambiguous. It may, for instance, mean either the light energy per se produced by some standard apparatus, as it is before striking the cornea, and thus described independently of any reference to sense organ or receptor; more rarely, as in Hecht's elegant calculation of the minimal stimulus energy required to stimulate under conditions of maximal sensitivity, it may mean the actual photic energy directly stimulating the receptor cells themselves [31].

The world of object-events (Phase 1). The object perceived may be characterized quite independently of any particular perceiving organism. Furthermore it is "the" object (the whole object) which is ordinarily said to be perceived, rather than only that part of it directly *visible* at any one instant. Thus it is generally some sort of unit which is characterized in terms of some one of the many available language systems. However, it is useful analytically to distinguish between that part of the object surface which is visible (the part from which reflected light rays reach the retina—Phase 1: surface visible) and the major parts which at any instant are nonvisible (Phase 1: surface nonvisible). Making this distinction forces us to recognize the ubiquitous role of temporal integration in preserving the phenomenal, cognitive, and reactive *identity* of objects constantly shifting in their momentarily visible parts.

Another distinction required is that between the surface and interior of an object (Phase 1: surface, versus Phase 1: interior). In opaque objects only the former may be visible, yet in definite senses certain interior properties may be said to be visually perceived. The senses in which an object's solidity, heaviness, elasticity, ripeness may be perceived —rather than merely inferred—are the same as the senses in which its surface is said to be perceived. That there is an *increment* of indirectness to the process—and correspondingly an increase of uncertainty with respect to the validity of the correspondence between phenomenal, cognitive, reactive properties of the perception and actual object properties —introduces a quantitative, not a qualitative, change in the perceptual process. Perception of one extremely important class of object interiors, namely, the interior processes of other living organisms, and particularly the subclass of their experiential processes, will be considered later.

The question as to whether only visible object surfaces are really perceived—object interiors being only inferred—raises more than definitional problems. If it is argued that only visible surfaces are perceived because the process of perception is more direct, then why not restrict by definition the object of "direct" perception to the light stimulus, retinal stimulation, optic tract impulses, or even cortical activity in the striate area? Or contrariwise, what is common to the energy transmissions through these phases which is not shared by the effect of a contracting muscle upon the rippling and visible skin superficial to it which is visibly perceived? Two kinds of consideration are relevant. In the perception of a visible surface, there is a certain orderliness and isomorphic relationship in the various actual transmissions and transformations which occur. Furthermore, the media in which the transmission occurs and the processes involved in the energy transformation are rather standard in character. For many purposes, they may be regarded as constant and therefore—with bad logic but with relative impunity—be ignored. This is not so to the same extent in the relationships between interior and surface properties of objects. In some cases, direct energetic relations are involved, particularly in living organisms. But generally the association of properties is not based on present energy relationships. It is either intrinsic, as in the relation of interior to surface structure in quarter-sawed oak, or arbitrary, as in the relation between color and the state of rottenness of an apple. In either case, presumably, a learned connection within the preceiving organism plays an important role in the central perceptual process.

The medium world (Phases X, 2). In the visual perception of distant nonluminous objects, the energies of the medium world are involved in two ways. They constitute the means of transmission from distant object to organism. But clearly the properties of light reflected from a surface are codetermined both by the object surface itself and the composition and character of the illumination falling on it from the medium world (Phase X). Thus, the event standing in *direct relation* to the character of the reflected light is the interaction of surface and incident light in reflection (Interphase X-1, between Phases 1 and 2). Since the factors X and 1 are independent, reflected light itself could give no unambiguous information about the surface properties of the object which is being perceived without some basis for taking into account the character of incident light. It would thus actually be more accurate to say that what is perceived is the *illuminated object.*

Frequently Phase 2, transmission of the light stimulus, is treated as a neutral process. It is, of course, recognized as being dependent upon the general laws of light transmission, but is considered as yielding a one-to-one relation between illuminated object surface and retinal stimulation. Clearly, transmission of light—as of sound—is a function of variable properties of the medium, as illustrated by light reflected from the bottom of a lake, refracted at its surfaces. Obviously variations in the distribution of relevant parameters in the transmitting medium, such as for instance in fog, smog, or haze, may codetermine transmission of light, constituting *contingent conditions* of the perceptual act. Strictly, a distinction should be made between the character of the light as it leaves the object surface (Phase 2: surface), the *distal stimulus;* at successively different points in the medium (Phase 2: medium); and at the point in space where it affects the receptor surface of the organism (Phase 2: receptor surface), the *proximal stimulus.*

Gibson's concept of the optic array is a major conceptual achievement in the past decade in visual stimulus terminology. The conception is this: Not only is there an organization of the external world in terms of segregated physical objects; but there is also a strict organization or, rather, pattern of the light energies at each point in the transmitting spatial medium. At each point the angular distribution of varying light rays corresponds to the major distributions of surrounding reflecting surfaces. When this is supplemented by the motion parallaxes resulting from the movement of the eyes through successive optic arrays and, further, by the distribution of disparities between the structures of the binocular optic arrays, the information for a complete reconstruction of the surfaces and their distances in the environment is given [24, p. 474]. Thus, not only is the world of objects structured, but so also is the optic flux at each point in the medium space. It is the task of the visual receptors to transform the structures of these arrays into patterns of neural excitation.

The object-events of Phase 1 are independent of those of any other phase of the perceptual sequence. They may be characterized in the language systems of any appropriate science and independently of any given observer. This is also true of the optical properties of the medium world. The structure of each of the infinite number of optic arrays in a visual space depends upon the structure and composition of object surfaces surrounding it, upon sources of illumination transmitted or being reflected to it, and upon the distribution of properties within its surrounding medium. Furthermore, its structures or organizations are not dynamically segregated or self-maintaining. The organization is one of patterned energies, but with minimal dynamic interactions.

Classical cognitive formulation of perception. Traditionally the analysis of the sequence of energy transformations underlying perception of a distant object has focused upon the problem of how properties of the external object could be in some sense transmitted to the perceiving brain. Boring has lucidly characterized the changes in conception of this process from one of transmission of copies to the current one of a sequence of energy transmissions and transformations in which not similarity, but relationships of correspondence, an isomorphic preservation of invariant relationships, is maintained from one phase of the sequence to the next [5, pp. 169 ff.]. The primary empirical problem is determination of the extent of the correspondences and specification of the mechanisms involved in the transformation processes. The perceptual process thus conceived consists in alternating phases of transmission and quasi-isomorphic transformation. Modifications introduced in the regions of transformation are considered primarily as a loss of information or "biased sampling" [8, p. 129] either by specific selective action or by blurring through intrusion of noise. Since, in such analysis, the emphasis is upon preservation of relations between properties at each transformation region (our interaction phase), the *specific properties of the system mediating the transformation* are relatively unimportant as compared to the functional fact of adequate transformation. Consequently, the role of *contingent conditions* is considered primarily in terms of their effect upon adequate functioning of the transforming processes. In the extreme, it becomes possible for as astute a theorist as Gibson to postulate a doctrine of psychophysical parallelism, in which exclusive emphasis is placed upon correspondences between what he considers termini in the perceptual process (Phases 1 or 2, and 4: experiential). Underlying this is an implicit assumption that all contingent conditions, that is, all properties of the transforming processes, even including the efferent, are practically constant and thus irrelevant to the central terminal process and to the correspondences empirically determined. Positively stated, Gibson is concerned mainly with the process of perception of the *veridically* perceiving organism [24, p. 459]. Since the formulation is concerned only with cognition of properties of external objects, it is too restrictive for a general statement. It should be clear that the emphasis upon the reality and intrinsic significance of experiential events as developed in the previous section would lead us to question the empirical adequacy of all purely cognitive formulations of the perceptual process.

Interaction phases and transmission phases; "the" independent variable and contingent conditions. The analysis of the first two phases has emphasized several general features of the process of perception. No perception of a distant object can be direct. Intervening processes of energy transformation occur in which properties of the medium or the system in which the transformation occurs plays a contributing, contingent role. For instance, the effective optic array, the last point in the transmission process independent of the organism, contains information which is a joint function of at least three independent factors: illumination, properties of reflecting object surfaces, and properties of the medium (and their distribution over the course of transmission). The components of the optic array, the light rays, are—at their point of origin in the object surface—a joint function of the first two factors. The object surface may therefore be considered a node or region of interaction. (Phase 1: surface). Contrasting with this localized region is the distributed interaction between the propagated light and the properties of the transmitting medium (Phase 2). The retinal surface upon which the light is focused constitutes a second localized region of interaction (Phase 3), where a number of independent factors interact in the production of the next perceptual phase (afferent neural conduction, Phase 4a). Functionally, the phases of interaction differ from transmission phases (the medium world, neural conduction) in two ways. In the internodal phases, the conditions which codetermine the transmission process—for instance, clarity of the atmosphere or temperature of the axon—tend to be both homogeneously distributed along the course of transmission and to remain relatively constant. In fact, strict constancy of such contingent conditions is a basic, and not often fulfilled, requisite for any strict one-to-one relationship between change in distal object properties and central perceptual processes.

In the nodal region a greater variety of converging factors, contingent conditions, interact and these factors are characteristically variable. Indeed, their variation as a function of changes in other remote processes is, in most cases, intrinsic to their role in the perceptual process. This feature becomes more conspicuous at higher levels of neural interaction, where experimental interest may be centered upon the effects of variation of one of the contingent conditions—motivation or directed set upon some property of the experienced object, for instance. Thus at these higher levels only the experimenter's focus of concern determines whether a given factor is classed as a primary independent variable or as one of a set of contingent conditions. Since at the higher, but still afferent, regions of interaction many contingent conditions represent remote and variable processes or states of the organism, it is clear that the output of such *combined projection and interaction* contains, in all cases, information about external-organismic, object-self relations rather than sheerly "objective" information. What is transmitted to the locus of the next phase approximates objective information only when all contingent conditions at all levels are relatively constant.

It is important that the major kinds of "standard" perceptual situations, characterized by relatively stable and specific constellations and intensities of contingent conditions, be recognized by the perceiving organism, as by the experimental investigator in perception, and by the perceptual theorist in his formulation of perceptual relationships.

Receptor processes (Phase 3). The receptor processes involve transmission of light through the optical media as modified by the refractive effects of the optical structures (Phase 3: transformation) so as to produce sharp images on the receptor mosaic and the photochemical processes involved in actual receptor-cell excitation (Phase 3: excitation). In the eye, in the receptor phase, both transmission and regional interaction are present, but separable. In principle, the transmission of light through the optical media in the eye could be considered as a continuation of the extra-organismic transmission of Phase 2 into the organism with active modifications producing sharp images on the retina. A difference in principle, however, consists in the fact that control of refraction in the interest of sharper image productions is regulated by processes within the organism and, thus, constitutes the first interference in the simple, straightforward projective energy transformation from object to brain. The details of actual retinal excitation are determined, furthermore, not only by the objective properties of the optic array and their modifications in transmission within the eye, but also by the relation of specific sectors of the array to specific parts of the differentiated and anisotropic retinal mosaic. This relation is determined by the orientation of the eye, and this in turn by a complex set of organismic processes from shifts at the neural level of compensatory eye movements to shifts on the basis of voluntary attentional processes.

For a phase analysis, all types of supplementary sensory-perceptual apparatus would be functionally analogous to the variable structures of the eye. The apparatus itself could thus be formally regarded as an extension of the organism's receptor structures, and as functionally located in Phase 3: transformation of the perceptual sequence. The range of such artificial apparatus forms a spectrum of complexity from simple spectacles or contact lenses to telescopes or electron microscopes, television apparatus, or oscilloscopes. The appropriate answer to the question of what is seen depends upon the context; that is, upon the purposes of the perceiver and his behavior with reference to the object perceived, and upon the specific meaning of perceiving employed. What is "seen" can thus be either an image on the oscilloscope screen or the firing of a cell in the lateral geniculate body (even though confirmation of the veridicality of the latter perception would require histological procedures). The following conditions are critical in determining the role of such apparatus as processes in Phase 3 of the perceptual sequence: *completeness* of the set of output properties which are in isomorphic correspondence with the properties of the object-event; *constancy* of the interpolated sets of contingent conditions; *control* of variation in these conditions by activities of the organism (analogous to perceptual behavior); and correspondence between such controlling activity and *information concerning it* sent to higher nervous centers (analogous to sensory feedback, kinesthetic or visual, or to innervation return). Of less critical significance for the role played by apparatus in Phase 3 are the number of sequential energy transformations; homogeneity of energies in the interpolated subphases; and complexity of the new sets of contingent conditions. Additional complications arise when the energy striking the "perceived" object (analogous to illumination, Phase X) is itself controlled by the organism (directly, as in the sonar perceptual behavior of bat or porpoise; or indirectly, as in radar or other similar techniques).

In Phase 3, the *primary independent variable* remains the light reflected from the object, transmitted to the organism, and focused upon the retina. The *contingent conditions* include the constant features and variable states of the anatomical refractive and sensitive structures of the eye, together with the intrinsic and extrinsic muscles modifying these structures and changing the orientation of the eye, and levels of adaptation of the retinal receptors. Certain deviations in the anatomical and functional characteristics of the eye can be thought of as pathological but constant—optical defects or color blindness, or phorias for instance. Of the normal variations in state, some are independent of and others are regulated by the ongoing perceptual process itself. Examples of the former are changes of pupillary size through emotional state, for instance; examples of the latter, variation in lens curvature by reflex accommodation. Shifts to foveal location of the object image through voluntary fixation including convergence, in active survey or search behavior, would be examples of higher-level determination of events at this phase.

Thus considered, the specialized receptor organ, the eye, is a nodal region in which a variety of conditions, differently related to the external object *and* to other parts and activities of the organism, interact. A crude listing of the types of functional effects produced by interaction at this phase in the sequence may be useful. (*a*) Clearly there is *transmission of the proximal stimulus* energies of the optic array to the receptor cells. (*b*) These are variously selected (selection of the optic arrays themselves by searching, orienting, behavior of eyelids, head and neck, limbs; of parts of the optic array by eye movements). Not only are the energies affecting each eye selected by the orientation of that eye, but the binocular disparity patterns are also so determined. Thus the *"perceptual behavior" of the organism selects* among the enormous range of available stimuli the small sample of effective stimuli actually involved in stimulation. (*c*) The selected proximal stimuli are *modified* or *transformed* into effective stimuli in ways which crucially affect stimulation of the receptor cells and also their patterns of excitation. Thus the sharpness and the pattern of the optical, retinal image are determined no more by the structure of the optic array than by the structures of cornea and lens, and the latter's variation in accommodation. (*d*) In other senses, conspicuously touch and kinesthesis, motor processes play a more intimate role not only in stimulus selection and modification, but in *codetermination* of such basic properties as intensity and temporal pattern (e.g., in roughness). (*e*) In vision, reflexly regulated eye movements play a critical role in *maximization of conditions of excitation,* e.g., sharpening of contours in accommodation, and in foveal fixation; and (*f*) in *"homeostatic" maintenance* of those same conditions. These include compensatory nystagmic movements. The recent work on stabilized retinal images also shows the crucial role played by physiological nystagmus in maintaining effective conditions of receptor cell stimulation. (*g*) Central mechanisms mediate *variations in receptor cell excitability* as a function of habituation and other changes in central state [44], possibly also excitatory (such influences may in part mediate attentional or motivational functions). A peculiarity of the visual system is that within the retina certain neural interactions (contrast effects, etc.) and other processings occur which usually take place within the central nervous system and, strictly considered, belong in Phase 4*a*. Thus the recent work of Lettvin and others [42*a*] has shown that, within the frog retina, there exist specific neurophysiological mechanisms which may differentially respond to different characteristics of the stimulus and transmit corresponding information to different localized laminar regions in higher (collicular) nervous centers.

The central processes (Phases 4*a*, 4*c*, 4*e*). Beyond the receptor stage the pattern of interrelationships between interacting organismic processes becomes so complex that differentiation of a specific *sequence* of phases would falsify the intimacy of interaction. For practical purposes, the three subphases, afferent (4*a*), central (4*c*), and efferent (4*e*) may be usefully differentiated with no implication of sharp separation.

We will not be concerned with reflex functions, but only with pathways conveying sensory information to the higher nervous centers (Phase 4*a*). Domination of research in this area by the doctrine of specific nervous energy has led to an almost exclusive preoccupation with the search for neural correlates of the simplest physically specifiable properties of the stimulus (Phase 2) for which precise techniques of control have been available. The striking failure to demonstrate marked loss in discrimination of the simpler properties by ablation of presumably relevant cortical projection areas—for instance, pitch discrimination in audition [50]—raise the question as to which properties are related to neural function in these areas. It seems possible that they are related to more complex properties (object properties, that is) or molar relational stimulus properties in the sense of Köhler and Gibson. To the extent that present neurophysiological techniques prove inadequate to the task of complete analysis of neural patterns of this level of complexity, the crasser methods of ablation in combination with further anatomical investigations of relevant connecting systems will continue to be essential. In fact, as shown by the recent elegant studies of Rose and others [54*a*], in which sharp, clean lesions are localized within specific cortical laminae of the visual system, the extirpation method is presently capable of a hitherto unrealized level of refinement. At this level the method becomes applicable to the anatomical and physiological analysis of the functions of specific architectonic regions. Further progress in neurophysiological analyses of sensory-perceptual events at higher neural levels will probably also depend upon increased precision in the specification of molar relational properties of the stimulus (Phase 2). In turn, it is likely, as has been the case in the past, that further identification of some of these stimulus properties will depend upon the prior identification and characterization of new experiential properties (Phase 4: experiential) for which stimulus correlates are being sought.

The classical sensory projection model of perception has, within the past fifteen years, been radically modified by a number of developments in sensory neurophysiology. The discovery by Woolsey and collaborators of multiple sensory and motor areas [65] and the anatomical demonstration of "sustaining" as well as "traditional essential" projections [54*b*] indicate the differentiated character of central sensory projections. They constitute a challenge for the identification of the perceptual properties mediated by the functioning of these different areas. Promise of more detailed specification of such relationships lies in the combination of technical improvements in stimulating microelectrodes with more localized effects, combined with a much more detailed and systematic mapping of neural responses in multiple projection areas, and with adequate histological controls—a combination characteristic of current studies by these investigators. That such differentiation in the sensory projection systems starts at least with second-order neurons has been shown in recent systematic studies of the activity of the cochlear nucleus [54]. Another major modification consists in the demonstration by Magoun and others of the pervasive and relatively nonspecific effects of sensory stimulation attributed to the so-called "ascending reticular system" [18]. That this system is not wholly diffuse, possessing only general dynamogenic properties, is indicated by recent research [55a]. Possibly it represents the functioning of phylogenetic older sensory systems [3b]. This not only complicates the picture of sensory projection, but offers possibilities of dynamogenic and selective effects collectively referred to psychologically as motivational and attentional. Another recent development consists in the increasing evidence of the role of variable excitatory states in cell body and dendrites (as contrasted with the earlier rather exclusive emphasis on conducted impulses), as the neural events underlying integrative processes [3a]. This would facilitate, increase interaction of temporally separated events. The complexity in the dependence of such states upon changes in the internal environment, natural hormonal, or artificial and drug induced, is becoming clearer. Finally, of fundamental significance for understanding the role of the behavioral context upon perception is the increasing evidence of the complexity of the effects of efferent processes (Phase 4e, Phase 5) at all levels upon afferent processes at all levels [44].

All of these developments strongly indicate the likelihood that the perceptual processes which are mediated by and through these neurophysiological mechanisms are more diverse qualitatively than the traditional cognitive theories of perception have presupposed [51]. Further understanding of them can scarcely be irrelevant to the *detailed* understanding of psychological processes which overschematized theoretical conceptions at the psychological level have discouraged.

The more central experiential, cognitive, and behavior-controlling processes (Phase 4c), under which the discriminatory process may be included, cannot be ordered in any fixed serial sequence. Within Phase 4, no perceptual functions are exclusively relatable to separated transmission and interaction processes. The contingent conditions involve all those factors, chemical as well as neural, which affect the excitatory and inhibitory states of dendrite and cell body, and possibly the state of the glial cells, as well as the conductive state of the axon [3a]. However, each of the above classes of perceptual processes presents a different balance with regard to the complex set of relatively constant contingent conditions in transmission and the variable contingent factors in interaction regions. In perceptual cognition of external objects, the relationship between specific property or properties of the remote "initiating" Phase 1 and properties of Phase 4*c* are critical. The isomorphic character of the "representation" of remote properties in the central process determines its veridicality. The test of veridicality consists in the appropriateness of behavior resulting under specific motivational conditions. A sequence of isomorphic energy transformations with minimal influence of variable contingent conditions at interaction regions is favorable to adequate cognition. Actually most psychological theories of perceptual cognition have assumed that such isomorphic relations hold primarily for simple object properties and that cognition of more complex properties involves inferential processes based on the effects of specific cues "weighted" in terms of past learning. In effect, this shifts the focus of interest of the cognitive theorist from the details of the transmission process to the determination of the underlying learning process [51].

In understanding the complete perceptual process, the basic problem is not the relation between its nonexperiential properties and those of the external object, but between its experiential properties and the complex set of conditions interacting at each region of interaction, as well as with the properties of the perceived external object. From this point of view, what is experienced is strictly the totality of this interplay of factors. Since the cortical processes involved in perception are directly and indirectly affected by innervational (Phase 4*c*) and effector (Phases 4*e*, 5) processes, perceptual behavior will constitute a most important contingent condition affecting experiential processes. Concretely this means that always object-self relations are experienced rather than external object properties. In visual perception, the frequently employed experimental condition of brief exposure with a single fixation is highly unrepresentative of actual perception of natural objects or situations. In such situations, the sequence and pattern of retinal excitations is controlled and integrated with a sequence and pattern of motor processes in looking, i.e., eye movements between fixations. The role of perceptual behavior urgently requires investigation. Kohler has demonstrated the existence of so-called "conditional sensations" of color which, through habituation, have become dependent upon specific ocular movement or postures [40]. It is clear that normal tactual experience results from motor activity of the organism without which purely touch-receptor information would give very inadequate information concerning the surface properties of touched objects. Anatomically and physiologically, the close proximity and actual overlap of cortical regions subserving tactual sensation and motor control indicates their functional interaction. The probability of a similarly close functional interrelation between visual and eye-movement processes has been curiously neglected in theory and in experimental investigation until the recent introduction by von Holst of the concepts of voluntary innervation as *Kommando* with an "efference" copy interacting with a reafferent process [59], thus yielding through cancellation stability of the visual world with moving eyes. That the active innervation processes—as distinct from passive externally produced movement—may be critical in the types of perceptual rehabituation demonstrated by Erismann and Kohler [17, 40] has been recently shown by Held [33].

The complexity and relative dominance of contingent conditions—specifically, interactions with reafferent and innervational motor processes—become apparent in those anisotropies of central processes commonly called laterality of higher-cognitive and motor functions. A specific laterality of higher level perceptual interpretation has been found only recently by Brenda Milner [48b], differentiating between the role of left and right temporal lobes. The finding that—while the left temporal lobe contributes to understanding and retention of verbally expressed ideas—the right temporal lobe aids in rapid visual identification may be related to the detailed and differentiated demonstration of perceptual anisotropies and the role of looking behavior discussed by M. Gaffron in the concluding sections of the present paper.

The effector process (Phase 5). A complete phase analysis of the perceptual-behavioral cycle should in principle discriminate the peripheral phase of actual effector activity, formally comparable to that of the receptor processes. Molecular description of this phase would be in terms of actual muscular movement and glandular secretion. Functionally, a more meaningful characterization of the effector process would include specification of the controlling and integrating neural activities of Phase 4e. Recognition of their complex character is indicated by the differentiation between the pyramidal and so-called extrapyramidal systems. One important consequence of events at Phase 5 are the kinesthetic excitations resulting from muscular activity.

The medium world (Phase 6). In behavioral interactions with objects at a distance and particularly in social situations, the effect of effector, muscular action is mediated by a process of energy transmission formally analogous to that of Phase 2 in the reverse direction. Thus the movement or vocal behavior of the perceiving organism affects the object (organism) being perceived by energy transmission of light or sound. A special set of problems consists in the relationships between properties of the effector system and the characteristics of the acoustical or optical effects upon the environmental medium. The sequence of processes from Phases 4c, 4e, 5, and 6 are identical in nature with the event sequence object interior to object surface (Phase 1) to stimulus (Phase 2) when the event perceived is an internal process in another organism.

The world of object-events (Phase 7, 1′). The consequences of a perceptual-behavioral act are often specifiable only in terms of a change in some external object (Phase 7), often the object perceived. The most significant of such objects is another person, and the focus of concern may lie in the changes produced in the other person's experiential processes, and perception of them would constitute a new perceptual cycle. It is clear that such object changes may be characterized in the language system of any appropriate science and in the case of social interaction require specification in phenomenal terms.

INTERRELATIONS AMONG PHASES

In one sense the major purpose of the preceding series of distinctions among discriminable phases of the perceptual process has been to facilitate the analysis of the complex web of interrelations among them, including constitutive relationships. This would comprehend the entire psychology of perception. Fortunately, the scope of the task precludes our attempting it here. The implication of our analysis is that the task should be approached by attempting to specify a limited number of qualitatively different *patterns* of interrelationships. The following two sections are concerned with an analysis of the overabstract concept *behavior* and a suggested discrimination of specific useful meanings of another overabstract term, *perceiving*.

The most hopeful trend in perceptual theorizing has been a curiously belated but currently increasing interest in the role of motor processes in perception. This has been stressed long ago by Dewey [15], more recently by Sperry [56], still more recently by Drever [16]. It has been central to the experimental programs of Erismann [17], Kohler [40], and Held [33]. Among phenomenal experimenters it has been most strongly emphasized, and also placed in a context of neurophysiological processes, by Gaffron [21; see also the subsequent section of the present article]. In her conception, "perceptual behavior" is involved at all levels of central processing. Here it suffices to indicate that motor processes affect perception not only by selecting and modifying incoming stimuli to the visual organs, but by directly producing a consequence in modified visual stimulation via change in body or head position, in kinesthetic and vestibular sensory return, in "efference copies," and also very possibly in direct effects of innervational processes at the neural levels at which they occur.

One kind of interrelationship not adequately studied is that of the effect of one experiential property upon the occurrence of another. Thus Gibson has suggested that the basic phenomenal property of visual surface upon which others depend is that of hardness, impenetrability, texture [23, p. 371]. Wallach and Adams [61] have shown that the experiential effect of visual fusion of two different brightnesses binocularly presented depends upon their surface character. What is involved, in more general terms, are the interrelations of physiological processes *at different levels* upon experiential properties. A somewhat different but significant problem is the mutual interrelationship (inhibitory as well as facilitatory) between experiential and cognitive processes.

A fundamental problem, discussion of which belongs here, is the character of the relationship between experiential and other properties of the perceptual process (between "Phase 4: experiential" and the other phases, especially the subphases of Phase 4: *a, c, e*). Whether the problem is one capable in principle of as sharp a formulation as that attempted by Wertheimer, Koffka, and most specifically by Köhler [41c] is perhaps open to question. It is possible that an acceptable answer will have to be much more differentiated and include within itself recognition of the facts of multiple interdependencies among the central phases, and even more indirect though essential contingencies among more remote phases. We hope to discuss this at a later time in terms of our present analytic framework. It is clear that modern solutions of the kind suggested by Licklider [43, pp. 49, 107], i.e., to consider experiential properties as ways people have been trained to use descriptive words, or as systematic intervening variables, would not be compatible with our basic emphases.

THE SCIENTIFIC STATUS OF THE CONCEPT OF BEHAVIOR; MULTIPLE MEANINGS OF BEHAVIOR

A curious circumstance constrains us in the present context to examine the concept of behavior. Nearly fifty years ago in the name of scientific objectivity and in order to liberate psychological research from the pressure to relate all of its findings to the experiential aspects of psychological events, J. B. Watson persuasively suggested substituting behavior for consciousness as the subject matter of psychology. In many ways, not all equally desirable, the suggestion has been enormously successful. Behavior has become the subject matter not only of psychology, but of the social (or behavioral) sciences, and modern departments of psychology or divisions of social science are housed in behavior laboratories. A recent president of the American Psychological Association has with approval labeled this verbal conquest of psychology, "The American Revolution" [30]. Thus, in the present context, it would appear necessary to indicate explicitly the relation of perceiving to behavior. Perhaps the most adequate statement would be that since, in practice, behavior means whatever psychologists are focally interested in, by definition perceptual processes simply constitute part of, or one kind of, behavior. A statement of the interrelationships among the various phases of our sequence would thus constitute the only meaningful answer to the problem of relations between perception and behavior. But this sounds too verbal.

Is it actually possible to be more specific in defining behavior? Hebb thinks so. As he is a respected "theoretically neutral" empiricist, his clarion conviction commands recognition as a serious contemporary statement. *"Behavior* is the *publicly observable* activity of *muscles* or *glands* of *external* secretion . . . mind is an activity of the brain and our knowledge of it is chiefly theoretical, *inferred from behavior* rather than being obtained directly from self-observation" [29, pp. 2–3; italics chiefly by present author]. This amounts to a strict identification of behavior or response with those parts of our Phase 5 which are "directly" observable, whereas Watson, with a more liberal definition, talked about "motor and glandular indicators of response" [62, p. 13]. The implications as to the experiential properties of perceptual events are, however, the same, although stated in more sophisticated terms. Since phenomenal properties are not publicly observable, they are clearly not behavior, but become "intervening variables" [30]. What relation (or similarity) exists between the subject's experience, considered as an intervening variable, and the actual experience of the experimenter in the same situation, upon which he could report even though it is not publicly observable, is not clarified. Until it is, conditions of communication with the subject, and thus of control of criteria of experiential report by the experimenter, are not specifiable. Lack of interest in this problem is one serious handicap of the "behavioral" approach to perception.

It is anachronistic in this age of physics to insist upon direct observability as a criterion of the subject matter (focus of interest) of any science—physics, biology, or psychology. One distinguishes between the pointer reading, which is not the subject matter of physics, and the event whose properties are measured, which is. Furthermore, it would be strange if the subject matter of any science—let alone all!—were shiftingly defined in terms of what is "directly" observable; it would be strange because inaccurate, and also because no clear definition of what is "directly" observable is presented or can be offered. In terms of our phase analysis, exactly *what* is meant by "direct"? Actually the relationship between any phenomenal report and its corresponding internal processes with their experiential properties is more direct than that between a report and *any* external object reported on. Furthermore few psychologists outside a physiological laboratory in any sense "directly" observe a muscle movement, but only movement or deformation of overlying skin. And if one protests that this is quibbling, one cannot—without shifting ground—protest the inclusion of central nervous activity (Phase 4) as behavior. Both it and muscular activity are "manifested" in observable skin deformations. *Relative* differences of degrees of indirectness can scarcely be made the basis of a major conceptual difference between "behavior" (muscle activity) and "intervening variables" (central nervous activity). The latter is just as accessible to the recording electrode as is the former, and a graphic record of it is just as directly a function of the process recorded as is a Skinnerian cumulative graphic record of lever-depression rates.

The obvious need not be further belabored. Perusal of the psychological literature would reveal that, in accepted practice, "behavior" (despite Hebb's definition) is currently used to refer to *any* and all phases of the perceptual-behavioral cycle. This would include events from the retinal potential to events within specific projection or nonspecific reticular systems, to the brain activity as electrically recorded, to muscular activity as recorded electrically or mechanically, to the movement of body parts or their environmental effects as recorded in *any* fashion, including that of observer protocols. It is also evident that the terms used to translate such records into statable scientific relationships are as diverse as scientific language systems permit. Thus behavior may be and is characterized in the language systems of every science. It is double talk to assert that this applies only to behavioral measures or indicators, but that "behavior" or "response" is a strictly psychological term. Specifically, *of what* is a behavioral measure a measure? Miller implicitly raises this question without providing an answer [48a].

Many specific answers may be given to this question but not one will be reasonably determinate and will really satisfy most psychologists. For, quite legitimately, any given psychologist may be *primarily* interested in the interrelationships between quite specific phases of the perceptual-behavior cycle—between stimulus energy and, for instance, differential activity in different cell layers of the lateral geniculate nucleus, differential experiences or their report, or differences in response systems or rates of activity. For the experimenter, the important facts to determine (as influencing the adequacy of his specific choice of experimental variables) are his own *foci* of *primary scientific interest or concern*—and the most appropriate *empirical procedures* for controlling or recording the events at these foci.[1] The question whether events at these foci are to be

---

[1] The initial explicit statement of the distinction between empirical (experimental) and systematic variables was made by Koch in his analysis of the theoretical system of Clark Hull [38a, pp. 27 ff.] and was elaborated in the invitation to contributors of this series [38c, pp. 678 ff.]. A statement of current failure adequately to observe the distinction in practice, and the significance of this fact, is presented in his subsequent analysis of current trends [38d, pp. 752 ff.].

labeled "behavior" or "intervening variables" is one of less immediate research significance. It is, however, vital that a conceptual terminology of sufficient discriminating power be available to permit the more precise location, in terms of phases, of the specific events constituting major foci of concern—and their interrelations—and to permit an adequate indication of the probable ranges of generalization which the obtained experimental results warrant. A major mischief of the word "behavior" lies in its seductive capacity to encourage purely verbal solutions for real problems (as, for instance, verbal report qua behavior, instruction stimuli, and the like). It has doubtless also contributed to the prevalent gross lack of concern with problems of warrantable range of generality by encouraging the couching of experimental results in the form of "behavioral laws" holding between stimuli and (conditioned) responses *in general.*

Furthermore, the present incredibly impoverished technical psychological terminology for descriptive characterization of responses seems in part attributable to contentment with the overabstract character of the word "behavior." Elsewhere [66], I have argued that in no other science is there a single, unqualified noun referring to the totality of events studied by that science, comparable to the term *behavior.* There are optical, mechanical, magnetic, intra-atomic events, all of which are physical events; there are a variety of biological events—metabolism, growth, reproduction, contraction, secretion; but no single, unqualified term exists in either science comprehending all of the events which constitute its subject matter. Furthermore, there are no biological laws comparable in *generality* to stimulus-response laws—no such physical or chemical laws. No other science handicaps itself with the incubus of a term which so discourages analysis and encourages overgenerality of interpretation of obtained functional relationships.

The overabstract character of the concept of behavior (and that of stimulus) tends finally to produce the illusion that a *conceptually homogeneous set of lawful relationships* has been achieved or is achievable in psychology. The fact that events in Phases 1 and 7 are in practice describable in terms of every natural and social science (including history of visual arts), those in Phase 2 in physical or chemical terms, those in Phase 4 in physical, chemical, biological, psychological terms, and so on —all this indicates the impossibility of avoiding a total set of relationships whose terms are completely heterogeneous. For the present, and probably always, psychology will remain the most heterogeneous and empirical of the sciences in the character of its constituent relationships. Since in sciences involving experiential terms this is inevitably true, the analysis of perception reveals a representative sample of the heterogeneity of psychological relationships.

MULTIPLE MEANINGS OF "O PERCEIVES X"

Since perception does not occur in a vacuum, but is always an activity of some organism (O), characterized by reference to some object, event, relation, or situation (X) said to be perceived, it is more fruitful to examine basic differences of meaning of the total statement "O perceives X" than simply diverse meanings of the verb, "perceive." As generally employed either in ordinary language or in technical discussions, this statement is highly ambiguous in that one or more of at least four different specific meaningful propositions may be intended. Although the context is generally adequate to satisfy the loose requirements of everyday communication, it definitely is not sufficient for technical discourse, planning of research, or discussion of research findings. Since the different component meanings only partially overlap and represent different foci of interest deriving from varied theoretical approaches, it is desirable to explicitly separate them. Such a discrimination will reveal differences in the phase locations of the primary foci of interest and in the character of the organismic process in Phase 4 upon which attention is centered.

1. One specific meaning of the statement "O perceives X" is: O *discriminates* X, in the sense of reacting differentially to X as distinguished from Y. The discriminative capacity of the organism to react differentially to the properties of X versus Y is determined by systematic experimental variation of X and Y and tests of differential response. The experimental foci of concern are the effective properties of X and the properties of the central discriminatory process. Thus, on the lowest level, Klüver's monkeys, lacking the striate cortex, could not discriminate visual stimuli differing in brightness but of the same total luminous flux, but they could discriminate differences in total flux [37]. On a higher level, the events discriminated (perceived) could be, for instance, physical objects, tilts of lines, another person's emotions or attitudes. In principle, there is no restriction on the kinds of differences that could be studied. In experimental practice, however, there has recently been a marked preference for differences definable in physical terms and for systematic variation of energy variables (Phase 2) rather than external-object properties (Phase 1).

A recent experiment of Guttman and Kalish [28] illustrates these preferences. The basic problem was testing the relationship between discriminability and stimulus generalization as functions of spectral wavelength (Phase 2). Both discriminability and generalization functions were determined by differential rate of pecking (Phase 5 or 7) at an illuminated disk. It is worth noting what aspects of the perceptual process are critical to the problem as formulated. The experiential quality of the perception is basically irrelevant; the character of the motor reaction is also irrelevant. The critical behavioral feature is change in rate of occurrence of *any* experimentally determined response—not the specific properties of the response occurring, however. The selection of the response in such experiments is governed by considerations of technical convenience, such as ease of elicitation, ease of graphic recordings, and the like. It serves as an indicator of the central discriminating process but is not itself a major focus of concern. Whether or not there is a cognitive aspect to the perceptual activity is also irrelevant. Thus, the appropriateness of the reaction or the character of its variation (other than in rate) as a function of change in the stimulus or stimulus context is also disregarded. The relationship investigated is one between properties of Phases 1 or 2 and Phase 4c (discriminatory process), with events in Phase 7 (physical movement of the pecked-at disk) used as indicators of Phase 4c.

It is clear that the equation of perception with discriminative reaction is a very abstract approach to perception. Neither the character of the perceptual process beyond Phase 2, nor the character of the response beyond Phase 4c has been of focal interest. The dependent variable focus lies simply in the *capacity* of the organism to discriminate between two different external situations, no matter how the capacity for differential response is mediated. Such an approach throws the entire burden of specific explanation of behavior production upon processes of learning which determine the character of the behavioral reaction. It constitutes the classic and almost exclusive research formulation of the perceptual problem for neobehavioristic systems.

2. A second specific meaning of the sentence "*O* perceives *X*" is: a *cognitive process* is occurring in *O*, a process whose properties stand in a certain relationship of appropriateness or "behavioral correspondence" to some external *X*. The core of this meaning of the statement is thus the *occurrence* of the *specified* cognitive process, not its accuracy (veridicality). This cognitive process may be partially or wholly wrong, as in the cognition of a tachistoscopically presented stimulus, for instance. The character of the relation of appropriateness existing between properties of the cognitive process and of its actual initiating condition, the external object, is one subproblem of importance, but the properties of the internal cognitive process itself is another—one whose solution is a precondition for a solution of the first.

Basically, the properties of a cognitive process are not to be ascertained by *direct* reference to its "corresponding" external object. Rather they are constituted by the features of the more efferent kinds of behavior which the process in part controls. If these kinds of behavior are appropriate in specifiable ways to the external object, it may be said to have been "correctly" cognized. Thus, if the distance to a given object is correctly perceived (cognized), the person may walk approximately the actual distance with his eyes shut, either *to* it or *away* from it, report it verbally, or do a large number of appropriate and adequate things. If only one appropriate response may be demonstrated, the usefulness of the term "cognitive" is debatable. The basic difference between a cognitive process and a discriminatory-behavior indicator is that generally the latter is purely arbitrary and bears no physiologically or psychologically significant relation to the stimulus difference being discriminated. (Thus, differential rate of pecking may indicate the discrimination of almost any kind of stimulus-object difference.) Occasionally the relationship is not arbitrary, as in the experiment of Russell [55]; here variation in appropriate force of the jump of the rat from starting platform to food platform as a function of varied distances could be taken to indicate not only discriminatory behavior but also adequate cognition.

Again it is useful to indicate what is basically irrelevant to the cognitive meaning of perception. The particular experiential character of the perception is irrelevant, although cognition in humans is generally based upon some experiential property. But in contrast to discrimination, the character of the response or, more precisely, the relationship of appropriateness of the response to the situation is not irrelevant. Rather, the crucial test of the *character of the cognitive reaction* lies in a systematic test of the *kinds* of object-reaction relations that actually exist. Tests of transfer are critical here.

Investigations of cognitive perceptual activity have become more frequent in recent times, particularly among psychologists primarily interested in the effect of motives and personality factors on perception. Thus, in the sequence of Bruner-Postman experiments [cf. 9], the subjects were not asked to report their experiences, but to report what was being exposed (word, syllable, letter); that is, they were asked to commit the "stimulus error," to infer the actual stimulus, i.e., to give a "correct" report. Any demonstration of the effect of motivation on this kind of perceptual report, however, could scarcely be taken to hold for different meanings of perception other than cognitive without independent investigations of the effect of motivational factors in such noncognitive perceptual situations. Yet in such investigations there has been no such caution evidenced in formulating conclusions.

The whole problem area of the constancies—particularly size constancy—suffers from a failure to discriminate sharply between the experiential and cognitive meanings of perception and their translation into unambiguous differential instructions for the subjects. Thus, does the word "size" (absolute, not relative) actually refer to an experiential reality (except perhaps for the extremes of "huge," "hulking" versus "tiny") or generally to a cognitive inference often clearly based on knowledge of object category? In the experiment of Bolles and Bailey [4], the high correlations obtained by Brunswik in the size-constancy monograph [10] were duplicated by subjects with eyes closed on the basis of a verbal identification of the kind of object to be judged for size. This strongly suggests that Brunswik's subject was not reporting on phenomenal size, but on cognized size, inferred from recognition of the kind of object perceived. Its apparent size might well have been size inferred on an object category basis, as contrasted with his other judgments of size inferred through a calculation of cognized distance and estimated retinal size. Clearly, a sharper differentiation is required in such experiments of the experiential versus the cognitive reference of the report.

3. Another specific meaning of the statement "O perceives X" is: a process with the *experiential property* or properties X occurs in O. In practice, occurrence of such an experience is indicated by a report of the experiences, either a verbal description or a nonverbal behavioral indicator whose reference to the experience is determined by prior verbal instruction. The experience must obviously be characterized in phenomenal, experiential terms. This meaning of the statement that O perceives X is simply and strictly this: As the result of *some* stimulation, an experience of such and such properties has *occurred*.

No implication of either similarity or cognitive appropriateness to the stimulating object exists. In the experiential sense, perception of an object or relationship may or may not be veridical, or illusory. This is a special subproblem whose solution requires the existence of criteria of correspondence between physical and phenomenal properties in addition to empirical test procedures. However, phenomenal veridicality should be sharply distinguished from accurate cognitive judgment—in the estimates in size constancy experiments, for instance. Maintenance of this distinction is rendered difficult by the fact that the most available descriptive terms for phenomenal characterization are often words whose current meanings tend to be determined by reference to objective properties of physical objects. Unless these are very carefully used, the presumed phenomenal description actually may be instead a cognitive estimate, an equivalent of the old "stimulus error."

In this sense, the primary focus of experimental concern is the experiential character of the perceptual event (Phase 4: experiential). The character of the indicator of this occurrence is irrelevant except in so far as there is an intrinsic relation between the two. This would be the case if a spontaneous reaction were taken as the indicator, but it need not be so. Usually an instructionally determined response is utilized. If the instruction is specific, the report or indicator may be nonverbal (pressing of a key; empirical datum, Phase 7); or it may be a specifically determined verbal report, "not present," "present" (Phase 5); or a written protocol (Phase 7). Since the character of the actual experience—not the verbal description or other report of it, or any other kind of "behavioral indicator"—constitutes the focus of interest, one inescapable set of technical problems lies in the *specification of the relationship between the experiential event and the process underlying the report*. The most frequent source of ambiguity in this sense of the word "perceive" is the *confusion of specification of an experiential occurrence with that of the physical situation to which it may "correspond"* (stimulus error).

In a classic experiment of Wever, black spots of various shapes on white cards were exposed tachistoscopically for varying brief durations [63]. The aim was to relate the frequency of occurrence of different properties of the figure-ground experience to different exposure times. The subjects first acquired considerable practice in observation; they were then instructed to report on presence or absence of partial contour, complete contour, difference in localization of figure and ground, and other phenomenal characteristics. They were aware that all the stimulus cards were black figures, all fully contoured and flat. Nevertheless, they had no difficulty in reporting in terms of experiential, not cognitive, criteria, and the steepness of the psychophysical functions (i.e., the percentage of positive reports changing often over 60 per cent between steps in exposure time of only 1.2 msec) indicated a high consistency of report. In this situation, as in most psychophysical experiments, no possibility of interobserver check on any *single* report exists; also, the differences in threshold values between observers were such that no intersubjective agreement on presence or absence of a given experiential criterion on any *absolute* exposure duration would have been obtained. The securing of clear psychophysical functions in a situation in which no objective check of individual reports exists—either among observers or in terms of correspondence with a similar property in the external stimulus object—nevertheless is a convincing demonstration of the contention that some real property of an event was being reported on. This real property was an experiential property of the perceptual event. It cannot be maintained that actually the report was simply on the occurrence of a specified brain event. It is irrelevant whether ultimately some brain event *corresponding* to the reported experiential property may be discovered—recordable, for instance, through electrodes. It is irrelevant since the fact of such a correspondence could itself never be established without a highly consistent report on the experiential properties of the perceptual events.

In this experiment the meaning of "O perceives X" is clearly *not* the cognitive one: O perceives an exposure duration of so many milliseconds; rather it is: *O* perceives (has an experience characterized as) partial contour. The present author was one of Wever's subjects and can say with confidence even now that a report of partial contour, for instance, did not identify a unique experience, but only a large class of experiential contours of varying incompleteness, all, however, possessing some contour as opposed to experiences in which the change of brightness was too gradual to warrant any report of contour.

One might wish to argue that in this situation the reports of partial contour were cognitive reports. I would not wish to protest the legitimacy of such use if it were recognized that what was being cognitively reported was the occurrence of an experiential event, co-determined by external and organismic factors, one experiential property of which was a phenomenal partial contour, other (physiologically statable) properties of which remain to be determined. The event cognized would have to be considered not an external situation, but an organism-environment relationship or interaction.

Most of the experiments designed in terms of this experiential meaning of perception have had as the second major focus of interest some specified external condition (Phase 1 or 2) as duration of the stimulus in Wever's experiment, for instance. There is no insuperable technical reason why the second major focus of concern should not be the character of the response [Phase 4*e* (molar), 5, or 6] to a given experience where the experience is formally the independent variable (controlled via conditions in Phase 1 or 2 and checked via verbal reports) [61]. It would be desirable if such relationships could be more systematically explored at all levels of complexity of behavior. A beginning in this direction at a high level of complexity has been made by C. R. Rogers and a number of his collaborators relating *"immediate present experiencing"* [22, p. 1] of a patient's problem to objective evidences of therapeutic changes [2, 53]. A clear distinction is drawn between reports of intellectual understanding and of immediate experience, and it is recognized that often nonverbal behaviors, such as gesture, tones of voice, and the context of talking, may constitute valid indicators of a "direct reference to experiencing" [22, p. 2]. There is research implementation of the assertion that "the basic problem then, especially for psychotherapy research, is one of developing means of measuring subtle experiential phenomena that may have predictive power in descriptions of interpersonal interactions" [2, p. 4].

4. A fourth strict meaning of the statement "*O* perceives *X*" is: a specific kind of behavior has occurred as the result of some stimulation by an external object or event. The focus of primary concern is the *specific response* occurring as a function of the stimulating or releasing action of some event, external or internal. The effective properties of the

total stimulus object are often not known and are frequently made the object of experimental investigation. The problem is *not,* as in the first sense, whether the organism can discriminate such and such previously identified stimulus properties; rather, it is the reverse—the identification of what stimulus properties are effective in producing a previously identified kind of behavior. Paraphrased, the problem may be stated: *What* does the organism perceive as fearful, or eatable, or retrievable, or courtable? The whole *perceptual process* is treated as the independent variable to be further specified—not as the dependent variable studied as some function of specified stimulation. It is this sense of *behavior control* in which perceiving is often used by the ethologists.

It should be evident that in none of the four strict meanings just differentiated is the problem of veridicality as such an essential one. In each case, one starts with the occurrence of a certain event,—specific external object, or an experiential event, or a cognitive object process, or a motor response—as a primary focus of concern. The basic question concerns the nature of the functional relations existing between it and either its consequents in behavior, experience or cognition, or its antecedents in the external world or in organismic processes. In some cases (in most instances from everyday life) the relationship would exhibit some correspondence or appropriateness between external and internal phases of the perceptual sequence but the perceptual problem is not narrowly focused upon the conditions of veridicality. Veridicality would thus be one of many kinds of relationships, though a frequent and significant one.

5. The most frequent meaning of the sentence "O perceives X" is a compound one in which the sentence is used at once in all of the first three specific meanings—the usage of the child or the naïve realist or the novelist. It implies that certain kinds of correspondences and appropriatenesses exist between the external object or event initiating the perception and the experiential object, the cognized object (categorized meanings or behavioral tendencies constituting cognition). In this sense, to perceive an orange, for instance, means that the initiating condition *is* an orange, and that its phenomenal properties and cognized meanings correspond. It need *not* imply release of eating behavior since variations in state of need and past learning may affect behavior—even given the occurrence of the phenomenal or cognitive process.

The point to be stressed here is this: Compound usage is disadvantageous for research in perception since the processes and conditions stressed in the four specific meanings are not identical—processes underlying the principle governing, and the conditions relevant to occurrence of, the properties of the event. Therefore, the generalization ranges of experimental findings are indeterminate when the sense in which the term "perception" is used is unclarified. This will be illustrated by the examination of several sample researches in the following section.

SOME IMPLICATIONS OF THE PHASE ANALYSIS AND OF THE DISCRIMINATION OF SPECIFIC MEANINGS OF PERCEIVING FOR RESEARCH IN PERCEPTION

The previous analysis and discussion has been directed toward increased clarity and specificity in the systematic, conceptual terms in which perceptual laws are stated; an increased concreteness in the direct and indirect specification of the *reality referents* of descriptive and explanatory terms; a more detailed understanding of the *relationship between systematic and empirical variables in actual experimental practice.* Achievement in practice would require a more explicit concern of experimenters with the choice and specification of the referents in the actual process they wish to investigate, together with a less focal but more responsible interest in the choice of indicator or type or report utilized. Basically this means a generally increased *relative* concern with the specification, control, and recording of the dependent as against the independent variables in current experimentation. In particular, clearer discrimination between the experiential versus the cognitive processes in perceiving is required. This is necessary, since it is altogether probable that cognitive and experiential processes differ in their dependence not only upon the external independent variables, but upon internal contingent conditions. They may especially differ in the extent and ways in which they vary with internal factors such as motivation, drugs, hormones; or with mediating processes such as perceptual behavior; or in their role in the elicitation and control of behavior, or in different kinds of perceptual learning.

The issues involved may best be clarified by examining in detail a sample of current research. For this purpose, several experiments by Gibson have been chosen to illustrate an original and significant approach to perceptual problems [cf. 23, 25, 26]. It is hoped that the analysis will reveal the advantages of specific applications of the mode of thinking here explicated.[2]

The experiments selected are concerned with a specific facet of Gibson's general program of developing a new, molar psychophysics of the visual world. "What is called for is a *listing* of the properties or qualities [of the visual world]—a phenomenological study—and a *search* for the corresponding stimulus variables—a program of psychophysical

---

[2] It should be noted that in respect to the points subjected to critical examination, Gibson's work is perhaps less vulnerable than much other contemporary research.

experiments." [23, p. 367]. The different emphasis upon the two major aspects of the task revealed by the words we have italicized symbolizes our most basic criticism of Gibson's research. A serious psychophysics should take with coordinate seriousness both kinds of events related by the program of investigation. This is formally done in Gibson's statement of his aim.

Gibson explicitly does this in an early formal statement of program [23, p. 367]; but his experimental work fails to implement it fully. Actually, the initial study pays more specific attention to the phenomenological problem than any later one, listing tentatively eight "phenomenal properties" of the "experience" of a determinate surface. In this initial formulation the experiential aspect of the psychological part of the psychophysical program is unambiguously indicated by the use of such terms as *phenomenal properties, apparent slant, visual impression.* Yet the ubiquitous ambiguity of the common-sense terms currently utilized by professional psychologists immediately introduces confusion. "In ordinary perception the *surfaces we see* possess contours. The *face of an object,* for instance, has a closed shape" [23, p. 375, *italics ours*]. Are surface and face here intended as external objects (Phase 1) or as experiential or cognitive events (Phase 4c); if the latter, which of the two (Phase 4c: experiential or 4c: cognitive)? One assumes that a phenomenal meaning is intended since no real face (Phase 1) possesses a contour. This is a property of its projection and appears only in Phases 2 (optic array), 3 (retinal excitation), or 4 (experience). Yet the next sentence continues: "Since many of the surfaces of civilized environments . . . " (obviously meant in the sense of Phase 1). And throughout the discussion the term *visual surface* remains systematically ambiguous (as to its reference to events of Phases 1 versus 4). For instance, "The slant of a visual surface in the region fixated [presumably Phase 1] may also depend [apparently Phase 4] on gradients of stimulation" (Phase 2). The term *perceived optical slant* is similarly ambiguous.

The point at issue is as serious as the basic problem itself is taken to be. Certainly the conceptual confusion is pragmatically pervasive in effects on experimental procedure and report. Objective criteria of the lack of serious concern with experiential properties as such (aside from the implicit one that the experiment is avowedly directed toward an analysis of their stimulus determinants) are the space devoted to specifying to the subject the referent of his report, and the character of the report itself. In Gibson's article [23], typical of perceptual articles generally, only two lines are devoted to specification of instructions to the subject, as contrasted with some 80 lines characterizing apparatus, the image on the screen, the procedure of stimulus presentation. The failure to indicate with any specificity either the precise instructions, or what the subjects may have taken them to mean, is characteristic of what experimenters or censoring editors feel is necessary to permit replication or interpretation of findings.

Of even more general methodological concern than lack of specificity of its characterization is the question of the *appropriateness* of the empirical indicator to the property of the perceptual event in which the experimenter is primarily interested. Presumably in the first two experiments of Gibson, this was the phenomenal property of slant of surface. The empirical indicator in the first study was the angle of slant of a flat board adjusted by the subject so that his tactual-kinesthetic impression was "the same" as that he visually experienced looking at the image on the screen. In the second, he *judged* when a surface rotated by the experimenter reached an objective position perpendicular to the line of sight or parallel to that of the screen, through an aperture of which it was viewed. In the first instance the report indicator was an external event (Phase 7) regulated by the subject so as to provide the stimulus conditions (Phase 1 or 2) for an equivalent experience (Phase 4: experiential). This is then essentially a matching technique. The phenomenal property to be matched should be carefully specified to the subject. Running checks as to whether the report is in fact a phenomenal or a cognitive one are required. Clearly in the second experiment the report is (and was designed to be) a *cognitive judgment* of the position of the stimulus object. The relation of this to Gibson's doctrine of psychophysical correspondence is nowhere explicitly considered. This is the more serious in that it is not even clear (aside from a comment that the impression was "fairly compelling") that the basic condition of a *phenomenal* surface, namely visual hardness, was actually achieved in these experiments [23, p. 371]. Certainly a judgment of "represented" slant can be easily made in its absence. It would methodologically seem to be required that positive direct statements by the subjects of such basic phenomenal facts be obtained before serious use of the data can be made in an *experiential* context.

In the final experiment Gibson is concerned to further specify the optical stimulus determinants (Phase 2: distal) of a visual surface. ("Does a pseudo-tunnel yield the perception of a phenomenally real tunnel?" [26, p. 5]) The experiment is an excellent example of persistence in stimulus refinement in the face of difficulties in controlling the stimulus object surfaces (Phase 1: surface). But the naïve subjects are never asked to describe their experiences: "The reports desired were not introspective descriptions but statements of what *O* perceived as 'there' " [26, p. 6]. More explicit questions to the subject make clear the intended cognitive character of the report, i.e., their inferences as to the character of the stimulus object (Phase 1). Clearly Gibson mistrusts the procedure of asking naïve subjects for experiential reports. But he also fails to indicate in the main experiment, with any specificity, the experiential reports of his trained subjects. One is consequently left with considerable uncertainty as to the actual phenomenal character of the experiences produced and, therefore, as to the applicability of the result of the experiment to Gibson's fundamental psychophysical postulate. Or has Gibson misstated his own interest, and is his basic doctrine one of *cognitive correspondence* to the stimulus? Until this is clarified in both conceptual language and experimental practice, one is left with the impression of a lack of concern with precision in the fundamental concepts. Suggestions for legitimizing a more direct attack on problems of psycho- or phenomenal-physical correspondence are presented in the following two sections.

EXPERIENTIAL REPORT IN RELATION TO THE REQUIREMENTS OF SCIENTIFIC OBJECTIVITY

In our previous discussion, the legitimacy of incorporating experiential reports in some integral sense into the body of scientific knowledge has been assumed. In the past it has often been assumed merely on the basis of general epistemological considerations equally applicable to all the sciences. As indicated earlier, Köhler has pointed out that the physicist in his dial readings reports on his experience: that in principle, therefore, physical observation is similar to the phenomenal report of the psychologist [41a, p. 29]. I believe that this line of supportive argument for the scientific status of experiential report in psychology is inadequate or incomplete on two grounds.

Cognitive versus phenomenal report: physics versus psychology. First, it is inadequate because the physicist is not *by intent* reporting on his experience; therefore, in a real sense, he is not reporting on it. He is acting as a naïve realist, committing the "stimulus error"; to him his report means that the pointer is aligned with a certain mark on the dial. It is a *cognitive,* not a *phenomenal,* report. Practically, it is irrelevant to point out that a direct and indispensable basis for this cognitive report is his experienced alignment, of which he, as observer, is more certain than of the corresponding cognitive statement. Theoretically, for such a phenomenal report to be a correct cognitive report, a number of *contingent conditions* would have to be fulfilled, such as a perpendicular line of visual regard, etc. However, the observer does *not* in practice explicitly report upon these contingent conditions as part of each observation.

It is incomplete because the physicist's report—even were it in intent experiential and therefore private—could be readily validated as a basis for science. A claim could be made that, in principle, it achieves pragmatic public character by the fact that other observers could simultaneously make and report on their individual observations. The external stimulus conditions, plus the observer's moral and intellectual qualifications, would be sufficiently compelling to achieve sufficient intersubjective agreement. It is often argued and with considerable force that this pragmatically public character is *sufficient* for science and also *required* for science. It is this last argument that makes Köhler's defense of phenomenology, by the tactic of stressing the subsumption of pointer reading into it, insufficient for psychology. Although correct in principle, it is inadequate in scope. It seems tacitly to agree with the restrictive condition that phenomenal observations are scientifically valid only if all literate, moral, and sensorily well-equipped observers agree with each other (the criterion of unrestricted interobserver agreement, of required quasi universality of the observer group). And it implicitly accepts as crucial the requirements of multiple simultaneous observation of a single common external situation.[3]

As I have argued elsewhere [66, p. 360], this would automatically disqualify for science all descriptions of experiences markedly influenced by varying states of the organism, by individual differences in sensitivity, temperament, past learning, present perceptual behavior or behavioral context—in fact, all complex perceptions would be technically disqualified. Clearly, such a radical constriction of its observation base would handicap psychology much more than it would modern physics—and for a variety of reasons. Contemporary physics can largely restrict its formal observations to dial readings because its knowledge currently permits construction of instruments connecting the moving pointer to that property of a system whose measurement constitutes the purpose of the observation (i.e., the property which is the focus of concern of the experimenter or theorist). The instrument ensures an orderly transformation of energy from the system measured to the moving pointer. This has the essential characteristics of the process of energy transformation between the phases: object interior to exterior; object surface to transmitting stimulus energy; stimulus to receptor excitation. *Cognitively* considered, therefore, a report on the dial could validly be regarded as a genuine report on the relevant property of the physical system measured (and probably is so taken by most experimental physicists). The process of transmission through the instrument simply has more sequential phases, is *more* indirect, and has a *more complicated,* although *stable, set of contingent conditions* than does an ordinary unaided perception. Such a connection of instrument to the property of the event in

---

[3] It is to be noted that another excellent phenomenal experimenter also almost explicitly accepts this implication (cf. Michotte, 48).

which one is focally interested is rarely technically possible in psychology. When possible, it has the advantages of yielding quantitative readings, since the extent of pointer deflection is reported in terms of a spatially quantified scale and is a specific function of graded quantities of the focal physical property. But, even in physics, proper attachment of the instrument to the system measured often presupposes a further artificial constriction upon the physical system itself—witness the frequent complication of the physicist's apparatus other than his mere measuring instruments. When the real process to be observed is the behavior of an organism, however, the situation often demands greater freedom for movement. An excellent example of this is the kind of experimental diadic situation employed in recent years in the researches of H. Murray, where freedom for bodily movement and hand gestures is necessary to provide one sort of observational data.

Reformulated criterion of objectivity. In the social behavior of animals, those movements and gestures which evoke appropriate responses in other members of their species can certainly be *identified* better by the perceptual apparatus of a trained human observer than by instrumentation. But such identification may involve a great deal of prior practice, as the ethologists have rightly pointed out. So, however, does the identification of cells and tissues by the histologist, fractures by the X-ray specialist, obscure heart murmurs by the cardiologist, and so on. Only a minute fraction of the population would be able to legitimize by intersubjective agreement the observations of the histologist or the medical internist, but these observations are not therefore regarded as nonscientific. Clearly, some criterion other than that of agreement by all members of an unrestricted pool of sensorily standard observers is relied upon in these areas. A more explicit formulation of criteria derived from these instances would also be useful in determining the limits of permissible psychological observation. I have suggested elsewhere that the only necessary condition is sufficient repeatability of the association between the reported experience and its specified conditions. If this criterion is accepted, "the objectivity required by science" would mean only that *under given specifiable and manipulable conditions, specifiable events* (in the present context, *specifiable experiences*) *can be shown to recur* (with sufficient regularity). These conditions would include all the relevant organismic, as well as external, conditions discriminated in our phase analysis.

This revised criterion of scientific objectivity which I have stated above differs in a number of respects from the usual and apparently more stringent criterion of intersubjective agreement among a conceptually unrestricted pool of observers in their simultaneous reports of observations (cognitive reports) of a single event. This is generally stated without reference to the necessity of intersubjective agreement on the (associated) occurrence of specified conditions of the event. The emphasis on scientific objectivity is thus traditionally placed on agreement in the descriptions of the properties of a single event (therefore the emphasis upon simultaneous observation). Yet science is rarely interested in the occurrence of single events, irrespective of their conditions. Its objectivity inheres in communal acceptance of its laws, its causal relationships, that is, in events stated as functions of specified conditions. These cannot therefore be tested without specification and observation *both* of the occurrence of particular events and of the conditions of those particular events. The repeatability required is that of the *association,* not merely secure evidence of the *occurrence* of an event or of its conditions considered separately. The revised criterion which I have formulated earlier is more stringent than this usual one, since its fulfillment demands that *different individuals repeatedly and independently realize specified conditions and independently and repeatedly, under these conditions, report similar experiences* [66].

The requirement of agreement among simultaneous observations of single events thus becomes essentially irrelevant because it is weaker than the requirement of consistency among the observations by *different observers* of events *independently produced* by *repeated realizations of specified conditions by different experimenters.* Failure to achieve agreement in reports on events *may* be due to failure to achieve the conditions adequately, but satisfactory agreement among reports obtained under identically specified but independently realized conditions tends to validate both reported observations of the event and the realization of its conditions.

It is evident that our strict criterion for the scientific usefulness of a phenomenal report is not applicable to experiential descriptions of events whose conditions are not known. Phenomenological description is not, in itself, fully developed science, but becomes so to the degree that adequate specification of the conditions of the experience becomes possible. It is reasonable to expect that a progressive expansion of the range of experiences repeatable with requisite scientific objectivity will occur. With increasing descriptive adequacy, it should become easier to identify more completely the conditions (external and organismic) of given experiential properties. With resulting increased control over their conditions, clearer inter-observer communication and explicit specification of experiential properties should become possible. And this, in turn—and in progressive spiral fashion—should tend to broaden the group of individuals able to identify the properties. Such expansion of the language community [38e] would not necessarily produce an increase in the "objectivity" of the relationship, but rather in the number of individuals in whom the requisite conditions would be realized, and therefore in the number in whom events characterized by the law will occur. This would mean an increase in the size of population to which the laws would apply and within which individuals would be capable of an experiential understanding of them. It is of practical importance to recognize the heuristic scientific value of phenomenal reports in new perceptual areas by individuals whose capacity for discriminating experiential report has been previously established, especially when the properties reported on are felt to be peculiarly impressive or significant.

EXPERIENTIAL REPORT: METHODOLOGICAL COMMENTS

Thus far we have developed the following basic propositions: Experiential events occur and are of central significance for a science of psychology. Their experiential properties are real, identifiable, specifiable and can, within limits, be reliably reported by the experiencing person. The report is not to be identified or confused with its referent, the experiential property. *Reports qua behavior do not constitute the basic scientific data in this area of science.* Rather, they refer to experiential properties of events, private to the individual. Although private as individual occurrences, these experiential properties nevertheless constitute the ultimate data of the science of psychology in the area of experiential perception. Understanding of scientific perceptual laws which include an experiential term presupposes the understanding individual's capacity not only to identify this term, but to identify in his own experience the experiential referent of the term. This differs from the situation in physics, where scientific laws do not directly involve experiential terms.

Report versus behavioral indicators of experience. A psychological investigator has direct access to his own experience. He has three sorts of access to the experience of other persons, all indirect: "perceptual access" (rendered precarious by the highly complex set of contingent conditions in Phase 1: object interior to object surface); phenomenal report of the other, verbal or nonverbal; and behavioral indicators. Scientifically a report can never be taken simply *as behavior.* (See the critique of Stevens' equation of experience with the discriminative reaction developed by Pratt [52]; Graham's usage of report qua behavior [27] is open to the same criticisms.) An essential feature of a report is that it embodies an intent to report on the part of the reporter, and must be so taken by the investigator. In the first place, the phrase "qua behavior" implies a great deal more determinateness in the term *behavior* than we have found to exist. It is therefore *not* a meaningful phrase. In any case, for a report to constitute a scientific statement not only must the report be identifiable as such, but also the operations for determining its referent. These clearly differ in character between experiential and cognitive reports.

The fashionable skepticism that the experiential properties of another's perception can never be known ("His red may be the same as my green.") may be acknowledged without being accepted as a basic barrier to communication. However, if experience is accepted as a reality, and if the universe is accepted as orderly, then to the extent that relevant conditions, internal and contingent as well as external, are similar, the experiences of two comparable individuals under similar conditions *should* be similar. Complete assurance of experiential identity is not obtainable. It is neither reasonable to expect nor necessary as a methodological postulate for research.

Although behavior *as such* is not a report it may constitute an *indicator* of experience. Examples would be the "aha" expression as an indicator of an experienced insight; change in respiratory or pulse rate, or galvanic skin reaction as an indicator of pain, etc. In humans, the validity of such indicators is established by previous association of the indicator with experience, either that of the experimenter or of a subject via report. Whether, in reporting, the effector is that of the laryngeal muscles (verbal) or a finger pressing a key (nonverbal) is irrelevant. In each case, the essential feature is the subject's acceptance of meaningful verbal instructions or an equivalent situational context which establishes his intent to report (Phase 4c) and specifies for him its experiential referent. With the "finger report" the instruction substitutes also for a descriptive statement by the subject.

Communication with respect to experiential properties. Individuals can, within limits, communicate with reference to the experiential properties of their perceptual events by reporting on them. The test of such communication consists in the capacity of different individuals to verify independently statements of causal relationships (antecedent or consequent) involving experiential terms. Communication of experience can never be certain in *single* instances, nor is this necessary. In single instances the probability of adequate communication always rests upon an extrapolation from a *sufficient series of past agreements* in reporting experiences of the same event or of similar events perceived under similar specified conditions. What is necessary is that a general basis of confidence in reporting be established between experimenter and subject, and an understanding of the limited number of alternative modes of processing—and thus of experiencing—the given external situation be achieved (see following section). Under such conditions communication may be preserved in single instances in which the subject's report does not correspond with the experimenter's present experience. A viable science of experiential events depends upon a sufficient *capacity to specify;* in individual instances, to *ascertain;* and in a sufficient number of cases to *control,* the operation of such variable internal contingent conditions. In experimental research they will need either to be experimentally controlled within the situation or, where this proves impossible, by comparing groups of subjects differing in specified characteristics.

Qualifications of reporters and specification of subject characteristics. An essential condition for experimentation is availability of adequate observers [36, p. 28]. Lorenz [45, p. 234] has commented both upon the special suitability of amateur naturalists for observation of animal behavior and the necessity of extended training. In practice it has proven difficult to sensitize, within the experimental situation, observers who never had a spontaneous interest in their own experience. Requirements for adequate reports are a genuine interest in experience; a capacity to maintain curiosity with reference to it; some sensitivity to the connotational nuances, as well as to the denoted meanings of words in describing experiences, combined with a constant awareness of possible discrepancies between descriptive terms and present experience. The experiencer-reporter[4] should have confidence in the reality of his own experience—as contrasted with the attitude of a subject who once remarked in a tachistoscopic experiment that he could not tell what he experienced because he was uncertain of the cues to which he was responding. In general, the frequency of such reporter attributes is codetermined by the general cultural and immediate intellectual climate (notably of graduate education). In psychology, such attributes have been too often considered completely unnecessary for scientific experimentation, even in perception.

The implications of our previous discussion impose a difficult task on the experimenter in the interpretation of discrepant reports. Lacking a full understanding of the processes underlying both experience and experiential report, the experimenter must nevertheless attempt to discriminate between those *disagreements* in experiential report which reflect genuine underlying differences of perceptual processes within the individual and those discrepancies arising from (1) ambiguity in phenomenal terminology; (2) substitutions of cognitive judgments for phenomenal report (stimulus error); (3) associative or inferential comments; (4) utilization of physical language instead of phenomenal; (5) reversion to habitual use of categories instead of a fresh determination of each report by each actual experience; or (6) sheer insensitivity or even carelessness in report. No formal requirements for such effective discrimination can be outlined, but it cannot be too strongly stressed that

---

[4] The term *reporter* (of experience) is preferable to *observer.* One experiences and one reports experience (Phase 4: experience). One observes and one reports the occurrence of external events (Phase 1).

responsibility for ensuring that the subject's reports remain genuinely experiential cannot be simply passed on to the subject by a set of general instructions [6]. Diversities in experiential report, when they occur among good subjects, are not a reason for abandoning the introspective method; rather, they provide occasions for inquiring seriously into the multiplicity of kinds of perceptual organizations which may occur and into possible individual differences. Important among such differences are characteristic modes of perceptual (looking) behavior which codetermine differences in relative dominance among perceptual organizations. Although the specific nature of so-called laterality factors remain to be clarified and differentiated, the most complete specification of the subject's sensory-motor anisotropies should become routine in perceptual experiments. Since certain combinations of eye-hand laterality are relatively infrequent, group tests which may serve to locate such subjects for systematic comparisons become important.

It would be highly desirable if, in all descriptions of sensory or perceptual research, more explicit specifications of subjects were routinely included. Thus often in monocular viewing conditions, the actual eye used is not specified, nor eyedness, nor handedness. It is often not clear in sensory psychophysical experiments whether subjects were excluded or on what bases, yet it is certain that intrasubject variability and sometimes gross intrasubject variation is legitimately used as a basis for exclusion. In the most rigorous area of perceptual research—sensory psychophysics—it has been customary from Fechner to Hecht to include as one major subject the experimenter himself. It is clear that pragmatically in this critical area it has not been felt necessary to exclude the observations of the experimenter, who knew the purpose of the experiment. Actually one has the conviction that advantages other than sheer convenience have played a role in shaping this practice [43, p. 47].

Differentiation of phenomenal dimensions and of perceptual behavior. The major phenomenal distinctions in simpler sensory perception were already made during the last century; since then, sensory research has taken a parametric turn. In this country it has until recently been generally assumed that the more complex phenomenal properties are to be explained by learning; this has prevented a search for new dimensions which might reflect qualitative differences in underlying processes. The present paucity of explicitly characterized phenomenal dimensions is appalling, and there should be a renewed attempt to identify experiential dimensions adequate for specification of events at the level of complexity of actual situations.

The nondiscriminating character of most phenomenal terms—especially those referring to properties largely determined by conditions of internal processing rather than by isomorphic energy transformation

—should be mentioned here. Instructive examples of *phenomenal differentiation* may be found in the detailed analyses in the following section. Such phenomenal distinctions as those mentioned below emerged only after long periods of experiential observations and in the sustained attempt to reconcile apparently valid, but somehow conflicting, reports of sensitive subjects and of the experimenter's own experiences. One example of such phenomenal differentiation is that of the description of the location of the self when viewing a photograph or pictures. This will vary depending on whether the subject reports his experienced standpoint, his viewing point, his relation to a specific object or to specific parts of the picture space or reference surfaces such as left or right wall, ceiling or ground (see below, pp. 577 ff.). The distinction between four discriminable types of perceived form described below (below, pp. 572 ff.) provides another example of the insufficiency of a nondiscriminating phenomenal category, that of shape.

The initial discovery of new dimensions can only be made by the individual experimenter-experiencer. Isolation and specification will, however, involve attaining sufficient knowledge of external and internal conditions to *reproduce the phenomena for oneself and to evoke it for identification by other perceivers.* Training of subjects will involve not only practice in identifying certain perceptual criteria, but also training in the awareness and control of perceptual behavior (looking behavior) upon which they in part depend (see following section). This should lead to the identification of standardized patterns of perceptual behavior, which may prove different for different cultures but may also show characteristic individual variations.

Systematic specification and study of complex perceptual situations. One reason for the slow progress in the experimental analysis of anisotropies in the visual field has been experimenter failure to recognize adequately the pragmatic implications of the sheer complexity of the interactions among external and organismic factors, including perceptual behavior. Thus, quite aside from the unrecognized necessity of specifying both handedness and eyedness of subjects, investigations of differences between exposures in right and left visual fields may give negative or conflicting results unless the laterality effect is investigated separately in upper and lower fields. Gaffron has emphasized the necessity for the analysis of anisotropies in terms of quadrants of the visual field rather than in terms of hemifields, since the factors underlying anisotropies include not only hemispheric differences, but differential relationships of visual cortical areas above and below the calcarine fissure, as well as different processings of eye movements in upper and lower, and right and left fields. The general point stressed here is the desirability of differentiated analysis and experimentation in this field.

Necessity of analysis of the mechanisms of report. It might seem plausible to assume that since instructions, via subject intent, determine his report, the specific mechanisms mediating between perceptual process (Phase 4*a, c*) and report (Phases 4*e*, 5) should be largely irrelevant to the functional relationships obtained with stimulus variables. This is probably a gross mistake. We urgently need more understanding of the processes in Phase 4*c* mediating the most central determination of various reporting processes. Particularly we need a functional analysis of the variety of basic perceptual reporting situations from this point of view. We would differentiate among (1) unrestricted phenomenal description; (2) report on presence or absence, or level on a rating scale, of a specified experiential property; (3) subject adjustment of a stimulus to yield a perceptual match with another presented stimulus [23] or a distinguished experience such as that of alignment or verticality, etc. [25].

One specific contingent condition that requires further analysis is the role of perceptual behavior in *mediating the report* as well as in mediating the experience. Thus Crovitz and Daves [14] have shown that a high positive association exists between direction of eye movement occurring *after* a brief exposure of a set of items on both sides of the fixation mark and relative accuracy of the items reported on the side of the movement. Sperling has interestingly demonstrated independence of the number of items being visually processed (Phase 3*a*) and the number accurately reported (Phase 5) [55*b*].

Limitations on communication, on universality of perceptual categories, on generality of perceptual laws; the possibility of restricted subsciences of perceptual phenomena. If it were not likely to be used as an argument against the scientific legitimacy of phenomenal investigations, it would not be necessary to stress the painfully clear fact that limits exist to adequacy and sureness in quasi-universal communication in many, and significant, areas of experience. Presumably the limits would recede with increased knowledge of and control over internal contingent conditions and understanding of the reporting mechanism. That the recession will be neither precipitous nor complete need not bother the perceptual scientist any more than the artist or poet. It should be explicitly recognized that with respect to some complex areas, of which aesthetics is certainly one, it is probable that multiple sub-, but genuine, sciences may develop. That is, certain phenomena may occur in a limited number of subjects and be reliably reported by a still smaller number. To devise fruitful experiments, the perceptual experimenter should be one of this group. And the functional relationships obtained would be fully understood only by this group. And yet it could be a legitimate area of science. It may eventuate that certain areas of the humanities may become sciences in this restricted sense. If this occurred it would be a gain both to psychology as a science and to the humanities. It is possible that, to date, too great a price has been paid in restricting perceptual investigations to the causal contexts of very abstract, and therefore quasi-universal, experiential properties. It could be a function of the humanities, especially the arts, to *exhibit* concrete and investigable properties of experience.

PHENOMENAL PROPERTIES AND PERCEPTUAL ORGANIZATIONS*

Many years ago I attempted to analyze the phenomenon of a definite but rather unspecified difference between the impression of a perspective picture and of the same picture presented in right-left reversal [19, 20]. Looking from one picture to the other, one experienced a definite change in qualities of objects and of perspective space. Repeated comparative surveys of picture pairs produced alternations in phenomenal properties of objectively identical parts of the picture. Thus one became explicitly aware of specific qualitative dimensions, which, before the systematic application of this method, had remained vaguely implicit and unidentified. Corresponding changes could be seen upon right-left reversals of photographs and in mirroring actual scenes. These phenomena all indicated a right-left anisotropy of visual perception in survey, i.e., of the highest-level sensory motor processings.

Current theories of perception did not account for the new dimensions of experience, nor for the laterality of their distribution. Since the conditions of their occurrence could not be theoretically predicted, I first tried to find similar phenomena by looking at objects in actual surroundings and noting the effects of systematic variations in looking behavior. In this way I found that qualities of objects and the experiences of spatial relationships between objects and the self could be shifted in a predictable way by active changes in looking behavior, notably by shifting fixation from in front of to behind objects [21].

It is known that certain two-dimensional patterns show spontaneous perceptual reorganizations. Again characteristic shifts in experiences of spatial relationship between the object and the self appeared, especially in the so-called "perspective reversals." Since these shifts happened not only in the near-far dimension but even more impressively in the up-down dimension, I investigated the effect of inverting photographs of actual situations. Compared with right-left reversals, such inversion produces much more striking phenomenal changes, often resulting in partial or complete phenomenal reorganization of the inverted scene. Over a long period of time, in which a large number of color slides, photographs and actual scenes in different orientations were compared, an increasingly explicit awareness of the kind of structure whose inversions pro-

* Section by M. Gaffron.

duced the major phenomena developed. On this basis, a large variety of natural scenes suitable for the analysis of reorganization phenomena were photographed. Some of the pictures described in this section are selected from this material.

In this article only a few pictures could be presented. In order to exhibit the diversity of phenomenal dimensions occurring in such picture material, we have often included in our detailed descriptions features which would have come out more strikingly in other examples. On the other hand, the more complete descriptions serve to demonstrate the ubiquity of typical dimensions which were originally identified with different, specifically favorable conditions. Experiences of spatial relationships involving the self are more convincing in projections of color slides with their larger picture size, increased brightness contrast and sharpness of contour, and a reduced awareness of the picture plane. In general, experiences depending upon integration of central processes underlying looking behavior are reduced in impressiveness in a picture material of small size. Furthermore, such experiences will vary with individual differences in active looking behavior, in the processing of motor activities, and thus in general with laterality characteristics.

The pictures were chosen and arranged so as to show the similarity of phenomena in the experience of objects or units, of surface and surface pattern, and of complex situations representing objects in space.

Each perceptual organization emerging spontaneously or upon reorientation of the picture material is characterized by a typical constellation of phenomenal properties. This suggests that reorganizations and reversals represent shifts in dominance of processing systems which are always connected with a shift in experiential properties.

Spontaneous reversals occurring in the first two pictures demonstrate two typical perceptual organizations. One of these shows the grouping of phenomenal properties most characteristic of the perception of three-dimensional objects with a material textured surface. The alternative organization emphasizes brightness and movement along contours and appears unfamiliar. It will be seen that form or shape is characteristically different in these two organizations. Thus reversals, in actuality, prove to be not merely opposites within the same organization, but alternations between qualitatively different organizations.

The method of changed picture orientation is illustrated by the analyses of the effects of both inversions and right-left reversals. The inversion of typical ground structures shows a striking variety of phenomena, but in no case is the inverted ground, the ceiling structure, experienced as an identical surface merely opposite in slant. The previously exhibited texture and brightness organizations emerge as differentially dominant in ground and ceiling. Typical of the ceiling structure is instability and a tendency toward piecemeal organization. Here a complete and stable reorganization may occur under favorable conditions. The experiential anisotropies of the major spatial reference surfaces are discussed in relation to differences in experienced looking behavior.

The possibility of principal differences in the typically dominant perceptual organization in the different cultures is raised in the discussion of alternative perceptual organizations occurring in the picture of a cuneiform tablet.

The last examples represent right-left reversals of complex pictorial representations which are characteristic for European art. Here the role of anisotropies of innervational processes and of actual motor processes in active survey of a framed-in area is demonstrated and discussed.

Our primary emphasis has been on faithfulness and relative completeness of phenomenal characterization. Even so, we are aware of the fact that the paucity of the available objective traditional terminology tends to wash out differences of experiential properties which may prove theoretically significant. Though newer neurophysiological data suggest concrete bases for our observations at the neurophysiological level, in the present context no attempt could be made to develop perceptual theories. But it should be assumed that all major phenomenal dimensions do indeed have theoretical implications. The assumption of multiple, though limited, perceptual organizations and thus of *processing systems* underlying them, and the study of the conditions favorable to the dominance of each of these possible organizations may also be fruitful in the study of behavior. At this point we want just to mention the similarity between the shifts in perceptual organizations, here experienced as spontaneous reversals or as reorganizations upon changed orientation of the stimulus material, and the characteristically changed perception upon intake of drugs, in psychopathological conditions, upon specific brain lesions, or even upon merely drastic changes in gravitational forces. Changes in animal behavior in social situations may well be connected with sudden changes in perceptual conditions which, together with slower endocrine changes, could cause a shift in perceptual organization and thus a corresponding shift in reactive behavior.

Differences between the pictorial representations typical of different human cultures suggest differences in dominance within the possible perceptual organizations. Slow fluctuations within the history of visual arts, specifically in Western culture, may reflect relative shifts through changes in looking behavior which would particularly emphasize changes in the experience of self-object relations.

Typical Constellations of Phenomenal Properties in Spontaneous Perceptual Reorganizations

Egyptian sunken relief. The first picture, Fig. 1, is a detail photograph of a set-in Egyptian relief, cut into the wall of the temple at Luxor,

Egypt. It shows mainly the chest and arm of the figure of an Asian prisoner. The illumination comes from above. The photograph of this objective situation may be perceived in different ways which we describe in detail, since each presents a constellation of experiential properties typically found in other perceptual organizations.

One way of perceiving this picture corresponds to the actual situation in its gross three-dimensional characteristics. Despite its veridicality, however, it does not show the constellation of properties typical of our perception of real objects. We will label this "constellation *B*" (brightness dominant). Objectively, the outline of the chest is cut into the wall surface. Our experience of a chest shape is primarily determined by this cut-in border zone, which, together with its shadow, is seen as a definite segregated zone between the two roughly frontoparallel planes of the chest region and the wall. It is constituted by impressive and sharp brightness contrasts. One's attention is felt as being concentrated neither in the central chest region, nor spread over the outer wall area, but as following the course of these extended zones of contrasting brightness. Thus the form of the chest seems actually given in the experience of a movement, a swinging around of the border zone, similar to the way the opening of an archway in a baroque church appears shaped by experience of movement in the profiles of the side walls. The inner chest region is seen as set back in a vaguely frontoparallel plane, behind the very definite surface of the surrounding wall. There is a marked difference in the surface character of the chest and wall regions. The surface of the chest appears to lack articulated texture; it is not experienced as being looked at directly. One may even have the impression of seeing through the cutout in the nearer wall into an underlying, vague frontoparallel layer. In contrast to it, the near wall surface is experienced as strikingly hard, level, and smooth, as if planed. Though it contains many minute, sharply bordered holes, this does not at all modify the dominant characteristic of hardness and smoothness. Indeed, these two characteristics of the wall are experienced as more tactual than visual in quality.

If we look at the region between the chest and the bent arm, this area of the wall is seen as a segregated unit, a characteristically shaped piece of typical wall material. It too appears as shaped by the brightness surrounding it; the cut-in surface is seen as a border zone, but in a somewhat different way. It appears as if the new unit were stamped out of the near wall surface. The form is not experienced as *developing through movement,* as in the chest, but as a *simultaneous step in depth.* Primarily determining this clear-cut form are the angles of the surrounding border zone, the changes in its direction. Most impressive and characteristic therefore is the sharp, pointed triangle underneath the axilla.

In this constellation, the wall region has a more tangible quality than the white page around it. It is not seen at some distance behind the plane of the page, but may appear to be even slightly nearer than the surrounding white paper. The paper region is here seen as just another brightness zone cutting off the wall arbitrarily; that means it does not possess specific frame quality.

If the picture is looked at long enough, a reorganization occurs in which another set of phenomenal properties appears, "constellation T"

Fig. 1.

(texture dominant). (Indeed, for some subjects this may be the first experience.) The chest region acquires for the first time the character of a real object, and the whole picture looks not only more "objective" in character, but also more familiar. In this positive relief, the chest area appears slightly elevated above the wall and is dominant in the picture, while the wall now appears as background. We naturally look at, attend to, the center of the chest, whose shape appears to be formed more from the inside out than by its borders. Its surface is more convex than frontoparallel and has a much more textured, material character. The white spots in the middle gain in impressiveness as material spots upon the textured, material surface.

Brightness and darkness do not appear as qualities of a special zone or surface intermediate between wall and chest. Rather, in this constellation, the zone has disappeared as a segregated area. In those regions where in constellation *B* the independent existence of the sharply demarcated border zone was most outspoken, the same textured, looked-at, material surface of the chest appears now to bend around toward depth. The gradients of brightness appear here as merely superimposed shadows at the curving side of the three-dimensional chest.

The region between chest and bent arm has now no specific form; the sharp, pointed triangular piece of wall has disappeared. On the other hand, the bending into depth of the chest surface is most impressive at the height of the pectoral muscle where the course of the border is softly curved, while the parts with angular changes in direction of the border do not play a conspicuous role in the formation of the chest shape.

The wall, now seen as background space, even extends behind the horizontally stretched rope around the prisoner's neck. In constellation *B*, when this rope was seen as a horizontal groove in the veridically perceived situation, it clearly divided the hard wall into partitions. If one manages to make a detail inspection of the wall without losing the convex relief organization, one will see tiny protuberances sticking out—instead of little dark holes—each one having, like the chest, a shadowed and an illuminated side. Thus the wall region has vagueness only when it lies peripheral to the chest we look at—as its background.

In this constellation, the surrounding white paper appears to lie in front of all the structures in the picture *as a frame*. The peculiar character of the frame lies in its functionally dual role in framing the picture space on the inside and establishing a spatial reference for the observer within his actual surroundings on the outside. It is only in this convex organization T, not corresponding to the actual situation, that we have the typical picture experience of surveying a framed-in picture space.

Cutout board. Another example illustrating similar phenomenal constellations is taken from Wolfgang Metzger's "Gesetze des Sehens" [47, p. 379], Fig. 2. Like the Egyptian set-back relief, it is a picture of an actual situation showing cutouts in a flat material surface. Metzger comments upon it merely as being forcefully seen as reversed, but we want to emphasize the qualitative changes in phenomenal properties occurring in such a "reversal." The most natural perceptual organization is one which again does not correspond with the actual situation (constellation *T*). In it, we predominantly see and attend to three-dimensional units, objects of an unusual shape resembling cookies upon an indeterminate background. They alone have substance, as opposed to the space between them. Though we cannot see their material texture, such a material quality is felt, and a texture gradient of increasing density appears

FIG. 2.

to underlie the dark zones along the borders where their surfaces curve sharply toward depth. Their relation to the ground is ambiguous. One tends to see them either lying upon a plane like a positive relief or floating in space, with each unit having an individual slant in depth. The background or picture space lies behind the white parts of the surrounding page.

When this picture reorganizes (which may be facilitated by rotating it) we are struck with a change in phenomenal properties which is so strong that the perceptual identity of the situation is completely lost (constellation *B*). In this constellation there remain no single objects. We see a board, or better, since it is not a complete "object," a part of a board with quite intricate, irregularly shaped cutout holes through which one may see the ground upon which the board is lying. There are no longer any rounded surfaces. Instead, we experience a sharp step in depth between two parallel planes, the top surface of the board and the underlying ground, with a separate cutting-in surface perpendicular to both. This border zone is given in the course of the darkness at the lower side of the cookies, and even in the fine white line at their upper rims in the former constellation *T*. The board surface is absolutely plane, smooth, and hard, and while the interior region of the cutouts is parallel to the board, it does not share its quality of touchable, palpable hardness, but has a "bottom" quality.

There is not enough enclosure of any part of the board to see a single characteristically shaped board unit. The form of the holes, on the other hand, is again given more by an experience of movement, of following the course of the dark or bright cutting-in border zones, than as a static, simultaneously given shape.

The spatial relation of the surface of the page and the surface of the wooden board is different. The hard surface of the board does not lie in a picture space behind the plane of the page. It is also not looked at from a certain distance, but seems just to stand out from the page. Thus it appears to be merely cut off by the brightness region around it, which is similar to the way the holes are cut into it. We do not have the experience of a framed picture.

"Reversal" as qualitative reorganization. The phenomenal analysis of spontaneously occurring perceptual organizations in these two examples shows that the so-called "reversal" from constellation *B* to *T* is actually *a shift to a qualitatively different perceptual organization, with a different, rather than a reversed, constellation of phenomenal properties.* Some of these may be characterized for practical purposes by terms representing true polarities along the same *physical* dimension. For example, "convex" versus "concave" applied to the same object might well indicate a strict reversal of an object property in a mere physical sense. However, in terms of underlying processings in a physiological system, the phenomenal qualities concave and convex might be as different as, for instance, processes in the "opposed" sympathetic and parasympathetic systems. The biggest pitfall in consciously analyzing and de-

scribing phenomena of reorganization lies in the logical tendency of our Western mind to stick to the same descriptive frame of reference, to think in polarities within one and the same dimension. Even when we try to free ourselves from such habitual conceptualization, we still tend to verbalize concrete experiences in a language of scientific acceptability whose vocabulary is mostly one of physical properties rather than one of physiological or experiential properties. This tendency of Western categorical thinking is therefore in part responsible for the poor and inadequate vocabulary used in the analysis of our illustrations. It emphasizes our earlier assertion that the development of a more adequate terminology for description of experiential properties is badly needed.

Texture versus brightness organizations. In our first examples the two alternating organizations show typical constellations of properties common to both pictures. Since shifts of the same constellations can be shown in figure-ground reversals as well as in spontaneous reorganizations in actual situations, we want to characterize them explicitly. Later we will show how changes in orientation of the picture, and thus in the spatial relationship between picture and observer, result in similar phenomenal shifts. These are of a much more complex and variable nature, which may be the reason that their occurrence has been either overlooked or suppressed in the discussion of phenomenal reversals.

In both pictures the most familiar aspect of objects in space occurs only in constellation T. We see illuminated three-dimensional objects (or a positive relief) with front and sides having the same textured, material surface. The curving into depth makes the same surface appear either shadowed or more highly illuminated at the sides. Thus *the whole object surface is unified by its common texture,* and brightness differences within the central or front area of the object are either spots of a different substance lying upon the typical object surface or are perceived as illumination effects. The object is seen in front, "upon" a background which extends unbroken behind it. The object is felt as looked at, focused upon, as being at a definite distance; while the background is not felt as looked at, focused upon, and thus has no definite distance. Rather it is experienced as having a vague depth, though upon specific inspection it may possess a structure of tiny illuminated protuberances. The object shape, as shape of the surface bending around, uniting front and sides, is felt as *simultaneously enclosing a three-dimensional interior.*

The picture is felt to be related to, to be framed in by, the enclosing whiteness of the page in constellation T. As the background lies behind the object, the picture space lies behind the plane of the page which, in contrast to the background, has a definite distance from the observer. This distance, however, is not just the same distance as that of the objects looked at in the picture. It is characteristic of the frame that its distance is one related also to regions outside, peripheral to the picture. This means it is related to the actual environment of the viewer in which he feels oriented while looking at objects in the picture space.

In constellation *B, the roles played by texture and brightness in organizing the picture are reversed*. Brightness differences are experienced more vividly and separate brightness zones are seen where in constellation *T* one saw light or shadow upon the textured surface.

The surface of the central area of the represented "object" in the Egyptian relief is much less clearly textured, has less material character than in *T;* it is not as rounded as the convex surface in *T* (enclosing an interior) and not as firm, as definite in distance, but more like a fronto-parallel layer. In the Metzger picture it has become a flat bottom of holes.

The areas which were background for the objects in constellation *T* have now become a special kind of surface. They are not seen as textured, as characterized by tiny protruding elements, but *tactually flat and very hard* (with irregularities seen as mere tiny holes in the basically level surface in the Egyptian relief).

In both pictures in constellation *B*, we see a *definite segregated border zone of brightness* in the periphery of the former object areas which does not exist as such in constellation *T*. In both, the shape or shapes seen are experienced via a kind of movement within the separate border zone. In the Egyptian sunken relief it moves around the inner region, giving it a following-the-contour-of-the-chest or quasi-object shape. In the Metzger cutout board, according to the curved or straight angular course of the border zone, it is felt as a swinging around the holes, or a cutting out of the board, but it does not result in a dominance of a typical movement form or in the formation of cutout board units. In the Egyptian relief, however, we see in organization *B a new kind of unit* outside the chest area, created by the bright border zones of chest and arm which single out between them a piece of the wall which, in constellation *T*, was simply part of the general background region. Characteristic for this new unit is the specific hard flat surface and the definiteness of its shape. The surface as such remains a mere flat "wall" surface; the brightness zone, however, is experienced as a decisive step in depth. Thus the new unit stands out from the surroundings, the vaguely inset areas of arm and chest. The shape is given entirely in *direction of the enclosing brightness step* and is most impressive at the sharp angular changes of direction.

Compared with the surrounding page, the surface of the wall or board in constellation *B* is experienced not as lying behind the plane of the page and as being looked at from a distance, but as standing out from the page, being in a peculiar direct relation to the observer, in a "touchable" distance. The wall or board now appears merely interrupted, cut off, arbitrarily shaped by the surrounding bright area of the page which does not act as a frame in this constellation, but more like a brightness border zone.

Shape may be experienced differently not only between the two basic organizations, but also within each organization. In the border-zone-brightness organization *B*, a flat hard surface with a definite static cutout shape and a deeper-lying area with a vague contour-movement shape are seen side by side alternating in dominance. In constellation *T* the textured rounded surface of the three-dimensional object bending around toward depth at the sides appears to enclose within the same area of the picture an interior volume shape lying directly behind it in depth, extending forward from an invisible back surface.

Figure-ground reversal as qualitative reorganization. What we have shown as occurring in our examples upon reorganization actually occurs also in most of the typical figure-ground "reversals." The same changes of properties, indicating a shift in the underlying perceptual processes, occur in the two-dimensional drawings frequently used for demonstration. They are merely seen more explicitly in our photographs of actual situations. In the famous Rubin "vase-profile" drawing, for instance, the experience of a centrally located object "vase" upon background in a framed picture shifts to that of two "profile" faces, indicating that the contour zones of the vase region have become dominant. It is typical that the surface of the former background region enclosed by the profile and the frame changes in character; it becomes a very definite, flat and hard silhouette surface which is not seen as framed in, but as arbitrarily cut off by the frame line. Contrary to the Egyptian relief, however, the central region is merely experienced as set back and hollow since the dominance of the meaningful silhouette shape of the two profile faces suppresses the experience of a vague movement shape of the interior region. It has to be emphasized that in all classical cases demonstrating the figure-ground reversal we have conditions favoring a constellation *B* organization. This means that we rarely have such a reversal when we look at a textured, rounded, material object in a typical perspective picture space.

Qualitative reorganizations, physiological processings, and differential behavioral consequences. The emergence of a new dominant set of experiential qualities, a new type of organization, as illustrated in our own examples, as well as in the classical figure-ground reversal, may well reflect a shifting of physiological processing to a different physiological system or systems. Most certainly it involves a shift in motor integrations, a different perceptual behavior. This is indicated by the shift from the experience of active looking at units, focusing at different distances, to an experience of passive shaping through enclosing, peri-central brightness zones in different depth planes. In such organizations (or systems), different phenomenal qualities (or physiological processes) may play quasi-equivalent roles in the total perceptual process. For instance, in the segregation of units we find a predominant role of texture differences in one constellation versus brightness differences in the other. The fact that in each organization of the Egyptian relief, the same area, the chest, is *cognized* does not obliterate the marked *phenomenal differences* in this area—the typical object properties in constellation T as compared to the vagueness of the movement shape in constellation B. Such shifts of properties, if permanent, may well have behavioral consequences which could, for instance, differentiate between "normal" humans and those with specific behavior disorders. In the Metzger picture, as well as in the classical figure-ground reversal, the identity of the object recognized by its shape disappears entirely. Such radical shifts of organization might play a role in sudden changes of behavior of animals toward visual "objects" which for us do not lose their identity. The peculiar experiences reported by congenitally blind patients upon regaining vision [60] correspond so closely to those in constellation B that we can assume absolute dominance of brightness organization in their visual perception. Later, in a picture of a tablet with cuneiform script, an example will be given of a situation in which—in contrast to the recognition of objects—a recognition of script, of signs, may occur better in the nonveridical, reorganized, perceptual experience. Our two first examples are alike in this respect: in both, the more natural, familiar experience of objects is not the veridical one. On the other hand, the point may be made that the Egyptian sunken relief, as a technique foreign to our Western culture, may appear unnatural only to our Western way of looking. The unique emphasis upon the brush stroke as movement experience and carrier of shape in Chiang Yee's interpretation of Chinese painting is another example of a different way of looking [12, 13]. The probability of a different perceptual behavior in different cultures again emphasizes the role of central integrations as contingent conditions in visual perception.

Anisotropies in Spatial Relationships

The method of changed picture orientation. The organizations in the previous sections were described in detail in order to present the reader with some concrete instances of perceptual organization whose adequate characterization requires the development of a more differentiated, less cognitive, more experiential vocabulary. It should be clear that utilization of a vocabulary referring to nonexperiential, merely cognized, properties of external physical objects would be nondiscriminating here. Picture material permitting "spontaneous" reorganizations was selected to illustrate the dependence of constellations of experiential properties upon central processes including perceptual motor processes underlying looking behavior. Clearly the phenomenal changes occurring cannot be attributed to changes in the objective situation. A dependence upon internal processes may be demonstrated also by the utilization of material which tends to be perceived differently when its spatial orientation to the observer is changed, while all intrinsic properties remain the same. This may be achieved either by rotating a picture or by presenting a mirror or right-left reversed image of it. Some of the most striking changes demonstrated with changed orientation are related to the shifts in organizations which we have seen in the spontaneous reorganizations of the two first pictures.

The next pictures are selected from photographs taken to demonstrate the influence of changed orientation upon experience of specifically structured and slanted surfaces in our actual surrounding. In each case, a short description of the actual situation will be given before describing phenomenal properties and their shifts. Some terms used repeatedly by various observers to characterize the over-all impression of a reorganized picture are taken as characteristic qualitative labels and are presented in quotation marks.

The role of texture gradients in the perception of slant of surfaces has been emphasized by Gibson [24]. We wish to emphasize here the anisotropies in the visual experience, not the veridicality in judgments, of slant.

Inversions. *Lake bottom.* This picture, Fig. 3, appears to represent something unfamiliar and not really meaningful. It is most often described as an aerial view of a "rocky desert," or as a "moonscape." When we turn it upside down, which is the actual orientation of the photographed situation it represents a dry bottom of a shallow park lake drained for cleaning. Again the phenomenal changes upon inversion are so striking that the two pictures appear to have nothing in common.

The lake-bottom picture in normal orientation, though unusual, does not appear unfamiliar. We see, as if looking through the frame of the page like a window, a ground upon which little hillocks of a material like dry moss or shredded wheat are densely packed. Most hillocks have a shadowed and a sunlit side; one can see in the nearer hillocks the single bright shreds with darker intervals between them. Between the hillocks are indentations, small furrows, and part of the underlying ground is visible toward the middle of the picture. In surveying this situation, we seem to look from the near hillocks in front, across the ground and the tops of the farther, smaller units, out into the distance. The dominant experience is that of a rather peculiarly

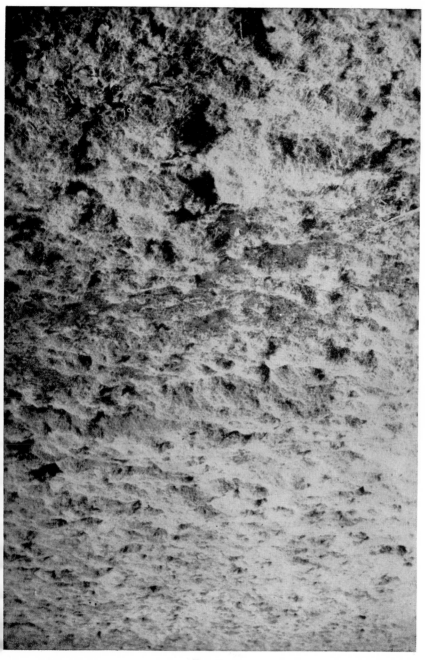

FIG. 3.

structured but uniformly receding ground which begins to be visible at the lower frame. Looking at it, it is felt that we are standing somewhere upon a forward extension of this ground as onlooker (or photographer).

In turning this picture slowly around, we may become aware of a reorganization resulting in a totally different experience. It may be gradual or sudden, partial or complete. There is, as a transitory stage, an enhancement of brightness and brightness contrast, a singling out of the former dark shadows as unit shapes. There is certainly no simple over-all inversion of a ground surface with hillocks into a ceiling with inverted hillocks, as one would expect. Instead of that, we see, in the complete reorganization, a scooped-out hard surface with sharp ridges between slopes in the upper half, and small crested waves or dunes in the lower half. The lower part reorganizes most easily; the larger units in the upper half may sometimes still be seen like hillocks, though peculiarly flattened. The slant of the surface is quite indeterminate and varies as to regions. In the lower part we may even have the contradictory experience of a receding from the lower frame, a backward slant, and that of a very far, though quite indefinite, distance; the upper part appears more frontoparallel, or may even slope somewhat forward. There is no consistent slant, no looked-at units at increasing (or decreasing) distances. Instead, the dominant impression is one of mere regional differences of size, of dimensions, and any assessment of distance proves to be a cognitive judgment determined by the assumed size or meaning of units. Seen as a rock wall, it may appear relatively near; as a moonscape, extremely far; and again, different regions may seem to have different distances, just as they have different slants and different unit sizes.

A most striking character of the scooped-out surface appears to be its hardness, as compared to the fluffiness of the hillocks on the ground. The shreds of materials and interval spaces have become a mere pattern of white scratches upon a hard gray rock surface. There is no experience of a space through which one is looking at objects, of atmosphere; no experience of a ground upon which each object has its individual distance from the onlooker. Instead, there is an experience of inherent movement connected with the dominance of the crests, the sharp ridges, so that the lower part especially looks like a hardened surface of a wavy sea or wind-blown dunes of a desert. The ridges carrying the movement along this hard surface are the edges of the regions constituting dark shadows in the ground structure. There is no feeling of steps in a sequence of looking at, or surveying, larger units separated by interval spaces; the whole surface is just quasi-simultaneously visible and clear.

We wish to emphasize that the natural illumination, experienced as causing lighted and shadowed areas of objects, is qualitatively completely different from the luminous or lustrous brightness and the hollow or silhouette blackness inherent in different areas in the reorganized picture.[5] The intermediate phase of reorganization—in which we see the shadows more and more dominant, until they appear as flat silhouette unit shapes—is important, because out of this intermediate silhouette phase develops the complete reorganization, which lacks the natural and characteristic quality of illumination.

Experienced looking behavior. In this picture the inversion of a familiar ground structure has not resulted in the experience of a ceiling structure, but in a reorganization—an organization showing again a typical constellation of properties not just opposed to, but different from, that in the ground orientation. The reorganization need not happen simultaneously or in all regions. Its occurrence will vary for each observer. There are also intermediate stages: a flattening out, with a mere enhancement of the brightness contrasts, resulting in a formation of dark, flat silhouette shapes seen in the area of the larger shadows. Again we can demonstrate phenomenal characteristics of the ground structure which we have not been aware of in its familiar aspect— by our surprise at their disappearance, the contrasting experience at their places in the inverted picture, and their reappearance upon re-orientation of the picture. For instance, we may not have been aware of the positive experience of looking at objects, of surveying the picture space, or of having an apparent standpoint as observer on the ground at a certain distance. But we are certainly struck by the complete disappearance of any spatial relationship to ourselves as surveyors and by the inherent movement and simultaneous visibility of the reorganized ceiling surface. Thus only through the method of repeated comparisons with inverted orientations have we become able to identify certain self-related and looking experiences typical of but normally not explicit in the ground structure.

Rusticated wall. The picture of a rusticated wall of a Florentine palace is shown in a ground orientation in near-symmetric perspective, Fig. 4a. In this picture, brightness and brightness contrasts are diminished, while the material texture of the big boulders is emphasized. Under these conditions we do not easily get a reorganization when the picture is shown upside down, and the phenomenal properties of a true ceiling organization can be observed, Fig. 4b.

In the ground orientation, we seem to look at the front surface of the nearest boulders and along the top of the farther ones toward distance. Our viewing point appears to be correspondingly low. The picture space extends above the ground toward distance, lying behind the plane of the frame of the page. Iron ring and torchholder are at a medium distance in this picture space; one would have to move

---

[5] Such phenomenal changes in brightness are maximal in projected slides, minimal in printed reproductions.

Fɪɢ. 4a.

forward in order to grasp them. Darker and brighter areas are seen here as shadowed and lighted parts of the convex, roughly textured boulders.

In spite of the fact that in the ceiling orientation this picture does not reorganize (at least not completely), its aspect is most unfamiliar and shows a peculiar shift in qualities. The picture space appears different in kind. It is felt as extending from afar, underneath a ceiling which seems to protrude forward into the very same space which surrounds us as viewers. Looking intensely at this picture, one may even feel more *in* its space than in front of it. It should be emphasized that this experiential difference between ground and ceiling orientation exists quite convincingly in looking at our actual surroundings. The floor of a hallway, for instance, extends *away from a certain distance in front of us;* the ceiling, however, is seen as extending *from the hall end forward toward us and above our heads* and even beyond us.

Iron ring and torchholder have lost the quality of being seen from a distance, of being at a definite distance in front of us. If one tries to think how one would reach for them, it appears as if we would have to reach not forward, but mainly upward, from below. The natural and dominant spatial relationship here may be expressed in terms of up-down, of more or less above ourselves, underneath the ceiling—the experience of ourselves changing into one of just *being underneath* instead of *looking from in front.*

Instability of the ceiling organization. The true ceiling experience is remarkably unstable. Brightness contrasts tend to gain out over texture

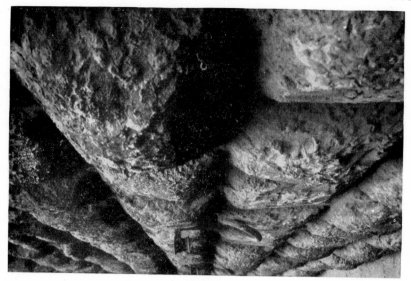

FIG. 4*b*.

wherever they are strong enough, and the experience of a protruding ceiling slant tends to oscillate with a tendency to see a spreading out in a more frontoparallel plane. There is no standpoint, no viewing point; thus perspective, with its constancy of unit size of the boulders, is apt to lose out against the experience of the change in dimensions of units now arranged as fanning out in cones. The decisive element in shaping these cones is the dark border zone of the grooves. Thus again we have a prevalence of a brightness border organization and an experience of movement. The horizontal indentations between the boulders, which are not impressive as brightness contrasts, are practically not seen here, while they play an important role as a bending around of the textured surface, setting the boulders off against each other in depth, in the ground picture. There is a loss of parallelity in depth of the boulder rows and a change in apparent size of iron ring and torchholder. The striking loss of perceptual constancy in the ceiling, associated with weakening of perspective, suggests the possible dependence of size constancy upon experienced ground structure.

Regional reorganization. The instability of the initial ceiling organization may show itself in the tendency of separate regions of the picture to reorganize independently. Thus the lower left corner tends to reorganize easily. Here one becomes aware of more outspoken differences in brightness and of the different angular directions of the grooves, until suddenly one sees sharp ridges between scooped-out troughs. The lower left corner then becomes a piece of "moonscape," a completely different world from that of the ceiling, which is still seen, though more vaguely, in the rest of the picture. Compared with the ceiling organization, there is an overclarity combined with an uncanny disappearance of spatial relationships to the self—as if one were looking through binoculars in reversed direction. There is an indefiniteness of distance, a shrinking away of the self when one tries to imagine oneself, and no reference for size. This reorganized region has now a definite backward, outward slant of the surfaces. However, there is no ground-structure experience since the movement seen here is inherent in the ridges, and there is no self-related looking along the ground.

Effects of looking behavior. A different, quite contrasting effect occurs if, in looking at Fig. 4b, one tries to effect an upside-down reversal of the self, to imagine oneself as swinging around and looking down from the near top of the picture—as if one were bending out of a window and looking down a building front. We then may have again the experience of perspective and parallelity of rows. The competing feature of spreading, however, tends to make us experience this perspective as very exaggerated, compared with the ground. Distance experience in this looking-down perspective is also different: it has acquired the character of depth underneath us; when looking at the textured units along this front toward depth, one may even have a sensation of giddiness remarkably opposed to the feeling of being firmly anchored or having a standpoint.

It is often said that imagining the light coming from an opposite direction may help to achieve a reversal. Possibly this is only the effect of imagining a rotation, a reorientation which, by changing the natural survey behavior, might well have the desired effect of bringing out the different organization.

It appears as if only the combination of a ground-structure gradient and a typical survey behavior results in the familiar experience of looked-at units, seen higher up in the picture, in perspective, i.e., with constancy of size and direction. As soon as we try to survey a ceiling structure, we lose stability as well as perspective constancy. *A habitual combination of survey behavior with a ground structure might therefore underlie the apparent stability of experience of the ground organization.*

In the ceiling structure there may thus be a competition in the integration of the processes underlying *active looking behavior* and processes underlying mere *orienting movements* toward the pattern of brightness distribution. There may be an oscillation in dominances or regional differences which we experience as instability or as piece-meal organization. *Only upon a complete loss of looking-at experience, loss of spatial relationship to the self, and a new identity of the situation (as in the moonscape) do we get a new sort of stability characteristic for complete reorganization.*

Mown field. This picture of a hand-mown grass field illustrates in its normal orientation another familiar ground structure. Inverted, it shows a dominance of the horizontal brightness contrasts in phenomenal organization (Fig. 5*a* and *b*). The photograph is taken so that we appear to look across the rows of brighter stalks lying on the darker ground out into the distance. We appear to stand, slightly elevated, on a forward extension of the same ground which is seen in the picture and which we experience as a reference surface extending from near to far, even where it is not directly visible. In the distance the tops of the rows, with their irregularities in height and spots of ground in between, are seen like a soft wavy surface. In the foreground and middle ground, the stalks are lying lightly heaped upon each other, and one can see the interval spaces and even some space underneath the front ends of the stalks in the nearest rows. Thus here the individual stalks have slightly different heights above the ground, different distances, and different tilts. All these qualities are related to the experience of ourselves looking at them or, vice versa, to the quality of being looked at (photographed) by us as we stand in front of them. The remarkable feature of this picture is *the dominance of an experience of looking from near to far in the upward direction.* There is certainly no scanning of the picture following the rows, for instance, from left to right, or going to and fro.

In the picture turned upside down, the reference surface of the ground does not turn into one of a ceiling. Instead of this, the main experience is now one of horizontal extension, concentrated in the dark regions between the brighter partitions. The *simultaneity of a horizontal spreading* goes with a loss of experience of active looking. In fact, the main character of such a picture is that one does not know how to look at it; one feels tempted to try out various ways of looking at it in order to get a more convincing, coherent, and familiar experience. The result, however, will always be a changing one, though certain qualities of the organization will be dominant in certain regions of the picture. Though there may be an over-all impression of frontoparallelity, each partition appears to have a slightly different distance and slant. Thus this organization of the picture appears, as a whole, less complex and less detailed, but nevertheless as a kind of *piecemeal organization in horizontal partitions.* At an indefinite, but apparently far, distance, the lowermost part looks similar to the lowest part in the moonscape. There is a slant away from the lower frame, decreasing, however, with increasing unit size. The units, as brightness units, are small troughs below crests. The scooped-out character of a hardened surface is less clear-cut in this picture because the whole region shows a hatching with fine bright lines softening the brightness contrasts. The larger bright partitions are characterized by strokes of brightness in a diagonal direction—like a white-on-black draw-

Fig. 5a.

ing. The differing directions of individual strokes in the uppermost partition is quite striking and is seen as crisscrossing. It appears as if with the
loss of dominance of active looking, emphasizing perspective parallelity
the *linear directions of brightness contrast* determine the experience of the
picture when it is organized in terms of horizontal brightness partitions.
The slant and tilt of the individual stalks were related to the ground

Fig. 5b.

below them in the normal orientation; in the inverted picture, the direction of the bright lines is related to the brightness contrast horizontally above them, while no experience of a ground- or gravity-related tilt or slant is involved. An exception is the uppermost region where, in certain parts with reduced brightness contrasts, the experience of a detail structure which may be focused upon and a partial ground experience begin to develop. Thus we oscillate between seeing this partition as more frontoparallel or as overhanging ground receding from a relatively near distance.

In this orientation, the role of brightness and darkness as mediating intensity and depth and variation in penetrability is quite striking. It appears as if the white stalks lie like slats of Venetian blinds in separate and near depth planes in front of the dark interval regions which lack the quality of hard surface, appearing as hollow depth. Turning to Fig. 5a, one sees in this very same dark zone the structured ground extending continuously toward distance. Thus, in the survey of the ground picture, we have an experience of looking at objects from in front combined with an experience of looking from near to far along the ground; while in the reorganized ceiling picture, we have an experience of directions of brightness contrasts and of simultaneous sidewise spread competing with the experience of penetrating and looking into depth between partitions.

Cuneiform tablet. The earliest-known system of writing is cuneiform script. A reed stylus was pressed into the surface of wet clay, creating the typically wedge-shaped indentations. The illustration in Fig. 6 shows a detail picture of a cuneiform tablet "written" around 2000 B.C. (from the cover of *Scientific American,* October, 1957). We see a typically textured material, a clay-brick surface, divided by grooves in horizontal regions, with a rather complex pattern of short indentations grouped somehow along the grooves. Instead of seeing only the script as structured groups of cut-in wedges, one tends to see also the shapes of the softly rounded interval regions between the impressed signs. This picture, however, changes strikingly when a reorganization occurs; then the wedges are seen not as indented, but as jutting out. When the whole area is reorganized, the tablet appears to be clearly structured—one has no more the impression that one has to search or look for groups with characteristic direction of its components, but rather clear-cut groups of positive wedges are seen quasi-simultaneously. There is a sudden increase in brightness contrasts. Instead of a general illumination of the clay surface, we see brightness concentrated on one side of each wedge, contrasting sharply at the ridge with the darkness of the other side. The ridge whose direction constitutes the most conspicuous feature of the markings is actually the bottom of the stylus impression.

The former material surface of the clay tablet is in this reorganization seen as a deeper-lying frontoparallel bottom plane. Though the wedges are clearly set off from this bottom plane, it is the brightness contrast along the ridges which is most intensely experienced, almost tactually felt, like a sharp edge. Since direction, size, and grouping of the wedge impressions determine the meaning of the written symbols, it is not astonishing that we seem to see a meaningful script more easily in the reorganization, while the meaningless shape of the indented

Fig. 6.

material surface of the clay tablet tends to prevail when we see it veridically.

Effects of inversion with continued brightness organization. Another shift of experience within the nonveridical positive-wedge organization can be demonstrated by turning this picture upside down. The wedge groups will now be shifted from below to above the long horizontal ridges. This causes a new and quite impressive change: we now tend to see something meaningful like scaffoldings or structural objects, and not just combinations of various directions. The star group of wedges, for instance, will no longer be seen as a burst of directions. Instead, we seem to see a stylized small tree standing upright on the groundlike upper surface of the horizontal ridge, with branches extending at different angles from its stem, the vertical wedge. With this shift toward an experience of meaningful objects, the experience of seeing in several directions simultaneously disappears and is replaced by one of actively looking from one structured unit to another, each one being a new center of attention.

In the original orientation, the long horizontal ridges appear as the dominant *reference direction* for those of the smaller wedges underneath. No basic qualitative difference is experienced between directions. This is different when the picture is inverted. Here the long horizontal ridges become the ground upon which the constructions rest. More precisely, it is only the upper bright side which becomes ground, while the lower dark side—when attended to—is actually seen as a ceiling of the space underneath in the next lower partition. Thus, with the horizontal ridges being qualitatively divided in themselves according to brightness and darkness above and below, we get horizontally arranged independent spaces, with ground and ceiling. When we attend to the wedge structure in this orientation, the experience of the ground is dominant as basis for the upright objects and as main reference surface in space.

With a ground orientation, the experience of direction is qualitatively different: within the groups, the vertical wedge, perpendicular to the ground, appears singled out in its quality. It appears as upright, and the various other directions seem now to be experienced more as deviations from uprightness, i.e., as tilt in relation to gravity. In our Western culture, such gravity-related base-down organization of brightness patterns appears prevalent in visual perception. It seems characteristic of our habitual way of looking at objects. For instance, when we look at a short line on paper tilted slightly away from the vertical—clockwise or anticlockwise—we say simply that it is tilted to the right or to the left. This means that we see the object line standing upon an imaginary horizontal base and being tilted away from the axis of uprightness on the ground. With a forceful base-up or ceiling reference and with enough brightness contrast, however, the experience of tilt in a field of gravity disappears; it is replaced by the directly visible quality of direction in the straight linear course of brightness contrasts on a vague frontoparallel ground. Therefore, the assumption that the "meaning" of a brightness pattern is always clearest in a veridical perception of the objective situation does not hold for perception of symbols with an emphasis on directional quality.

We tend to think of script as mediated by a visual experience in which extension and direction of brightness contrasts are the significant qualities. Other qualities too could be considered as used for characterization—certain movements or silhouette shapes. All these qualities have something in common: on the basis of brightness organization, there is no felt spatial relationship to a looking self involved in their experience—as contrasted to looking at units characterized by a textured rounded material surface or even objects standing upon the ground. (Therefore it seems typical that the very first step in the development from picture writing to sign writing is a 90° turning of the pictograph from upright to horizontal.)

One must be careful not to assume that our Western way of looking at three-dimensional objects in space is the only possible way of experiencing the world around us. It is only the best way to see the "perspective," or "objective," situation. Whenever we look at a striking horizontal line in a brightness pattern or at a surface with a ceiling-texture gradient, objects or object groups below them or related to them change their quality, losing their typical object character at the same time that our experience of active looking, of focusing upon material surface, and of antigravity uprightness disappears.

Tile roof. The photograph of the tile roof (Fig. 7) shows the tiles arranged in rows as an ascending ground structure. They are not like the boulders in the picture of the rusticated wall—rounded, segregated units constituting a ground. They are more like steps of a ground ascending and receding to the ridge of the roof. Their dark front surfaces may be looked at individually; they may also be seen as continuous dark bands with a swinging movement across the picture plane. The illumination is very pronounced, causing sharply outlined shadows in the troughs which tend, even in the normal organization, to divide the tile surface into parts. Still, the prevailing impression is one of looking up the roof along the troughs between the rounded ridges, seeing tiles with a uniform, typical texture in bright sunlight.

Upon inversion, the increase in brightness intensity is striking; the sunny part of the tiles becomes luminous, the shadows very dark. Instead of a brilliantly illuminated ceiling of tiles, one may see—especially in the upper part of the picture—an arrangement of sharply outlined, bright, vizor-like heraldic shapes upon a uniformly dark ground. These bright units now possess a surface, while the dark regions, in which the front surfaces and the shadow parts are no longer differentiated, are seen as mere depth without a surface. Correspondingly, the experience of surveying, of *looking along* a coherent surface structure in the picture space, has disappeared; only the bright heraldic shapes stand out. In the lower part (above the more distant ridge of the roof), the black front surfaces of the tiles are differentiated from the somewhat lighter shadow

Fig. 7.

regions on the back of the tiles; here reorganization may occur and spread over the whole picture. We then see rows of convex shields of a hard material, like coats of arms with one part painted in glossy silver, the other in dull gray. Shields of increasing sizes are arranged in cones, rising fanlike from the ridge of the roof underneath, which now appears to be much nearer. The shape of the new units, the shields, is given now through the border zones of darkness—the front surfaces and the sharp

588   KARL ZENER AND MERCEDES GAFFRON

shadow lines directly along the ridges. This border form results in a uniform convexity of the enclosed surface, while the textured surface, looked along in the ground structure, was modeled in undulations from concave to convex. The former frontal surfaces are thus seen as dark depth zones between the hard shield surfaces. We experience a movement inherent in the radiating pattern, in the grooves between the rows. The cone rows have a different slant in depth according to the angle they form with the horizontal ridge of the roof underneath. Those at the lower left recede most distinctly, while the perpendicular row appears most frontoparallel.

In projecting the original color slide, another phenomenal change upon reorganization is most striking. Instead of mere shadow and light on the gray tiles, we see—after the initial enhancement of luminosity—an emergence of color in the two parts of the shield surface; there is a dull blue in the shadow area and a lustrous silver gold in the light. Also in the color slide of the lake bottom, a yellow color appears in the moonscape organization which was not in the original illuminated-ground experience.

In this picture we see three different kinds of unit shapes: the *textured* modeled tile *objects* in the ground structure; upon inversion, *bright figures* on a dark set-back *ground* (chiefly in the upper part); and, with complete reorganization, *hard-surfaced patterned units shaped by dark border zones*. The pattern is given by the course of the original shadow line, the contour which divided figure from ground and now separates two colored areas of the same hard shield surface.

Phenomenal shifts in surface patterns. Some years ago we illustrated the phenomenal changes in the experience of a black-and-white drawing—a small "potato-shaped" outline figure. The paper area enclosed by an irregular curved black outline was described as having a shape of inner coherence, having a surface and some voluminousness in space [21, p. 299]. When the inner area was made solid black it became a flat and solid surface, as a silhouette shape. Introducing an irregularly curved inline across the enclosed area created a situation in which, in alternation, one part was seen as (shaped) figure, while the other became ground. This was connected with a loss of the former shape of the whole drawing and a step in depth along the inner contour line. However,

A uniform experience of the former figure shape can only be regained if the figure-ground oscillation gives way to the experience of one single, more material surface bearing a pattern line with a shape of its own. The shape of this surface is not determined by the pattern in-line, but exclusively by the former figure outline, which has become its "border" [21, p. 300].

The phenomenal shifts in the organization of this simple line drawing are, therefore, the exact counterparts of the shifts in the organization of the photographic picture of the actual tile surface upon inversion.

The best-known spontaneous perspective reversal of a surface pattern is that of the Necker cube. Since the shift in properties and spatial relationship corresponds to those upon inversion of a picture, and since an equivalent shift happens in one object (the polyhedron in Dürer's engraving) in a later picture upon right-left reversal, this classic reversal will be shortly described here.

The Necker cube is seen in its normal organization as resting upon an imaginary ground, looked at from a distance, with its side receding into a space behind the paper plane. Upon reversal, it appears to stick out from the paper plane, protruding instead of receding. In addition, however, we now feel that we are looking up from the space underneath it against its bottom side. As described elsewhere, the common feature of all so-called "perspective reversals" is the emergence of spatial relationships experienced as related to the self whenever "a ground-related, receding, habitual perspective changes into a ceiling-related perspective" [21, p. 306].

The Necker cube drawing has a diagonal asymmetry and can be drawn in two ways. If the two lines forming its diagonal axis are drawn in the direction lower left to upper right, the front aspect in the normal and the protruding movement of the edges in the reversed organization appear more dominant; if the diagonal axis extends in the opposed direction of upper left to lower right, the right wall or side aspect of the cube in the normal, the being underneath, the looking against its bottom in the reversed organization are more characteristic features of its aspect. Thus a right-left asymmetry in the drawing of an object in perspective emphasizing one or the other diagonal direction shows a further differentiation of qualities of spatial relationships superimposed upon the basic ground (near-to-far) or ceiling (far-to-near) organization.

In the article mentioned above, qualities of surface patterns, of objects and of their relationships to the self, were described as shifting with external conditions and with looking behavior. The phenomenal, experiential differentiations found at that time correspond to our current notion of a shifting dominance of organizing processes which emerged from the observation of clusters of properties in our photographs of actual situations.

Reorganization in actual situations. The same shift in experience of qualities as seen in our illustrations takes place when we look at a real scene through inverting lenses or with inverted head position.

One need only stand in the middle of an empty street and look along it, then compare this aspect with the aspect one gets with one's head upside down, in order to see shifts corresponding to the effect of inverting a photograph. All "perspective" lines—car tracks on the pavement, curb-stones, for instance—are seen as fanning out rather than as parallel and receding toward depth. The line of the curbstones is specifically enhanced as border of the spread-out, fan-shaped street area. The tree stems do not appear to stand along the curb, but are lined up in their own differ-ent angular direction. The dark shadows of trees lying horizontally across the pavement are emphasized, creating partitions. A bend in the perspec-tive lines produced by a distant upward slope in the street is seen as an exaggerated definite angle in the course of the curbstones.

When one looks at the upper corner of a uniformly painted room, one may easily get a "reversal" in which the hollow corner is suddenly seen as the jutting-out corner of a solid box. Again, the experience of typically slanted wall and ceiling surfaces, enclosing space, is shifted to that of sharp edges meeting at right angles and is accompanied by an enhancement of brightness contrast along these edges.

The behavioral adjustment of persons wearing inverting lenses for a long period of time has been described and investigated very thoroughly by Erismann and Kohler [17, 40]. We want here only to point out that such behavioral adjustment will certainly be associated with a shift in dominant qualities shaping our experience. Therefore, we do not have a true reversal and an adjustment to opposed experiences, but a shift in basic organization and adjustment of cognition and behavior to this new kind of perceptual organization. When we look through inverting lenses, we will see, for instance, brightness and color very much enhanced. Borders of objects stand out as brightness contrasts, and movement ap-pears exaggerated along these borders in a frontoparallel plane, while the experience of depth is much reduced. Thus people seen walking upside down seem, especially at an intermediate distance, to bob up and down and wave their arms exaggeratedly. They do not walk forward as much as they seem to shift their feet sidewise, putting them down one directly in front of the other. Instead of *coming* nearer they appear to *grow* nearer—with sudden increases in size. There is a ripple of movement running around the body outlines and along the shifting wrinkles of the clothes. (It is exactly the same kind of experience which one gets when watching the performance of East Indian dancers, where the movement does not seem to originate from within the often motionless body but along the periphery of the moving limbs.) Even near-far shifts—accord-ing to partitions of brightness in the actual scene—may occur and a paradoxical setback of convex objects into the surrounding background, just as in the actual sunken Egyptian reliefs. We then have also the experience of luster and hardness of surfaces. All these shifts happen only in parts of our visual field, constituting a piecemeal organization. Again, exactly such a piecemeal effect has been described as typical in a pseudoscopic situation in which the near-far disparities are reversed. We found, however, that such partial reversal in depth always appeared to be connected with the characteristic *qualitative shifts* described here.

Right and left walls and objects. The difference between right and left walls needs for demonstration—without the complicating effects of inversion of illumination and interchange of upper and lower perspective regions—a mirror reversal of the illustration. However, a short comparison of the (upper) right- and (lower) left-wall orientations of the tile roof might be instructive, since we have to deal with a relatively simple uniform structure, instead of a highly complex pictorial representation, as in our later pictures.

In the orientation of the tile roof left wall, as in all perspective left walls, the experience of looking activity is most pronounced, even more than in the ground. We seem to be looking directly against the nearest left part and from there along the troughs into the distance toward the ridge. The tiles form more distinct units than in the ground orientation: the brightness differentiation within the units is more enhanced and the front surfaces are experienced as perpendicular to our looking direction. *The experience of space is here connected with the experience of increasing distance in looking along the wall from the near left to the far right.*

In the right-wall orientation, no comparable looking experience occurs. (There is an immediate, striking increase in brightness contrast, which may soon cause a reorganization; the following description, however, refers only to the initial "illuminated-wall" organization.) The wall appears as quasi-simultaneously seen without being looked along; but there is now an element of protrusion from the far end forward inherent in its extension. *It appears to close off space toward the right.* The nearest part of the wall appears in a vague way protruding past us, as if we ourselves were in space to the left. The rounded ridges, or better, the bulging-out bright parts of the tiles determine the character of the right wall. Shape is given more in the movement of contours. Instead of the dark front surfaces of the tiles, we tend to see vertical swinging bands of unequal width in a frontal parallel plane.

In general in a left wall the spatial reference surface appears to lie in the setback parts along which we seem to look; but the "surface" closing off space at the right is more determined by the protruding parts. *Active looking and focusing upon texture are the prevalent experiences in left walls as contrasted with movement and brightness seen as inherent in right walls.*

In our example, the inverted brightness distribution within the tiles will soon cause a reorganization and the original tile units will be destroyed. The complete reorganization will then be seen with an apparently "reversed" (i.e., left-wall) slant in the arrangement of the new units, the shields. It is important that it is also possible, although less easy, to achieve a reorganization in the left-wall picture by not focusing, but staring, at the far end of the wall. A reorganization of the ground, however, is practically impossible to achieve even if one tries hard not to focus.

The hay-field picture, turned into a left-wall orientation, shows a clear continuation of the ground underneath the rows as forming the wall proper along which we seem to look. The rows themselves are segregated from this wall, set off at a right angle and looked at from in front. In a right-wall orientation, the ground is not seen as extending underneath the rows; the wall itself is formed by the bright rows with deep setback vertical partitions in between.

As an introduction to the right-left reversals of our final illustrations, we would like to mention a difference in the properties of object units on right and left walls. In general, when a picture of an object upon ground is turned so that the same object projects from a left wall, wall and object tend to be seen as separated at the object's former base and as at right angles to each other. The segregated object has a differently textured surface, is seen from directly in front and at a specific distance. At its lower contour, which is now experienced as the object's base, one misses explicitly the support of the ground surface against gravity and experiences hollowness in space underneath. The same object at the right wall appears not so much segregated from the wall in its texture, but more as segregated from a uniform space along its free contours. It appears, as a whole, more spread out in a frontoparallel plane and parts of different brightness or color tend to be seen as independent shapes. It does not have a specific base and there is no experience of gravity. It appears more like a protruding part of the wall. Thus, seen as the same object unit, it now acquires a characteristic profile to the left; seen as part of the wall, it helps to give it a profilation, shaping the space to the left into which it protrudes. As illustrated in the Egyptian sunken relief, there is a shift from centered, textured, looked-at object shape to a brightness-border movement shape which may be related on the one side to the unit, on the other to the setback area, the space. All over the world, not only in Western culture, a face-profile line is drawn preferably as facing to the left, forming so to say a natural "right-wall" profile shape [35].

The creation of conditions favoring such right-wall perceptual organization appears typical in the art of India with its emphasis on movement shape and volume. Ornaments and reliefs with curving, deeply cut-in partitions that are seen as darkness zones fill walls profilated richly with recesses and niches. Sculpture represents moving bodies with voluminous body parts in a mere torsional gravity-less balance protruding from such walls, real or imaginary. Even "perspective" in painting is described as moving from right to left, diverging from a point in depth behind the painted wall into the picture space [42].

Dual role of object surfaces.   Objects in reality and when represented in perspective may be seen from different sides, showing surfaces with characteristic texture gradients. They may be seen as parts of the object's exterior surface, as enclosing and shaping it. They may also act as spatial reference surfaces shaping the space around the objects, and in this role they would be more determined by their *slant* than by their *shape*. Geometric objects with straight sides and edges are experienced differently from those with curved convex surfaces. They appear more as mere cutout material units than as true objects with an interior shape. Their shape is given in the edges and corners in which the slanted, but in themselves unshaped, surfaces cut into each other. In any perspective picture, therefore, objects may help to establish the structure of the picture space, and thus the experience of spatial relationships which is changed in a right-left reversal.

Right-left reversals.   A right-left reversal of a situation representing objects upon the ground within a perspective picture space will not show such dramatic phenomenal changes as, for instance, the inversion of the lake bottom, and it will never through reorganization make objects as such unidentifiable. We know, however, that a picture of a familiar interior space, shaped by the orientation of the enclosing surfaces but otherwise devoid of recognizable objects, may look so different in the right-left reversal that it is not recognized. The qualities of a right and left perspective wall—even right and left parts of ground or ceiling—are not the same.

We know about the anatomical bilaterally symmetrical structure of the central nervous system and its asymmetry in the rostral—caudal and dorsal—ventral directions. Ecologically, there is no difference in the overall distribution of brightness pattern in the natural surroundings as to right and left visual fields, though there is a definite differentiation between upper and lower fields. Thus the phenomenal changes upon right-left reversal are most difficult to understand without assuming a physiological laterality of highest-level sensory-motor processes underlying visual perception, as well as anisotropies of innervational and feedback processings of the different eye movements. Any anisotropies in experience would occur more consistently with a culturally developed standardized looking behavior in surveying a framed-in area, a picture. As long as the orientation of the frame remains the same, the survey pattern need not necessarily change with a right-left reversal or any other shift in orientation of the picture itself. Within the frame, however, the typical motor processings of survey eye movements would integrate differently with reversed brightness patterns and this would result in a different, though not unfamiliar, aspect upon survey. Such changes will be described in the two following pictures which are perspective representations of complex and meaningful situations. In these pictures, composition as the distribution of meaningful objects in perceived space plays a determining role, and enhances phenomenal changes through loss in significant meaning upon reversal.

Prints of engravings and etchings represent mirror images of the drawing on the plate. The consequences of such reversal for the graphic art of Dürer and the etchings of Rembrandt have been discussed in former publications [19, 20].

Dürer's "Melancolia." In Dürer's famous etching of the "Melancolia," we see a very complicated asymmetrical picture space crowded with objects. It is represented in central perspective, emphasizing texture gradients of slanted surfaces. In the print (Fig. 8), the main visible reference surface toward the left is the ground and water surface; in the middle region, right-wall gradients are dominant; on the right, we have a quasi-separate small foreground space closed off by the body of the sitting figure against the main space on the left. The vanishing point of perspective lies in the upper left of the picture plane, emphasizing the ground as reference plane. The illumination comes from the upper right, leaving front and face of the main figure in the shadow but lighting up the side of her body. The reversal shows the opposite asymmetric features of gradients of perspective and illumination on the plate (Fig. 9).

The subject matter of the picture has been discussed at length by art historians. The true fame of this engraving, however, is based upon the fact that people have not only seen in it a very learned allegorical representation and an intricate performance in the art of etching—they have truly experienced, in looking at it, an unusual involvement of the self, a mediation of a mood vaguely related to the meaning of the word written into the sky. Clearly, if every object is taken only in its objective or in its symbolic meaning—that is, if the experience of the picture is reduced to the recognition of the assembled objects (as in a kind of picture writing)—nothing much would be changed by a right-left reversal. It is possible, therefore, that for some observers the picture and its subject matter do not appear changed by reversal. However, we want to emphasize here how the qualities of experienced *spatial relationships* do indeed change when the observer is actually making a survey of a meaningful situation represented in the framed-in area of the picture.

In this picture we have a single object which shows a simple consistent change upon reversal: the big polyhedron. It is a typical geometrical object, a cutout material unit determined in shape entirely by the slant of its intersecting surfaces. In Fig. 8, we are most impressed by the jutting-out corners and the sharp edges. We seem to look more from below against the shadowed underneath surface, which appears to slant forward like a low tent roof, above the ground. In Fig. 9, however, it is the pentagon shape of the upper bright side which appears most prominent. We now appear to see it more from above and look along this re-

Fig. 8. (Print)

ceding and ascending surface out into the distance. What in Fig. 8 was seen as a prominent sharp corner edge between upper and lower side now becomes part of the contour shape of the upper surface. This change is not just dependent upon a survey of the whole picture but also holds, though somewhat reduced, for a detailed survey of the polyhedron alone.

In short, what is happening here with a solid textured polyhedron upon a right-left reversal carries the features of the spontaneous reversal of the famous Necker cube.

The characteristic aspect of the polyhedron in the plate is emphasized in a survey of the whole picture by an experience of dynamics, of accelerated movement in looking diagonally across its upper surface out into the distance. In Fig. 8, however, the polyhedron seems to block the distant view. Here we have—in accordance with perspective—an apparent standpoint on an extension of the left foreground from which we seem to look straight out along the ground at a much lower level. However, the conspicuous objects, arranged one behind the other directly in front of us, cannot be overlooked. They appear emphasized in detail and rounded in depth.

In addition to the feeling of being obstructed in looking at the distant view, one has the experience of being *oneself enclosed* in a central space formed by the polyhedron, the surface of the millstone, and the two figures. It is an experience which again conflicts with the one of looking at even the nearest objects directly above the lower frame from a certain distance in front of them.

The feeling of being included in the picture space is the most characteristic among these competing qualities of spatial relationships in the print. Indeed, it appears as if here we do not so much look directly at the two main figures as we are aware of their presence. Their shaded fronts with single highlighted areas, the movements in the folds of their clothes—both are experienced more as a richly profilated lower right wall of this space in which we are included and into which they are gazing. These figures appear in survey, on the right side, to be arranged more in a frontoparallel plane so that the angles in space between their sides and front are flattened out. The foreground space in the right lower corner, beside the sitting woman, though connected with the nearest foreground over to the left, does not seem to play any role. It merely looks here as if some kind of outside space—not belonging in the picture—is mistakenly visible and thus is skipped in our experience.

In the plate a survey results in different spatial experiences. There is no more a feeling of a self-enclosing space. We are no more aware of a continuously receding ground upon which we stand, upon which the objects rest, and across which we look into distance. Instead, we appear to look at several figures and objects separated by space pockets. The visible parts of the ground at the right seem to be more steep, to rise up. Correspondingly, the objects appear to be arranged more above than behind each other, and we do not see clearly their relative distances in a continuous perspective space. The winged figure is now seen in extreme plasticity. She appears taller and heavier than in the print, and the bright illumination appears much more to enhance the side of her body, the

Fig. 9. (Plate)

intricate folds of her gown. We appear to look at knee and elbow as being much nearer to us and directly in front of us. Thus, contrary to perspective, the apparent standpoint, experienced as spatial relationship to the self in surveying the picture, is again shifted over to the left.

Still farther to the left, to the side of the woman, we look into a deeper space pocket. From the depth underneath her right wing, the side of her body—especially thigh and upper arm—is seen as protruding forward in a right-wall slant. The effect is one of being caught with our glance in this space, having to complete a survey of a separate space unit and begin a new survey for the rest of the picture further to the right. Thus, beginning from where the "right wall" of this separate space ends, from the jutting-out knee and underarm, we appear now to look along surfaces with a left-wall slant in the direction of the compass over to millstone and *putto* and across the upper surface of the polyhedron toward the horizon. This dynamic experience, however, is much reduced when we attend to details farther left, since there are many small areas of darkness seen as depth, as pockets of surface-interrupting space. With the emphasis upon looking up and to the right, the dog and more so the sphere in the lower right corner appear as outside the main direction of survey. Except when we look at them in detail, we do not feel a relationship to ourselves. In this situation they appear more as related to the main figures, as lying at their feet, as belonging to them.

The resulting impression is one in which the unclarities and conflicts in the spatial situation are not experienced as relevant to ourselves. We see a powerful figure but, while the details of her gown appear much emphasized, we seem to look past her shaded face over to the *putto* on the millstone, who seems unduly important in this picture. Thus we experience the reversed composition as a representation of an allegoric figure in a disorderly surrounding of symbolic objects as her attributes. In the print, however, the experiences of being blocked in looking into the distance, being ourselves included in the situation, and, while looking directly at the main objects, being more aware of the presence of the main figures than directly looking at them may well give to the picture its character of uncanny grandeur and the 'bewitched mood of the conflicting self-related spatial relationships.

Rembrandt's "Death of St. Mary."   In contrast to the preceding picture, perspective. texture and illumination gradients play a less important role in this etching of Rembrandt (Figs. 10 and 11). Brightness and darkness per se and the direction and movement of linear elements are emphasized.

Looking at each picture as if it were a scene built up on a theater stage, one would tend to say that we have the most successful stage setting in the picture as Rembrandt drew it on the copper plate—with a uniform deep and wide space in which the groups are differentiated and at the same time easily surveyed by the spectator. The mirror image, the familiar print, however, has in a split-up space an arrangement of groups difficult to survey and less clear in meaning.

In this etching we have definite areas of brightness and darkness and surfaces at various slants including a ceiling slant. Thus, in looking

Fig. 10. (Plate)

around, we will have shifts in dominance of perceptual organizations of certain areas or certain objects. However, the composition in the plate picture is such that all shifts in perceptual organization occurring when looking at specific parts or objects merely emphasize the intended meaning of the object within the represented situation.

Looking at the ground in Fig. 10, we experience ourselves as onlookers somewhere in the extended left foreground; from here we begin the survey of the situation, with a free space in front of us, between ourselves and the background curtain. This space may acquire also the quality of an interior when we look at the underneath surface of the cloud which seems to be hovering above. Through this space, we seem to look quite naturally toward the group at the foot of the bed, and from there over to the right through the interval space between the bedposts, along the bed directly toward the head of St. Mary at the right wall. There is certainly nothing in the way this head is drawn with fine lines which would attract our attention as such, but it seems to be located at a focal point in space toward which we seem to move naturally in survey, looking first toward depth, then turning in a left-right direction. In this way we seem to *look around behind* the large figure of the man sitting at the table in the near right foreground. The group seems to be located this side of the natural path of survey through the picture space, and to be separated by an interval space in depth from the group at the bed. Though drawn in a larger scale and in dark color, this figure rightly does not appear to be the main person or to take part in the actual event, but his presence is noted and his position fits his role in this situation.

Most of the other figures on the far side of the bed appear to be arranged just along the path of our glance. Since there is also an experience of time order in surveying, the grieving persons at the foot of the bed appear as seen first, thus preparing the surveyor for the main event further to the right.

In the upper left corner, the cloud appears as not included in a first spontaneous survey; one is aware of specifically looking up to it. It then appears voluminous and real as looked at from below, as the ceiling of an interior space in front of the rear curtain. At its right side, however, it dissolves into immaterial brightness with a loss of surface. The figures of the angels seem just in the process of appearing, shaping out of the same kind of lines which model the surface farther to the left. The brightness around the group at the head end of the bed appears to be caused by the cloud above and behind as visible source of this brightness.

Such natural surveyability, a harmonic and meaningful composition, is not experienced when one looks at the mirror reversal, the print (Fig. 11). The dominant impression is one of a much flatter picture space in which the groups at the left are built up more above each other than in depth, while at the right we see a perspective space not enclosing the main groups, but leading out of the picture behind the right frame. One is immediately struck by the figure of the reading man at the table at which we seem to look from the closest distance. Here this group seems to loom up higher, the dark areas appear enhanced, and the angle in which the book is tilted appears steeper as compared to the plate picture,

Fig. 11. (Print)

where its main extension seems to be in the horizontal and the tilt of the book appears to be flattened out. In looking at the group around St. Mary, the foreground objects are now experienced as obstacles. In spite of the perspective, the reading man seems to be sitting directly in front of us. One has the experience of being forced to look in two different main directions into the divided space. We appear to look *upward across* the foreground group to the group at the head end of the bed and further up along the cloud. Or, beginning further over to the right, we *look along* the back of the man and the foot end of the bed—past the main events and following perspective—toward the figures at the rear curtain. Looking up at the group around St. Mary above the reading man, one seems to look directly across the bed sheets at the people on the other side of the bed, or through the space underneath the canopy against the bright surface of the cloud. Though in distance apparently less far away than in the plate, the head of St. Mary has lost its position in the focal point of the survey. We now seem to look past it into the faces of the apostle and the "doctor." The many figures are not seen as mainly one large group lined up along the bed, but as split up into the group behind the bed, below the canopy, and the more independent larger figures at the foot end of the bed, and those in front of the curtain, seen in the perspective space opening toward the right.

In contrast to the plate, the cloud is seen immediately, and it appears to rise like steam from behind the bed. We seem to look along its upper bright surface upon which the figures of the angels are seen as standing, more real and more distinctly set off than in the plate. The cloud appears less voluminous and less uniform but more divided into different regions, the darker side more streaked with lines than modeled, and its brightness not as a source of light for the group at the bed.

The dynamic character of arrangements in the direction of the "ascending diagonal" has been commented upon by Wölfflin [64] and other authors. Wölfflin writes, specifically with regard to this print picture, that one would understand how much the clouds steaming up in it were a welcome motive in the baroque. It is true that the dynamic experience in the ascending diagonal is impressive, but like many of the other experiences in the print, this one does not fit at all the subject matter of the picture. On the other hand, the true cloud breaking through the ceiling, hovering above and helping to unify a greater picture space as interior space is convincing and meaningful in the composition as Rembrandt drew it on the plate.

Survey and Perceptual Organization

The description of the phenomenal changes in our last illustrations upon right-left reversal is by necessity fragmentary. Many additional changes observed are not mentioned, but many others may not yet have been discovered. Even so, their multitude and complexity are certainly bewildering and would seem to defy attempts at generalization. Differences in individual reaction will be outspoken. Still there will be quite an astonishing "consensus of experience" with regard to the left-right differentiations described here. They are clearest for right-eyed, right-handed individuals, but are not limited to this group. They may be confirmed by similar observations upon comparative survey of photographs or other pictures showing scenes in perspective.

Comparing many detailed analyses, we find again characteristic clusters of properties in right and left halves or, more precisely, in the four quadrants of the picture. Those in the lower left and upper right quadrants tend to prevail in the visual experience of a typical perspective representation. In both our last illustrations, the experience of active looking, of a beginning of survey, of having a standpoint is characteristic for the left side only. This is so in spite of the fact that, according to perspective, our apparent position should follow a shift in location of the vanishing point upon reversal. On the left side, we seem to look across the ground or along a left wall toward distance, and against the front of near objects. On the right side the experience of looking out toward distance shifts into that of an independent frontoparallel movement in a general direction from left to right. The plane of this movement varies in depth according to the perceived depth of space at the left, and its particular direction tends to follow the dominant direction of brightness contrasts. In the diagonal toward the upper right, it acquires an outspoken dynamic character.

Objects on the left appear most clearly in their three-dimensional plastic shape. The material texture of their surface and their extension upward from the ground is emphasized. Objects on the right appear flattened out and, instead of texture, their color and brightness are enhanced. The shape is determined more by their outlines, specifically by the left contours; in survey they appear to be seen from the left instead of from in front.

This characteristic difference of right and left upon survey involves mainly the lower and middle left and the middle and upper right. The upper left and especially the lower right quadrant are visibly neglected locations, at least under our specific condition of surveying a perspective picture. While it is thus much more difficult to identify phenomena in these quadrants, they may nevertheless play an important role in our experience. If there is no object in the lower left, we may look upward instead of "outward" at an object in the upper left. Such an object will appear to be looked at from below, to be more voluminous and floating. On the other hand, the object at the lower right is neglected as such in survey if there are any competing objects or distant views at the left, and just a movement along contours may be experienced. However, in both these quadrants, ceiling and right-wall surfaces may shape an interior space felt as enclosing the self, and thus may influence our experience of the whole picture.

To summarize: Object units and surfaces, the experiences of looking and of space show qualitative differences in left and right sides of a picture, differences very similar to those in the alternating, competing perceptual organizations seen in the former illustrations. However, their relative dominance is different in the four quadrants and appears to be sequentially and selectively emphasized through survey behavior.

When we tried to analyze the phenomena upon reversal, we were most of all impressed by the characteristics of survey experience, namely, the apparent change in the direction of looking and the asymmetrical experience of our standpoint as surveyor. Indeed, we did not become aware of the shifts in perceptual organization of object units until we had observed the typical constellations of properties, the differences in unit formation demonstrated in our first illustrations. Instead, the writer and many individuals who have an outspoken experience of surveying a picture as a whole and who are sensitive to the composition of objects in picture space do not experience a shift in perceptual organization as such; rather, they find a change in their way of looking at objects which appears convincingly connected with some change in object qualities. This is enhanced by the fact that only objects lying within this asymmetrical path of survey are spontaneously seen, recognized as meaningful and in relation to each other. Therefore, I called this survey phenomenon the "glance curve" or the "perception curve." Now we can say more adequately that survey experience corresponds to the experience of active looking, in a combined left-wall and ground structure, on the lower left side and shows a shift to an experience of inherent movement, characteristic for a combined ceiling and right-wall structure, on the right.

We can also more adequately characterize our changed experience of objects in the different regions of the picture space. Their shapes correspond to the four different types of unit shapes which appear in the two basic organizations of the Egyptian sunken relief. The object at the lower left shows the qualities of the exterior, textured, looked-at, convex chest surface, while interior volume shape becomes more prominent in the object at the upper left. The object at the right appears as a profilated cutout unit, while at the lower right it seems to have a vague movement shape. Thus, within each half-field of the picture, we experience the two kinds of shape which we saw competing for dominance within the same general perceptual organization of the Egyptian relief.

The relative shift in dominance of different organizations holds also for any smaller region singled out to be surveyed in detail within the larger picture, and for any relationship between objects represented side by side. For instance, if within one framed area, two heads are represented in profile symmetrically facing each other, they are actually experienced quite differently. The emphasis in the left head lies in the center of the object area—the ear, or cheek region—as directly looked at. In the right head, however, forehead, nose, and mouth are emphasized in the profile line. This may be experienced as if here one looked more into the face from the left, but it involves also characteristic changes in object property and in meaning. While the head on the left is seen as a true plastic object, the meaning of the right head is determined by the profile which represents, symbolizes, the face. Thus for the average (right-handed) individual in Western culture, there will always be at least two different kinds of object meanings: the looked-at "real" object related to ourselves, and the object with the *symbolic* meaning of its profile shape, dynamically related to an object looked at in the start of survey at the (lower) left.

The descending, "causal," diagonal. If an object in the upper left, nearer the upper frame, above the perspective ground attracts our attention, we may experience a peculiar kind of relationship between this object and events at the lower right. One may feel that the object in the upper left *causes* a characteristic movement, a posture, an event, in the lower right. For instance, in Renaissance and Baroque paintings the inspiration of St. John on Patmos and the stigmatization of St. Francis are situations in which the source or cause of the event at the lower right is traditionally represented at the upper left. A right-left reversal of such a composition shifts the main figure to the lower left. In this location, the movement, the posture, of this figure is not experienced as caused, but as self-initiated. What appeared as light rays moving through space with *causal efficacy* may now appear as material shafts with metallic surface, along which one experiences an ascending *dynamic movement.* These effects are detrimental to the meaning convincingly communicated by the original composition. They are also evident as disturbing in the reversal of our own illustrations. On the other hand, they are traditionally and effectively used in the representation of certain other situations in which movement of an object is made visible through an experience of dynamics as, for instance, in the ascension of St. Mary.

Western culture has developed two unique means of communication in pictorial representation: perspective and illumination. It has also emphasized the picture frame. In survey of a framed picture, experience of objects in perspective space is dominant in the direction of the ascending diagonal. However, illumination is characteristically represented in the direction of the descending causal diagonal. A light source at the upper left is naturally experienced as causing the immaterial movement shapes of shadows below. In this way, by relating diagonally opposed quadrants in opposed directions, the basic organizations and competing properties can more fully develop in alternation and with minimal interference. The artist thus has the possibility of evoking experiences of a "causal," felt relationship of interior-related subjective events in a brightness-movement organization within the same picture in which, upon active survey, an objective world may be seen in perspective.

Experiential anisotropy of eye movements. The basic difference between vergence and version movements at the physiological level is well known and experientially it is equally outspoken. Here we want only to draw attention to a very striking difference in the experience of slow, controlled eye movements in looking along lines or edges in opposed directions, i.e., looking out versus looking back, upward versus downward, and, even though to a smaller degree, from left to right versus right to left.[6] If one tries to look slowly along a vertical line or edge in the upward direction, one will have the experience of an easy gliding along, as if one were pulled up by the vertical line which is clearly visible in the region above. Trying to follow the same line or edge downward, however, gives an awkward feeling of small, saccadic jumps; moreover there is unclarity about the course of the contour to be followed in the region below. One is rather tempted to jump back to the base in one big movement and then follow upward again. Following a perspective line toward distance is easy and natural, but following it backward is strenuous and appears unnatural. The difference between looking from left to right versus right to left is least outspoken, as is that for the opposed directions in the descending diagonal. Most impressive, however, is the difference between the ease with which one follows the ascending diagonal upward, while in the direction to the lower left one has to initiate each movement anew without being guided by a clearly visible line.

It is characteristic that we talk and think about looking out into distance, looking at a landscape as extending toward the horizon. We look up a tree or column which is seen as rising from the ground and we think about scanning a representation of an event in time, or any scale, from left to right. We do not, however, think of or imagine looking in the opposite directions.

Thus in the complex sensory-motor process of looking, there is a relative dominance of experience of motor activity when looking toward the near, lower, and left regions of the visual field; there is a dominance of

[6] The pattern in experiential anisotropy described here only holds for a group of right-handed right-eyed individuals. Its characteristics in individuals with deviating laterality factors should be investigated, as well as possible anisotropies in labyrinth sensitivities.

experience of visual surface qualities when looking into distance, upward and to the right. In survey, continuity of visual surfaces is experienced from lower left to upper right. The self-related experiences characteristic for the lower left, i.e., the beginning of active looking, the standpoint of the self, may be connected with motor processes in looking in this direction. There has not yet been an adequate registration of eye movements in survey with specifically selected, suitable material and including vergence changes [7, 11].

Effects of looking behavior in actual situations. It is not necessary to actually move one's eyes; paying attention to one object while fixating another will suffice to demonstrate anisotropies in experience which have been described elsewhere in more detail [21].

If we look at an object from in front, fixating its near end, it will be seen in uncrossed disparity just behind the plane of fixation. It will appear at a definite distance and will have the familiar aspect of an object remembered and represented in typical perspective. If we shift our fixation to its far end, it will be seen in crossed disparity. It now loses its definite distance and will appear vague in surface but bulky and in an exaggerated, protruding "Van Gogh perspective." In general, objects behind our point of fixation will most often be seen in the upper half of the visual field; objects in front of our fixation, mostly in the lower half of the visual field. If we attend to objects behind our plane of fixation they will be located in space in relation to the fixation point as if we experience their spatial location within a three-dimensional coordinate system centered in it. However, if we attend to objects in front of the fixation plane, they will appear naturally related in space toward ourselves, located within a self-enclosing space whose directions, centered in our own bodily position, are experienced more as moving than as looking directions. Actually we look beyond objects which we avoid as obstacles in locomotion and in manipulative behavior objects are seen in crossed disparity, particularly at the lower right for right-handed people. Thus it appears that their qualities (or the underlying processes) are not compatible with the qualities (or the underlying processes) of the habitual visual memory image, though they are obviously important in guiding our motor behavior.

Van Gogh has represented this experience of objects in front of the fixation plane, related to the self in a surrounding space. If we look at an original painting—his room at Arles, for instance—from arm's length (as he must have viewed it when painting), and if we try not to converge upon the picture plane but to look toward depth into the picture space, a striking change takes place. Now the outline-movement shapes and the protruding distorted perspective appear to represent our natural experience of near objects, not focused upon, in a surrounding space which includes ourselves. Instead of looking at a peculiar picture which needs a cognitive or aesthetic interpretation, we now have direct communication of an experienced world in which the dominant perceptual organization is connected with a looking behavior which characteristically deviates from objective survey.

CONCLUDING STATEMENT

As a preliminary requirement for a survey of the pattern of relationships constituting the psychology of perception, we have attempted to analyze in theoretically neutral terms the sequence of events typically involved in human visual perception of external objects. The intent has been to provide, as a conceptual framework, an analysis of phases which would be adequate for the explicit statements of all major viewpoints currently shaping research. Four basic meanings of perception exemplified in different current systematic accounts are distinguished. Located in terms of the framework presented, these varied accounts of perception do not appear as alternative formulations of the same problem. Rather, they are seen as complementary statements of interrelationships among events located in different phases of the total perceptual behavioral act.

Such an analysis invites, on the part of both theorist and experimenter, sharper and more explicit identification than usual of those phases of the actual event sequence in which he is primarily and most directly interested. And it invites a more explicit recognition of the derivative and technical, rather than convenience-dictated, character of the problems involved in the choice of empirical methods for the investigation of these interrelationships.

A major specific feature of the essay is a renewed focus upon the experiential properties of human perceptual activity as essential, significant, psychological realities. In the earlier sections, the scientific status of experiential properties of perceptual events is discussed differentially in relation to physics and psychology. They are regarded as much more significant to psychology, not only epistemologically but also empirically.

Perceiving cannot be understood apart from the cyclical character of the ongoing process of interaction between organism and environment. Single perceptual acts occur not only in a context of preceding and ongoing activity, but typically require integration of subsequences of perceptual activity over time. In any analysis of the total events, the selection of any particular phase as an analytic starting point must thus be contextually determined, and only the pattern of interrelationships among the phases of the cycle, not temporal priority, is to be taken seriously.

The desirability, in both theoretical formulations and experimental practice, of sharper discriminations between and within certain phases of the sequence is stressed. In the external world, the old but neglected distinction between the *external object* (Phase 1) and the *medium world* (Phases X and 2) is reemphasized, together with a further discrimination between *interior object properties* (Phase 1: interior, especially significant in social perception) and *surface properties* (Phase 1: object surface). The energies of the medium world, as *illumination* (Phase X), striking the surface of the *stimulus object* (Phase 1: object surface), interact with its properties to jointly constitute the *distal stimulus* (Phase 2: object surface), which, as transmitted through the medium (Phase 2: medium), arrives at the surface of the receptor as the *proximal stimulus* (Phase 2: receptor surface)—in vision, the optic array. Selected and modified (Phase $3m$) by the refractive receptor structures, themselves affected by effector events of *perceptual behavior* (Phase 5), the proximal stimulus is transformed into the *effective stimulus* (Phase 3: effective stimulus). The effective stimulus interacts with the receptor cells to form a *pattern of excitation* in the anisotropic mosaic of rods and cones (Phase 3: excitation), itself also affected by central processes. After further neural interaction within the retina, the excitations are projected via the optic tract and the radiation (Phase $4a$) successively to thalamic and other centers and to the striate cortical projection area. There further interactions and processings occur and *a complex set of interrelated central events* (Phase $4c$, 4: experiential) is initiated.

This sequence from object to cortex may be roughly considered as constituting an alternating and interlocking series of relatively isomorphic energy transformations and transmissions with interactions at the nodal regions of object surfaces, receptor mosaic, and successive synaptic relay regions. In these nodal regions, especially within the organism, the interplay of the structure and present state of the regions, themselves often significantly determined by effects from other, remote regions, contribute so significantly to the output from the region that it is more meaningful to explicitly regard it as codetermined than as essentially a process of simple transformation and transmission of energies. Thus at all points in *all* phases, but most conspicuously at the interaction regions, the one-to-one correspondences between successive phases (most characteristic of the transmission phases) are dependent upon *sets of contingent conditions*. Full understanding of the perceptual process therefore clearly requires an explicit characterization of these conditions, as well as a specification of the terminal correspondences codetermined by them. Within the organism, these include the anisotropies of receptor distributions and projective areas, the selective and modifying effects of perceptual behaviors, and different transmission and processing systems and the varying state of excitation of the region. This makes any implication that the organismic phases (Phases 3, 4, 5, or their subphases) are strictly successive both inaccurate and misleading. In a sense, particularly in social situations where the external stimulus object is not only selected but also modified by the activity of the perceiver, this is true of the temporal relations of all phases.

This means, furthermore, that any specifications of isomorphic "psychophysical" correspondences of the sort postulated by Gibson cannot be considered as fundamental unconditional psychophysical relationships as the type postulated earlier in classical gestalt isomorphism. Nor is it satisfactory even to regard them as dependent only upon a hypothetical "standard" or "normal" sensory-motor apparatus. Rather such correspondences must be considered as dependent upon sets of contingent conditions at *every phase*. These sets of contingent conditions are relatively constant through the transmission phases but vary significantly within the ranges of normality within the interaction regions, particularly in those within the organism. One such relatively high-level contingent condition illustrated in the final section is the interaction of ecologically normal or reversed gradients with standardized patterns of looking behavior.

An ubiquitous component of the sets of contingent conditions at each intraorganismic phase is some effect of concurrent perceptual behavior (central or efferent phases). This means that the central phases of which the behavioral phases are direct functions, are not "representations" corresponding strictly to external events but are more precisely object-self relations or interactions. The phenomenal self-related character of perceptual object properties, often only implicit, has failed to receive explicit recognition in experimental analysis. The illustrations in the preceding section clearly demonstrate them in the experience of spatial situations.

In the context of examining the interrelationships between the various phases, and more generally the relation of perceiving to the total perceptual-behavioral cycle, different meanings of behavior and of perceiving are analyzed.

The concept behavior is seen as completely nonspecific, more general, and more ambiguous than general concepts of related sciences. It refers indiscriminately, as the user may elect, to any or all of the phases of our sequence except perhaps the first two, and to events characterizable variously in the language systems of any of the sciences. It is highly improbable that general laws of behavior (stimulus-response laws) can be formulated which, without extensive and varying qualification, would be applicable to all or even to many of the multiple submeanings of the concepts of behavior or stimulus.

Four different meanings of perceiving are discriminated: perception as discrimination, as cognition, as behavior control, as experiencing. The importance of distinguishing between the actual foci of concern and the observed indicators or reports of these focal events is stressed for all senses of perceiving. The desirability of a sharper distinction between experiential and cognitive reports, currently often confused, is discussed. Several sample experiments are analyzed methodologically to exhibit the need of such clarification in experimental practice.

The problem of the scientific objectivity of findings based upon experiential or phenomenal report (introspection) is examined in the light of the classical and partially valid objections of the behavioristic approach. A revised criterion of scientific objectivity is presented in which the requirement for objectivity is shifted from the single observation to the entire functional relationship involved (that is, to the reported experiential event *together* with *either* its determining conditions or its behavioral consequences). The revised criterion is regarded as more stringent than the more restrictive conventional one it is designed to replace. Nevertheless it sets no limits to the character of the properties reported on nor to the smallness of the group of observers among whom consistency is obtained, provided only that their characteristics relevant to the report be specifiable and determinable.

Reports are distinguished from behavioral indicators as involving quite generally a more or less specific intent to report. The difference between restricted verbal and nonverbal report is not viewed as significant since the conceptual determination of the report in the latter instance is simply mediated through verbal instructions accepted by the reporter.

The current tendency among many psychophysicists (and among many learning theorists turned perception theorists), to substitute response for experience in their systematic treatments of perception is viewed with concern as constituting a major hindrance to significant research in perception. It is seen as creating an unbridged gap between the reality of experience and the content of perceptual laws. The dependent variables of such laws are conceptualized as responses (which, if they refer to anything, refer to differences in stimuli, the events of Phases 1 or 2). The treatment of any report as mere response (report *qua behavior*) misses the essential point that the report must be taken by the experimenter *qua report*, as it certainly is intended by the experiencer-reporter who gives it. In current neobehavioristic analyses, however, the significance of the reference of the report to the actually occurring experience is ignored and the report response itself is taken to constitute the essential reality for psychology. The capacity of science to deal with experiential reality is thus effectively denied, by substituting behavior as the only reality—a reality whose conceptualization comprehends without discrimination (and at the temporary convenience of theorists or experimenters) the heterogeneous collection of events at any phase of the perceptual-behavioral sequence. A potentially even more serious chasm tends to be created between the experiencer-reporter and his own denied and evaporating experience. The neobehaviorists' analysis of descriptive report dulls sensitive reporting within the scope of accepted descriptive terminology and completely stultifies the development of urgently needed new experiential discriminations.

Qualifications of reporters and specification of subject characteristics relative to reports on certain kinds of experience, and upon the initial discovery of new dimensions, are discussed. The especial dependence of experience, and thus of report, on different kinds of perceptual behavior and of perceptual processing is considered, as well as its significance in limiting the universality of communication concerning experiences.

In the next sections on phenomenal properties and perceptual organization, pictures of actual or represented objects or scenes are presented, together with their corresponding phenomenal descriptions. The introduction into the essay of these stimulus materials provides actual reader experiences which permit perceptual as well as conceptual understanding of the descriptive terms used. The illustrative materials range from single units or objects, surfaces and surface patterns, to more complex situations representing objects in space. It becomes apparent that at *each* level of complexity a serious effort to achieve even relatively adequate description requires identification of hitherto formally unrecognized experiential dimensions.

Previous serious attempts to provide comprehensive perceptual experiential terminologies, such as those of Titchener and of the classical gestalt systematists, have tended, in the interest of quasi-universal applicability, to restrict formal descriptive terms to extremely abstract dimensions of sensory quality or of perceptual form. The recent remedial attempt of Gibson to develop a psychophysics of the concrete perceptual world has failed to recognize *the necessity of a fresh reexamination of the experiential properties* of this world including its surfaces *as an essential part* of any vital *psychophysical program of research.*

The last sections on phenomenal properties contains the results of such a reexamination. It presents further differentiation of and additions to certain new dimensions of visual perception previously described [21]. The didactic method here employed consists in *exhibition* of various dimensions through the experience of a number of varied concrete illustrations rather than a simple catalogue of descriptive properties. Identification of these dimensions reflects acceptance of a rich but *specifiable qualitative diversity of molar perceptual properties* (as distinct from conceptual, cognitive attributes) of the units and frameworks of our experience. They represent the outgrowth of a sustained effort to maintain under systematically varied conditions a fresh though sophisticated sensitivity toward experience. Thus the aim has been to realize the intrinsic and indigenous requirements of faithful experiential description rather than those of cognitive characterization, or of some presumed ideal general scientific methodology.

Experiential description of even relatively simple two- or three-dimensional object-units, their outlines, borders, forms, surface and interior properties, and relationships to reference surfaces, requires a multiplicity of phenomenal dimensions not adequately statable in the objective, neutral terms of physics or even of common sense. Thus, for instance, four distinct experiential properties are shown to mediate visual perception of form. Comparison of perceptual reversals in different situations reveals *recurring and typical clusters of phenomenal properties.* These perceptual "reversals" thus prove to be alternations of qualitatively different basic perceptual organizations involving characteristic differences in object surface, form, and interior properties. These typical alternative, phenomenal clusterings recur in the perception of ground versus ceiling structures for instance.

In the perception of both object and reference surfaces the phenomenal properties appear to be determined not only by the character of the external surface gradients but by the *interaction of gradients with characteristic patterns of looking behavior.* Such interaction persists in more complicated situations where with objects in space further differences in object properties and particularly in self-object relations are revealed by systematic right-left reversal of identical arrangements. The class of object-self relations and properties constitutes a significant set of phenomenal attributes often only implicit in experience and rarely included in even comprehensive discussions of perception [39, 47, 57]. They have not hitherto been systematically investigated.

The method of inversion, or right-left reversal of an otherwise identical complex stimulus field without the necessity of behaving to it other than by perceptual behavior, constitutes one method for the systematic disentanglement of external and certain of the intraorganismic factors in perception. The development of standardized patterns of looking behavior and their usual association with ecologically typical gradients of ground and ceiling constitute important examples of *constant contingent conditions* which have been ignored theoretically and in experimental investigation of the perception of surface and space. The method of right-left reversal, here illustrated, offers a possibility of investigation of the effect of laterality factors which may play an important role in the determination of more complex spatial and self-object relationships. The possibility of basic cultural differences in such factors is considered.

Recognition of such multiple types of perceptual processings and determination of the factors on which these depend may be expected to enhance the possibilities of communication with regard to experiential properties and thus the scientific objectivity of experiential relationships.

The systematic significance of such experiential properties lies in part in their correspondence to certain of the more central intraorganismic events discriminated in our phase sequence, where their physiological properties are clearly joint functions of the stimulus energies isomorphically transmitted and transformed and of the intrinsic properties of the multiple, alternative, central processing systems. More adequate identification and differentiation of the phenomenal properties and their clustering may open the way for the establishment of new types of *intraorganismic psychophysiological correspondences.*

At the psychological level much fuller utilization of systematic phenomenal analyses of perceptual experiences should be widely fruitful not only in the suggestion of new problems but in providing new theoretical reorientations. A recent radical reformulation of the problem of motivation is an excellent relevant example [38b]. The differentiation of a multiple but limited number of basic perceptual processes, which may vary in development or in dominance in different organisms or even among cultures, provides a systematic basis for comparative study. Social psychology is a field which could be expected to profit more than it yet has from sensitive but sophisticated phenomenal analysis [1, 32, 46]. Other fields, notably that of aesthetics, which deserves a more central place in psychology, would not only benefit from such analyses but can scarcely hope to make significant advances without them [19].

Several final comments may be appended without elaboration since they derive from the trend of the entire previous discussion. It is evident that if the general analysis of the total perceptual-behavioral cycle is at all adequate, understanding of perceiving in all discriminated senses of the term is relevant and even central for all subfields of psychology. Experimentation and theoretical discussion would profit from sharper discrimination among these senses.

The most significant human events are experiential events. Their experiential properties are actual, and in perceiving are identifiable, reportable, and, within expanding limits, communicable and accessible to scientific study and understanding. In stating the conditions and consequences of experiential events, science achieves its most direct and significant relation to human realities. And only through retranslation into personal experience can the individual most directly and fully understand such scientific statements about human events.

REFERENCES

1. Asch, S. A perspective on social psychology. In S. Koch (Ed.), *Psychology: a study of a science*, Vol. III. *Formulations of the person and the social context*. New York: McGraw-Hill, 1960. Pp. 363–384.
2. Bergin, A. E. Work notes toward a science of inner experience. *Psychiat. Instit. Bull.*, 1961, 1, No. 4.
3a. Bishop, G. H. The natural history of the nervous impulse. *Physiol. Rev.* 1956, 36, 376–400.
3b. Bishop, G. H. The relation between fibre size and sensory modality: phylogenetic implications of the afferent innervation of cortex. *J. nerv. ment. Dis.*, 1959, 128, 89–114.
4. Bolles, R. C. and Bailey, D. E. Importance of object recognition in size constancy. *J. exp. Psychol.*, 1956, 51, 222–225.
5. Boring, E. G. *Sensation and perception in the history of experimental psychology*. New York: Appleton-Century-Crofts, 1942.
6. Boring, E. G. A history of introspection. *Psychol. Bull.*, 1953, 50, 169–189.
7. Brandt, M. F. *The psychology of seeing*. New York: Phil. Libr., 1945.
8. Bruner, J. Neural mechanisms in perception. In H. Solomon, S. Cobb, and W. Penfield (Eds.), *The brain and human behavior*. New York: Williams & Wilkins, 1958. Pp. 118–143.
9. Bruner, J. On perceptual readiness. *Psychol. Rev.*, 1957, 64, 123–152.
10. Brunswik, E. Distal focusing of perception: size constancy in a representative sample of situations. *Psychol. Monogr.*, 1944, No. 254.
11. Buswell, G. T. *How people look at pictures*. Chicago: Univer. Chicago Press, 1935.
12. Chiang Yee. *The Chinese eye*. London: Methuen, 1935.
13. Chiang Yee. *The silent traveler in Oxford*. London: Methuen, 1944.
14. Crovitz, H., and Daves, W. Tendencies to eye movement and perceptual accuracy. *J. exp. Psychol.*, 1961, in press.
15. Dewey, J. The reflex arc concept in psychology. *Psychol. Rev.*, 1896, 3, 357–370.
16. Drever, J. Perception and action. *Bull. Brit. psychol. Soc.*, 1961, 45, 1–9.
17. Erismann, T. *Das Werden der Wahrnehmung*. Bericht vom Kongress des Berufsverbandes Deutscher Psychologen (Bonn, 1947), Hamburg, 1948.
18. French, J. D. The reticular formation. In J. Field and H. W. Magoun (Eds.), *Handbook of physiology*. Sect. 1., *Neurophysiology*. Vol. II. Washington: Amer. Physiol. Society, 1960. Pp. 1281–1305.
19. Gaffron, M. *Die Radierungen Rembrandts, Originale und Drucke*. Mainz: Kupferberg Verlag, 1950.
20. Gaffron, M. Right and left in pictures. *The Art Quarterly*, 1950, 13, 312–331.
21. Gaffron, M. Some new dimensions in the phenomenal analysis of visual experiences. *J. Pers.*, 1956, 24, 285–307.

616   KARL ZENER AND MERCEDES GAFFRON

22. Gendlin, E. T. Experiencing: a variable in the process of therapeutic change. *Amer. J. Psychother.*, 1961, **15**, 233–245.
23. Gibson, J. J. The perception of visual surfaces. *Amer. J. Psychol.*, 1950, **63**, 367–384.
24. Gibson, J. J. Perception as a function of stimulation. In S. Koch (Ed.), *Psychology: a study of a science*, Vol. I. *Sensory, perceptual, and physiological formulations.* New York: McGraw-Hill, 1959. Pp. 456–501.
25. Gibson, J. J., and Cornsweet, J. The perceived slant of visual surfaces— optical and geographical. *J. exp. Psychol.*, 1952, **44**, 11–15.
26. Gibson, J. J., Purdy, J., and Lawrence, L. A method of controlling stimulation for the study of space perception: the optical tunnel. *J. exp. Psychol.*, 1955, **50**, 1–14.
27. Graham, C. H. Sensation and perception in an objective psychology. *Psychol. Rev.*, 1958, **65**, 65–76.
28. Guttman, N., and Kalish, Harry I. Discriminability and stimulus generalization. *J. exp. Psychol.*, 1956, **51**, 79–88.
29. Hebb, D. O. *A textbook of psychology.* Philadelphia: Saunders, 1958.
30. Hebb, D. O. The American Revolution. *Amer. Psychologist*, 1960, **15**, 735–745.
31. Hecht, S., Shlaer, S., and Pirenne, M. H. Energy at the threshold of vision. *Science*, 1941, **93**, 585–587.
32. Heider, F. Social perception and phenomenal causality. *Psychol. Rev.*, 1944, **51**, 358–374.
33. Held, R., and White, B. Sensory deprivation and visual speed. *Science*, 1959, **130**, 860–861.
34. Hull, C. L. *Principles of behavior: an introduction to behavior theory.* New York: Appleton-Century-Crofts, 1943.
35. Jensen, B. T. Left-right orientation in profile drawing. *Amer. J. Psychol.*, 1952, **65**, 80–83.
36. Johansson, G. *Configurations in event perception: an experimental study.* Uppsala: Almquist and Wiksells Boktryckeri, 1950.
37. Klüver, H. *Behavior mechanisms in monkeys.* Chicago: Univer. Chicago Press, 1933.
38a. Koch, S. Clark L. Hull. In *Modern learning theory.* New York: Appleton-Century-Crofts, 1954. Pp. 1–177.
38b. Koch, S. Behavior as "intrinsically" regulated: work notes toward a pre-theory of phenomena called "motivational." In M. R. Jones (Ed.), *Nebraska symposium on motivation.* Lincoln, Neb.: Univer. Press, 1956.
38c. Koch, S. Appendix: suggested discussion topics for contribution of systematic analyses. In S. Koch (Ed.), *Psychology: a study of a science,* Vol. I. *Sensory, perceptual, and physiological formulations.* New York: McGraw-Hill, 1959. Pp. 673–683.
38d. Koch, S. Some trends of Study I. Epilogue. In S. Koch (Ed.), *Psychology: a study of a science,* Vol. III. *Formulations of the person and the social context.* New York: McGraw-Hill, 1960. Pp. 729–788.
38e. Koch, S. Psychological science versus the science-humanism antinomy: intimations of a significant science of man. *Amer. Psychologist,* in press.

39. Koffka, K. *Principles of gestalt psychology.* New York: Harcourt, Brace, 1935.

40. Kohler, I. *Über Aufbau und Wandlungen der Wahrnehmungswelt.* Wien (Rohrer) : Osterr. Akad. d. Wiss., 1951.

41a.Köhler, W. *Gestalt psychology.* New York: Liveright, 1947.

41b.Köhler, W. The mind-body problem. In S. Hook (Ed.), *Dimensions of mind.* New York: New York Univer. Press, 1960.

41c.Köhler, W. and Wallach, H. Figural after-effects. *Proc. Amer. philos. Soc.,* 1944, **88,** 269–357.

42. Kramrisch, S. *The art of India.* New York: Phaidon, 1954.

42a.Lettvin, J. Y., Maturana, H. R., McCullough, W. S., and Pitts, W. H. What the frog's eye tells the frog's brain. *Proc. IRE,* 1959, **47,** 1940–1951.

43. Licklider, J. C. R. Three auditory theories. In S. Koch (Ed.), *Psychology: a study of a science.* Vol. I. *Sensory, perceptual, and physiological formulations.* New York: McGraw-Hill, 1959. Pp. 41–144.

44. Livingston, R. B. Central control of receptors and sensory transmission systems. In J. Field and H. W. Magoun (Eds.), *Handbook of physiology,* Sect. I. *Neurophysiology.* Vol. I. Washington: Amer. Physiol. Society, 1959. Pp. 741–760.

45. Lorenz, K. Z. The comparative method in studying innate behavior patterns. *Symp. Soc. exp. Biol.,* 1950, **4,** 221–268.

46. MacLeod, R. B. The phenomenological approach to social psychology. *Psychol. Rev.,* 1947, **54,** 193–210.

47. Metzger, W. *Gesetze des Sehens.* Frankfurt am Main: K. Kramer, 1953.

48. Michotte, A. Autobiography. In C. Murchison (Ed.), *A history of psychology in autobiography,* Vol. III. Worcester, Mass.: Clark Univer. Press, 1952.

48a.Miller, N. Effects of drugs on motivation: the value of using a variety of measures. *Ann. N.Y. Acad. Sci.,* 1956, **65,** 318–333.

48b.Milner, B. Psychological defects produced by temporal lobe excision. In H. Solomon, S. Cobb, and W. Penfield (Eds.), *The brain and behavior.* New York: Williams & Wilkins, 1958. Pp. 244–257.

49. Murray, H. Preparations for the scaffold of a comprehensive system. In S. Koch (Ed.), *Psychology: a study of a science,* Vol. III. New York: McGraw-Hill, 1960. Pp. 7–55.

50. Neff, W. D., and Diamond, I. T. The neural basis of auditory discriminations. In H. Harlow, and C. Woolsey (Eds.), *Biological and biochemical bases of behavior.* Madison, Wis.: Univer. Wisconsin Press, 1958. Pp. 101–126.

51. Postman, L., and Tolman, E. C. Brunswik's probabilistic functionalism. In S. Koch (Ed.), *Psychology: a study of a science,* Vol. I. *Sensory, perceptual, and physiological formulations.* New York: McGraw-Hill, 1959.

52. Pratt, C. C. *The logic of modern psychology.* New York: Macmillan, 1939.

53. Rogers, C. R. The process equation of psychotherapy. *Amer. J. Psychother.,* 1961, **15,** 27–45.

54. Rose, J. E., Galambos, R., and Hughes, J. R. Microelectrode studies of the cochlear nuclei of the cat. *Bull. Johns Hopkins Hosp.,* 1959, **104,** 211–251.

54a.Rose, J. E., Malis, L. I., Kruger, L., and Baker, C. P. Effects of heavy ionizing, monoenergetic particles on the cerebral cortex. II. Histological appearance of laminar lesions and growth of nerve fibres after laminar destructions. *J. comp. Neur.,* 1960, **115,** 243–296.

54b.Rose, J. E., and Woolsey, C. N. Cortical connections and functional organization of the thalamic auditory system of the cat. In H. Harlow and C. Woolsey (Eds.), *Biological and biochemical bases of behavior.* Madison, Wis.: Univer. Wisconsin Press, 1958. Pp. 127–150.

55. Russell, J. T. Depth discriminations in the rat. *J. genet. Psychol.,* 1932, **40,** 136–161.

55a.Sharpless, S. K., and Jasper, H. Habituation of the arousal reaction. *Brain,* 1956, **79,** 655–680.

55b.Sperling, G. The information available in brief visual presentations. *Psychol. Monogr.,* 1960, **74,** No. 11, pp. 29.

56. Sperry, R. W. Neurology and the mind-brain problem. *Amer. Scientist,* 1952, **40,** 291–312.

57. Teuber, Hans-Lukas. Perception. In J. Field, and H. W. Magoun, (Eds.), *Handbook of physiology,* Sect. I. *Neurophysiology.* Vol. III. Washington: Amer. Physiol. Society, 1960. Pp. 1595–1668.

58. Titchener, E. B. *A textbook of psychology.* New York: Macmillan, 1910.

59. von Holst, E. Aktive Leistungen der menschlichen Gesichtswahrneh-mung. *Stud. Gen.,* 1957, **10,** 231–243.

60. von Senden, M. *Raum-und Gestalt auffassung bei operierten Blindge-barenen vor und nach der Operation.* Leipzig: Barth, 1932. Translated as *Space and sight,* by P. Heath. London: Methuen, 1960.

61. Wallach, H., and Adams, P. A. Binocular rivalry of achromatic colors. *Amer. J. Psychol.,* 1954, **67,** 513–516.

62. Watson, J. B. *Psychology from the standpoint of a behaviorist.* Phila-delphia: Lippincott, 1919.

63. Wever, E. G. Figure and ground in the visual perception of form. *Amer. J. Psychol.,* 1927, **38,** 194–226.

64. Wölfflin, N. Über das Rechts und Links im Bilde, *Gedanken zur Kunst-geschichte.* Basel: B. Schwabe, 1941.

65. Woolsey, C. N. Organization of somatic sensory and motor areas of the cerebral cortex. In H. Harlow, and C. Woolsey (Eds.), *Biological and biochemical bases of behavior.* Madison, Wis.: Univer. Wisconsin Press, 1958. Pp. 63–82.

66. Zener, K. The significance of experience of the individual for the science of psychology. In H. Feigl, M. Scriven, and G. Maxwell (Eds.), *Minnesota studies in the philosophy of science.* Vol. II. *Concepts, theories, and the mind-body problem.* Minneapolis, Minn.: Univer. Minnesota Press, 1958.

PERCEPTION AND RELATED AREAS

FRED ATTNEAVE
Department of Psychology
University of Oregon

Introduction 619
Perception and Psychophysics 621
   Two Approaches 621
      The S-R formulation 621
      Multistage formulations 622
   The Systematic Study of Subjective Variables 623
      "Direct" magnitude judgments 623
      Inferences concerning internal processes 627
      A new psychophysics 629
      What is a "mechanism"? 630
      Multidimensional psychophysics 631
Perceptual and Cognitive Mechanisms 633
   Processing of Sensory Data 633
      The ecological basis of adaptive behavior 633
      State-grouping 634
      Receptor-grouping 636
      Continuous versus discrete formulations 638
      Hierarchical and schematic analysis 639
   Some Convergent Views 642
   Relationship between Perception and Cognition 644
Perception and Learning 645
   Efforts to Determine the Facts 645
   Toward an Adequate Theory of Perceptual Learning 647
      From behaviorism to associationism 648
      Osgood's system 650
      Rosenblatt's system 652
      The invariance problem 653
References 655

INTRODUCTION

It would seem appropriate, perhaps even requisite, to begin a discussion of the present sort with some definition of the central term *per-*

ception. My initial concern is to avoid committing myself to any formal definition. A large body of research, past and present, is said to fall within the general area of "perception," and there is in practice remarkably little disagreement among psychologists about which studies belong in this area and which do not. On the crudest and most superficial level: perception has to do with the input side of the organism, with certain short-term consequences (*how* short is difficult to specify) of variations in stimulating conditions. Agreement on even this vague level is sufficient to give the term a rudimentary usefulness in discourse. The moment we try to be more elegant, and to give "perception" systematic status as a scientific concept, we find some measure of disagreement. Almost any possible formal definition is likely to employ terms associated with some particular theory of psychology, and hence to bias subsequent discussion in a manner repugnant to adherents of other theories.

For example, suppose we define perception as a set of processes intervening between the outside world and the individual's representation of the world. Such a definition seems to have considerable extensional validity as well as intuitive appeal. However, many S-R theorists will object to it, on the ground that it assumes the existence of a "representation" that is perhaps nonexistent, and certainly unobservable. Some extreme behaviorists, in effect accepting a definition of this type, have consequently rejected the whole field of perception as inherently unscientific and concerned with insoluble problems: indeed, one may actually find departments of psychology which offer no courses in perception at all, presumably for this reason. A slightly more moderate position involves redefining the area: it may be said, for example, that "perception" experiments are "really" discrimination experiments, or studies of the behavioral effects of systematic stimulus-variation.

My aim in avoiding a definition is not to avoid theory, however, but rather to avoid placing any unnecessary initial restrictions upon the field to be considered. The project to which this paper is contributed undertakes to determine the degree to which present divisions of psychology make sense, and to examine the possibility that other divisions might make better sense. The criterion for good scientific organization is perhaps not fundamentally different from the criterion for good perceptual organization: the phenomena within an area or subarea should be more similar to one another—either in the principles that describe them, the functions they perform, or some other important respect—than to phenomena in other areas. Achieving such an organization is an a posteriori matter, and is strictly dependent on the state of our knowledge about the phenomena in question. Whether we yet know enough about psychology to organize it in anything like a permanent manner is highly doubtful. Certainly no present attempt in this direction can turn out much better than the theoretical insights associated with it.

We shall inquire how various phenomena that are called "perceptual" are related to one another, and to other psychological phenomena that do not bear that label. Most of the natural boundaries between these phenomena lie buried inside the nervous system, and our attempts to chart them will necessarily be provisional. The most important boundaries may not demarcate "perception" at all: we may possibly find that we wish to retain the term as a convenient superficial rubric, but not as a systematic concept.

PERCEPTION AND PSYCHOPHYSICS

Two Approaches

It is evident that a close kinship exists between perception and psychophysics, though specifications of this kinship show considerable diversity. From one point of view, psychophysics is literally the study of relationships between the physical world and the subjective or psychological world, and perception is the set of processes underlying and determining such relationships. This view makes no distinction between sensation and perception, but few contemporary psychologists would object to it for that reason. On the other hand, a good many would argue that neither psychophysics nor perception should be tied to anything so infirm and tenuous as a "subjective world."

The S-R formulation. Graham [27, 28, 29] has been particularly vigorous in urging a stimulus-response approach to psychophysics and perception. In one article [27] he considers the traditional psychophysical methods one by one (constant stimuli, single stimuli, limits, adjustment, sense ratios, and reaction time), concluding in each case that what is studied is behavior—more specifically, discrimination behavior. "We may take it that the objective of a science of behavior is the explication of the relations implicit in the equation

$$R = f(a,b,c,d \ . \ . \ . \ n \ . \ . \ . \ t \ . \ . \ . \ x,y,z)$$

In this equation, the first letters of the alphabet (a,b,c, etc.) refer to properly specified aspects of stimuli; the last letters (x,y,z) to properly specified conditions of the organism; R, to response; n, to number of presentations; and t, to time." Experiments in psychophysics may be considered to involve relationships between R and stimulus variables ($a,b,c, \ . \ . \ .$), with the other terms as parameters. Instructions are parametric stimuli which serve to restrict R: "The instruction stimulus may be thought of as the 'selector' of a given class of discriminations . . . " In a subsequent article, Graham shows how other experiments in perception (having to do with figural aftereffects, the effect of motives on coin-size-estimation, and visual extent) may also be fitted into this S-R formulation. He concludes: "The term *perception* might be advantageously restricted to functions obtained with those psychophysical methods that use response restriction and specifiable stimulus variables."

One may agree with most of what Graham has to say and still feel that his approach is unlikely to advance the study of perception very much. It is certainly true that the independent variables in perception experiments are usually stimulus-variables. To say that the process studied is one of discrimination is no doubt true enough, but it should be understood that "discrimination" is itself a highly indiscriminate term. Any information-handling process whatever can be considered to involve discrimination: e.g., the information-capacity of a channel is measured in terms of the (equivalent) number of discriminations between dichotomous states that it can transmit in a unit of time. Further, it is true, quite irrespective of the theoretical position of the experimenter, that his subjects must exhibit observable behavior of some kind; otherwise he simply obtains no data. As for response restriction, this would seem to be a matter of convenience rather than necessity: e.g., it is often possible for the experimenter to impose some reasonable system of classification on reports that are relatively unrestricted.

Graham's treatment is concerned almost entirely with the methodology of the individual experiment. On one hand, it tells us nothing about how to decide which of innumerable stimulus-variables are worth studying; on the other, it throws little light on the problem of integrating results from different experiments into a coherent system. Even on the level of experimental methodology, it cannot be claimed that acceptance of the S-R formulation is necessary for good experimentation, since the psychophysical methods that Graham cites with approval were devised and first employed by psychologists of a highly mentalistic bent.

Multistage formulations. Let us consider the opposing point of view: that the psychophysical observer is attempting to report upon certain aspects of the world *as it appears to him,* and that the experimenter's primary interest is in relationships between the physical world as it is (i.e., according to the best observations of which he, the experimenter, is capable) and the world as it appears to the observer under the experimental conditions. What is assumed here is a process of (at least) two stages, the first of which may be loosely designated "perception," the second "report" or "response." The most obvious justification for such an assumption is the fact that there are broad areas within which the mode of response does not alter psychophysical results. To cite a somewhat threadbare example: it does not matter whether the observer is given a choice between two buttons to push or between the spoken words "yes" and "no." It is doubtful that even the most ritualistic experimenter really cares whether an observer says "bigger" or "larger" on a given trial, though considered merely as patterns of muscular activity, these words are no more alike than "larger" and "smaller." The list of such examples may be (and has been) extended indefinitely. The assumption of a two-stage process leads fairly directly to certain methodological improvements: e.g., one can construct a more precise equal-discriminability scale from ratings by first removing from the data variation attributable to individual differences in the use of the rating scale [8]. Of still more importance is the strong presumption that, in attempting to integrate the results of many experiments, we shall be able to conceptualize and represent the body of data more simply in terms of a process of two or more stages. The argument here is essentially that which Hull [43] offered some years ago for the postulation of "intervening variables" in a stimulus-response system, and it seems to me that anyone committed to such a system might consider the "world as it appears to the observer" to have the status of a class of closely related intervening variables.

Another way of looking at the matter (not necessarily incompatible with the intervening-variable formulation) is to consider that the subject's response-mechanisms constitute a set of *instruments* by means of which the experimenter may observe, and in some cases measure, the "subjective" variables in which he is interested. The problems entailed by this approach are in many respects no different from those faced by a physicist who uses an instrument like a thermometer to study a physical system like a heat-engine. The instrument may be unreliable, in which case efforts may be made to improve its precision; it may require calibration; or it may interfere with the system being measured (as when the thermometer absorbs and dissipates heat from the engine), in which case experimental arrangements which reduce the interference may be sought, or appropriate corrections for the disturbance may be made in the data.

The Systematic Study of Subjective Variables

"Direct" magnitude judgments. I should like to consider in some detail the work of S. S. Stevens and others on the measurement of sensory magnitudes, since it provides some highly illuminating illustrations of these problems—particularly the problem of "calibration." Stevens's method is to present his subject with a reference stimulus (e.g., a tone) and tell him that it has some arbitrary numerical value (e.g., 10) on the continuum being studied (e.g., loudness); the subject then attempts to assign proportional values to other stimuli. Reliable "subjective" scales may be obtained from such "direct magnitude judgments." They are virtually identical with scales obtained by fractionation methods, but *not* with scales obtained by bisection and other equal-interval methods.

Recently Stevens and Galanter [75] and Stevens [74] have compared "direct-magnitude" scales with "equal-interval" scales for a dozen different perceptual continua. In the case of quantitative continua, "direct magnitude" judgments are well described by a function of the form

$$J = C\phi^m \qquad \text{that is,} \qquad (1a)$$

$$\log J = m \log \phi + \log C \qquad (1b)$$

in which J is judged magnitude and ϕ is physical magnitude. The constant C is unimportant, having to do merely with the absolute magnitudes of the numbers used (depending, e.g., on whether the subject is told that the reference stimulus is 10 or 100), but the exponent m is an important characteristic of the continuum under consideration: it varies from about 0.3 for loudness to about 2.0 for visual flash rate. Bisection and equal-interval methods yield scale values that are consistently curvilinear (concave downward, or negatively accelerated) when plotted against these "direct magnitude" values.

Several years ago, Garner [21, 22] suggested that "direct magnitude" judgments are not as direct as they seem: that what the subject is really doing is matching the subjective magnitude of the stimulus with the equally subjective correlates of a number, and that if the psychophysical function for the number-continuum could be taken into account the discrepancy between "equal-interval" and "direct magnitude" scales might disappear.

Let us follow up this suggestion, noting first its plausibility on purely a priori grounds. Unless we suppose that numbers are innately or divinely implanted in the nervous system, we must believe that they acquire meaning from *some* sort of experiences: to some degree perhaps from counting operations, to some degree from the measurement of distances, and so on. Whatever these specific experiences may be, it is with the subjective magnitudes arising from them (e.g., of numerousness, length, and distance) that numbers must become associated. One would expect, therefore, that the function relating the subjective magnitudes of numbers to their objective values should have the same general form as other psychophysical functions. If this inference is correct, the "direct magnitude estimation" experiment has precisely the same status as an experiment in which the subject is required, say, to adjust a tone to a loudness equivalent to the brightness of each of a number of lights being judged. If the number continuum is itself a psychophysical variable, any other psychophysical variable of equivalent form would serve equally well as a yardstick. The value of the exponent m of Eq. (1) would, of course, vary with the yardstick, but the m's for various continua would retain the same proportionality: e.g. the exponent for flash rate would remain about six times as great as the exponent for loudness, regardless of the yardstick used. Since the preceding discussion was written, Stevens, Mack, and Stevens [72] have actually obtained magnitude judgments on seven different continua using pressure on a hand dynamometer as the response medium. The results are exactly as predicted: exponents for the various continua consistently differ from those obtained with numerical judgments by a factor of 1.7, and 1.7 is the exponent independently obtained when the magnitudes of hand pressures are judged numerically.

Equation (1) may thus be considered a phenotypical function of the following form

$$\phi_1\{\psi_1 = \psi_2\} = C\phi_2{}^{m_2} \tag{1c}$$

relating the physical values of the two psychophysical variables, a measuring continuum ϕ_1 and a measured continuum ϕ_2, for all those conditions in which the subjective values of these variables, ψ_1 and ψ_2, are equated. What can we say about the genotypical functions (relating ψ to ϕ) that might underlie this equation? The most general answer, assuming a basic communality of form from one continuum to another, seems to be as follows:

$$\psi_1 = f\{k_1\phi_1{}^{n_1}\} \tag{2a}$$

$$\psi_2 = f\{k_2\phi_2{}^{n_2}\} \tag{2b}$$

in which k and n are constants peculiar to the continuum [actually k has an even more restricted status, being comparable to C in Eq. (1)], and f is any monotonic function common to both (or more generally, to all) continua. Our most parsimonious assumption is that $f(x) = x$, i.e., that f is the identity function, and that

$$\psi_1 = k_1\phi_1{}^{n_1} \qquad \text{and so on,} \tag{3}$$

and we may adhere to this assumption until we have some reason to change it; though it should be pointed out that $f(x) = \log x$ gives us the somewhat Fechnerian form

$$\psi_1 = n_1 \log \phi_1 + \log k_1 \tag{4}$$

Stevens's implicit assumption that the subjective values of numbers are proportional to their objective values amounts to setting $f(x) = x$ and

$n = 1$ for the number continuum, and is therefore a special case of the present formulation. In any case, f drops out when we set $\psi_1 = \psi_2$, and we have

$$k_1 \phi_1{}^{n_1} = k_2 \phi_2{}^{n_2} \qquad \text{which becomes}$$

$$\phi_1 = \left(\frac{k_2}{k_1}\right)^{\frac{1}{n_1}} \phi_2{}^{\frac{n_2}{n_1}} \qquad (1d)$$

Comparing this with Eq. ($1c$), we find that the phenotypical exponent m_2 is interpreted as the ratio of two genotypical exponents: that of the measured continuum, n_2, to that of the yardstick continuum, n_1.

In deriving a scale from bisection or other equal-interval judgments, we are asking an apparently simpler question: what psychophysical transformation will render equal the intervals judged to be equal? Here again a power function usually describes the data quite well, and it might be supposed that such a function, obtained under optimal conditions, approximates the genotypical function. (Actually, there are various disturbing factors here: there is the phenomenon, which Stevens calls "hysteresis," of obtaining a higher bisection point with the stimuli in an ascending order than in a descending order, and it is well known that the spacing of stimuli on the continuum is important when an equal appearing intervals method is used. However the "hysteresis" effect may be balanced out, and Stevens and Galanter have developed an iterative method for obtaining a stimulus spacing such that the various categories are used with equal frequency.) Stevens [74, Fig. 3] publishes equal-intervals data obtained for lifted weights by Cowdrick; from this graph I estimate that the power function describing the points has an exponent of roughly .62. Let us suppose that this is the genotypical exponent, n_2. If the phenotypical exponent for weight, m_2, is about 1.45 (Stevens gives this as a pooled estimate from several investigations), and $m_2 = n_2/n_1$, as in Eqs. ($1c$) and ($1d$), it may be calculated that n_1, the genotypical exponent for the number continuum, is about .43. Again making rough calculations from a graph of equal-interval judgments of loudness presented by Stevens [74, Fig. 7], I obtain a value of $n_2 = .12$ for the "genotypical" loudness exponent. Since the phenotypical exponent m_2 for loudness is about 0.3, we may calculate that n_1, the number-continuum exponent, is about .40: this agrees with the .43 inferred from weight-lifting data at least as well as we have any right to expect.

What happens if we try to obtain equal-intervals data on the number-continuum directly? Recently I asked fourteen behavioral scientists for a quick, intuitive answer to the following request: "Suppose we agree that *one* is a very small number and that a *million* is a very large number. Now: give me a good example of a medium-size number." The median of the "bisections" obtained was 100,000; the mean 186,575. The number halfway between one and a million on a scale of the .4 power is about 174,000. Some research along this line of a more elegant nature might be profitable.

Inferences concerning internal processes. It is not my intention that the numbers in the preceding excursion be taken too seriously. Indeed, the supposition that equal-interval judgments yield the genotypical function may be incorrect: Stevens argues rather convincingly that such judgments represent a compromise between the equation of subjective intervals and the equation of just-noticeable-differences. The discussion does, nevertheless, illustrate some important aspects of the study of perception. The first of these is the general method by which we may hope to make inferences about psychological processes that are not directly observable. Such inferences are achieved by means of what Garner, Hake, and Eriksen, in a significant article, have called "convergent operations" [22]. These consist of experiments, the results of which tell us more when considered jointly than when considered separately. Thus neither direct magnitude judgments nor equal-interval judgments, considered in isolation, tell us how the subjective number-continuum is calibrated but, taken together, they may. It is by this sort of methodological triangulation that we acquire a knowledge of psychological mechanisms. (What is meant by "mechanism" will be discussed later.) Obversely, it is the understanding of mechanisms that integrates diverse experimental findings into a body of scientific knowledge.

Second, we may observe that the word "subjective" has at least two possible meanings. It may refer to something inside the organism that is not directly observable, or it may mean simply "judged" or "reported," in which case psychophysics becomes essentially a study of relationships between the physical world and the language processes of the observer. Stevens is well aware of the possibility that the "true" subjective number-continuum is curvilinear—having, in fact, been the first to propose the possibility of "correcting" magnitude judgments by the use of bisection data [73], but prefers to use "subjective" to mean "reported," arguing that if an observer says that one line looks half as long as another, it should be considered "subjectively" half as long. The objection to this point of view has already been made; nevertheless it may be granted that a phenotypical magnitude scale is preferable to a genotypical scale in most immediate practical applications. For example, one individual can say, "We need twice as much light in this room as we have now," and another can understand him and increase the illumination to suit him, even if neither the physical magnitude nor the "true" subjective magnitude is doubled by the increase.

A third and closely related point is that the "response" processes involved in magnitude judgments do not really seem very response-like at all; rather it appears that one psychophysical variable is being used to measure another, as when the brightness of a light is matched with the loudness of a tone. Whenever such a situation obtains, we need to concern ourselves with both psychophysical functions—that of the measuring instrument, as well as that of the variable being measured. However, this situation is by no means peculiar to magnitude judgments: we face it in one form or another whenever an observer reports, whether in quantitative or phenomenological terms, on the world as it appears to him. Just as we need to determine what numbers "mean" to the observer, so we need to inquire into the "meaning" of any other terms he may use.

Sometimes the problem is so innocuous that it may presumably be ignored without ill effects, as when an observer merely orders stimuli on a continuum by means of responses like "Greater," "Less," and "Equal." The problem is minimal here for two reasons. First, physical reference situations for many continua are abundant and well defined. When an observer says, "Line A looks longer than line B," he is in effect saying "My present experience in looking at these lines is similar to previous experiences in which I have found, by manipulation or measurement, that a line corresponding to A was physically longer than a line corresponding to B." It is safe to assume that he has had many such experiences, hence that he "knows what he means" by "longer," and that if his judgment is in error, the error is attributable to a present misperception. Second, ordinal relationships are invariant over all monotonic transformations; hence, we may be sure that the order of subjective experiences on a psychophysical continuum is the same (within limits of error) as the physical order of the stimuli, assuming only that the psychophysical function is monotonic.

In the language of introspection (or phenomenology) we encounter the problem in a form much more serious, but not nearly so unmanageable as it has sometimes been pictured. Phenomenological terms necessarily refer to *objective* reference situations, however obscure; otherwise they could never have been acquired by the person using them, and in any case could not be used for communication with another person. Sometimes the physical reference is obvious: thus, when an observer reports a red afterimage, he is merely asserting that his experience is like the one he gets from light of a certain wavelength, and when he reports phi movement he is clearly saying that his experience is like that obtained from objective movement. If he reports that a figure looks "awkward," however, we do not know, in any scientific sense, what he means. This is not to say that we have no way of finding out: if we wish to go to the trouble, we can have the observer (or a group of observers) look at a large number of figures and tell us which ones are awkward and which are not (or else scale the figures for degree of awkwardness). Having identified an objective class of awkward figures, our task becomes one of discovering what physically measurable characteristics differentiate such figures from others. We do this by trying out various hypotheses on the data; the experiment may have been so arranged as to facilitate the testing of particular hypotheses, but this is not essential. In choosing hypotheses to test we are usually, if not always, guided again by phenomenological considerations of some sort. Phenomenology, even at its worst, is not so much unscientific as prescientific. We usually need to think about issues in vague terms before we can think about them in precise terms. Descriptions of objects in terms of "physiognomic" properties should not be accepted with complacency, but neither should they be viewed with such abhorrence that the psychologist is afraid to work on them for fear of contaminating himself. The course of progress lies between these extremes.

A new psychophysics. Some of Hochberg's current research [41] demonstrates dramatically how such fuzzy concepts may be clarified in psychophysical terms. He has had considerable success in identifying physically measurable correlates of "cuteness" and "sexual attractiveness." A recent experiment of mine [5], aimed at finding out what physical variables underlie apparent complexity in shapes, is of the same general sort. I think that both Hochberg and I may have been started off in this direction by the work of Brunswik [15].

It should be noted that experiments of this type represent a relatively new variety of psychophysics, differing from the older variety in a couple of important respects. First, they have the primary aim of *discovering* the physical referents of certain subjective properties or variables, whereas traditional studies have usually dealt with subjective and physical continua that were known in advance to be in close correspondence. Second, they typically have the effect of turning up physical correlates that are not simple: i.e., the subjective variable is likely to correspond to some combination, not necessarily linear, of simply measurable physical variables.

The research of Gibson [23, 24, 25] on space perception presents a somewhat similar contrast with traditional psychophysics. Gibson discusses the importance of finding the physical variables responsible for subjective experiences, as well as the necessity for considering the combinatorial or "ordinal" properties of stimulation. I have great admiration for Gibson's experimental and analytical achievements, but his usage of the term *stimulus* leaves me uncomfortable. He considers (if I understand his position correctly) that if one refers to certain higher-order properties of stimulation—e.g., complex relations obtaining among the rays of light impinging upon the retina—as "stimuli," then correspondences between the physical world and the subjective world reduce to simple stimulus-response relationships, and the need to assume any process of "unconscious inference" or the like is eliminated. Now, I have shown elsewhere [4] that texture (one of the subjective variables with which Gibson is particularly concerned) may depend upon purely statistical properties of a brightness-distribution. If we start referring to such statistical properties as "stimuli," where are we to stop? Suppose a page of numbers is presented to an observer. Whatever the numbers may be, they necessarily have a mean, a standard deviation, and higher moments. All these moments are, in a sense, represented in the bundle of light-rays falling on the observer's retina, and we may call them "stimuli" if we wish to use the word in that way, but the observer still has to *calculate* them if he wants to know them. (The same considerations apply to products, quotients, and other nonstatistical relationships among the numbers.) Wherever some combinatorial property of stimulation is important, there must be some mechanism—perceptual or cognitive—that does the combining. It seems to me that Gibson's conceptualization tends to discourage the study of such mechanisms.

What is a "mechanism"? A brief discussion of what is involved in the adequate description of a psychological mechanism is worth interpolating at this point. Describing a mechanism does not necessarily require "neurologizing," despite a widespread misunderstanding to that effect. What is important is that the description represent the functional properties of the mechanism, irrespective of the materials out of which it is constructed. An example from physics is the following: Ohm's law holds for both electrical and hydraulic systems. The variables *pressure* (or voltage), *resistance*, and *current* are related to one another in the same way, whether they apply to water in pipes or to electricity in wires. Thus an individual observing certain external characteristics of the behavior of a hydraulic system might induce a perfectly accurate description of the mechanisms involved, even if he were under the erroneous impression that the system was electrical. Systems between which such a one-to-one correspondence obtains are said to be *isomorphic*. We should like to be able to describe psychological mechanisms in such a way that our descriptive or representative system, or "model," whether abstract (mathematical or logical) or concrete, is as nearly as possible isomorphic with the "real" mechanism. Superficially different models may be isomorphic with one another, and hence equally good as representations. For example, Arnoult and I [7] recently cited three different systems which have been proposed for the abstraction of contours of visual objects: one a hypothetical nerve-net, another a series of photographic operations, the third a specially programmed digital computer; the three are virtually isomorphic with one another. Since different descriptive media may thus have equal validity, the choice of a medium may legitimately be dictated by heuristic or temperamental considerations: much of the argument in this area (over intervening variables versus hypothetical constructs, etc.) is as undecidable as the question of whether water colors or oils are better to paint with. Describing any psychological mechanism "up to an isomorphism" is by no means an easy goal, whatever the medium; in fact, the best we can usually hope to achieve is some *homomorphic* representation: one in which each state corresponds to a class of states in the mechanism represented. (See Ashby [2] for a good elementary discussion of isomorphism and homomorphism.)

The mechanisms with which we are particularly concerned here are those which transform, combine, distort, and otherwise process incoming sensory data; i.e., those which mediate between the physical world and the subjective world. When we attempt to study the subjective world of an external observer, we are dealing with a picture of a picture, as it were. Here again the concept of isomorphism is useful. A major aim of psychophysics is to discover how the observer's subjective world deviates from isomorphism with the physical world. We, as scientists, cannot directly observe subjective phenomena, however. (Whether any observation is "direct" is questionable, but beside the present point.) What we can attempt, with some hope of success, is to construct, by means of converging operations and related inferential methods, a representation that approaches isomorphism with the subjective world. The old question of whether the experience associated with "red" is the same for two people becomes, in so far as it is investigable, a question of whether two subjective systems involving "redness" are isomorphic. This point has been made in various ways by a number of people, most recently Galanter [20]. I wish to add merely that any features of "mental content" that are not preserved in an isomorphism are not only unknowable but trivial as well: whatever is unrelated to anything else literally *makes no difference*.

Multidimensional psychophysics. Nearly the whole of so-called "psychophysical research," recent as well as early, has dealt with subjective variables one at a time. These variables correspond to certain adjectives that describe the appearances of things: e.g., "long," "bright," "complex," "cute." How good a picture of the subjective world can we ever construct from the study of such variables? A picture that readily presents itself is one of a multidimensional "psychological space" in which every subjective variable is represented by some axis. Objects (symbolized by nouns) would presumably be represented by points in such a space; classes of objects by volumes.

Some years ago Richardson [64] obtained judgments on the relative similarity of color patches differing simultaneously in brightness and saturation, and found that the stimuli could be represented as points in a two-dimensional Euclidean space in such a way that distances between the points were very closely proportional to psychological "distances" (in discriminal units) obtained from judgments. This finding was later verified beyond all reasonable doubt by Torgerson [77]. In the meantime, however, I did some comparable experiments [3] with materials other than color patches—e.g., squares varying simultaneously in size and brightness—and obtained psychological distances that could *not* be fitted together in a Euclidean space: the psychological difference between any two of my stimulus-objects was about equal to the *sum* of their differences on the underlying continua, not to the square root of the sum of the squared differences, as in a Euclidean space. The important feature of such a geometry, in which the observer has to "go around the corner" to get from one stimulus-object to another, is that the axes are psychologically fixed, i.e., not arbitrarily rotatable. Although differences in methodology might conceivably account for these divergent results, a more plausible and pessimistic conclusion is that the rules by which psychophysical continua combine are simply not the same for all possible combinations of continua. The critical point may have something to do with the "obviousness" of the variables, as such, to the observer.

The concept of a psychological space of many dimensions, in which virtually any object may be represented, runs into several difficulties of a still more fundamental nature. Only one of these need be discussed here: the problem of *relevance*. Consider the kind of dimensions that might be important for the representation of a human face: e.g., height of forehead, distance between eyes, length of nose, etc. Now where, on such dimensions, is an object like a chair located? We cannot say that the distance between the chair's eyes is "medium," nor that it is "zero"; since the chair has no eyes, any question about the distance between them is completely irrelevant. This is to say, in geometrical terms, that a face and a chair belong to different representative spaces (or to partially overlapping spaces), rather than to different regions of the same space.

A similar problem arises when one undertakes a psychophysical approach to shape and pattern perception [7], even with such tame material as nonsense polygons: e.g., complex figures require more dimensions for their specification than simple ones; further, it is often unclear whether a given dimension is or is not "the same" from one figure to another. In dealing with the psychophysics of similarity in general, we presumably need to consider, with respect to any two objects, the degree to which their representative spaces overlap (i.e., "How many of the questions or propositional functions relevant to one are also relevant to the other?") before we try to measure "distances" between them on the dimensions they do share. There is no good reason why the former type of similarity cannot be studied by psychophysical methods as well as the latter, though it never has been.

It seems to me that the foregoing considerations apply to results obtained with the "semantic differential" by Osgood and his co-workers [59]. (The semantic differential may or may not constitute a psychophysical instrument in the strict sense, depending upon whether or not the objects rated are presented physically or symbolically, but this point does not concern us here.) By factor analyzing the scales of the differential, Osgood arrives at three or four subjective variables that do indeed seem relevant to practically everything: the continua *good-bad, potent-weak,* and *active-passive* repeatedly emerge from diverse materials. Variables with such universality are undeniably of great importance, by reason of their universality. It should be recognized, however, that the part they play in *representing* objects cannot be very great, simply because there are so few of them. From what we know about absolute judgments, it is a safe bet that the three continua mentioned above can convey, in combination, no more than five or six bits of information [56, 61]; i.e., that somewhat fewer than a hundred objects could be uniquely represented by values on these continua. It is thus fairly clear that the main burden of representation must be carried by variables of more restricted relevance.

Further consideration of the ways in which subjective variables may be related to one another will be postponed until the following section, in which we shall approach the problem of representational structure from a somewhat different angle. The notion of "overlapping spaces" with which we are left here can perhaps be incorporated into a formulation that is generally more satisfactory.

PERCEPTUAL AND COGNITIVE MECHANISMS

Processing of Sensory Data

The ecological basis of adaptive behavior. That the world is lawful is perhaps the most fundamental of all facts, since in the absence of lawfulness (or regularity, or constraint, or predictability, or redundancy, to give some synonyms) nothing else that we call a fact could obtain at all. The type of lawful relationship that underlies all adaptive behavior is as follows: If certain antecedent conditions of class A_i exist, and behavior B_j occurs, there is some probability $p(A_iB_j:C_k)$ that a consequence of class C_k will follow. This relationship may be thought of as one element of a two-dimensional probability matrix relating various possible behaviors B (of which "doing nothing" is one) to various possible consequences C, given the antecedent conditions A_i. If each consequence has some positive or negative value, $V(C_k)$—based ultimately on considerations of survival, to suggest the most obvious criterion—the expected value of each behavior B_j is given by $\sum_{k}^{k} p(A_iB_j:C_k)V(C_k)$, the average of the values of possible consequences with each weighted by its probability. Whatever cost or negative value the effort expended in B_j involves may further be taken into account as a subtractive term [2].

The formulation suggested above is not psychology, and is not meant to be. Specifically, A_i, B_j, and C_k are not the same as "stimulus," "response," and "reinforcement," though they may seem so at first glance: A_i could be some set of conditions about which the organism has no information whatever, and the "reinforcing effect" of C_k may or may not correspond to its value. Moreover, the form of the relationship under consideration is not "A_i causes B_j," but "A_i and B_j jointly cause C_k." Such relationships constitute the natural framework within which adaptive behavior must develop in either the species or the individual.

It is obvious that the organism can take no advantage of such relationships unless he obtains some information about the antecedent conditions A. Thus evolutionary pressure has led to the development of elaborate receptor systems in higher animals. There are many kinds of information to which these systems are insensitive: e.g., there are no radioactivity receptors, though such receptors might have great value in some future state of the earth. Nevertheless, the receptors that people do possess transmit a quantity of information that is quite tremendous, relative to either the storage or the reactive capacities of the individual; in other words, most of the information that goes into the individual never comes out again. The information that is lost is not necessarily wasted, however. The situation is somewhat like that of an executive who considers a mountain of data on some prospective business venture in order to arrive at a one-bit decision: "Yes" or "No." A less striking but more illuminating case in which information is used and then discarded is the following: if one is interested in the specific gravity of a substance, he measures the weight and the volume of any convenient sample and divides the former by the latter; once this quotient is obtained, the original measurements have served their purpose, and may be thrown away.

State-grouping. Let us pursue a little further some formal aspects of the matter. Each of the possible combinations of stimulated and non-stimulated receptors may be designated a "receptor-state." Any set of receptor-states may be considered to constitute a possible classification, A_i, of antecedent conditions. Any such grouping of two or more receptor-states, of course, involves an information loss, since the grouping discards distinctions between members of the set of states characterizing it. Most of the possible classifications are quite worthless, however, and of those which are not, some are much better than others. There are several ways in which one grouping A_i may be "better" than another:

1. Most generally, a grouping is better, the greater is the variation in expected value (see above) of different forms of behavior under the conditions so defined. Assuming independent variability in the value of consequences, it follows that a grouping tends to be better the greater the *determinacy* of the relationship between B and C (i.e., the more nearly the p's relating them approach zero and one) under that grouping.

2. Other things being equal, a grouping is better, the more frequently its component receptor-states actually occur. This criterion is not necessarily compatible with the first; the two may and often do conflict. Its rationale is fairly obvious, however, since the organism or the species must acquire, either by learning or evolution, something corresponding to an *estimate* of certain p's relating B and C if any use is to be made of the lawfulness we have been discussing. The more often members of the group of states occur, the more accurate are the estimates potentially obtainable.

3. Other things being equal, a grouping of receptor-states is better the simpler the principle that characterizes it, and, accordingly, the simpler the mechanism capable of accomplishing it. This follows from the obvious fact that no organism can have unlimited neural or information-processing resources.

The third criterion above is extremely important and requires further discussion. It brings us to the consideration of a kind of lawfulness not assumed earlier: i.e., what we have called "antecedent conditions" are themselves lawfully interrelated; hence interdependencies or intercorrelations (perhaps of a very high order in some cases) exist among the states of various receptors at the same time and at different times. Of the vast number of receptor-states that *could* occur in a world without constraint, only a small proportion have any appreciable probability of occurrence in the world as it is. This lawfulness provides relatively simple bases for the classification of receptor-states. It seems to be an empirical fact that classifications so achieved (e.g., based upon recurrent subpatterns of receptor-stimulation) tend also to have high value by criterion (1) above, i.e., to make for relatively determinate behavior-consequence relationships. This convergence is not too remarkable, since the organism's behavior acts upon the same world from which he receives stimulation. If, in contrast, the organism were required by criterion (1) to form arbitrary groupings of random receptor-states, he would need an unthinkably complicated perceptual machinery.

Although the organism we have been considering is a purely hypothetical one, the same considerations apply to real organisms as well. "Perceptual" and "cognitive" processes alike may be conceived to have the basic function of classifying receptor-states in favorable ways. A naïve stimulus-response theory that postulates direct receptor-effector connections may be considered to describe a particular way in which the organism might group the receptor-states, i.e., according to whether a particular receptor is or is not stimulated. Any complex animal embodying such a theory would have great difficulty surviving, however, since the stimulation of a particular receptor rarely, if ever, implies determinate behavior-consequence relationships.

The opposite supposition that a grouping depends upon the states of *all* the organism's receptors is equally unrealistic. (This may or may not be the supposition of certain psychologists who theorize in terms of "the whole field"; it is hard to tell.) For example, it is adaptive for the organism to group receptor-states that result from the presence of a particular object, say, a cow; obviously, however, the assignment of any momentary receptor-state to this group depends almost entirely upon the state of that subset of receptors which is affected by the presence of the object. A cow is readily classified as such even in the middle of a living room; at this level, "context effects" are far less remarkable than the *invariance* of the classification over different contexts.

Receptor-grouping. It should be clear that the *grouping of receptor-states* that we have been discussing corresponds, in everyday terms, to the classification of objects and other experiences. Let us now consider the *grouping of receptors* (or of portions of the sensory field) within a particular receptor-state; this is "perceptual grouping" in the gestalt sense. (Receptor-grouping is one of the ways by which state-grouping is achieved, since the basing of a classification upon the activity of receptors within a particular group collapses all the states that differ by virtue of differences in receptor activity outside that group, as in the example above.) Portions of the momentary sensory field tend to be grouped, i.e., treated as a unit or as a single "stimulus" by the organism, (1) if they contribute, either separately or jointly, to the definition of a category A_i that is favorable by the criteria discussed above, and (2) if they are interpredictable or intercorrelated to a relatively high degree. The distinction between (1) and (2) becomes somewhat arbitrary in the case of investigatory or manipulative behavior, a major consequence of which is further stimulation. (For example, if I see a man facing me, A_1, and I walk around him in a certain way, B_1, I shall see the back of his head, C_1.) The importance of such sensory consequences of behavior has been given emphasis by psychologists of the transactionalist group [45, 50]. Contingency relationships existing among parts of the sensory field may have great generality, as in the case of Wertheimer's laws of perceptual grouping, or they may be highly specific, as in the case of the association between eyes and noses. All these contingency relationships presumably derive from physical linkages in the external world, e.g., contiguous receptors are often stimulated with about the same intensity because they are all receiving light reflected from the "same" physically homogeneous surface—but it is well to keep in mind that surfaces, objects, and other physical entities are in quite a real sense *hypothetical constructs* that enable the organism who "postulates" them to handle sensory data in a reasonably economical manner.

Indeed, it is tempting to think of the organism as a sort of intuitive factor-analyst, extracting from sensory data those entities the components of which tend to go together. The "factor-structure" in question is almost certainly hierarchical: e.g., on one level a factor might correspond to a line in the visual field; on another to a surface; on another to a whole object; on still another to a (recurrent) cluster of objects. The present idea is closely akin to one arrived at by Hochberg and other participants in a recent symposium [41]: i.e., that the observer "partials out" successive components in perceiving a complex situation. This "partialing-out" process is well illustrated by experiments of Johansson [47] on the perception of moving lights. If, for example, one point of light is moved through a circular path and another nearby is oscillated vertically, the lights are seen to move up and down together (centroid factor), while the first alternately approaches and recedes from the second (residual factor). Different orders of communality or constraint of movement may clearly underlie hierarchical perceptual groupings in the case of natural objects. Consider the object hierarchy thumb-hand-arm-man: if one literally measured and intercorrelated the successive spatial positions of various points on a normally active human body and performed a hierarchical factor-analysis of the correlations, he would undoubtedly obtain one set of factors corresponding to these parts.

If the reader is inclined to consider factor-analysis too complicated a task for the perceptual machinery, his misgivings are in the wrong direction; such a model is actually too simple to account for what happens. One could never extract factors corresponding to objects from intercorrelations between the states of individual receptors, because the relationships that are important involve joint probabilities. It is quite possible that analysis of joint probabilities is required at all levels of the hierarchy, but the requirement is most obvious at the receptor-level; simple intercorrelations between the states of single receptors would yield some monotonic decreasing function of distance between the receptors, and very little more. Analysis at this level must involve, at the barest minimum, three receptors at a time; i.e., the organism must at least be sensitive to contingencies existing between the state of one receptor and the joint state of two others, or (what is formally equivalent) to deviations from uniform probability among the joint states of the three. Some of these joint states (perhaps only those of highest probability, excluding states of uniformity) might then be represented at the next higher level as elements, the joint states of which would be analyzed in a like manner.

Continuous versus discrete formulations. The question of whether this analytical process may better be conceived in terms of psychophysical dimensions or in terms of discrete classes or elements is difficult, important, and unresolved. Both continuous and discrete variables seem to exist subjectively; in certain contexts, one formulation seems the more appropriate; in other contexts, the other. It would appear that either is potentially reducible to the other. If a multidimensional psychophysical space is taken as the fundamental framework, then classes (e.g., of objects) may be conceived as regions or hypervolumes in that space. The discreteness of such classes may be attributed simply to the fact that objects occur frequently within the class-regions, and rarely, if ever, outside or between them. Alternatively, if classes of elements are taken to be fundamental, a dimension may be conceived as either (1) a series of partially overlapping classes, (2) a series of classes, each of which includes all the elements of the preceding class, (3) a series of classes that vary in communality with some reference class, or (4) a series of classes that vary in relative communality with two reference classes, thereby defined as opposites.[1] The conceptualization in terms of classes seems, on the whole, the more convenient and versatile. It is easier to understand a hierarchical organization of classes than of dimensions, and the clumsy notion of "overlapping spaces," encountered in the preceding section, becomes considerably more intelligible when reformulated in class terms. Too great a zeal for parsimony should not, however, lead us to dismiss the alternative that classes and dimensions may both exist in an irreducible form, perhaps corresponding to the identity of active neurons on one hand, and the firing-rate of such

---

[1] The concept of *opposition* is a fairly complex one, however. Applied to configurations, it refers to a reversal of relationships among elements on one or more dimensions: thus 4-3-2-1 is opposite to 1-2-3-4 with respect to horizontal order; and a black triangle on white is opposite to a white triangle on black with respect to brightness. Configurational opposition accordingly implies isomorphism. This principle holds on higher cognitive levels: consider the familiar psychological theory that stimulation is inherently noxious, that reward always involves reduction of stimulation, and that stimuli are apparently rewarding only if they result in the removal or inhibition of other stimuli. The opposite theory would be that stimulation is inherently rewarding, etc., and that stimuli are apparently noxious only if they result in the removal or inhibition of other stimuli. These theories are completely isomorphic, and virtually any behavioral phenomenon explicable by one is explicable by the other.

neurons on the other. Stevens [74, 75] has convincingly shown that psychophysical continua are of at least two different kinds; the laws that hold for "prothetic" or quantitative variables are markedly different from those pertaining to "metathetic" or qualitative variables. One possibility is that the former are "true" or irreducible dimensions, whereas the latter are class-series. Another is that class-series subserve both types of variable, but that the series are based upon different relations—(2) versus (4) above, for example. (Since the foregoing was written, Frank Restle [63] has made an important contribution to this area, showing in mathematical detail what relationships among sets of elements are necessary and sufficient for the definition of the concepts "betweenness" and "distance." He further discusses the conditions for "parallel" and "multidimensional" sets. The interested reader will find Restle's discussion highly clarifying.)

Hierarchical and schematic analysis. Though these important questions remain unresolved, certain salient properties of a hierarchical analysis process may still be indicated in a crude way.

1. The basic idea of "levels," or of a "perceptual hierarchy," is simply that a potentially definable *sequence* of classifications of incoming information occurs. It is presumed that the output of one stage of this sequence constitutes the input of the next, but the possibility of feedback from higher to lower levels is by no means to be excluded.

For example, activity of a particular element on one level might imply (i.e., result from) a pattern of activity of elements on the next lower level describable as follows: "*a* and *c* but not *b* and not *d*, or *e* and *g* but not *f* and not *h*, or . . . ," etc. The conjunctive terms involve grouping of elements (receptors, at the lowest level); the disjunctive terms grouping of states.

On this basis it is evident that a higher-level element may represent a *relation* between lower-level elements, if the latter are ordered.

2. It will be true, at least in a statistical sense, that higher-level classifications will represent, or depend upon, the states of larger subsets of receptors than lower-level classifications. Such an increase in extensity of representation is obvious in the case of a hierarchy like active receptor-line-letter-word-phrase. Likewise, higher-level categories will tend to have lower individual probabilities, i.e., to be more specific to the total receptor-state and accordingly to carry more information.

3. It seems necessary to suppose that feedback loops exist, whereby classifications on higher levels may regulate or modify lower-level activity. In everyday perception most classifications are highly overdetermined (i.e., the bases for the classification are redundant); hence the essential economy of the classification system in summarizing sensory data. It follows, however, that objects which are not "perfect" members of a

given class may nevertheless be assigned to the class: e.g., a man with a long bushy tail will still be seen as a man. Any such anomalous characteristic which actually violates an otherwise appropriate classification is highly conspicuous, and becomes the most important basis for further classification of the object. What is more common is that an object, once classified, is perceived to have certain characteristics which, though not anomalous, do constitute deviations from the central tendency of the class-schema, or model. A man may be classified as having widely spaced eyes and a long nose; such terms could have no meaning if there were not some schema for "man" or "human face" that includes norms for spacing-of-eyes and length-of-nose.

The preceding examples are taken from a quasi-cognitive level, but comparable processes operate at lower levels as well: the gross classification of that which is homogeneous or familiar establishes a "frame of reference" within which the unclassified residual is perceived. This is the process referred to in the "partial-correlation" and "factor-analysis" analogies above. The figure-ground relationship may itself be of this sort; i.e., it may be said that the ground establishes a rudimentary schema from which the figure emerges as a deviation. Helson [37, 38] and others have shown that classifying processes of both high and low order are dependent upon "adaptation-level"; elsewhere [4] I have suggested that a complex class-schema may be thought of, at least in part, as the multivariate counterpart of an adaptation-level.

The nature of the mechanisms underlying the schematic function of classifications remains obscure. A temptingly simple hypothesis is that any particular classification operates to suppress or inhibit lower-level activity to the degree that the ongoing activity coincides with the class-schema, i.e., the pattern of activity that optimally evokes the classification. The effect of such negative feedback would be to enhance, relatively, those aspects of lower-level activity most deviant from the schema, leaving them free to determine further classifications.[2]

4. Some mechanism of this sort may exist, but is almost certainly inadequate, in itself, to account for all the schematic functions of classification. By "schematic function" is meant, most generally, the

---

[2] Any such feedback would presumably require time; therefore in the case of tachistoscopic exposure one might expect deviations to go unnoticed, i.e., to be "assimilated" to the schema, or "normalized." Experimental results like those that Bruner and Postman [14] obtained using playing cards with reversed colors may be interpreted in this manner. Under normal viewing conditions, an incongruous object like a red spade arouses *curiosity:* see the work of Berlyne [9, 10] on this aspect of the matter. Further detailed investigation of the conditions under which deviations are "normalized," and the conditions under which they "stand out" is badly needed.

effect of a classification on further classifying operations. Here the matter of *relevancy* arises again: whether a given question, or propositional function, or system of classification, or dimension is relevant depends upon what classifications have already been made. Thus, if a visual object is identifiable as a man, questions concerning his posture (whether standing, sitting, running, etc.) are relevant; the same questions would be irrelevant if the object were a telephone. It seems at least superficially unlikely, however, that any one human posture may be considered a standard or norm from which others are perceived as deviations. The more obvious and plausible possibility is that a given classification has a direct facilitating effect upon further systems of classification (i.e., classes of mutually exclusive classes). These systems might be on either the same or a higher or lower level; feedback is neither implied nor excluded here. Although the facilitating mechanisms are conceived as primarily neural, they may also contain motor components, i.e., the "pure stimulus acts" suggested by the behaviorists.

5. The phenomenological statement that an object is "seen as" or otherwise "perceived as" a member of some class is not merely an assertion that the object is so classified, but refers further to the "organizing" effect—i.e., the schematic function—of the classification. If a drawing is "seen as" a cat, a simple line segment in a particular position will be readily accepted as an eye, though it is not in the least eyelike in isolation. A *perceptual hypothesis* is a classification, the function of which is almost entirely schematic, resulting primarily from activity on higher, rather than lower, levels. Such a classification process may be voluntary, i.e., it may result from instructions or other activity on a verbal level, and have a phenomenal quality otherwise associated with the use of skeletal muscles.

The confirmation of a perceptual hypothesis consists, most obviously, of the recognition of some minimal degree of congruency between the present pattern of lower-level activity and the pattern optimally leading to, or represented by, the classification. (If a mechanism like that suggested in item 3 above exists, the congruency would be proportional to the amount of inhibition of lower-level activity resulting from the hypothesis.) The assumption here is that there is a marginal range of lower-level patterns, insufficiently similar to the ideal or defining pattern to cause the classification to be made, but sufficiently similar for the congruency to be recognized once the classification is otherwise elicited.

A further way in which confirmation might occur is somewhat less obvious, but perhaps equally important. If the systems of classification facilitated by the hypothesis turn out to be relevant—i.e., if the situation is in fact classifiable within these systems—the hypothesis tends thereby to be confirmed. In other words, the hypothesis tends to be confirmed to the degree that it generates answerable questions.

Some Convergent Views

How one conceives perception to be related to cognition obviously depends upon his theoretical point of view. From the point of view suggested above, the two terms apply merely to different levels of a hierarchy, and there are intermediate levels to which one term is about as appropriate as the other.

The bare outlines of a theory sketched in the foregoing contain little that is original or new. On the contrary, it appears that a considerable number of psychologists who are attempting, from various points of departure, to make sense of the perceptual-cognitive area are converging upon a position not too far removed from that suggested here. We may at least hope that this convergence is based solidly on the demands of the facts.

An appreciation of the inferential or quasi-cognitive nature of perception is to be found in Helmholtz [36] and perhaps much earlier. At a time when the view was scarcely fashionable, Woodworth [81] argued that perception is to be understood as a sort of problem-solving activity. Brunswik [16] applied the term *ratiomorphic* to perceptual processes; this seems somewhat more apt than Helmholtz's *unconscious inference.*

A great deal of the research and theorizing that has been done in the area known as "concept formation" is of such unmistakable relevance to "perception" that it might be reclassified under the latter heading without objection. Some of Heidbreder's work is noteworthy in this respect [33, 34, 35]; so is that of Welch [78] and Long and Welch [55], whose idea of a concept-hierarchy clearly applies to perceptual processes.

Hebb [32] definitely recognized the need to suppose a hierarchy of processes extending from the perceptual to the conceptual; within the same system he made important contributions to the theory of schemata, developing Woodworth's [80] earlier suggestion that a new object is remembered in terms of a "schema, with correction." Oldfield [58] has spelled out, perhaps more clearly than anyone else, the point that schemata constitute a well-nigh essential device for efficient information-storage in either a nervous system or a complex computer. His model, again, is a hierarchical one in which low-order patterns become the elements out of which higher-order patterns are formed. Empirical results like those of G. A. Miller and his associates [56], demonstrating the importance to learning of unit formation or "chunking," fit readily into a system like that suggested by Oldfield and in the present paper.

Some recent experiments of my own [6] verify Hebb's observation that learning to identify the members of a class of objects is facilitated by prior familiarization with an object exemplifying the central tendency or communality of the class.

One of the most acute analyses of cognitive aspects of perception is contained in an article by Adams [1]. This paper deserves special emphasis not only because it is important, but also because it apparently has not been read by many psychologists currently thinking along similar lines. Adams deals with perceptual classifying operations, with what we have called the schematic function of classifications, and with the problem of relevance (decidability). He suggests an intimate relationship between concept-structure and the general theory of scaling and measurement (e.g., most categorizing may be viewed as *nominal* scaling) and touches upon the matter of hierarchical structure. His treatment points the way to an application of mathematical set-theory to the description of perceptual and cognitive processes.

An extraordinarily fine theoretical contribution to this area has recently been published by Bruner [13]. Taking off from the position that "perception involves an act of categorization" and that "a theory of perception . . . needs a mechanism capable of inference and categorizing as much as one is needed in a theory of cognition," Bruner proceeds to develop a remarkably coherent theoretical system embracing a wide range of perceptual phenomena, and dealing with many of the issues discussed in the present section. Like Adams, Bruner believes that set theory is the mathematics most appropriate to this area.

Pribram [62] has under development a neurological theory dealing with both "discriminative" and "preferential" behavior which includes, along with certain unique features, a good many of the basic concepts discussed above. He, too, subscribes to the utility of a set-theoretical formulation. Both he and Bruner are intrigued by the theoretical potentialities of recent work by Hernandez-Péon, Galambos, and others [39, 26, 54] which shows that efferents from the central nervous system regulate afferent activity, perhaps as far out as the receptor level. Pribram considers that these efferents function in somewhat the manner of a telemetering circuit to impose a sequence of partitions or classifications on the receptor-input.

The idea that the nervous system actively performs certain operations on its input in order to classify the input in useful ways (somewhat as a scientist performs tests or experiments on his materials) has also been advanced by Selfridge [69], an engineer who is interested in programming computers to perceive forms. Operations with this function may, of course, occur quite overtly, as Wyckoff [82] has shown.

Relationships between perception and personality are not discussed in this paper; nevertheless, the congruence of G. A. Kelly's "psychology of personal constructs" [49] with the ideas presented here is so striking as to deserve special comment.

Osgood [60] has recently made a contribution of broad theoretical scope titled *A behavioristic analysis of perception and language as cognitive phenomena*. Consideration of this paper will be deferred, somewhat arbitrarily, to the following section, though I believe Osgood's ideas to be essentially convergent with those discussed above.

Relationship between Perception and Cognition

Virtually the whole of this section has been taken up with a discussion of the communalities between perception and cognition. What, then, can we say about the differences? Can we find no natural boundary between one class of phenomena and the other? It perhaps goes without saying that perception is usually considered to consist of that portion of an information-handling process which occurs either during or very shortly after the entry of the information into the organism, whereas cognition may operate, in whole or in part, on stored information. The question, then, would seem to be whether we wish to make a distinction between perceptual and cognitive operations on the present (or near-present) input.

A widespread notion worth considering is that perception has a certain *immediacy*, whereas rational processes require appreciable time. Such a distinction need not depend entirely on phenomenological judgment: in the case of subitizing versus counting, for example, Reese, Volkmann, and their associates [48, 57] have demonstrated marked discontinuities in time and error functions between one process and the other. What is more to the present point, Hunter and Sigler [44] found that time and brightness are interchangeable (i.e., that the Bunsen-Roscoe law holds) within the subitizing range, but that above that range no increase in brightness can adequately compensate for a lack of time. It would appear that subitizing and perhaps a wide variety of comparable perceptual processes require but a single classifying operation, whereas in more complex situations, the important classification occurs as the final member of a temporal sequence of operations in which early members exercise a schematic or programming function on later ones. This distinction may be an important one, but it seems hardly to provide an adequate basis for a division between perceptual and cognitive processes.

With calculated vagueness we may, as suggested earlier, associate "perception" with lower levels, and "cognition" with higher levels of a hierarchical representational system. An alternative usage, which may be better, is to call the whole representational system "cognitive," and to refer to that portion of the system which is active in the representation of the present sensory input as "perceptual."[3] My own view is that the precise definition of these words does not constitute an issue worth much worry. In any case, no psychologist, however suggestible, is likely to abandon the problem on which he is working as a result of any redefinition which places that problem outside the area in which he considers himself to be interested!

PERCEPTION AND LEARNING

Efforts to Determine the Facts

The question, "To what degree are perceptual functions learned," is not in itself foolish or meaningless, but overconfident attempts to answer it prematurely have burdened the psychological literature with a formidable body of polemical drivel, to which I have little desire to add. Over several decades the gestalt psychologists have argued with great eloquence that the organism's perceptual capacities are nearly all inherited, while the behaviorists have maintained with equal fervor (or, sometimes, have merely assumed) that they are nearly all acquired. Neither side has had any respectable array of relevant empirical evidence at its disposal; hence the somewhat medieval character of the controversy.

Definitive experiments in this area are inherently hard to do, because they require drastic manipulation and control of relationships between the organism and his environment. Easy experiments—Gottschaldt's [19] may be cited as a classic example—simply contain too many loopholes to be of much value. Only within recent years have a few people been going to the necessary trouble to get unequivocal results: Sperry's transplantation experiments [71] are outstanding in this respect; so are the studies of Riesen [65, 66] in which chimpanzees are reared in restricted visual environments.

The recent studies of Hess [40] on place perception in the chick are a model of good experimentation. Hess never allowed his chicks to see except through special lenses which (in one condition) displaced the visual field sideways: these chicks showed the pecking coordination that

---

[3] This distinction is entirely functional, and leaves open the possibility that primarily perceptual mechanisms may perform nonperceptual functions as well. Thus "images" may play an important role in certain types of problem-solving activity. Most people are unable to tell offhand how many edges a cube has, but can give the correct number after a little thinking. Introspectively, this seems to involve something very much like counting the edges of an imagined cube. The "image" would presumably have to exist at a fairly low level in a representational hierachy for such an operation to be performed on it.

would have been appropriate in the absence of the lenses, and pecked to one side of the real grain. As in previous studies, pecking became less variable with continued "practice," but the closer clustering was about the modal native response, not the "reinforced" response. Similar results were obtained for depth perception when stereoscopic images were displaced with prisms. These experiments seem truly definitive; they leave little room for controversy or polemics; whatever one's predilections may be, one can hardly escape the conclusion that place perception in the chick (i.e., the coordination of pecking behavior with the visual field) depends upon native, wired-in connections.

Only a little less conclusive, and in striking contrast, are the results that Ivo Kohler [51, 52] obtains by having adult human subjects wear distorting glasses of various types for long periods. Kohler, more persistent than Stratton [76] and some intervening experimenters, has found that, after a slow and painful learning period extending over three or four weeks, the wearer of inverting lenses comes to see the world as "really" upright again, and experiences a corresponding, though briefer, period of disturbance when the glasses are removed. The phenomenal inversion seems to occur by virtue of generalization from a mass of highly specific learning, since objects connected with the subject, or displaying conspicuous gravitational cues, appear upright at a much earlier stage than unfamiliar objects.

Kohler's most dramatic results, however, involve what I should like to call "constancy-learning." In one experiment a split lens, the left half blue and the right half yellow, was placed before each eye, so that on looking to the left the subject saw a blue-tinted field, and on looking to the right, a yellow-tinted field. After several weeks, the wearer became completely "adapted" to the glasses, and objects appeared normally colored, irrespective of eye-position. When the glasses were removed, fixated objects were seen as blue when the eyes were moved to the right, and yellow when they were moved to the left: i.e., perceived color had become conditional upon the position of the eyes.

In experiments involving the wearing of prisms, the chromatic fringes initially imparted to achromatic contours likewise disappeared after long habituation and reappeared, with colors reversed, when the prisms were removed. In this case, perceived color at a given point had become conditional upon the presence of contour, and upon the spatial relationship between the contour and the point in question. As Hochberg [41] remarks, "These data appear innocent enough, but are actually quite resistant to a satisfactory yet detailed explanation." It is worth emphasizing, I think, that in these cases of "conditional adaptation," the subject is actually learning certain new constancies, of a sort that an organism in a natural environment never needs to acquire.

Kohler's results do not prove that normal spatial localization and the normal constancies (e.g., of size and brightness) are learned in the first place, but do demonstrate that they *may* be learned, i.e., that the human perceptual system is sufficiently malleable to acquire such functions by experience.

To take either extreme position on the nativist-empiricist issue at this time remains foolhardy. The answers that come out of future experimentation may be highly specific, with respect to both function and species. For example, we should not be unduly surprised to find that some of the same functions that are inherited by lower animals have to be learned at the human level. The informational capacity of the germ cell is not indefinitely great, as McCulloch [46] has pointed out; accordingly, it appears likely that competition exists even among desirable traits for representation in the hereditary substance. It may be, therefore, that the blueprint for man's complex and versatile cognitive machinery is transmitted at the expense of blueprints for more specific mechanisms that must be regained by learning.

In any case, the universality of a trait or function is no guarantee of its hereditary nature. Some years ago Smith and Guthrie [70] suggested that there may be a large class of *coentropes,* i.e., behavioral processes that are universal (within one or more species), but learned. We can go a good way, on a priori grounds, toward describing certain functions that any organism with the necessary capacity *will* learn, if he does not inherit them; a few steps in this direction were taken at the beginning of the preceding section. For example, the perceptual processes to which Wertheimer's principles of grouping refer exist in both men and jaybirds [19], and we can predict with some confidence that any intelligent creatures that may greet the interplanetary voyager will display very similar processes. The reason for this confidence is dual: (1) the grouping processes are based upon ecological laws of the greatest generality (e.g., the tendency of things close together to be alike in other respects); (2) these processes entail an economy in information-handling [4] of which no higher organism efficient enough to survive can fail to take advantage. In contrast, a priori considerations tell us little or nothing about whether these processes are inherited or coentropic, and the answers may indeed be different for the jaybird and man.

Toward an Adequate Theory of Perceptual Learning

The substitution of decent experimentation in this area for a quasi-religious dependence on scholastic dogma accompanies a more general breakdown of the behaviorism-gestalt polarization that has for so long dominated American psychology. (True believers still hold out in both camps, but in declining numbers; soon one may have to look among psychoanalytical converts to find real purity of faith.) Hebb's *Organization of Behavior* has probably been the most prominent single influence in this breakdown: like Hebb, a great many psychologists are now able to recognize both the central importance of gestalt facts and the extreme inadequacy of gestalt explanations.

From behaviorism to associationism. The facts of perception are nearly all gestalt facts. Without supposing that all perceptual functions are learned, we know from experiments like Ivo Kohler's (as well as on other grounds that Hebb has discussed, e.g., the existence of reading and similar skills) that an adequate learning theory must be able to encompass such facts. But what of "learning theory" as that term is currently used—i.e., stimulus-response theory? Can perceptual learning be explained in terms of stimulus-response connections? Before attempting to say much on this question we need to consider what limitations, if any, are to be placed on the meanings of "stimulus" and "response."

Wolfgang Köhler [53] has justly chided the behaviorists for the inconsistency with which they use the term *stimulus:* sometimes to refer to an event at a single receptor, sometimes for a complex entity like a chair, a facial expression, or a sunset. If it is something of the latter sort that becomes associated with a *response* (a term of equally flexible inclusiveness), certain gestalt principles would seem to be prerequisite to a stimulus-response psychology (rather than the other way about) since the "stimulus" is obviously a pattern, or a class of patterns, of stimulation, the functional unity of which requires explanation.[4]

This and kindred difficulties have led S-R psychologists to broaden the reference of their basic terms even further, to include unobservable events inside the organism. It should be well noted, in passing, that in doing so they have abandoned what was claimed thirty years ago to be the chief and distinctive virtue of behaviorism: the observability of the elements (stimuli and responses) out of which a theory was to be constructed. Hull's "$r_g \sim s_g$" or "pure stimulus act" [43], Dollard and Miller's "cue-producing response" [18], and certainly Guthrie's "movement-produced stimulation" [31] were all originally conceived to involve real effector activity (observable potentially, perhaps, though not in practice) which in turn produced or modified activity of peripheral receptors. Recently there has been a growing tendency to drop the implausible pretense that mediating processes invariably require such peripheral loops, and to consider that some stimuli and responses exist entirely within the nervous system—Osgood [60], for example, is quite explicit in admitting this possibility. But if this usage is pushed to its logical conclusion, "$r_g \sim s_g$" may stand for any neural event whatsoever

[4] See the discussion in the first section of Gibson's usage of the term *stimulus.*

(since presumably no such event occurs without some cause, or without some effect), and there are at least as many elementary "$r_g \sim s_g$"'s as there are neurons in the nervous system.

Now, this usage seems faintly ridiculous on the face of it, and is certainly hypocritical to the degree that it capitalizes on the connotation of observability that still adheres to "stimulus" and "response." These objections are nevertheless somewhat trifling, and to say no more would be to miss the real point of what has been developing: i.e., that many psychologists who still feel some identification with the behaviorist movement are—in terms of their own behavior—steering back into the main stream of American psychology, the broad associationism that is perhaps best represented, over several generations, in the thinking of William James, R. S. Woodworth, and D. O. Hebb. Those who make the most lavish use of "$r_g \sim s_g$"'s are in fact attempting nothing more or less than to analyze psychological processes into discrete events, and to describe how these events are causally related to one another and how the relationships come into being. About the only way anyone can take issue with this objective is by contending that the events in question are not discrete at all; that the system is essentially "analog," not "digital." But such an argument must seek its support on neurophysiological grounds (in the face of the fact that there is a known element of neural structure, the neuron), since it may be demonstrated quite generally that any function that an analog system performs may also be accomplished by some digital system. Likewise, any analog system may be subjected to analysis in digital (quantal) terms with whatever degree of accuracy is desired [46, 79].

If all psychoneural events are considered "$r_g \sim s_g$"'s, the S-R psychologist is quite free to delve into the internal mechanics of perception and cognition, and to construct systems like those discussed in the preceding section. The classification of any complex of stimulation may be considered a perceptual response (or *vice versa:* any response to external stimulation may be said to classify the input, since there are some inputs that evoke the response and others that do not), and the functional unity of certain complexes of stimulation may be attributed to the unitary nature of the stimuli resulting from such responses. The possibility of a hierarchical organization of "$r_g \sim s_g$"'s is evident; indeed, virtually all the ideas discussed or suggested in the preceding section may be formulated in these terms. Feedback of the type investigated by Hernandez-Péon may be conceptualized in terms of responses that alter the prevailing stimulation (much as overt head-and-eye movements do), or in terms of s_g's that interact with lower-order stimulation to alter further responses; the schematic functions of classification may in general be described in a like manner.

Osgood's system. One of the most sophisticated of the current users of ostensibly behavioristic concepts is Osgood [60] whose "Behavioristic Analysis of Perception and Language as Cognitive Phenomena" is a genuinely important contribution to this area. Osgood defends the transfer of peripheral terminology to central events on the ground that it enables one to apply behavioral laws obtained from the study of observable stimuli and responses to unobservable internal processes. What is actually involved here is a parsimonious and not implausible hypothesis which, in some form or other, is likely to be present in almost any associationistic system. Taken literally, Osgood's formulation may run into a difficulty similar to that discussed earlier in connection with "direct" magnitude judgments: the process by which an observable stimulus (however defined) is associated with an observable response may entail a chain or a more complex pattern of associations among elementary internal events, and hence may not directly yield "pure" laws applying to such elementary associations. It seems better, therefore, simply to postulate a uniformity of the laws by which elementary psychoneural events (whatever we wish to call them) become associated with one another, realizing that fairly devious inferential processes may be required to tease these laws out of experimental data. Statistical learning theory is based upon one version of this hypothesis, and attempts to arrive at phenotypical relationships by the elaboration of some very simple postulated genotypical laws. In the context of a hierarchical system like that suggested earlier, the hypothesis would assert that the laws by which elements become associated are uniform, irrespective of the level on which the elements occur: this may or may not be strictly true, but some such postulate seems necessary to account for the importance of "chunking" and related phenomena in the learning process.[5]

[5] I have been trying to show that terminology is relatively unimportant; that differences in words do not reflect equally great differences in ideas. However, the nomological difficulties I have encountered in writing the above paragraph and others like it make me frustrated enough to suggest a new term.

It is proposed that the term *psychon*, abbreviated with the lower-case psi (ψ), be used to denote any psychological event of a unitary and elementary nature. A psychon is necessarily (in a determinate system) caused or evoked by other psychons, or external stimuli, or both; likewise psychons have the effect of evoking other psychons, or effector responses, or both.

Let it be noted that this term is offered to the psychological public freely, with no strings attaching it to any particular system. Hullians are invited to use it as a direct substitute for such ungainly expressions as "$r_g \sim s_g$," "fractional anticipatory goal response," and "pure stimulus act," without altering any of their assumptions about the associative properties of the referent. To statistical learning theorists and others interested in set theoretical approaches, the upper-case psi (Ψ) is recom-

The attempted use of behavioristic concepts is irrelevant to most of the important components of Osgood's system: e.g., the proposal that sensory and motor organizational processes are formally symmetrical, and that the principles applicable on one side are essentially applicable on the other. This idea makes extremely good sense, in view of the striking similarities, both overt and introspective, between the processes by which perceptual and motor skills are developed. The principle by which perceptual organization is supposed to come about is one that has been widely invoked, and that should be examined very closely. Osgood states it as follows (the associations referred to are considered to be of an "S-S" rather than an "S-R" type, but this distinction is somewhat irrelevant to our present interest):

The greater the frequency with which stimulus events A and B are associated in the input to an organism, the greater will be the tendency for the central correlates of one, a, to activate the central correlates of the other, b. This principle says in effect that patternings, regularities, and orderings of events in the stimulating environment of an organism come to be mirrored in the structuring of its central nervous system [60].

Now, the principle may very well be correct, but the second of the two statements quoted does not follow from it. Unless further assumptions of equally basic importance are introduced, this principle equips the organism to deal only with *first-order* contingency relationships among receptor-events. At least in the case of vision, the most cursory ecological observations are sufficient to indicate the general form that such relationships will take: the relative frequency with which the intensity or spectral composition of the light falling on two different receptors is the same (within any given tolerance limits) is some monotonic decreasing function of the visual angle separating the two receptors. Any first-order ecological contingencies that are not of this form will be averaged out over time. Thus the principle in question is capable of explaining how the ground "fills in" over the normal blind spot or a migraine scotoma, but not how more complex redintegrative processes occur. For the kind of association that must be postulated to account for the latter, it seems necessary that at least one of the associated terms be, or represent, a *joint state* of several receptors, or else a *relation* involving

---

mended as the symbol for a set of psychons. No a priori assumptions are made about the relationship between psychons and neurons; theorists who are inclined to use purely hypothetical or fictitious neurons as systematic elements, without wishing really to "neurologize," might equally well employ psychons as their units.

These suggestions are relegated to a footnote because I am pretty sure that nobody will take them anyway. Nevertheless a good many cobwebs might be cleared away if they were taken.

several receptors. (Formally, a relation may be considered a set of joint states.)

Rosenblatt's system. Frank Rosenblatt [67] has recently made a real effort to come to grips with the difficult problem of higher-order contingency relationships in an associative system. Rosenblatt's system has two aspects, being on one hand a theory of perception and on the other the design for a device (now under development at the Cornell Aeronautical Laboratory) that is expected to be able to "learn" to identify visual objects. The basic construction of the "perceptron," as Rosenblatt calls the system, is very simple (deceptively so) and may be described in a few sentences.

The input consists of an array of "S-units," or receptors; the output of a number of "R-units," which may be thought of as classifying responses, e.g., the names of common objects. In between is a relatively large number of "A-units," or association elements. Each A-unit receives connections from a few (e.g., 10 to 20) S-units, about half the connections being positive or excitatory and the other half negative or inhibitory, and in turn sends connections (excitatory) to one or more R-units. All these connections are fixed (i.e., unalterable by learning) and arbitrary; they might even come about by random wiring operations or growth processes. An A-unit is excited when the algebraic sum of stimulation from associated S-units exceeds some fixed threshold value; R-units also have fixed thresholds. An R-unit, once activated, completely suppresses all other R-units (within a mutually exclusive set) by means of inhibitory connections, and likewise suppresses all A-units (within the same set) from which it does not receive connections. Learning consists entirely of the following change within A-units: the more often an A-unit is activated, the greater its output becomes; hence the greater its weight (relative to that of the other A-units) in exciting R-units. Initially learning is induced by "forcing" or artificially activating the appropriate response while a stimulus object is being presented; later learning may accrue without such forcing, as the same object is presented in a series of sizes, aspects, and orientations.

Despite its simplicity of basic structure, the system appears capable of developing an extremely high order of functional complexity. Its operation may, in principle, be analyzed exhaustively in set-theoretical terms, but the calculations involved in any but the simplest cases are so laborious, and the difficulty of specifying practical ecological parameters is so great, that a Monte Carlo method—i.e., constructing the system and observing how it operates, as Rosenblatt is doing—is actually easier. It is likewise difficult to attain insight into the detailed functioning of the system, because the details make little sense except in the statistical aggregate—much as in Brunswik's "lens analogy" [15].

The essential idea may be stated as follows, however: what is desired is a particular, highly complex, arbitrary function associating a set of responses with a set of stimuli. Each A-unit, together with its fixed connections, provides a different elementary arbitrary function associating a subset of responses with a subset of stimuli. If these fixed elementary functions exist in sufficient number and possess sufficient variety, *some weighted average of them will approximate the desired function.* A stochastic approach to the necessary weights is achieved simply by increasing the weight of an elementary function whenever it happens to contribute to the evocation of an appropriate individual response. That this idea is mathematically and logically sound seems evident enough: what needs to be determined is the efficiency or degree of economy with which it would work out in practical situations. Some degree of order in the connections to and from A-units might result in greater efficiency than purely random connections. (Rosenblatt does not assert that the connections *should* be random.) Moreover, it is easy to conceive a multistage extension of the system; for reasons discussed earlier, such a hierarchical organization would have important potentialities for economy.

The invariance problem. Even if Rosenblatt's approach should turn out to be psychologically quite wrong, his system marks an interesting departure from the theoretical ineptness that psychologists of all schools have displayed before the problem presented by "constancy" phenomena. These phenomena are special cases of what was called "state-grouping" in the preceding section, involving the organism's ability to respond in a constant or invariant manner to a physical object —i.e., to perceive the object as the "same"—over a tremendous variety of intervening receptor-states. Wherever one draws the boundaries of perception, these phenomena are unquestionably inside them (see Boring's article titled "Visual Perception as Invariance" [12]). Size constancy and albedo constancy, though by no means completely understood, are relatively simple and amenable to psychophysical study. In either case, the dependent variable is continuous and undimensional, and may be considered a function of two interacting independent variables: retinal size and (perceived or inferred) distance in the case of size constancy; intensity of reflected light and (perceived or inferred) intensity of illumination in the case of albedo constancy. Form constancy, which is clearly of much greater importance in the perception of objects, presents a picture altogether more complex. There are six independent ways in which a rigid object may move in physical space: these are the linear and rotary motions associated with each of the three axes. Accordingly, there is at least a six-dimensional set of receptor-states, i.e., transformations of the retinal image, over which identification of the form of the object must be (or may be) invariant. Here the dependent variable is not continuous or unitary; it is a set of classifications that may include, exclude, or intersect one another in various ways.

Three possible approaches to an explanation of form constancy may be indicated.

1. The image might, in some analog system, literally be translated and rotated into a constant or standard aspect, regardless of its original aspect. Culbertson [17] has described hypothetical nerve-nets capable of performing this function with flat forms. The idea has some subjective plausibility, since many objects do have a particular aspect that seems "normal." Moreover, factor-analytical studies of perceptual tasks have repeatedly found one or more factors that appear, at least superficially, to involve an ability to translate and rotate images [30].

2. By means of certain analytical operations, the perceptual system might obtain descriptive measures that are invariant over many, if not all, of the possible aspects of a form. Attneave and Arnoult [7] have discussed several analytical systems that, applied to flat shapes, yield invariant descriptions over all transformations except those involving the two dimensions of slant in depth. Comparable systems encompassing all six dimensions of transformation (but still holding only for two-dimensional forms) are possible in principle. Such systems are attractively economical.

3. Separate arbitrary connections between the various aspects of a form and an identifying response might be established by an associative learning process. It is not difficult to ridicule this idea in its most naïve version, as Köhler [53] and other gestalt psychologists have done. Some version less naïve, like Rosenblatt's, may be quite tenable, however. Several very obvious considerations support the view that form constancy is, at least to some degree, dependent on specific learning. For example, one cannot see both sides of an opaque solid object at once; a back view and a front view may be quite different, and no analytical operation can be expected, either in principle or in practice, to yield a result that is invariant from one side to the other. Here we have no alternative but to invoke learning. There is also the interesting fact that invariance of classification may or may not hold over all the transformations mentioned. The organism seems quite capable of delimiting any particular classification in whatever way is most useful: thus an inverted "a" is perceived as an inverted "a," but an inverted "b" is perceived as a "q." Again: whereas the nonequivalence of "b" and "q" illustrates an adaptive delimitation of invariance, the equivalence of "q" and "Q," which is undeniably learned, illustrates invariance over a completely arbitrary transformation. Along with these matters of common observation may be considered Ivo Kohler's discovery that people are able to

acquire bizarre new "constancies"; though the latter do not pertain directly to form.

The difficulty that a learning explanation must overcome is obvious, and formidable. We have seen that the transformation-space is of no fewer than six dimensions; if each receptor-state corresponding to a point in this space must become separately associated with a common "response," an utterly fantastic number of associations would seem to be required in the case of every identifiable object. The answer to this objection, if there is an answer, must be that "generalization" of some sort will fill in the gaps, once associations are separately formed to a reasonable number of receptor-states. But "generalization" itself involves invariance; it can presumably occur only if certain properties, abstracted from the receptor-states, and serving as antecedent terms in the associations formed, are invariant at least over local regions of the transformation-space. Thus we are brought back to a consideration of processes essentially similar to those indicated under item 2 above. Abstractive principles adequate to subserve local invariance would need have no great elegance or universality, however. Even a quasi-random sampling of relational or configurational properties from receptor-states (each of which is itself a sample from the transformation-space) might be adequate.

It is conceivable that highly versatile manipulative and abstractive systems, of the types suggested under items 1 and 2 above, may somehow emerge from an associative learning process. New theoretical developments must occur, however, before any speculation of this sort can be considered genuinely plausible.

In any case it is quite evident, in view of the contributions of Hebb and other nerve-net theorists, that gestalt-phenomena can be explained in terms of systems made up of connections between discrete elements. We may look forward to a better understanding of the conditions under which such connections may be established by experience; to a clarification of the systematic status of the elements connected; and to further mathematical analysis of the effects that may result from statistical aggregates of connections.

REFERENCES

1. Adams, J. Concepts as operators. *Psychol. Rev.*, 1953, **60**, 241–251.
2. Ashby, W. R. *An introduction to cybernetics.* New York: Wiley, 1956.
3. Attneave, F. Dimensions of similarity. *Amer. J. Psychol.*, 1950, **63**, 516–556.
4. Attneave, F. Some informational aspects of visual perception. *Psychol. Rev.*, 1954, **61**, 183–193.

5. Attneave, F. Physical determinants of the judged complexity of shapes. *J. exp. Psychol.*, 1957, 53, 221–227.

6. Attneave, F. Transfer of experience with a class-schema to identification-learning of patterns and shapes. *J. exp. Psychol.*, 1957, 54, 81–88.

7. Attneave, F., & Arnoult, M. D. The quantitative study of shape and pattern perception. *Psychol. Bull.*, 1956, 53, 452–471.

8. Attneave, F., & Chambliss, D. J. An improved method for deriving equal-discriminability scales from ratings. *Psychol. Bull.*, 1957, 54, 253–255.

9. Berlyne, D. E. A theory of human curiosity. *Br. J. Psychol.*, 1954, 45, 180–191.

10. Berlyne, D. E. Conflict and information-theory variables as determinants of human perceptual curiosity. *J. exp. Psychol.*, 1957, 53, 399–404.

11. Binder, A. A statistical model for the process of visual recognition. *Psychol. Rev.*, 1955, 62, 119–129.

12. Boring, E. G. Visual perception as invariance. *Psychol. Rev.*, 1952, 59, 141–148.

13. Bruner, J. S. On perceptual readiness. *Psychol. Rev.*, 1957, 64, 123–152.

14. Bruner, J. S., & Postman, L. On the perception of incongruity: a paradigm. *J. Pers.*, 1949, 18, 206–223.

15. Brunswik, E. *The conceptual framework of psychology.* Chicago: Univer. of Chicago Press, 1952.

16. Brunswik, E. "Ratiomorphic" models in perception and thinking. In *Proceedings Fourteenth International Congress Psychology.* Amsterdam, North Holland: 1955. Pp. 108–110.

17. Culbertson, J. T. *Consciousness and behavior.* Dubuque, Iowa: Brown, 1950.

18. Dollard, J., & Miller, N. E. *Personality and psychotherapy.* New York: McGraw-Hill, 1950.

19. Ellis, W. D. *A source book of gestalt psychology.* New York: Harcourt, Brace, 1938.

20. Galanter, E. H. An axiomatic and experimental study of sensory order and measure. *Psychol. Rev.*, 1956, 63, 16–28.

21. Garner, W. R. A technique and a scale for loudness measurement. *J. acoust. Soc. Amer.*, 1954, 26, 73–88.

22. Garner, W. R., Hake, H. W., & Eriksen, C. W. Operationism and the concept of perception. *Psychol. Rev.*, 1956, 63, 149–159.

23. Gibson, J. J. *The perception of the visual world.* Boston: Houghton Mifflin, 1951.

24. Gibson, J. J. The visual field and the visual world: a reply to Professor Boring. *Psychol. Rev.*, 1952, 59, 149–151.

25. Gibson, J. J., Purdy, J., & Lawrence, L. A method of controlling stimulation for the study of space perception: the optical tunnel. *J. exp. Psychol.*, 1955, 50, 1–14.

26. Galambos, R., Sheatz, G., & Vernier, V. G. Electrophysiological correlates of a conditioned response in cats. *Science,* 1956, 123, 376–377.

27. Graham, C. H. Behavior, perception, and the psychophysical methods. *Psychol. Rev.*, 1950, **57**, 108–120.
28. Graham, C. H. Visual perception. In S. S. Stevens (Ed.), *Handbook of experimental psychology*. New York: Wiley, 1951.
29. Graham, C. H. Behavior and the psychophysical methods: an analysis of some recent experiments. *Psychol. Rev.*, 1952, **59**, 62–70.
30. Guilford, J. P. (Ed.) *Printed classification tests*, Res. Report No. 5, U.S. Army Air Force, Aviation Psychology Program, 1947.
31. Guthrie, E. R. *The psychology of learning*. New York: Harper, 1935.
32. Hebb, D. O. *Organization of behavior*. New York: Wiley, 1949.
33. Heidbreder, E. Toward a dynamic psychology of cognition. *Psychol. Rev.*, 1945, **52**, 1–22.
34. Heidbreder, E. The attainment of concepts. VI. Exploratory experiments on conceptualization at perceptual levels. *J. Psychol.*, 1948, **26**, 193–216.
35. Heidbreder, E. Studying human thinking. In T. E. Andrews (Ed.), *Methods of psychology*. New York: Wiley, 1948.
36. Helmholtz, H. *Physiological optics*. Vol. 3. J. P. C. Southall (Ed.) Optical Society America, 1925.
37. Helson, H. Adaptation-level as frame of reference for prediction of psychophysical data. *Amer. J. Psychol.*, 1947, **60**, 1–29.
38. Helson, H. Adaptation-level as a basis for a quantitative theory of frames of reference. *Psychol. Rev.*, 1948, **55**, 297–313.
39. Hernandez-Péon, R., Scherrer, R. H., & Jouvet, M. Modification of electric activity in the cochlear nucleus during "attention" in unanesthetized cats. *Science*, 1956, **123**, 331–332.
40. Hess, E. H. Space perception in the chick. *Scient. Amer.*, 1956, **195**, 71–80.
41. Hochberg, J. E. Psychophysics of shapes, things, and people. Paper read at APA Symposium on Psychophysics of Form, September, 1956.
42. Hochberg, J. E. Effects of the gestalt revolution: the Cornell symposium on perception. *Psychol. Rev.*, 1957, **64**, 73–84.
43. Hull, C. L. *Principles of behavior*. New York: Appleton-Century, 1943.
44. Hunter, W. S., & Sigler, M. The span of visual discrimination as a function of time and intensity of stimulation. *J. exp. Psychol.*, 1940, **26**, 160–179.
45. Ittelson, W. H. *The Ames demonstrations in perception*. Princeton, N.J.: Princeton Univer. Press, 1952.
46. Jeffress, L. A. (Ed.) *Cerebral mechanisms in behavior: the Hixon symposium*. New York: Wiley, 1951.
47. Johansson, G. *Configurations in event perception*. Uppsala: Almquist & Wiksell, 1950.
48. Kaufman, E. L., Lord, M. W., Reese, T. W., & Volkmann, J. The discrimination of visual number. *Amer. J. Psychol.*, 1949, **62**, 498–525.
49. Kelly, G. A. *The psychology of personal constructs*. Vol. 1. *A theory of personality*. New York: Norton, 1956.

50. Kilpatrick, F. P. *Human behavior from the transactional point of view.* Hanover, N.H.: Institute for Associated Research, 1952.
51. Kohler, I. Uber Aufbau und Wandlungen der Wahrnehmungswelt. *Oesterr. Akad. Wiss. Philos.-Histor. Kl.; Sitz.-Ber.,* 1951, **227**, 1–118.
52. Kohler, I. Rehabituation in perception. (Mimeo, Cornell Univer., Dept. of Psychology. Originally published in *Die Pyramide,* 1953, Heft 5, 6, and 7, translated by H. Gleitman and edited by J. J. Gibson.)
53. Köhler, W. *Gestalt psychology.* New York: Liveright, 1947.
54. Kuffler, S. W., Hunt, C. C., & Quillian, J. P. Function of medullated small-nerve fibers in mammalian ventral roots: efferent muscle spindle innervation. *J. Neurophysiol.,* 1951, **14**, 29–54.
55. Long, L., & Welch, L. Influence of levels of abstractness on reasoning ability. *J. Psychol.,* 1942, **13**, 41–59.
56. Miller, G. A. The magical number seven, plus or minus two: some limits on our capacity for processing information. *Psychol. Rev.,* 1956, **63**, 81–97.
57. Minturn, A. L., & Reese, T. W. The effect of differential reinforcement on the discrimination of visual number. *J. Psychol.,* 1951, **31**, 201–231.
58. Oldfield, R. C. Memory mechanisms and the theory of schemata. *Br. J. Psychol.,* 1954, **45**, 14–23.
59. Osgood. C. E. The nature and measurement of meaning. *Psychol. Bull.,* 1952, **49**, 197–237.
60. Osgood, C. E. A behavioristic analysis of perception and language as cognitive phenomena. In *Contemporary approaches to cognition: a symposium held at the University of Colorado.* Cambridge, Mass.: Harvard Univer. Press, 1957.
61. Pollack, I. The information of elementary auditory displays II. *J. acoust. Soc. Amer.,* 1953, **25**, 765–769.
62. Pribram, K. On the neurology of thinking. *Behav. Sci.,* 1959, 4, 265–287.
63. Restle, F. A metric and an ordering on sets. *Psychometrika,* 1959, **3**, 207–220.
64. Richardson, M. W. Multi-dimensional psychophysics. *Psychol. Bull.,* 1938, **53**, 659. (Abstract)
65. Riesen, A. H. Arrested vision: in which chimpanzees raised in the dark shed light on the relationship between visual experience and visual development. *Scient. Amer.,* 1950, **183**, 16–19.
66. Riesen, A. H. The development of visual perception in man and chimpanzee. *Science,* 1957, **106**, 107–108.
67. Rosenblatt, F. *The perceptron, a perceiving and recognizing automaton,* Report No. 85-460-1, Cornell Aeronautical Laboratory, January, 1957.
68. Rosenblatt, F. The perceptron: a probabilistic model for information storage and organization in the brain. *Psychol. Rev.,* 1958, **65**, 386–408.
69. Selfridge, O. G. *Pattern recognition and learning.* Cambridge, Mass.: M.I.T., Lincoln Laboratory, 1955.
70. Smith, S., & Guthrie, E. R. *General psychology in terms of behavior.* New York: Appleton, 1921.

71. Sperry, K. W. Mechanisms of neural maturation. In S. S. Stevens (Ed.), *Handbook of experimental psychology*. New York: Wiley, 1951.
72. Stevens, J. C., Mack, J. D., & Stevens, S. S. Growth of sensation on seven continua as measured by force of handgrip. *J. exp. Psychol.*, 1960, **59**, 60–67.
73. Stevens, S. S. (Ed.) *Handbook of experimental psychology*. New York: Wiley, 1951.
74. Stevens, S. S. On the psychophysical law. *Psychol. Rev.*, 1957, **64**, 153–181.
75. Stevens, S. S., & Galanter, E. H. Ratio scales and category scales for a dozen perceptual continua. *J. exp. Psychol.*, 1957, **54**, 377–411.
76. Stratton, G. M. Vision without inversion of the retinal image. *Psychol. Rev.*, 1897, 4, 341–360; 463–481.
77. Torgerson, W. S. *A theoretical and empirical investigation of multidimensional scaling*. Educ. Testing Serv. Res. *Bull.* 1951, RB-51-14.
78. Welch, L. The transition from simple to complex forms of learning. *J. genet. Psychol.*, 1947, **71**, 223–251.
79. Wiener, N. *Cybernetics*. New York: Wiley, 1948.
80. Woodworth, R. S. *Experimental psychology*. New York: Holt, 1938.
81. Woodworth, R. S. Reinforcement of perception. *Amer. J. Psychol.*, 1947, **60**, 119–124.
82. Wyckoff, L. B., Jr. The role of observing responses in discrimination behavior. *Psychol. Rev.*, 1952, **59**, 437–442.

PERCEPTION AND TRANSACTIONAL
PSYCHOLOGY

Department of Psychology
Brooklyn College

Historical Introduction 661
The Problem of Definition 662
   Common-sense Distinctions 662
   Some Experimental Problems 663
   A Multiplicity of Definitions 664
Major Approaches toward Definition 664
   Contrasting Views: Phenomenological, S-R, and Functional 664
   Phenomenological Definitions 665
      Conceptual emphases 666
      Advantages and disadvantages. 667
   S-R Definitions: The Psychophysicists 667
      Conceptual emphases 668
      Advantages and disadvantages. 669
   S-R Definitions: The Learning Theorists 670
   Functional Definition 671
A Transactional Approach to Perception 674
   Perception as Transaction. 675
   Perception as Externalization. 677
   Perceptual Change. 678
   Perceptual Validation. 679
Some Experiments Deriving from the Transactional Approach 680
   Experimental Variables 680
   Size-distance Relationships 682
   The Rotating Trapezoid 689
   Aniseikonic Lenses 690
   Binocular Rivalry 692
   Perceived Movement 694
   Perception of Social and Complex Processes 695
Some Empirical Generalizations 696
A Sample Interrelationship Issue 697
Concluding Note 701

Bibliographical Note 702
References. 702

HISTORICAL INTRODUCTION

The past fifty or sixty years have seen an intellectual revolution in all areas of human understanding. In the field of perception this has been reflected by making the interest in and dependence on perceptual theory quite explicit in studies where previously this relationship had beeen only vaguely seen or intuitively felt. No matter how peripheral or how implicit this connection may have been, however, the entire history of human thought is interwoven with the history of thinking about perception. No matter how limited and concrete his current problem may be, the contemporary theorist always has stretching out behind him and constantly on the periphery of his awareness, at least, a vast body of accumulated wisdom and observations.

The long development of speculation about perception in philosophy, dating from its earliest beginnings and continuing to the present day, is well known, as is its outgrowth, a century ago, of the beginnings of experimental psychology. Today, the importance of perception as a key psychological process is being stressed from many directions. Experimental psychology, starting with the Wurzburg work, then gestalt, and today on many fronts, has shown the problem to be complex and related to many other psychological processes. Projective techniques have shown that perception mirrors many conditions which previously had been considered independent processes. Psychoanalytic theory and personality theories growing from it can also be cited as stimulating and making explicit an interest in perception.

The impact of perceptual theory on philosophy and psychology, important though it is, nevertheless does not exhaust the points of contact between the study of perception and other human activities. Indeed, if this be thought of as the rational and intellectual aspect of perception, it can be matched by an equally fascinating and important interrelationship with man's aesthetic experiences. The mutual interdependence of art and perception can be seen, on the one hand, in the creative process of representing and communicating perceptual material; on the other, in the aesthetic experience involved in the perception of a work of art. For example, it is of particular interest to the study of visual space perception to note that, on the evidence of cave drawings and other examples of prehistoric art, the visual space cues—still subjects of active study today—were at least implicitly and intuitively dealt with by earliest man. With the early perspectivists and Leonardo, the interdependence of pictorial art and perceptual theory became quite explicit. Similarly, the production of artifacts or architectural structures always demands a theory of perception which may be the crudest kind of implicitly held realism, but frequently becomes quite sophisticated and explicit. In both art and architecture today, a growing body of contemporary writings makes quite explicit a dependence on perceptual theory and not infrequently expounds views quite far removed from those of writers in other fields.

Still a third line of human endeavor greatly influenced by and dependent on perceptual theory is represented by the development of science. It is a fundamental principle that scientific method rests on observable phenomena, and since science rests on observation, problems of perception have always been explicit or implicit in science. Indeed, in science perhaps more than any other sphere during the last fifty years, the whole concept of observation has come in for renewed study, epitomized by but not limited to Bridgman and the interest in the operational approach.

Wherever one looks—to rational, aesthetic, or scientific man—one finds perception standing as a key concept closely interrelated with other areas of thought and experience. Indeed, every one of us perceives; each of us has, through his life experiences, developed a profound understanding of this all-pervasive process, an understanding based on a vast accumulation of evidence, on repeated and verified observations. And yet this very fact—that each of us has already arrived at his own understanding of what perception is—makes it imperative that we start with an attempt to define, however broadly, what it is we are talking about. Certainly the first step in any inquiry is to delimit the area of study and to mark out the subject matter. This preliminary task is important both to keep us from bypassing problems which properly belong within our study and to help us avoid questions which are actually outside of it. Since perception can never be a novel topic to the reader, it is well to be cautious in avoiding at the outset those misunderstandings which stem from differing preconceptions.

THE PROBLEM OF DEFINITION

Common-sense Distinctions

If, however, one looks at the question of defining the subject matter of perception from the standpoint of one's own experience, it seems at first glance to be simplicity indeed. We all perceive, and we all know what we mean when we say we perceive. To the man in the street, the question of differentiating perceiving from other psychological activities does not seem to offer any obstacles. The differences between perception on the one hand and such processes as judgment, memory, knowledge on the other, for example, seem striking and adequately determined by common sense. As I look up from my desk I cannot avoid seeing a wooden chair against the opposite wall. It certainly seems obvious to me that my perception of that chair is clearly and unequivocally differentiated from other aspects of my experience such as my memory of another chair, my judgment that this particular chair is over one hundred years old, my knowledge that it belongs to me, my feelings that it is a very beautiful chair indeed, and by prediction that unless some glue is applied it will very shortly cease to be a chair at all.

Some Experimental Problems

Unfortunately, however, to the man in the laboratory these distinctions are not always so clear nor so sharp. We can ask some questions which may point out the difficulties. Do the distant mountains look twenty miles away? Or do they look some indeterminate distance, and, because they look thus and so, I judge that they are twenty miles away? How big does the moon look? Most people make an estimate of about the size of a dinner plate. But in what sense does the moon appear dinner-plate size? Certainly not in the same sense that the plate itself does. An apple looks red, or do we sometimes remember that apples are red? The floor looks hard, or do we know that it is hard? A Rembrandt or a Picasso looks beautiful, or do we simply see a mass of light and dark, color and shadow, and add the experience of beauty as something quite separate from that of perceiving?

These examples have not been chosen at random. Every one of them has a history of experimentation and speculation behind it. Taken together, they serve to illustrate the fact that, upon close examination, a straightforward, common-sense definition of the subject matter of perception is not so easily obtainable. While we all may think we know what we mean by perception it is easily showed that the drawing of sharp lines about certain aspects of experience and stating, "Inside this area is perception and outside of it not," is a difficult if not fruitless task.

A close appraisal of one's own experience, then, fails to reveal any easy and clear-cut answer to the question of what we are talking about when we talk about perception. But when we leave our own personal experience and seek an answer by referring to what has been written by others on the subject, our confusion becomes worse. Far from having no answer, we suddenly find ourselves faced with a multiplicity of answers. We can in desperation turn to the dictionary and learn that perception is "the awareness of objects." But this helps us little when we realize that we would have to search long indeed today to find a psychologist or a philosopher who would assert that when he talks about perception he is talking about the awareness of objects and nothing more.

A Multiplicity of Definitions

Men have been writing about perception ever since men have been writing, but after millennia of writing on the subject there is still no general agreement between authors as to what it is they are writing about. Those who accept disagreement among philosophers as the rule are sometimes surprised to learn that even in experimental psychology there are almost as many definitions of perception as there are writers. Even within the context of scientific psychology it cannot be assumed that the reader will have a clear and unequivocal understanding of what is referred to by the term *perception*, nor, if he does, that it will in any way correspond to that intended by the author.

We are faced, then, with the paradox that one of the oldest topics within the province of scientific psychology yet remains without a formally accepted definition. On closer examination, however, it may be that the very fact of the venerability of the study of perception accounts for its lack of definition. For psychology has in its history passed through many phases of changing emphases, has had its ardent proponents of many divergent schools, has defined its own subject matter in a variety of ways. And as psychology itself has grown and changed, so has the way it has posed the problem of perception. In this sense, the many definitions of perception are merely reflections of the many facets of psychology.

A brief glance at two sample issues may serve to illustrate this point. Does perception always involve conscious awareness, or can the term be applied to unconscious processes as well? Even a passing familiarity with the history of psychology shows that this question of conscious versus unconscious processes is not limited to problems of perception, but represents an old and continuing issue cutting across all areas of psychology. Or again, does the external stimulus determine perception or do "inner" factors have to be taken into account? Clearly this question of whether or not our study should be limited to responses to external stimuli transcends the study of perception and symbolizes two contrasting approaches to the entire subject matter of psychology.

MAJOR APPROACHES TOWARD DEFINITION

Contrasting Views: Phenomenological, S-R, and Functional

Perhaps every approach to psychological theory has been reflected in a somewhat different definition of perception. These can conveniently be summarized, however, under three familiar contrasting views: the phenomenological, the stimulus-response, and the functional. Today one rarely encounters any one of these in pure form; perhaps they had best be considered as different elements which appear to greater or lesser degrees and in varying combinations in most current definitions of perception.

Similarly, it is not surprising to find that a diversity of ways of defining the subject matter has resulted in diverse ways of formulating the problem of the study of perception. It is probably fair to say that there are as many different problemizations as there are different definitions. Nevertheless, one can—without doing too much violence to the many views represented—indicate two general approaches, each of which has some degree of historical continuity and coherence and each of which has formulated its problems in such a way as to deny or do violence to the problems of the other. It need hardly be added that no implication is intended that either of these approaches is "wrong" in some absolutistic sense. Rather, neither view is complete or adequate in itself. Each sets too narrow a problem, which ensures correspondingly narrow solutions and makes dangerous the assumption that either one or the other represents the correct way of setting the problem. Nor can the two simply be added together, since each contains the denial of the other as one of its basic postulates.

These two contrasting lines of thought are, of course, the first two mentioned above, the phenomenological and the stimulus-response. These will be briefly considered separately from the standpoint of the kind of definition and the nature of the perceptual process implied by each. This will be followed by a more detailed discussion of one particular contemporary functional approach to perception.

The two most obvious characteristics of perception as indicated by the common-sense dictionary definition referred to earlier are these. First, it represents some sort of subjective experience, and second, this subjective experience is directed outward, is oriented toward the objects of the external world. The two approaches represent simplified, univocal emphasis on one or the other of these common-sense aspects. And herein lies the positive value of each, as well as the basis for its limitation. Each takes one important aspect of the total process being considered and makes it synonymous with the process itself.

Phenomenological Definitions

The phenomenological approach, of course, attempts to define perception in terms of the subjective experience of the perceiver. It does this by taking certain aspects of conscious experience and declaring that when, and only when, these aspects are present can we properly speak of perception.

The chief modern protagonists of a phenomenological approach are certainly the gestalt psychologists, but with the passage of time the term has become so diluted that phenomenolism today embraces many individuals and many theoretical orientations that have only the most tenuous connections with strictly defined gestalt. The common link is the insistence on definition in terms of phenomenal experience. But when one tries to find explicit statements of the phenomenal definition of perception, the search is difficult indeed. The early gestaltists, so effective in demolishing the atomistic-sensory approach to perception with its sharp distinctions between sensation and perception, were far less successful in defining exactly what it was they were salvaging or building out of the ruins of the older psychology. Some common definitional threads can be discerned. The phenomenal "immediacy," the "giveness" of perception is for them its most distinguishing characterstic. Of almost equal significance is the phenomenal unity of perception, its "unanalyzableness." But unity and immediacy, while essential ingredients of a phenomenological definition of perception, have proved to be too broad themselves; more recently we have found other phenomenological aspects added in efforts to sharpen the definition. The net result has been a gradual moving away from strict phenomenalism and toward efforts to relate the phenomenal aspects to the stimulus in various ways. This definitional trend thus recognized a specific interest with stimulus which was explicit in gestalt writing from the outset, namely, an emphasis on the relational invariances of the stimulus input.

Conceptual emphases. Such a definition leads to a particular way of approaching perceptual problems which can be labeled "percept-orientated." This approach has been primarily concerned with perceptual mechanisms or processes operating within the organism. It has emphasized sensory experience and deals with the stimulus only in terms of its physiological or proximal definition, although conceived frequently as being definitive of relational or configurational invariances to be found in the physical stimulus. It has emphasized the *structure* of the *percept*, the *process* whereby this evolves, mainly in terms of *internal or physiological events* and with the nature of the resulting *experience*. These concepts serve to characterize the interests and emphasis of this approach.

Growing out of this particular set of interests and biases has developed a particular way of approaching perceptual theory which has stressed certain selected views to the exclusion of others. Perhaps first on this list must be placed the notion of *nativism,* the belief that experience is somehow built into the native structure of the organism. Nativism, for better or worse, has come to be almost inseparably linked with phenomenology. Almost as close is the tie to *wholism*, the belief that experience is irreducible to elements, and to *relationism*, the belief that experience consists of the relations between wholes. Perhaps as a necessary corollary to the above is added the emphasis in most phenomenological theories on *apriorism*, the belief in knowledge independent of experience. The philosophic forerunner of contemporary views was an aprioristic nativism which clung to a doctrine of innate ideas. In modern views this has largely disappeared, as has the embracement of epistomological apriorism in the Kantian sense, namely, that there are certain absolutely true propositions, the truth of which is independent of experience. Although this latter view is indeed to be found implicit in some early gestalt writing, with meanings arising independently of experience, gestalt apriorism essentially rests in the emphasis on organizational principles of perceptual processes as being given by the physiological constitution of the organism.

Advantages and disadvantages. The chief advantage of a phenomenological approach is that it makes the most "sense." To the common-sense view, perception is an aspect of awareness. It seems to be a conscious process, possessing many of the characteristics we have seen the phenomenologists ascribe to it. It is perhaps this very fact of consciousness that is its most distinguishing feature, and one would seem to violate everyday experience by talking about perception in any other terms. On the other hand, there are disadvantages to a phenomenological definition. The exact and rigorous specification of the phenomenology of perception turns out to be more difficult than appears at first glance and, indeed, has not as yet been satisfactorily accomplished. In addition, while perception is preeminently a conscious process, the question remains whether it is profitable either to exclude from the realm of perception all unconscious aspects or to include all similar conscious processes (e.g., dreams and hallucinations) which are phenomenologically difficult to distinguish from what is more commonly considered to be perception. But perhaps most important, no matter how elaborate the theorizing may become, a phenomenological approach by its very nature deals with only one part of the total process of perceiving.

S-R Definitions: The Psychophysicists

In sharp distinction, a psychophysically oriented stimulus-response approach attempts to define perception in terms of observable characteristics of the stimulus and the response. On the stimulus end, this kind of definition usually simply asserts that there *must* be an external stimulus and then limits the kinds of stimuli acceptable. Usually, for example, it is held that the stimulus must bear some obvious relationship to the object perceived, referred to by some such term as the "stimulus value" of the situation. The stimulus must also be "adequate" and not "impoverished" or "reduced" with the exact definition of these forms sometimes involving elaborate considerations. But no matter how complexly stated, these stimulus requirements always can be reduced to a simple assertion of the fundamental assumption of a psychophysical approach to perception, namely, stimuli determine perceptions.

Oddly enough, however, while stimulus determination is undoubtedly a central thesis of all psychophysical perception theories, it is the response rather than the stimulus that provides the central elements of the definition of perception. Perceptions may be determined by the stimuli, but they are recognized by the responses. On this response end of the definition, two aspects are crucial. First, only certain kinds of responses are considered to be acceptable as indicating perception. For example, the responses "A is larger than B" or "A is the same size as B" are eminently respectable indicators of perception. In contrast, the responses "A is prettier than B" or "A is just as pretty as B" are ruled out as perceptual indications and relegated to the category of evaluative judgments far removed from direct perception.

Second, in addition to the nature of the response, is the relation of the response to the stimulus. For example, the response must bear some sort of imprecisely defined but intuitively obvious resemblance to the stimulus. This is aptly illustrated in the often-cited case of the Rorschach cards. "A piece of white cardboard with an irregularly shaped black mark on it," is an acceptable perceptual response while "A bird in flight," is not. Another similar restriction is the one of stimulus determination again. The response must be in some way interpreted as being determined by the stimulus, perhaps only in the sense that it could not reasonably be expected to occur in the absence of the stimulus.

Conceptual emphases.   This kind of definition leads to an approach to perception which can be called an "object-oriented" approach in contrast to the "percept-orientation" of the phenomenologist. Object-orientation is concerned with the attainment of functionally useful responses. It has emphasized the way in which the organism deals with reality and has concentrated on studying events external to the organism. It has, in short, studied the *attainment of object-oriented responses as representation of an external reality.*

Again, this particular set of interests has produced an approach to perceptual theory which has emphasized certain aspects in contrast to, and to the exclusion of, those most intimately linked with phenomenological theory. If the latter can be properly characterized as nativistic in orientation, certainly S-R approaches to perception must be labeled "empiristic." That is, present behaviors are seen as being built up out of prior behaviors. Along with this has frequently traveled *elementarism,* or the belief that behavior is compounded out of combinations of smaller elements, and *sensationism,* or the belief that perceptions specifically are compounded out of minute elements once called sensations but today clothed in more sophisticated and modern terminology. Pervading this entire approach, and providing its own characteristic theoretical flavor, is what might be termed *objectivism* or the belief that the only way to learn about the organism is by studying externally observable events.

Perhaps the most characteristic feature of all psychophysical approaches to perception, as we have seen, is the notion of stimulus determination. Although this general principle can be stated in many ways, it basically maintains that the stimulus imposes fixed and rigid limitations on the observer. It may be that the observer can select, attend, organize, etc., but only within the framework uniquely determined by the stimulus. Some such statement would undoubtedly be accepted by a large number of perceptual theorists today. This, coupled with the fact that it is quite incorrect, makes a careful scrutiny of the concept of stimulus determination imperative. Indeed, its value for perceptual theory can be questioned on many grounds.

Advantages and disadvantages. First, prior to inquiry, it arbitrarily assumes that stimuli determine perceptions and then sets about reconciling this assumption with contemporary evidence. In so doing, it violates the cardinal principle of scientific inquiry, that the conclusions follow from the data, and not in the opposite direction.

Second, stimulus determination, in common with all stimulus-oriented psychology, is based on the false dichotomy of stimulus versus response. It studies the stimulus-to-response sequence and rules out as irrelevant any study of the other half of the "closed-loop" system.

Thirdly, it assumes that the observer is the completely passive "victim" of his stimuli, thus reflecting an antiquated mechanistic determinism: stimuli are "causes" of responses. This approach is in contrast to contemporary thinking in most areas of psychology which emphasizes the active and creative role of the individual in all psychological processes.

Fourth, there is the problem of achieving an adequate definition of the term *stimulus.* A stimulus is generally considered to be some observable and identifiable process, usually initiated outside of the observer, which is followed in temporal sequence by some observable and identifiable process initiated by the observer. An excellent modern statement of this general stimulus-response orientation is that of Stevens [43]:

In a sense there is only one problem of psychophysics, namely the definition of the stimulus. In this same sense there is only one problem in all of psychology and it is the same problem. The definition of the stimulus is thus a bigger problem than it appears to be at first sight. The reason for equating psychology to the problem of defining stimuli can be stated thus: the complete definition of the stimulus to a given response involves the specification of all the transformations of the environment both internal and external that leave the response invariant, this specification of the conditions of invariance would entail of course a complete understanding of the factors that produce and alter responses.

This quotation avoids a hopeless circularity simply by avoiding the problem of defining the response. Responses in this quotation are assumed to be self-evident and not in need of definition. However, analysis of any concrete situation indicates, as Slack [37] has so well demonstrated, that the stimulus must necessarily be defined in terms of the response, and similarly the response is defined in terms of the stimulus. This circularity can be avoided only by an arbitrary apriorism. Finally, a stimulus-determined approach necessarily, if carried to its logical conclusion, rules out perception as a subject matter for study. The subject matter usually treated as perception is subsumed either under the heading of internal stimulus or under the heading of response, depending upon the preferences of the individual writer. In either event, the subject matter becomes lost.

In contrast to these severe limitations, the advantages usually suggested for a psychophysical approach to perception turn out to be illusory. Scientific rigor, objectivity, operational definition, and experimental verification—so frequently cited as in themselves offering ample justification and support for this point of view—are no more the special property of this approach than of any other. The only real value of a psychophysical definition of perception is that it does focus attention on one particular aspect of the perceptual process, an aspect which is largely neglected by a strict phenomenological orientation.

S-R Definitions: The Learning Theorists

In recent years, a somewhat different stimulus-response approach to perception has been receiving growing emphasis. S-R learning theorists have more and more attempted to attack complex perceptual problems by an application of the general principles developed in behavioral learning theory. From the standpoint of a definition of perception, there is relatively little to be said concerning this approach. These theorists have not attempted to delimit the area of perception nor to set it aside as a particular field for study. Rather, they are interested in explaining any and all of the data of perception, regardless of the particular implied definitions, in terms derivative from the S-R learning theory framework.

With this aim in view, they accept the data of perception, regardless of its origin in phenomenology, in psychophysics, or in functionalism.

Although the learning theorists have virtually nothing to say regarding the definition of perception, they have very much to say regarding the central process. At this point, it may be well briefly to outline some of their major conceptual emphases. There is, in fact, only one major conceptual strategy employed. This consists of nothing less than the bodily transfer of peripheral explanations to central processes, thereby permitting the application of the behavioral S-R laws to the analysis of central mechanisms. This conceptual tour de force is accomplished in a number of ways. For example, the concept of perceptual response can be introduced, along with attendant response-produced stimulation. This can then be presumed on the one hand to correspond to almost any central event which it may be useful to invoke relative to given phenomena, and on the other hand, to follow peripheral S-R laws. The same purpose is accomplished with only slightly different terminology, by redefining the fractional anticipatory response with associated stimulus, so as to make it applicable not to overt behavior, but rather to central events.

Whether or not such a rewriting of S-R theory is justified will perhaps be determined in the future. In any event, it leads to an approach to perception which, while certainly interested in and emphasizing the stimulus, is also concerned with modifications brought about by past learnings as well as by a variety of other processes, such as motivation, inhibitory states, and so forth. In this regard, it is in fairly direct contrast with the psychophysical approach. However, in so far as the learning theory approach has anything to say about the definition of perception, it is certainly akin to the psychophysical approach in their common emphasis on the behavioral as opposed to phenomenological data.

The reader will already have noted that these two contrasting definitions—the phenomenological and the stimulus-response—grow out of two different philosophical trends, each with deep historical roots. The first mode is that of the idealist who concentrates on the thoughts and feelings of his own experience. The second represents the realist who is concerned with the observable objectives and events of the external world. The *reductio ad absurdum* of the first view is reached by the solopsist, who believes that there is nothing outside of his own head; of the latter view by the behaviorist, who believes that there is nothing inside of his.

Functional Definition

A functional definition tries to bridge the gap between these divergent views by specifying the perceptual process in terms of the relationship of that particular process to the total life functioning of the individual. A functional approach is by its very nature future-oriented and goal-directed. Its chief advantage derives from this very fact. A functional definition puts the person into a real situation and considers him as he actually appears in concrete living.

Perceptual studies initiated the modern era of scientific psychology. A look at the course of development of the study of perception since that time gives us a bird's-eye view of the course of development of the entire field of psychology and indicates why a functional approach to perception has become imperative in the climate of contemporary psychology. The early perceptual work fell within what has come to be known as the tradition of "stimulus determines the perception." Emphasis was placed on a detailed analysis of the characteristics of the external stimulus and the search was for universal "laws" relating the physical environment on the one hand and the subjective experience on the other. Within the limits of this approach, it was gradually found necessary to enlarge the subject matter to include the study of the sensory apparatus and of neural processes and central functioning as well. This line of approach has been and continues to be actively pursued and productive of important findings.

Within the past decade or so, however, the experimental study of perception has received a tremendous impetus from a point of view almost directly opposed to this. The early work started with the object and went to the person. It asked the question, "What does the environment do to the perceiver?" Present-day thinking reverses this, starting with the perceiver and working toward the object. This apparently simple change has produced a revolution in thinking, so that today we ask, "What does the perceiver do to the environment? What is actually done by the individual when he perceives?" The shift, then, is from considering perception as a passive reaction to external events toward considering perceiving as a process actively carried out by the perceiver.

In short, the over-all trend of contemporary perceptual studies has been away from the earlier stimulus orientation, based on the assumption that external stimuli determine perceptions, and toward the treatment of perceiving an essentially creative process actively carried on by the organism. This trend is based on the assumption that the individual acts in any situation in terms of the way he perceives that situation. Perception, then, becomes a crucial process intimately involved in the effective functioning of the individual. It need hardly be pointed out that such an approach has necessarily led the experimental study of perception into a consideration of problems which had previously been considered sacred to that branch of psychology labeled "personality."

Actually the meeting has been at the halfway point. More and more, personality theorists and practicing clinicians have become interested in the perceptual process, and an analogous trend can be traced from this starting point. Certainly, the most fruitful clinical approaches currently in use in psychodiagnosis and psychotherapy rely on a theoretical basis which assumes a relationship between perception and personality. Psychoanalysis, of course, has always assumed that the individual structures his world through his experiences. The direct importance of perceptual processes in shaping the content of these experiences is specifically stressed by most contemporary psychoanalytic writers. The relationship of perception to phenomenological personality theory is more direct and obvious. The projective theorists have, of course, always maintained this position, and in a sense are today coming into their own. Rorschach himself referred to his test as an "experiment in perception." It is safe to say that personality studies have been approaching perception as rapidly as perceptual studies have been approaching personality. The two have met with an impact that has vitally affected contemporary psychology.

This changing emphasis only serves to underline the fact that the study of perception is indeed a very old one, with roots in a wide variety of human activities and experiences—social, aesthetic, philosophical, scientific. In all of these areas it has received a contemporary impetus which represents more than an acceleration of the age-old studies. It is, rather, a push in a radically new direction. Contemporary thinking in all these fields has, at the very least, elements of intellectual revolution and radical departure from earlier views.

Within the domain of scientific psychology, the central and dominant position currently held by perception can be attributed to two quite compelling reasons. First, considered as a psychological process, perception occupies a central, unifying position within the total functioning of the individual. If we may permit ourselves for the moment the simplifying assumption of a dichotomy between the individual and the environment, the reason for this importance of perceiving becomes obvious. For it is through perception that each one of us becomes aware of the world outside of himself.

Second, considered as a subject matter for study within the science of psychology, perception represents the common meeting ground between the whole tradition of experimental psychology on the one hand and that of clinical practice on the other. The study of perception, to use another figure of speech, is the bridge spanning the chasm between these two divergent approaches. Perception then becomes a central unifying study linking the laboratory with the clinic.

Of course, intercourse between the individual and his environment is a two-way affair, involving both incoming and outgoing channels. These are most naturally conceptualized respectively as perceiving and acting.

Certainly any adequate theory must account for both of these processes, and it may appear on the surface that an extreme emphasis on perception leaves out action and hence is limited to only half, and possibly the less important half, of the problem. However, the error of this view becomes apparent from a closer look at the relationship between perceiving and acting. For in dealing with the world about him, each person necessarily acts in terms of the world as he perceives it. He has no alternative, for that is the only world he lives in, the only world he experiences. As Adelbert Ames, Jr., so well put it, perceptions are prognostic directives for action.

But actions are not only initiated, they also have consequences. They have an effect first, it is true, on the object of the action. This is their outgoing aspect. But from a psychological point of view, the most important effect is on the person who initiated the action. In short, the most important aspect of acting is the way the individual himself experiences the consequences of his own actions. And this is in turn accomplished through the perceptual process. Perceiving, then, provides both the framework on which action is based and the channel through which the consequences of action are experienced. Small wonder that many investigators today consider perceiving to be the most important psychological process. Considered either as a psychological process or as a subject matter for study, perception offers a truly important meeting ground for many and varied areas of psychology, a central point from which one can travel in many directions.

A TRANSACTIONAL APPROACH TO PERCEPTION

A working definition of perception adequate to such a broad view has been previously suggested in another context and does not seem to be in need of serious modification. This defines perceiving as that part of the process of living by which each one of us, from his own particular point of view, creates for himself the world within which he has his life's experiences and through which he strives to gain his satisfactions.

The theory of perception which is implied by such a definition will be approached by emphasizing four different aspects of the perceptual process. First, there is the way in which perception enters into the total life situation of the individual, which is most adequately handled under the concept of transaction. Second, there is the way in which perception links the experience of inner and outer events, which can be subsumed under the heading of externalization. Thirdly, we will consider the question of perceptual change, and finally, the problem of perceptual validation, which leads into the role of action.

Perception as Transaction

Perceiving is not only an inseparable part of all waking activity, but even more important, perceiving never occurs independent of some other activity. The attempt to find everyday activity not involving perception leads one to a consideration of yogi practices and other possibly mystical trance states in which the attempt is made to maintain conscious thought while completely removed from all contact with the environment through perception. There is some evidence that some people may be able to achieve this condition. Even if fully established, such instances are certainly so rare that we will not consider them as disproving the general rule that activity always involves perception.

In an effort to find examples of perception independent of all other waking activity, we look not to advanced mysticism but to budding science. The introspectionism of early experimental psychology had as one of its fundamental tenets the belief that one could, in fact, observe oneself perceive without reference to any other activity. This statement, however, contains an unavoidable circularity, and this aspect of early experimental psychology has not been fruitful, nor has it been carried on to the present time. Certainly reference to one's own experience indicates that perceiving and other activities are inextricably interwoven.

But how are we to study perceiving if we can never find a perception? The answer is that perceiving is an abstraction from a concrete experience and must be treated as such. We cannot somehow isolate a perception in its pure state as a chemist might isolate a pure chemical or a biologist a pure strain, and then proceed to study it in isolation. Perceiving never takes place by itself. It can only be studied as part of the situation in which it operates.

Of course, the abstraction of some very simple act of perceiving from the rest of an ongoing situation for purposes of experimentation is frequently necessary, but this is always done at the risk of seriously distorting the subject matter. The starting point for perceptual studies must always be perceiving as it is encountered in concrete real-life situations. This, of course, places severe restrictions upon the experimental study of perception involving important methodological and procedural as well as theoretical implications. No matter how much he may wish to do otherwise, the student of perception is frequently forced to obtain data under conditions quite remote from those in which perception normally operates. But when he does so, he must always be sensitive to the limitations of attempting to treat such data as if they had relevance to real-life situations. Possibly the safest way out of this dilemma is to treat an experiment in the perceptual laboratory not as a reflection of how one perceives in another kind of situation, but rather in itself as a concrete situation in which the observer is perceiving.

Neither a perception nor an object as perceived exists independent of the total life situation of which both perception and object are a part. It is meaningless to speak of either as existing apart from the situation in which it is encountered. The word *"transaction"* is used to label such a situation, for it carries the double implication (1) that all parts of the situation enter into it as active participants, and (2) that they owe their very existence as encountered in the situation to this fact of active participation and do not appear as already existing entities merely interacting with each other without affecting their own identity.

Just as no single aspect of the transaction can be said to exist in its own right apart from the transaction, so not even the transaction itself can be treated as existing in its own right. Using the term is not to be construed as simply a new way of breaking the subject matter into larger but still discrete elements or events. This view, which we will try to avoid in this discussion, is analogous to the narrow, archaic view of Newtonion physics in which the belief was held that the observer somehow stood outside of the system which he was observing and which was independent of the fact of observation. Rather, we will assume that every transaction has within it as an integral part of its being its own unique reflection of all past transactions and its own unique presentment of future transactions.

Even the scientist studying the transaction enters into it as a participant. He does not somehow stand outside the transaction and observe it from some remote and inaccessible height. The very fact of observation has been shown in the physical sciences to affect that which is observed. How much more true and important this becomes in the behavioral sciences and particularly psychology. The psychologist is always a participant who affects and is affected by the transaction he is observing.

This fact that a transaction does not exist in its own right waiting for observation but rather can be observed only through participation had one very important implication for our present discussion. Each participant enters into the transaction in a different manner and experiences a transaction which is to this extent different from that experienced by all other participants. There are as many possible points from which the transaction can be entered as there are participants. Any aspect of the transaction which cannot be reached from that point of view is unknown. Similarly, aspects of the transaction which cannot be reached from any other point can be known only by the particular participant and are unique to him.

Each one of us is, therefore, constantly playing a dual role. First, we are experiencing our own unique participation, with all its intellectual and valueful overtones, many of which cannot even be verbalized without being lost. Secondly, we are constantly trying to abstract from this total experience those aspects which are or can be experienced at the same time by other participants. It is here that we are constantly in danger of falling into what Whitehead has called "the fallacy of misplaced concreteness" if we assign greater concreteness, that is, a higher degree of external reality, to the abstracted aspects than to the total experience from which they are abstracted.

Perception as Externalization

Probably the most obvious aspect of the experience of perception is that it is externally oriented—that is, the things we see and hear and taste and touch are experienced as existing outside of ourselves and as possessing for themselves the characteristics which we perceive in them. But it is also clear that perception is part of the experience of the individual. One essential feature of perception, then, is the external orientation of certain aspects of experience. In perceiving, parts of our own experience are attributed to events external to ourselves in whose independent existence we firmly believe. When we perceive, we externalize certain aspects of our experience and thereby create for ourselves our own world of things and people, of sights and sounds, of taste and touches. Without taking any metaphysical position regarding the existence of a real world independent of experience, we can nevertheless assert that the world as experienced has no meaning and cannot be defined independent of the experience. The world as we experience it is the product of perception, not the cause of it.

Certain aspects of experience are definitely and surely attributed to the external world. Clearly, not all experience is externalized, however. Other aspects are just as definitely considered to be personal, subjective, and having no external reference. Still other aspects lie in a never-never land in between. It is important, therefore, to ask such questions as: What aspects of experience are viewed as representing something independent of the experience? And what aspects are not? Why, indeed, does anyone ever come to believe in the independent existence of an external world? And what are the factors that determine which aspect of experience is selected as representing this external reality? The answers to these questions lie beyond the scope of the present work, but the problems raised by them always lurk behind any study in the field of perception.

It should be noted that it is not immediately and simply evident what kinds of experience can profitably be externalized. Some people on some occasions may externalize experiences which might more effectively be considered as subjective or vice versa.

One important part of psychotherapy, then, may well be learning to externalize some aspects of experience which have heretofore not been externalized and, probably more important, learning not to externalize many experiences which in the past have been—that is, to recognize as one's own experience certain things which have in the past been attributed to external events.

Perceptual Change

Any present perceptual experience consists of a total complex of significance. All previous experiences have been similarly composed. Through the course of experiencing, certain significances are found by the perceiver to have high probabilities of being related to each other. Other relationships have a low probability of occurring. The probabilities, high or low, are in turn weighted in terms of the relevance of the unique situations in which they have occurred to the large purposes and values of the experiencing person. All this is accomplished through a largely unconscious process and results in a set of *assumptions* or weighted averages of previous experiences which are brought to the present occasion and play a principal role in determining how the occasion is experienced. For each of us the sum total of these assumptions can be said to constitute our *assumptive world*. The assumptive world of any particular individual at any particular time determines his perceptions, that is, provides him with predictions of probable significances. His assumptive world is, therefore, in a very real sense the only world which he knows.

Perhaps the most significant point to be made concerning assumptions as they concretely enter into the transaction is that they are not always, if ever, in complete harmony. On the contrary, any concrete experience involves the achievement of some sort of resolution of a host of more or less incompatible and sometimes directly contradictory assumptions. This resolution is accomplished by means of an unconscious *"weighting process"* (the italics are taken to indicate that this is a figurative description of an as yet imperfectly understood function). The particular weight given to each assumption in this unconscious calculation is a product of at least three factors. First, each assumption is undoubtedly weighted on a probability basis. That is, assumptions which have frequently and consistently proved valid in the past will tend to be weighted most heavily. This point has been made, in other terminology, by Brunswik, in whose "probabilistic functionalism" weightings are determined on the basis of "ecological validity." Brunswik is in error, however, when he assumes that weights are based solely on probability. A second criterion for the weight given an assumption lies in the over-all importance to the individual of each particular experience into which it entered and the importance of the assumption within that experience. This consideration makes possible extreme cases of traumatic weighting, but also undoubtedly figures less dramatically in every experience. Finally, an assumption will be weighted in the immediate situation, depending upon its relevancy to the specific purposes of the moment. Each assumption, then, enters into the weighting process with a weight determined on a probability basis adjusted in terms of its previous importance to the individual and its relationship to the immediate transaction.

It follows from these considerations that perceptions can change through two quite different processes. One process takes place within the already existing framework of assumptions and consists of altering the weight without changing the assumptions themselves. The effects of this perceptual reweighting process become evident only when conflicts are present. In a conflict situation, however, the particular resolution achieved, and hence the resultant experience, will be changed in accord with the newly assigned weights. The second process of perceptual change is quite different and calls for the acquiring of totally new assumptions. This *perceptual relearning* process is more fundamental and can change the entire perceptual experience of the individual [29].

Perceptual Validation

Perceiving, as we have seen, provides us with predictions of the significance of the external situation only by experiencing the consequences of our own actions.

The experienced consequences of every action provide a check on the perceptual prediction on which the action was based. Every action can be thought of as an experimental test of an hypothesis which is appropriately modified or confirmed as the result of our test through action. One psychological result of any action, then, is a change in the probabilities unconsciously assigned to the particular assumptions on which that action was based. The probability is changed in proportion to the weight given to that particular experience, resulting in new assumptions, new predictions, new externalized significances.

There are, however, two ways in which assumptions, and consequently perceptions, change through experiencing the effects of our actions. It is important that these be differentiated. First, every action we undertake is a check on an assumption. Hence, every action affects the subjective probability assigned to that assumption. But second, and of much greater importance, are those actions which bring about changes in the assumptions themselves or the formation of new assumptions. These are actions whose experienced consequences are either directly contradictory to an assumption or not related to any existing assumption. In such cases, the consequences of our actions directly contradict the predictions on which they were based. These are "unsuccessful" actions, resulting in surprise, disappointment, frustration, or the awareness of a new problem to be resolved.

SOME EXPERIMENTS DERIVING FROM THE TRANSACTIONAL APPROACH

Up to this point our discussion has been directed toward theoretical issues of definition and problemization. But the ultimate translation of these issues into experimental investigations constitutes the final measure of their utility and the final arbiter of their validity. In the preceding discussion, all the major empirical variables of perception have been either explicitly stated or implicitly referred to. At this point it may be useful to assemble them under one heading so that we may obtain a clearer picture of the relevance of current empirical efforts to the broad issues already elaborated.

Experimental Variables

Actually, the crucial process of arriving at fruitful empirical variables is neither simple nor direct. It is here that the creative ingenuity of the researcher is most fully called into play, and it is here that his theoretical biases become concretized.

Any experimental variable is in itself only one of a large number of possible ways of making specific a more general aspect of the perceptual situation, an aspect which the investigator believes to be relevant to the problem at hand. Thus, underlying the use of any specific variable is the implicit endorsement of one particular aspect as being more important than others. Hundreds of different variables suitable for experimental manipulation may all derive from a single larger aspect. Even a partial listing of all the vast variety of empirical variables that have been used in perception experiments would be an impossible undertaking. The relevant aspects of the perceptual situation from which this flood of variables derives are relatively few, however. All have been referred to in the preceding sections and can be listed here.

The external object. In general, this refers to all aspects of the situation other than the living organism from whose standpoint we are conducting our inquiry. It is important to note, however, that we are concerned at this point not with externality as it may exist in its own right in the sense of the mystical ultimate essence of things, nor with externality as perceived, but rather with externality in so far as it is knowable to the physical sciences and as it enters into the transaction with relevance to the living organism.

Relating phenomena or impingements. These are physical energies related to the externality which impinge upon the organism and to which the organism has some physiological sensitivity.

Physiological excitation. Impingements are of relevance only if they cause some physiological stimulation or excitation in the organism. Excitation, then, includes the stimulation of peripheral nerve endings, together with the entire path of nerve endings, together with the entire path of nerve transmission leading to the higher centers at which contact with other nerve impulses is achieved, as well as neural activity which results from internal rather than external stimulation.

Awareness. This aspect of the situation is essential, as we have seen, as long as we conduct our inquiry from the standpoint of the perceiving organism and wish to include the full range of perceptual phenomena.

Unconscious aspects. Many of the psychological activities which enter into the perceptual process do not directly enter into the awareness of the perceiver, even though he may be taking them into account.

Psychological processes. Set, assumptions, values, purpose, weighing and integrating processes, weighted averages, and other such aspects appear explicitly or implicitly in most perceptual work.

Action. Included here are not only contemporary actions, but also the consequences of previous actions as well as contemplated future action. Perhaps a more descriptive term here might be the *participation* of the individual in the immediate transaction, which would include the effects of previous participations and the presentment of future participations.

The generality of any conclusions we may draw about perception is limited by the fact that only a relatively few of these relevant aspects have been translated into experimental variables. In addition, one theoretical orientation has emphasized one set of variables, another a different set. The result has been a collection of experimental variables which is extremely diverse, even though in a very general way they all derive from the same restricted set of relevant aspects.

In the remainder of this section a survey of some of the experimental work done by the group of investigators operating within the broad framework of transactional theory will be presented. It is hoped that this will serve the dual purpose of making more concrete the abstract discussion of transactional theory in the preceding section as well as illustrating the way in which a particular theoretical orientation influences the kind of experimental variables utilized. The work will be discussed under general headings (*size-distance relationships, the rotating trapezoid, aniseikonic lenses, binocular rivalry, perceived movement,* and *perception of social and complex processes.* It will be noted that these topics themselves form a progression in terms of both number and kind of relevant variables taken into consideration in each group. Within each topic as well, the same progression is to be seen, and work stimulated initially by a restricted problem inevitably expands to encompass more and more variables and gain greater and greater generality.

It is probably not necessary to emphasize that the following descriptions are not in any sense intended to be a complete summary of all the experimental work done in the various areas labeled, nor is it even a complete summary of all the work done by the transactional theorists. What is intended is simply a sampling of representative important and illustrative experiments.

Size-distance Relationships

It is in this area that Ames made some of his most important and influential original observations from which much of the work recorded in this section directly stems. The observations were made using an apparatus which Ames devised and dubbed the "Thereness-Thatness" table, thereby pointing up the fact that it offered an experimental way of linking the "thereness," or apparent location, of an object with its "thatness," or its meaning. Since the observations can be understood and their significance assessed only in the context of the apparatus with which they are made, the basic elements of the apparatus and the procedure will first be described. More elaborate descriptions can be found in Ittelson and Slack [26] and Ittelson [22].

The apparatus consists essentially of two visual fields which can be viewed simultaneously by the subject. In one field, the experimental field, is presented the stimulus object being studied. This object is viewed monocularly and hence, as shall shortly be elaborated, the apparent distance of this object depends on the physical size which the observer attributes to it or assumes it to be. The second field is a comparison field against which apparent distances are measured. This field is designed to have a minimum influence on the apparent distances of objects placed in the experimental field.

Using this apparatus, Ames made many observations with a wide variety of objects. Using a playing card, constructed to be off-size (larger than or smaller than an ordinary playing card), subjects consistently and reliably made distance settings which could be predicted from knowledge of the size of an ordinary playing card together with the size of the card actually being observed. They treated the card being observed as if it were, in fact, an ordinary-sized playing card. Their settings were objectively inaccurate but, nevertheless, "correct" in the sense that they were appropriate to playing cards as usually experienced. Similar observations were made with a variety of other familiar objects which come in essentially only one size, such as match boxes, cigarette packages, and the like. When familiar objects were used which did not meet this criterion and which normally are encountered in a wide range of sizes, somewhat different observations were made. Individual reliability of settings was maintained, but interindividual consistency dropped, and there was no rational way of predicting for any individual what the specific setting would be. For example, leaves, which are both familiar and variable in size, were effectively used in this type of experiment. Similar observations were made even when extremely unfamiliar or ambiguous objects were used. In general, Ames found that—no matter what object he placed in the apparatus—the individual subject was able to make definite and reliable settings.

The general conclusion reached by Ames as a result of these observations was that the object was set at a distance appropriate to the physical size the subject assumed it to be, which Ames labeled its "assumed size." Ames postulated that this assumed size was in the nature of a mean value of the various sizes of the object which the individual had encountered in the course of his previous experiences. In the case of objects such as playing cards, the range of these sizes would be extremely narrow and one would expect very great interindividual consistency. In the case of leaves, the variability is much greater. With ambiguous objects such as a blob of cotton, a piece of paper, a piece of string, etc., one would expect the range of sizes encountered to be very great and to vary considerably from individual to individual. Nevertheless, in all cases the same general principle was found to apply.

The work originally stimulated by these findings and conclusions was primarily aimed at verifying and elaborating the observations themselves in order to provide a more extensive experimental basis upon which the conclusions and generalizations might rest. Ames's original observations were essentially of a qualitative nature, although capable of being translated into quantitative terms. Ittelson [20] undertook a controlled quantitative replication, using an elaborate modification of Ames's original apparatus. Of the number of variables manipulated, the size and the meaning of the objects being observed are of interest in the present discussion. Specifically, distance judgments were obtained for two different sizes (in a ratio of 2:1) for three different objects, a playing card, a piece of white paper cut in the form of a diamond, and a piece of white paper cut in the form of an ink-blot-type shape. The results were completely confirmatory of the original observations. All subjects made reliable settings for all six objects. The playing-card settings were almost perfectly predictable in terms of normal playing-card size. There was, of course, no basis for predicting the settings for the other two sets of objects. However, as predicted in these cases, interindividual variability was greater than for the playing card. Consistency within each individual subject, however, continued to be quite high, although somewhat lower than for the playing cards. The general findings and conclusions were in accord with those described above for Ames's earlier work.

Many directions for inquiry are immediately suggested. Some have not as yet even been approached, others only sketchily and imperfectly explored. Illustrative examples of topics stemming from this work will be presented. For example, it is implicit in the above findings that the identical external situation will be perceived in different ways if the observer attributes different meanings to it. This intriguing possibility stimulated Hastorf [17] to an experiment using a modification of the original Ames apparatus in which suggestion was utilized to alter the meaning of otherwise identical stimulus objects. Specifically, Hastorf had his subjects make distance settings of a white rectangle and a white circle. Settings for the rectangle were made under two conditions: in the one case it was described to the subject as a calling card, while in the second case it was described as a legal-size envelope. Similarly the white circle was at one time labeled a "ping-pong ball," and at another time a "billiard ball." The prediction that these changes in suggested meaning would alter the perception of an otherwise identical situation was borne out by the results. Although the settings were not exactly predictable from the suggested meanings, there were significant changes in the directions predicted.

In another experiment directed at the same general question, Ittelson [19] had subjects compare two stimulus configurations which were geometrically identical, but which differed in the meanings attributed to various elements. A wrist watch, a playing card, and a magazine cover, all of their normal size, were matched by three playing cards, two of which were of unusual sizes, one the exact size and shape of the wrist watch, the other the exact size and shape of the magazine cover. These two sets of objects (watch, card, and magazine, and three playing cards), geometrically identical, were perceived as being quite different. In fact, what was perceived was predictable from a knowledge of the sizes of the objects derived from their meanings. The general conclusion drawn from these two experiments was that the stimulus conditions include the subjective meaning of the stimulus in the individual observer in terms of his previous experience with similar stimulus situations.

The role of previous experience in all of the above experiments, however, is only inferred rather than directly observed. W. M. Smith [42] undertook to make experience with the objects being observed a specifically manipulated variable. The general structure of his experiment, using a modification of the Ames thereness-thatness apparatus, consisted of obtaining distance judgments for a set of objects before and after an interpolated experience with these objects, specifically designed to alter the sizes the observers might attribute to them. For this purpose, he used geometrical shapes, one of which was carried through as a control object, while the others were used in the interpolated experience. The subjects made initial distance settings on all the shapes to be used. They were then divided into groups, depending upon their initial settings—all subjects making settings consistent with large objects were grouped together, for example. The various groups were then given experience with similar objects, but of sizes different from those derived from the original settings. This interpolated experience, emphasizing a careful observation and manipulation of the sizes of the geometrical shapes, was structured as a group competitive game to maximize the interest and involvement of the subjects. Following this, all subjects again repeated their initial settings. The results were in the predicted direction, with the second settings shifting in the directions derived from the sizes utilized in the interpolated-experience condition. In this experiment, then, specific experiences with an object were shown to affect the way the object was perceived.

The fact that assumed size derived from past experience plays a role in depth perception may be taken to be demonstrated by the preceding sequence of experiments. How important is this factor, however, compared to the other variables and cues involved? Two experiments stimulated by an interest in this question will be described. Slack [38] was interested in assessing the importance of familiar size in a situation in which all other normal cues were present. He had his subjects judge the size of familiar objects, which were constructed to be considerably off-size, in the context of normal everyday space perception. In order to achieve this, he had his subjects judge the sizes of chairs viewed at different distances. The chairs were constructed to be very much larger or very much smaller than normal chairs. A normal chair was used as a control object. The viewing conditions consisted of an out-of-doors situation in which, presumably, all the usual space cues were normally operative. He found that even under these optimum viewing conditions (optimum in the sense that one might expect maximal accuracy) the familiar size of the objects had a significant influence on the perception. Slack concluded that familiar size, far from being an esoteric and ephemeral cue produced in the laboratory only fleetingly and with difficulty, is a normally operative cue which must be taken into account in any analysis of everyday space perception.

A different approach to the same general question was used by Ittelson and Ames [23] in investigating the role of accommodation and convergence in relation to familiar size. Their basic experiment consisted of measuring accommodation while observing an object at a fixed distance under conditions in which its apparent distance was varied by means of a familiar size cue. Familiar size proved to be sufficiently stronger than any accommodation effect, so that apparent distance was relatively easily altered even in very near ranges under which accommodation is greatly affected. But the much more interesting and important finding was that the change of apparent distance of an object at a physically constant distance altered the accommodation of the eye viewing the object. This finding and others in the same set of experiments was broadly interpreted in the context of the role of physiological mechanisms in perception. In the present context of this paper, however, we are interested in it only as a further demonstration of the fact that familiar size represents a cue is sufficiently significant so that it must be taken into account in relation to other cues in the perceptual situation.

The experiments cited to this point, all of which were stimulated by the original work of Ames with the thereness-thatness apparatus, have been directed in one way or another at the consideration of size as a cue in space perception. Another series of experiments can be cited which were concerned with a rather different aspect of the problem. These experiments have accepted the facts and conclusions outlined above and have used them as a means for developing a technique for studying personality and motivational factors in perception. The rationale underlying all of these experiments can be stated quite simply.

If, as has been demonstrated, the apparent distance settings under the conditions initially developed by Ames depend upon a size which the observer attributes to the object being viewed, then it is a reasonable hypothesis that this size will, among other factors, be influenced by personality and motivational considerations. All of these studies, then, postulate that the size-distance setting an observer will make when viewing a particular object will be influenced by the relationship between that object and the observer.

The experiment of Kaufer, reported in Ittelson and others [25], is an interesting illustrative case. Using a modification of the Ames apparatus, he had a large number of neuropsychiatric patients of mixed diagnostic categories make distance settings for a number of relatively unstructured objects chosen to have a minimum of direct relationship to the previous experiences of the observers with respect to size, and yet to have more or less specific and consistent meanings. For this purpose, he chose some of the Twichell-Allen three-dimensional projective forms. In the part of Kaufer's rather elaborate study which is of direct relevance in the present context, he had his subjects simply make distance settings on six of these objects. He also presented complete psychological test materials for each of his subjects to a group of three experienced clinical psychologists. These psychologists were asked to decide on a very gross description of the personality dynamics of each subject. Specifically, they were required to decide for each subject whether or not the major personality characteristic could be described as a moving toward other people or a moving away from other people. In this way, Kaufer obtained a group of "moving-away" subjects and a group of "moving-toward" subjects. His hypothesis was that the two groups would make significantly different distance settings with the same objects. Specifically, he expected the moving-toward group in general to perceive the objects as closer and the moving-away group to see them as farther away. This expectation was borne out by the results, and Kaufer concluded that the general personality dynamics of the observer play a significant role in determining his size-distance perceptions.

In another somewhat analogous experiment, Abramson postulated that if one could change the emotional significance of the object being viewed, the size-distance perception would also be changed. With this purpose he had his subjects make distance settings, again on the Ames apparatus, using a selection of reproductions of the TAT cards. The experimental group made these settings before and after they had verbalized stories about the cards, while a control group went through the same procedure without the verbalization. Abramson predicted and found that the verbalization of the story altered the apparent size-distance settings of the cards.

In another series of related experiments, the effective relationship between the observer and the object being viewed was made the specific variable for study. This was accomplished by using photographs of faces as the objects being judged. The effective significance was varied either by changing the expression on the photographed face, or by using photographs of specific individuals. G. H. Smith [40], for example, found that size-distance settings of faces seen as pleasant were different from settings of similar faces seen as unpleasant or unfriendly. In a further study, Smith [41] found that these differences in settings of faces were also influenced by the general personality adjustment of the subject making the settings. Another series of experiments utilizing photography of faces is reported briefly [25, 26]. Here photographs of specific individuals of known relationships to the observers were used. In one case, for example, the observers were members of a group therapy group and made size-distance settings of photographs of other members of the group. In another study, the subjects were all living on a psychiatric ward and made settings of photographs of fellow ward mates. The affective relationship between the subject and the individual whose photograph he was setting was determined in the first case by the judgment of the group therapist, and in the second case by a sociometric analysis. In both experiments, the prediction that the size-distance settings would be influenced by the affective relationship between the subjects and the person whose photograph he was setting was borne out by the results.

This group of experiments thus briefly summarized illustrates the way a particular group of investigators taking off on the work of Ames have used the size-distance relationship as a technique for the study of motivational factors in perception.

Before leaving the size-distance question, it should be pointed out that Ames and all the investigators following him in this line of inquiry have either explicitly or implicitly assumed that the apparent size-distance relationships have in fact reflected the physical size-distance relationships. In its simplest form, this assumption states that the relationship between perceived size and perceived distance will be the same as that determined by the physical relationship between the visual angle, the physical size of the object being viewed, and the physical distance of this object. Kilpatrick and Ittelson [31], in discussing this "invariance" hypothesis, pointed out that this relationship usually correctly describes the experimentally obtained data. However, they point out that the invariance hypothesis, in addition to being used for description, also has frequently been invoked as explanation. By reference to the literature and through an experiment on their own, they point out that the invariance hypothesis is violated frequently enough in actual observations to make this use as an explanation of perceptual phenomena extremely dubious.

A more recent study of the utilization of the invariance hypothesis in describing and interpreting data obtained with the Ames thereness-thatness apparatus was undertaken by Meyerson and Ittelson. Their subjects made distance settings using an undersized playing card. The subjects were then shown an oversized card with the suggestion that the card they were actually viewing in the test situation was, in fact, of the same size. They then repeated the setting with the original undersized card. Immediately following these settings, the subjects chose—from a graded set ranging from extremely small to extremely large—cards representing their idea of a normal playing-card size, as well as cards representing the apparent size of the cards they thought they had been dealing with in the various parts of the experiment. The data were analyzed in terms of the invariance hypothesis to see whether the apparent size-distance relationships were consistent with the physical size-distance relationships. In general, Meyerson and Ittelson found that the invariance hypothesis held. For example, a subject who saw the playing card he was setting as being very large would see it as being farther away. In most cases, the quantitative relationships were almost exactly those predicted by the invariance hypothesis. However, individual cases of gross deviation from the invariance hypothesis were also obtained.

The Rotating Trapezoid

Beyond doubt, the most widely known and extensively discussed of all the Ames demonstrations in perception is the rotating trapezoid. Literally hundreds are distributed at educational and research institutions throughout the world and, through the medium of television, literally millions of people have had the opportunity of watching the trapezoid perform its strange gyrations. Ames himself considered the trapezoid as being one of his most significant contributions and derived from it evidence supporting many of the theoretical points outlined in the previous section. In a detailed analysis, Ames [5] presented his explanations and interpretations of this apparatus which he had created.

Among the many fascinating and important observations to be made with the rotating trapezoid, the following probably represent those considered by him to be most important. First, the appearance of the trapezoid depends on assumptions the observer makes regarding the actual shape and other characteristics it possesses. For example, Ames stressed the importance of the assumption of rectangularity in order to account for the apparent oscillation of the trapezoid. Second, and closely related to the first point, the appearance of objects seen in the context of the trapezoid also depend upon assumptions the observer makes regarding the nature of these objects. Third, the rotating trapezoid provides a perceptual situation involving many complex perceptual conflicts. Ames, for example, points out size changes in conflict with the apparent direction of the movement of the trapezoid as well as many other examples of conflict. Fourth, marked individual differences in the perception of the trapezoid can be observed. Ames not only believed that the total sequence of perceptions involved in continuous rotation of the trapezoid varied from individual to individual, but he also particularly emphasized that the perceived time relationships differed for individuals viewing the trapezoid from different points in space. Fifth, the rotating trapezoid, together with objects associated with it, offers a remarkable example of the perception of events which are directly contrary to all the experiences of the viewer. He sees things happening which he knows are, in fact, impossible.

Each of these points and others has led to controversy and experimentation which will not be summarized here. Rather, we will simply describe two illustrative experiments deriving from the first and second points listed above. The statement that the apparent movement of the trapezoid depends upon the assumption of rectangularity made by the observer was studied experimentally in a cross-cultural investigation conducted by Allport and Pettigrew [3]. By utilizing subjects from a culture which emphasizes circular rather than rectangular structures, they hoped to alter the assumptions made by the subject about the trapezoid. Specifically, if the assumption of rectangularity is not made, the prediction is that rotation rather than oscillation will be reported. The data turned out to be equivocal, partially confirming and partially contradicting the hypothesis. The interpretation of these data has been a matter of controversy. Slack [39], after a detailed analysis, questioned the concept of a "circular culture," and concludes that in the light of the dubious status of this concept, the data can best be interpreted as supporting the assumptive hypothesis.

The general question of the role of assumptions in determining the apparent properties of objects seen in the context of the trapezoid was studied by Kilpatrick. Out of a series of experiments, perhaps the most dramatic concerned the appearance of a rod placed through the center of the trapezoid. Kilpatrick noted two major modes of observation reported by the subjects. The rod was either reported as straight and "cutting through" the trapezoid, or it was reported as flexible and "bending around" the trapezoid. In the experiment, Kilpatrick showed his subjects what was ostensibly the rod subsequently to be placed in the trapezoid. Subjects shown a steel rod reported the rod in the trapezoid to be straight and cutting through, while subjects shown a rubber tube reported the rod in the trapezoid to be flexible and bending around. In all cases, of course, the actual rod in the trapezoid was identical. These results were interpreted as being in support of the general concept of the role of assumptions as outlined in the preceding section.

Aniseikonic Lenses

Although less well known to the general public, Ames's discovery of aniseikonia is considered by many to be his most significant single contribution to knowledge and certainly stands as one of the landmarks in the history of physiological optics. Ames's contributions in this area and in the specific context of the theory of binocular vision are reported elsewhere in this series, and will not be discussed at this point. Rather, we will be concerned with a series of studies stimulated by Ames's work in aniseikonia, but proceeding along a somewhat different line from those earlier described.

In a very real sense, experimental studies in perception from a transactional point of view can be traced to their origin in Ames's [4] paper dealing with the perception of commonplace environments while wearing aniseikonic lenses. In this paper, Ames reports his own observations while wearing aniseikonic lenses in a variety of different situations. Out of a large number of such observations, perhaps two major conclusions can be indicated. First, the appearance of the commonplace environments could not be predicted solely on the basis of stereoscopic disparities introduced by the aniseikonic lenses. Second, the actual appearance of the situation seemed to be influenced by the nature of the surroundings being viewed and the nature of the monocular space cues present in addition to the disparities introduced.

It is the second point that stimulated a series of experiments by Wittreich and others, studying the apparent distortion of persons viewed through the aniseikonic glasses. The specific focus of interest in all of these studies was the relationship between the observer and the person or persons being viewed. Actually, Wittreich's original report [46] utilized the Ames distorted-room situation rather than the aniseikonic glasses. However, in relevant respects, these two situations can be considered as comparable, and Wittreich's remaining work was done with the lenses. Wittreich's original report can be taken as representative of a whole class of observations. A female subject veiwing her husband in a situation productive of perceptual distortion reported that he appeared less distorted than did other people in the same situation. This observation regarding the apparent resistance to distortion of spouses was extended by Wittreich [47] to mutilated or apparently mutilated persons, and by Wittreich and Radcliffe [49] to authority figures. This work and other later findings are described by Wittreich [48] in a general summary article. The broadest conelusion from the data of these varied experiments is that the greater the importance of the person being viewed, the less will be the apparent distortion when viewed through aniseikonic glasses.

The preceding experiments utilized the aniseikonic glasses as a technique for studying certain motivational factors in perception. Another series of experiments made somewhat similar use of an observation made by Ames in connection with the aniseikonic glasses, which in turn repeated an earlier observation by Wheatstone with the pseudoscope.

The apparent distortion which is finally perceived when looking through the pseudoscope or through aniseikonic glasses does not appear immediately; rather, it takes place gradually over a fairly extended period of time. Out of a large number of experiments dealing with this particular phenomenon, two will be described which deal with the influence of psychological stress upon the duration of this time lag. Block [8] had subjects view the Ames "leaf room" (a small room lined with leaves) through aniseikonic glasses and measured the time taken for the distortion to become fully apparent under stress conditions and under nonstress conditions. Block used a real-life stress situation by utilizing as subjects surgical patients initially seen immediately preoperatively (i.e., under stress) and finally postoperatively (i.e., under reduced stress). Findings with this group were compared with a control group performing under nonstress conditions in both cases. A similar study was conducted by Roth, using, in this case, college students and an artificially induced stress situation. Finding in the two experiments were comparable. In both, the effect of stress was to increase the time taken for the resolution of the perceptual situation and the attainment of the final stabilized perception.

A quite different and novel utilization of the aniseikonic glasses as an experimental technique was introduced by McCarthy [32]. With two subjects viewing the same external situation through different aniseikonic lenses, he created a miniature situation in which two people perceive the same situation differently. He then involved them in an interpersonal verbal exchange oriented around a description of what they were observing. He was concerned with two aspects of the situation; first, the influence of the differing perceptions on the nature and content of their interrelationship; and second, the influence of their verbal exchange on their subsequent perceptions. He found, for example, that tendencies to minimize or compromise the perceptual differences in the verbal exchange were reflected in actual changes in the apparent distortion introduced by the aniseikonic glasses bringing the perception to a more close agreement.

It would be inappropriate to conclude these brief references to experiments in aniseikonic distortion without some reference to the question of long-term adaptation to such distortion. Early experiments involving wearing aniseikonic lenses for extended periods of time, reported elsewhere in the series, were interpreted as showing that such long-term adaptation did not occur. Unchallenged and almost unmentioned for a number of years, these conclusions have stood in implicit contradiction to a number of other conclusions made in this area.

At this point, it will simply be noted for the record that in recent unpublished experiments, Engel has reopened the question of long-term adaptation to aniseikonic distortion. Although his findings are as yet merely suggestive, by utilizing evidence from a wide variety of sources he is gradually accumulating data which seem to support the hypothesis that long-term adaptation can and does occur. If this should turn out to be the case, this area will undoubtedly represent an exciting and important field for experimentation in the future.

Binocular Rivalry

The problems of binocular rivalry were reopened for transactional experimentation by the observations of Engel [15, 16] regarding the role of meaning in the binocular fusion of dissimilar pictures. Prior to Engel's work, the resolution of binocularly presented images which were different to the two eyes was considered to be determined entirely by structural properties. In general, if the images were sufficiently similar in structure, it was believed they would be fused, while if they were sufficiently different, binocular rivalry or an alternation first of one image and then another was to be expected. Engel's work quite clearly demonstrated that, while structural properties certainly need to be considered, the role of content or meaning of the figures was also an important factor in determining the nature of the binocular resolution and, indeed, could in certain circumstances overcome very strong structural characteristics. Engel's work has been amply summarized by him and by Ittelson and Slack [26]; only a very brief indication of his work and some of the experiments growing out of it will be presented here. Engel's original findings were basically derived from three different types of presentations. First, with two different faces presented, one to each eye, he reported that the binocularly perceived face is a composite, selectively constructed out of the two in such a way that the perceived face has many apparent characteristics which cannot be directly derived from the features of either of the two presented faces, and that the perceived face is experienced by most observers as being particularly pleasing and attractive. Second, using two faces once again, one presented upright and the other presented inverted, the correctly presented face dominated the binocular resolution, thus ruling out the factor of structural properties. Third, where the binocular presentation contained emotionally acceptable material presented to one eye and emotionally unacceptable material presented to the other eye, the emotionally acceptable material tended to predominate.

This bare statement of Engel's major original observations does not do justice to the many fascinating qualitative as well as quantitative findings in his early publications as well as in later unpublished work. It does serve, however, to illustrate the finding that even such an apparently physiologically rooted process as binocular resolution can be influenced by meanings and past experiences. This finding has been extended by a number of experiments. Hastorf [17], for example, has essentially replicated Engel's study with the correct and inverted faces, thus providing independent corroboration of the role of meaning as opposed to structure. Adlerstein [2] reports a modified stereoscope suitable for binocular viewing of two human faces, thus replicating some of Engel's findings eliminating the intervention of photographs. Belloff and Belloff [7] compared the binocularly perceived face composed of one photograph of a stranger together with a photograph of the self. They report that the composite containing the unrecognized self was rated more highly than composites of two strangers. Bagby [6] and Pettigrew and Allport [34] both studied the binocular resolution of pairs of photographs, one of which was culturally familiar and acceptable and the other was culturally unfamiliar and unacceptable. In general, the findings indicate a tendency to perceive the culturally acceptable presentation.

A related but distinct finding of Engel involves the following sequence of presentations: first, a photograph of a face is presented to one eye, with the other eye dark; second, a photograph of another face is presented to the other eye by gradually increasing its illumination, at the same time maintaining the original face presented to the other eye unchanged. When the condition of binocular rivalry is reached, that is, when both faces are presented equally illuminated, the second face is maintained constant and the third step of the procedure is initiated: the illumination of the original face is gradually reduced until it is finally completely dark. Engel reported that, under these circumstances, the effect of the second face, thus gradually introduced, is much less, i.e., the binocular resolution shows much less influence from this second presentation than would be the case if they were both presented equally illuminated initially. Indeed, many subjects reported—even when the original face was completely removed from the field, and they were actually looking at the second face—that they were still seeing the original face unchanged. This rather remarkable observation, qualitatively reported by Engel, was made the subject of an extensive investigation by Seidenberg and Ittelson [36]. Their findings substantially confirm Engel's original report and provided certain additional observations. The extent to which the second face intrudes into the binocular resolution was shown to depend in part upon the meanings attributed to the face and attitudes of the observer toward these meanings (e.g., white-Negro or male-female pairs). Other contributing factors were the structural differences between these faces and the previous experiences of the observer with such presentations and his expectations regarding them.

This brief sampling of studies dealing with the role of content on the binocular resolution of dissimilar figures not only illustrates the kind of findings that can be obtained under these conditions, but perhaps suggests that this line of inquiry will be more actively pursued in the immediate future.

Perceived Movement

The perception of movement is one of the most interesting and difficult areas of study in visual perception. While it has not been extensively investigated by the group of experimenters referred to in this paper, sufficient work has been done to merit separate mention of this category. Many of the Ames demonstrations involve the perception of movement. The rotating trapezoid, of course, has already been referred to. Additional demonstrations are described in Ittelson [22] and Kilpatrick and Ittelson [30]. In general these demonstrations involve an extension of the basic approach indicated with regard to the static characteristics of space perception. They show that a variety of perceived movements can be produced by objective movements quite different in both direction and speed. Some of the factors studied are assumptions the observer makes regarding the nature of the object, the role of the context within which the object is perceived, etc. Ittelson [21], for example, studied some of the characteristics and determinants of radial motion, i.e., motion apparently directed toward or away from the observer, produced by changing size. Under optimum conditions, such movement cannot be distinguished from real movement, and the apparent direction, speed, and distance of the movement are primarily determined by the assumptions the observer makes regarding the size and other characteristics of the objects being perceived.

Stroboscopic movement was studied as part of a larger study in which Toch [44] investigated the following basic phenomenon: A square is illuminated briefly, followed by a brief illumination of two adjacent flanking squares. Under optimum conditions, the initially presented center square is not seen, and the observer reports only the flashes of the two outside squares. Toch showed that both structural and content variables are important in determining the occurrence of this report. This phenomenon is closely related to that of apparent movement, and a further study by Toch and Ittelson [45] elaborated the role of meaning in such presentations and showed that meaning can be a determinant of the direction of the apparent movement.

Perception of Social and Complex Processes

A logical extension of the transactional experimentation described above is in the direction of social perception, or in the perception of complex processes. Indeed, many of the individual experiments described in the preceding sections are directly relevant to social perception, involving—as they do—perception of persons, of social situations, etc. These will not be repeated here; rather, it will be indicated that an additional line of experimentation has been undertaken in which laboratory studies have been attempted. Together with these few empirical investigations, a number of theoretical papers indicating possibilities for empirical approaches to the problems of social perception have also been presented from the general transactional orientation. The earlier experiments dealing with social and person perception from a transactional point of view have been summarized in some detail by Ittelson and Slack [26] and by Cantril [11].

Cantril has attempted to use public-opinion-polling techniques to obtain data relevant to transactional views. Buchanan and Cantril [10], for example, report data on the way peoples of one country perceive those of other countries, while Cantril [12] studies the perception of social events in regard to which the individual is essentially powerless, but which he wishes to oppose. In both of these studies, the attempt is made to interpret the data along perceptual lines consistent with transactional theory.

A more limited, but perhaps more directly relevant, empirical study was reported by Cantril and Hastorf [14] when they studied the different perceptions of an athletic event by partisans of the two opposing sides. Their most general conclusions—in addition to the finding that the two sets of partisans in many ways perceived different situations—was that the exact nature of what really happened cannot be determined and actually presents a misleading fiction.

In this section we have attempted to present a sampling of experiments deriving from the transactional approach in order to indicate the nature of transactional perceptual experimentation and the kinds of data developed by these experiments. With this in mind, experiments covering the range of such work have been briefly reported. However, this singling out for emphasis of a particular group of experiments conducted by a particular group of individuals is not intended to suggest that a transactional approach to perception is the exclusive property of a few individuals, nor that it is outside of or contradictory to many long-time trends in perceptual theory. Quite the contrary, transactionalism represents historically a logical development out of earlier functional approaches, and transactional writers have drawn not only on their own experiments, but on the entire range of perceptual literature for the empirical foundations of their work. The empirical basis of the transactional approach to perception, therefore, is the entire body of perceptual literature. Many experiments by many different experimenters proceeding from many different theoretical positions add up to the total body of knowledge available to perception theorists today.

SOME EMPIRICAL GENERALIZATIONS

In spite of the great diversity and heterogeneity of approaches to the study of perception, certain general principles have emerged—principles to which most perceptual theorists would probably subscribe and which seem to have relevance to the larger interrelationship issues, both within the field of psychology and other areas of inquiry. These general principles will be only outlined here. They are all implied in the preceding discussion and are explicitly restated here as representing the most general conclusions about perception which can safely be made from the existing data and which have the widest range of implications for other areas of study.

First, *perceiving and acting are intimately related. Perceiving provides the individual with directives for action, with the framework within which action takes place, and with the means for registering the consequences of action.*

Several subprinciples emerge as being part of the general constellation of conclusions defined by this principle.

1. Perceiving is essentially predictive in nature; it is future-oriented in time. Perceiving provides the individual with a set of expectancies for the future, a range of probable outcomes of various possible courses of action.

2. Behavior takes place within a perceived world. Any external event enters into the specific occasion only as it is perceived or experienced, not as it may be conceived as possessing some independent reality.

3. Perceiving involves a constant checking and reevaluating procedure in which the consequences of behavior are themselves perceived and continuously serve to modify the perceptual process. The problem of the veridicality of perception reduces to the question of the extent to which the perceived consequences check with the earlier perceptual prediction.

Second, *perceiving is an active process, actively carried out by the perceiver.*

Again, several directly related subprinciples can be indicated.

1. The total functioning individual enters into the process of perceiving including all his diverse psychological and physiological processes.

2. Perceiving is a creative process in which the individual constructs for himself his own world of experiences. It is neither a passive reaction to nor an objective recording of the environment.

3. Knowledge about the perceptual process can be generalized to other psychological processes. For example, studies of perceptual conflict provide insights into conflict processes in general.

4. The specific individual idiosyncratic characteristics of the perceptual process give information which is relevant to the understanding of that unique individual.

A SAMPLE INTERRELATIONSHIP ISSUE

Let us examine briefly what value these extremely broad and abstract conclusions have for concrete application to a field not usually subsumed under the topic of perception. The whole area of perception-personality interrelationships provides just such an opportunity in a field of study that is being actively pursued today. We can, in the interests of providing a brief sample, confine discussion to a single restricted topic within the broader study, specifically, the relation between perception and psychopathology with emphasis on the psychotherapeutic process.

Interest in the interrelationship between perception and psychopathology is indeed a most ancient one, and the present discussion in this sense fits into a long tradition in human thoughts. Certainly the capacity to see things that no one else sees and to hear things that no one else hears has always been a mark of psychological distinction. Usually, but by no means always, it has been considered pathological. Sometimes, of course, and more frequently in some cultures than in others, quite the opposite occurs and saintly qualities are attributed to the individual so endowed. But whether judged favorably or otherwise, such perceptual anomalies have probably always been thought important. It is not surprising, therefore, that early work in psychopathology put great emphasis on perceptual disorders, describing them in great detail in texts and relying heavily upon them in setting up diagnostic categories.

Today, however, interest in the interrelationships between perception and psychopathology is proceeding in a radically new direction. While the importance of perceptual abnormalities as a clinical problem is by no means underestimated, emphasis is more and more shifting toward perception as a basic psychological process through which we can gain greater understanding of the over-all functioning of the person. And, as we have seen, this shifting emphasis has been brought about largely through growing contact between two initially diverse subjects for inquiry within the science of psychology: the experimental study of perception on the one hand, and the clinical study of personality on the other.

Let us consider the therapeutic situation as the concrete transaction with which we are at the moment concerned. And the word "concrete" is used advisedly; this is the reality with which both therapist and patient must deal. Whitehead's fallacy of "misplaced concreteness" is appropriately considered here when either participant introduces abstractions from outside of the situation and attempts to treat them as if they represented reality. It cannot be emphasized too strongly that from the point of view here presented, the only real concrete situation is the total transaction as it unfolds as an ongoing process.

The characteristics of this transaction are a product of the participants and, more important, the characteristics of the participants are determined by the nature of the transaction. The therapist does not enter as therapist nor the patient as patient, but both as active participants and neither one of them can be defined or studied or known in any way without considering this very fact of their participation.

Each such transaction represents a unique occurrence which cannot be duplicated. The therapist has never been just that therapist, nor the patient just that patient in any other situation. To the extent that the therapist ceases to be a unique participant and seeks to become a generalized therapist or to the extent that the patient seeks to become the generalized patient, the nature of the transaction is altered and the therapeutic value diminished.

This fact of the uniqueness of every transaction had led to a multitude of divergent theories and notions about the nature of the therapeutic process. However, out of this diversity certain general principles have emerged. The first of these we have just referred to. That is the importance of the concrete therapeutic situation. Next, we will consider some of the implications of the way the participants perceive each other within this transaction.

The patient perceives the therapist in terms of all his past experiences, primarily with authority figures and love objects. He brings to the situation all his acquired assumptions about such people and he will in turn base his actions within the therapeutic situations on predictions which he characteristically makes on the basis of these assumptions. The patient successively runs through his whole range of important people as he tries out his entire repertory of assumptions in an effort to find some way of perceiving the therapist which will give him relatively stable directives for acting. And he gradually discovers that such predictions can be made only to the extent that he experiences the therapist as a unique individual uniquely participating in the concrete transaction.

The therapist, in turn, perceives the patient in a variety of ways dependent on his own previous experiences with other patients and other important figures of one sort or another. He must necessarily do this since his own experiences are all he can or does bring to the transaction. However, he also has a greater flexibility in changing his perceptions as they prove inadequate. Danger to therapy stems not from misperceiving the patient—this is inevitable—but from the need to persist in misperceptions. Because the therapist is more closely linked to the concrete transaction, he is less likely to do this. But it should be noted that since the patient is presumably constantly changing, misperceptions by the therapist are not only inevitable, they are desirable. A correct perception of the patient is not a static thing to be acquired once and for all, but rather a constantly changing product of the situation which will always remain to a certain extent elusive as long as the transaction retains its dynamic qualities.

This serves to emphasize the fairly obvious fact that change is the *sine qua non* of therapy. And from the point of view of this paper, change in therapy can be conceptualized as a progressive sequence of perceptual changes. The patient initially changes his perception of the therapist and gradually expands his new ways of perceiving to include other aspects of his world. And since perceptions provide the bases for action, these changing perceptions bring about changing ways of behaving and eventually a whole new mode of acting and experiencing emerges.

What was said earlier about perceptual change, then, can be carried over bodily into this context. First, we must assume that the person who comes for therapy has certain misperceptions of the world about him. And here, by misperceptions, we mean specifically perceptions which give him predictions for actions which do not in turn provide him with the satisfactions he seeks. That is, his perceptions lead to actions which do not, for him, have the consequences he predicts.

In the process of therapy he will change these perceptions through the two processes of perceptual change, initially always in direct, concrete transactional relationship with the therapist. What we have referred to as perceptual reweighting undoubtedly takes place first. Although dramatically different perceptions and, hence, different ways of acting may emerge from this process, there is no basic change in the individual's assumptions but rather a reordering, a reshuffling, a shifting of relative importance of modes of perceiving which he has already brought with him to the occasion. This is probably the kind that occurs in relatively short-term or supportive therapy, in which no basic changes in personality are achieved. The second kind of perceptual change, which we have referred to as perceptual relearning, involves the formation of entirely new and different assumptions. As such, it does in a very real sense involve the creation of something new, something which the patient did not bring with him. It corresponds to the changes which occur in deep therapy with attendant basic personality changes.

All of this implies that the focus of therapy is, as we have previously stated, not inappropriate behavior, but rather inappropriate modes of perceiving. Psychotherapy aims at changing perceptions, not changing overt behavior. Of course, changing perceptions are related to changing actions in the way we have indicated. Changing perceptions lead to new predictions on which actions are based. To the extent these predictions are valid, that these actions provide the experienced consequences the individual seeks—to that extent will they become established as part of that person's characteristic, habitual ways of experiencing the world and acting in it.

So this process of perceptual change involves a never-ending sequence of new perceptions, new directives for acting, new actions, and a reassessment of the perception in terms of the experienced consequences of the action. All of this takes place usually quite gradually and almost entirely without any specific awareness. Characteristically, a patient may become aware of his changed behavior only after it has become a well-established part of his life.

The general problem of therapeutic change, then, can be approached from the standpoint of a theory of perceptual change. Such a theory stems from laboratory findings and must constantly be in contact with experimental procedures. The current interest in the study of person-perception, perceptual learning, perceptual conflict, etc., assures that such contact will be maintained and gives evidence of the vitality of this line of approach.

CONCLUDING NOTE

In concluding, one cannot avoid the impression that current thinking about perception has moved a long way from its conceptual origins and in so doing has departed from what may seem to be the evidence of everyday experience. Perhaps a final note of caution may be sounded. Since every one of us has been perceiving at least as long as we can remember, it is inevitable that each of us has acquired a set of pre-conceived notions as to the nature of perception. The study of per-ception, is, therefore, probably more susceptible than is any other area of scientific inquiry to the danger of being decided in advance of the study itself.

Metaphysical speculations as to the ultimate reality of things are generally avoided in science. However, avoidance does not necessarily eliminate such speculation. It may merely drive it underground. Con-sciously thought out or unconsciously acquired metaphysical presup-positions provide a framework within the limits of which each investigator is closely bound. The advantages of expanding this limiting framework in so far as possible is illustrated by the tremendous advances in the physical sciences attendant upon the changing view of time and space from conditions for the occurrence of physical events to physical events themselves capable of being studied and understood.

Perhaps no aspect of philosophic or scientific endeavor is more sensitive to presuppositions as to the "real" nature of the world than is the study of perception. The reason for this is clear. In so far as any presupposition as to the nature of the observed world independent of the observer is made, to that extent the problem is given an a priori answer and its very nature distorted. To that extent, we cease to ask how the individual perceives his world through the only data available to him —the chaotic and fragmentary data of present experience—and we start to ask rather how these data conform to our preconceived notion as to the nature of things. The belief that the theorist has a source of inside information as to the true nature of things represents the most insidious and most dangerous pitfall in the path of scientific study of perception. Indeed, the whole history of research in perception itself refutes this position. If we have learned anything from the study of perception, it is that we, as perceivers, can never learn the ultimate nature of things. What we can and do acquire is limited knowledge, tentative prognosis on which each individual acts as best he can as he strives to find his own satisfactions in living.

BIBLIOGRAPHICAL NOTE

Special attention is called to the following references on which most of this chapter is based. Some of the material appearing in this chapter was originally prepared for one or another of these works, and the entire chapter actually represents not a new presentation, but rather a summary of material previously available only in scattered sources.

Cantril, H. (Ed.) *The morning notes of Adelbert Ames, Jr.* New Brunswick, N.J.: Rutgers Univer. Press, 1960.

Ittelson, W. H. *The Ames demonstrations in perception.* Princeton: Princeton Univer. Press, 1952.

Ittelson, W. H. *Visual space perception.* New York: Springer, 1960.

Ittelson, W. H., & Kutash, S. B. (Eds.), *Perceptual changes in psychopathology.* New Brunswick, N.J.: Rutgers Univer. Press, 1961.

Kilpatrick, F. P. (Ed.) *Explorations in transactional psychology.* New York: New York Univer. Press, 1961.

REFERENCES

1. Abramson, L. Changes in perception as a result of verbalization. In W. H. Ittelson, et al. (Eds.), *Perceptual changes in psychopathology.* New Brunswick, N.J.: Rutgers Univer. Press, 1961.
2. Adlerstein, A. M. The humascope: a modified stereoscope. *J. Psychol.,* 1958, **45**, 109–113.
3. Allport, G. W., & Pettigrew, T. F. Cultural influence on the perception of movement: the trapezoidal illusion among Zulus. *J. abnorm. soc. Psychol.,* 1957, **55**, 104–113.
4. Ames, A., Jr. Binocular vision as affected by relations between uniocular stimulus patterns in commonplace environments. *Amer. J. Psychol.,* 1946, **59**, 333–357.
5. Ames, A., Jr. Visual perception and the rotating trapezoidal window. *Psychol. Monogr.,* 1951, **65**, No. 14 (Whole No. 324).
6. Bagby, J. A cross cultural study of perceptual predominance in binocular rivalry. *J. abnorm. soc. Psychol.,* 1957, **54**, 331–334.
7. Belloff, H., & Belloff, J. Unconscious self-evaluation using a stereoscope. *J. abnorm. soc. Psychol.,* 1959, **59**, 275–278.

8. Block, D. The effect of anxiety on the resolution of a perceptual conflict. In W. H. Ittelson et al. (Eds.). *Perceptual changes in psychopathology.* New Brunswick, N.J.: Rutgers Univer. Press, 1961.
9. Brunswik, E. *Perception and the representative design of psychological experiments.* Berkeley, Calif.: Univer. of Calif. Press, 1956.
10. Buchanan, W., & Cantril, H. *How nations see each other.* Urbana, Ill.: Univer. of Ill. Press, 1953. Chap. 9.
11. Cantril, H. Perception and interpersonal relations. *Amer. J. Psychiat.,* 1957, **114,** 119–126.
12. Cantril, H. *The politics of despair.* New York: Basic Books, 1958.
13. Cantril, H., Ames, A., Jr., Hastorf, A. H., & Ittelson, W. H. Psychology and scientific research. *Science,* 1949, **110,** 461–464; 491–497; 517–522.
14. Cantril, H., & Hastorf, A. H. They saw a game: a case study. *J. abnorm. soc. Psychol.,* 1954, **29,** 129–134.
15. Engel, E. The role of content in binocular resolution. *Amer. J. Psychol.,* 1956, **69,** 87–91.
16. Engel, E. Binocular fusion of dissimilar figures. *J. Psychol.,* 1958, **46,** 53–57.
17. Hastorf, A. H. The influence of suggestion on the relationship between stimulus size and perceived distance. *J. Psychol.,* 1950, **29,** 195–217.
18. Hastorf, A. H., & Myro, G. The effect of meaning on binocular rivalry. *Amer. J. Psychol.,* 1959, **72,** 393–400.
19. Ittelson, W. H. The constancies in perceptual theory. *Psychol. Rev.,* 1951, **58,** 285–294.
20. Ittelson, W. H. Size as a cue to distance: static localization. *Amer. J. Psychol.,* 1951, **64,** 54–67.
21. Ittelson, W. H. Size as a cue to distance: radial motion. *Amer. J. Psychol.,* 1951, **64,** 188–202.
22. Ittelson, W. H. *The Ames demonstrations in perception.* Princeton, N.J.: Princeton Univer. Press, 1952.
23. Ittelson, W. H., & Ames, A., Jr. Accommodation, convergence, and their relation to apparent distance. *J. Psychol.,* 1950, **30,** 43–62.
24. Ittelson, W. H., & Cantril, H. *Perception: a transactional approach.* New York: Doubleday, 1954.
25. Ittelson, W. H., Kutash, S. B., Abramson, L., & Seidenberg, B. (Eds.), *Perceptual changes in psychopathology.* New Brunswick, N.J.: Rutgers Univer. Press, 1961.
26. Ittelson, W. H., & Slack, C. W. The perception of persons as visual objects. In R. Taguiri & L. Petrullo (Eds.), *Person perception and interpersonal behavior.* Stanford, Calif.: Stanford Univer. Press, 1958.
27. Kaufer, G. Personality orientation and size-distance perception. In W. H. Ittelson et al. (Eds.), *Perceptual changes in psychopathology.* New Brunswick, N.J.: Rutgers Univer. Press, 1961.
28. Kilpatrick, F. P. Some aspects of the role of assumptions in perception. Unpublished doctoral dissertation, Princeton Univer., 1950.
29. Kilpatrick, F. P. Two processes in perceptual learning. *J. exp. Psychol.,* 1954, **47,** 362–370.

30. Kilpatrick, F. P., & Ittelson, W. H. Three demonstrations involving the visual perception of movement. *J. exp. Psychol.*, 1951, **42**, 394–402.
31. Kilpatrick, F. P., & Ittelson, W. H. The size-distance invariance hypothesis. *Psychol. Rev.*, 1953, **60**, 223–231.
32. McCarthy, G. Small group interaction and perceptual changes. In W. H. Ittelson et al. (Eds.), *Perceptual changes in psychopathology*. New Brunswick, N.J.: Rutgers Univer. Press, 1961.
33. Meyerson, B., & Ittelson, W. H. Apparent size and invariance hypothesis (unpublished manuscript).
34. Pettigrew, T. F., Allport, G. W., & Barnett, E. O. Binocular resolution and perception of race in South Africa. *Br. J. Psychol.*, 1958, **49**, 265–278.
35. Roth, A. Some effects of experimentally induced stress on perception. In W. H. Ittelson et al. (Eds.), *Perceptual changes in psychopathology*. New Brunswick, N.J.: Rutgers Univer. Press, 1961.
36. Seidenberg, B., & Ittelson, W. H. The perception of faces: a further study of the Engel effect (unpublished manuscript).
37. Slack, C. W. Feedback theory and the reflex arc concept. *Psychol. Rev.*, 1955, **62**, 263–267.
38. Slack, C. W. Familiar size as a cue to size in the presence of conflicting cues. *J. exp. Psychol.*, 1956, **52**, 194–198.
39. Slack, C. W. Critique on the interpretation of cultural differences in the Ames trapezoid. *Amer. J. Psychol.*, 1959, **72**, 127–131.
40. Smith, G. H. Size-distance judgements of human faces (projected images). *J. gen. Psychol.*, 1953, **49**, 45–64.
41. Smith, G. H. Size-distance settings as indicative of personal adjustment. *J. soc. Psychol.*, 1954, **40**, 165–172.
42. Smith, W. M. Past experience and perception: a study of the influence of past experience on apparent size and distance. *Amer. J. Psychol.*, 1952, **65**, 389–403.
43. Stevens, S. S. Mathematics, measurement and psychophysics. In S. S. Stevens (Ed.), *Handbook of experimental psychology*. New York: Wiley, 1951. Pp. 1–49.
44. Toch, H. H. The perceptual elaboration of stroboscopic presentations. *Amer. J. Psychol.*, 1956, **69**, 345–358.
45. Toch, H. H., & Ittelson, W. H. The role of past experience in apparent movement: a revaluation. *Br. J. Psychol.*, 1956, **47**, 195–207.
46. Wittreich, W. J. The Honi phenomenon: a case of selective perceptual distortion. *J. abnorm. soc. Psychol.*, 1952, **47**, 705–712.
47. Wittreich. W. J. The influence of simulated mutilation upon the perception of the human figure. *J. abnorm. soc. Psychol.*, 1955, **51**, 493–495.
48. Wittreich, W. J. Visual perception and personality. *Scient. Amer.*, 1959, **200**, 56–60.
49. Wittreich, W. J., & Radcliffe, K. B., Jr. Differences in the perception of an authority figure and a non-authority figure by Navy recruits. *J. abnorm. soc. Psychol.*, 1956, **53**, 383–384.

NAME INDEX

Page numbers in boldface type indicate bibliography references; *n.* indicates footnote reference.

Abood, L. G., 33, **39**
Abramson, H. A., **97**
Abramson, L., 687, **702, 703**
Adams, J., 643, **655**
Adams, P. A., 538, **618**
Ades, H. W., 212, **231, 237, 238, 328,** 354, **375**
Adey, W. R., 134, **155, 375**
Adlerstein, A. M., 693, **702**
Adrian, E. D., 96, **231, 232,** 382, **411,** 436, 437, **477, 478**
Albert, A. E., 371, **375**
Allen, G., **39**
Allen, J., **375**
Allen, W. F., 203, **232**
Allison, A. C., **40**
Allport, G. W., 690, 694, **702,** 704
Alper, R. G., **238**
Altman, J., 191
Amassian, V. E., 341*n.*, **375**
Ames, A., Jr., 674, 682, 683, 684, 685, 686, 688, 689, 690, 691, **702, 703**
Anastasi, A., 20, **40**
Anderson, F. D., 187, 190, **232**
Andrews, T. G., **657**
Anfinsen, C. B., **40**
Anokhin, P. K., 360*n.*, **375**
Aristotle, 54, 89, 110, 381
Arnoult, M. D., 630, 654, **656**
Arrow, K. J., xxxiv, xxxvii
Asch, S., **615**
Ashby, W. R., 631, **655**
Asher, H., 454, **478**
Asratyan, E. A., 360*n.*, **375**
Attneave, F., xxxii, xxxiv, xxxvi, xxxvii, **278,** 619, 654, **655, 656**
Auerbach, S., **115**

Babel, J., **42**
Babinski, J., 102, **115**
Babkin, B. P., 458*n.*, **478**

Bagby, J., 694, **702**
Bagshaw, M., 157
Baikie, A. G., 44
Bailey, D. E., 545, **615**
Bailey, P., 115, 116, 118
Baker, C. P., **618**
Baldwin, E. A., 174, 175, **232**
Bard, P. A., 64, 84, **98, 155,** 184, 228, **232,** 411
Bare, J. K., **411, 414**
Barlow, H. B., 328, 453, **478**
Barlow, J. S., 361, 365, **375**
Barnett, E. O., **704**
Barris, R. W., 191, **232**
Barron, D. H., 79, **96**
Barry, J., **238**
Bartley, S. H., **328**
Bastock, M., **40**
Battersby, W. S., 155, 156, **238**
Bauer, K. H., **40**
Baumgartner, B., 116
Baumgartner, G. B., 116
Baumgartner, R. V., 116
Baxter, D., 107, **117**
Beach, F. A., **40, 96**
Beadle, G. W., **40**
Beale, G. H., 171, **232**
Beare, A. C., 488*n.*, 490
Beck, E. C., 219, **232**
Beebe-Center, J. G., 404, **411**
Beer, B., 235, 330
Beidler, L. M., 385, 387, **411, 413, 415**
Belloff, H., 693, **702**
Belloff, J., 693, **702**
Bender, M. B., 156, **238**
Benedict, R., **40**
Bennett, E. L., 45, 47, **236**
Bergin, A. E., **615**
Bergmann, G., 297, 310, **328,** 487, 498, 504, 506, **512**
Berkeley, G., 458

705

Berlin, I., **411**
Berlin, L., **375**
Berlyne, D. E., xxxiv, xxxvi, xxxvii, 640*n.*, **656**
Berman, A. J., **157**
Berman, A. L., **331**
Bernard, C., 58, 226
Bernhard, C. G., 112, **116**, 372, **376**
Bernstein, F., 8
Bernstein, J., 435
Berry, C. M., 187, 190, **232, 235**
Bessel, F. W., 504
Biersdorf, W. R., **512**
Binder, A., **656**
Bindra, D., 403, **411**
Bishop, G. H., 77, **96**, 185, 186. 187, 193, **232, 235**, 266*n.*, 272, **278**, 292, **328**, 343, **376**, 438, **478, 615**
Blackwell, H. R., 301*n.*, **328**
Block, D., 691, **703**
Blough, D. S., 463, 469, 470, 471, 472, **478**, 481
Blum, J. S., 200, 201, **232**
Bode, W., **40**
Bodian, D., **232**
Bohm, E., **116**
Bohr, N., 104, **116**, 229, **232**
Bok, S. T., 105, 106, **116**
Bolles, R. C., 545, **615**
Böök, J. A., **40**
Boost, C., **45**
Boring, E. G., **412**, 420*n.*, 458*n.*, **478**, 528, **615**, 653, **656**
Born, M., 90, **96, 116**
Bosma, J. F., **116**
Boudreau, J. C., **43**
Bouguer, P., 439*n.*
Bowsher, D., 186, **232**
Boyd, W. C., **40**
Boyle, R., 55
Braceland, F. J., **155**
Brachet, J., **40**
Brady, J. V., **412**
Brandon, M. W. G., **40**
Brandt, M. F., **615**
Brazier, M. A. B., **96, 155, 156, 157, 234, 241, 278**, 355, 356, 361, **375, 376, 379**, 433*n.*, **478**
Brehme, K. S., **40**
Bremer, F., 64, 67, 73, **96**
Brennan, W., **155**
Brentano, F., 317
Bridges, C. B., **40**
Bridgman, P. W., 662
Brindley, G. S., 356*n.*, **376**
Brink, F., Jr., 433*n.*, **478**
Broadhurst, P. L., **40**

Brodal, A., 107, **116**
Bromiley, R. B., **329**
Bronk, D. W., 436, 437, **477, 478**
Brookhart, J. M., **98**
Brooks, C. M. C., **234**
Broom, L., **41**
Brown, J. S., 406, **412**
Brown, R. M., 351, 352, **375, 377**
Bruner, J. S., 544, **615**, 640*n.*, 643, **656**
Brunswik, E., 525, 545, **615**, 629, 642, 652, **656**, 678, **703**
Buchanan, W., 696, **703**
Bucy, P. C., 111, **116**, 129, **155, 235**
Bullock, T. H., **376**
Bumke, O., **116**
Burch, G. J., 436
Burt, C., **40**, 171, **232**
Bush, R. R., 485, **512**
Busnel, R. G., 354, **376**
Buswell, G. T., **615**
Butler, R. A., **232**
Bynum, E., **44**

Cajal, R., 282
Cameron, A. T., **412**
Campbell, B. A., 402, **412, 415**
Campbell, D. T., xxxi, xxxii, xxxiv, xxxvi, xxxvii
Campbell, K. H., 399, 400, **415**
Campbell, N. R., 485, 504, **512**
Cannon, J. F., **40**
Cantril, H., 695, 696, **702, 703**
Carlson, F. D., **478**
Carmichael, L., 49, 168, **232**
Carpenter, J. A., **412**
Carpenter, M. B., 191
Carr, R. M., **41**
Carr, W. J., **412**
Carton, A. S., **333**
Caspari, E., **41**
Caton, 59
Cavalli, L. L., **41**
Chambers, R. M., **412**
Chambers, W., 409, **415**
Chambliss, D. J., **656**
Chandler, J. H., **46**
Chang, H. T., **96, 97**, 292, 328
Chang, J. J., 99
Charles, M. S., **48**
Chase, A. M., 445, **480**
Chiang Yee, 573, **615**
Child, I., xxxi, xxxiv, xxxvii
Chiles, W. D., 222, **233**
Chow, K. L., xxxi, xxxiv, **41**, 74*n.*, 158, 211, 212, 214, 216, 221, 223, **233, 234, 238**
Chung, C. S., **41, 45**

Churchman, C. W., 514
Clare, M. H., 232, 266n., 278, 292, 328
Clark, K. E., vi, vii, xv
Clark, S. L., 332
Clark, W. A., Jr., 376
Clark, W. E. LeG., 179, 184, 233
Clausen, J. A., 41
Clemente, C. D., 155
Cline, W., 41
Cobb, S., 615, 617
Cockayne, E. A., 41
Coghill, G. E., 64, 78, 79, 111, 116
Cohen, M. J., 390, 412
Collier, G., 333, 402, 412, 466, 482
Collins, W. F., 188, 233
Comer, P. B., 502, 514
Condillac, E. B. de, 381
Connelly, C. M., 478
Conrad, K., 116
Coombs, J. S., 329
Coppock, H. W., 412
Cornsweet, J. C., 456, 481, 616
Cornsweet, T. N., 456, 478, 481
Costello, R. T., 378, 412
Cotton, J. W., 333, 466, 482
Cottrell, L. S., Jr., 41
Court-Brown, W. M., 44
Covington, M., 47
Cowdrick, 626
Craik, K. J. W., 116, 464, 470, 471, 478
Cranefield, P. F., 234
Creutzfeldt, O., 116, 378
Crossman, E. R. F. W., 376
Crovitz, H., 561, 615
Crowe, F. W., 41
Crozier, W. J., 41
Culbertson, J. T., 654, 656
Cumming, W. W., xxxi, xxxii, xxxiv, xxxvii

Dahlberg, G., 41
Danilevsky, V. Y., 59
Dantzig, T., 475, 478
Dartnall, H. J. A., 438n., 478
Darwin, C., 57, 59, 160, 161, 162, 163, 165, 166, 168, 173, 174, 233
Daston, P., 615
Daves, W., 561, 615
David, P. R., xxxi, xxxiv, 1, 41, 49
Davies, P. W., 331
Davis, H., 234, 329
Davis, R., 371, 376
Davis, R. C., xxxiv, xxxvii, 242, 278
Dawson, G. D., 329
deGroot, J., 155
Delafresnay, J. F., 117, 233
Delgado, J. M. R., 223, 239, 329

Delhagen, J. E., 413
Dempsey, E. W., 182, 237
Dencker, S. J., 41
Denenberg, V. H., 35, 47
Descartes, R., 54, 57, 59, 91
Deutsch, J. A., 412
De Valois, R. L., 329
Dewey, J., 523, 537, 615
Diamond, I. T., xxxi, xxxiv, 155, 158, 188, 189, 192, 193, 194, 205, 232, 234, 617
Dichter, M., 376
Ditchburn, R. W., 431n., 478, 479
Doane, B., 330
Dobzhansky, Th., 41, 48
Dollard, J., 648, 656
Donner, K. O., 472, 479
Doty, R. W., 219, 221, 222, 232, 234, 272, 376
Dow, R. S., 329
Drever, J., 537, 615
Driscoll, K. W., 43
Drucker, P., 71n.
du Bois Reymond, E., 58
Duffy, E., 277n., 278
Duffy, M., 415
Dunlop, C. W., 155, 375
Dunn, L. C., 48
Dürer, A., 594
Durup, G., 376

Eccles, J. C., 116, 234, 284, 292, 329
Edwards, W., 317, 331
Einstein, A., 39, 431, 479
Ellis, J., 99
Ellis, M., 99
Ellis, W. D., 656
Emerson, A. E., 163, 234
Engel, E., 692, 693, 694, 703
Engle, R., 404, 405, 412
Ephrussi, B., 169, 234
Eriksen, C. W., 627, 656
Erismann, T., 536, 537, 590, 615
Erlanger, J., 185, 234, 392, 412, 436, 479
Estes, W. K., 485, 512
Eugster, J., 42
Evarts, E. V., 376
Eysenck, H. J., 42

Fairman, D., 241
Falls, H. F., 42
Fantz, R. L., 238
Faraday, M., 431
Farley, B. G., 367, 376
Fatt, P., 329
Fechner, G. T., 316, 317, 559
Feigl, H., 618

Fender, D. H., 478
Ferguson, A., 512, 513
Ferrier, D., 83, 97
Ferster, C. B., 155
Fessard, A., 376
Field, J., 239, 328, 329, 330, 332, 333, 375, 615, 617, 618
Fisher, G. J., 238
Fishman, I. Y., 412
Fitts, P., xxxiv, xxxvii
FitzGibbon, J. P., 237
Fitzhugh, R., 328, 478
Fizeau, 421
Flanigan, S., 156
Fleming, T. C., 376
Flynn, J. P., 156
Foerster, O., 116
Forbes, 64
Forbes, A., 479
Forssman, H., 42
Foucault, M., 421
Foulds, G. A., 42
Franceschetti, A., 42
Frank, K., 284, 329
Franklin, B., 55
Fraser, C., 46
Fraunhofer, J. V., 428
Freeman, G. L., 278
Freeman, M. Z., 375
French, D., xxxi, xxxiv, xxxvii
French, J. D., 97, 329, 615
Frenkel-Brunswick, E., 459, 479
Freud, S., 154
Friedman, S., 46
Frings, H., 390, 403, 412
Frishkopf, L. S., 329, 330, 376
Frolov, Y. P., 459n., 479
Fry, G. A., 449n., 479
Fuller, J. L., 15, 33, 35, 40, 42, 48
Fulton, J. F., 97, 117, 206, 239, 332, 481
Fuster, J. M., 372, 377

Gaffron, M., xxxii, xxxiv, xxxvi, xxxvii, 515, 524, 536, 537, 560, 562n., 615, 616
Galambos, R., 83, 97, 217, 234, 235, 272, 329, 330, 377, 412, 618, 643, 656
Galanter, E. H., 156, 313, 314n., 315, 329, 333, 490, 514, 624, 626, 631, 656, 659
Galatius-Jensen, F., 42
Galileo, G., 57, 420
Gall, H., 168n., 235
Galton, F., 166, 167, 168, 169, 171, 226, 234
Galvani, L., 55, 433, 434
Gantt, W. H., 61n.

Gardner, L. P., 234
Garner, W. R., 489n., 512, 624, 627, 656
Gasser, H. S., 185, 234, 329, 392, 412, 436, 479
Gautier, M., 45
Gedda, L., 42
Geisler, C. D., 330, 354, 377
Gellerman, L. W., 130
Gellhorn, E., 112, 116
Gendlin, E. T., 616
Gerard, R. W., 34, 39, 155
German, W. J., 206, 239
Gerstein, G. L., 366, 367, 377
Gibson, J. J., 109, 116, 155, 527, 528, 533, 537, 549, 550, 551, 552, 574, 610, 612, 616, 629, 630, 648n., 656, 658
Gilbert, W., 55
Gilmore, J. T., 376
Ginsberg, B. E., 15, 33, 34, 35, 42, 47, 172, 234
Ginsborg, B. L., 479
Giurgea, C., 222, 234
Gladwin, T., 98
Glass, B., 42, 45
Gleitman, H., 658
Goldberg, J. M., 205, 234
Goldiamond, I., 503
Goldscheider, A., 391
Goldschmidt, R., 43
Goldstein, K., 199, 234
Goldstein, M. H., Jr., 351, 352, 354, 377, 378
Goltz, F. C., 83, 111, 116
Gotch, F., 436
Gottschaldt, K., 645
Graham, C. H., vi, xxxii, xxxiv, xxxvii, 297, 310, 330, 441, 442, 479, 480, 483, 484n., 485, 493, 494n., 503, 505, 506, 512, 513, 514, 556, 616, 621, 622, 657
Graham, J. B., 43
Granit, R., 97, 197, 235, 321, 326, 330, 412, 437, 438n., 455, 472, 479
Grassé, P. P., 47, 236
Grastyan, E., 133, 155
Gray, J. A. B., 330, 412
Green, A., 156
Green, D. M., 333
Green, J. D., 155, 413
Greene, J. T., 416
Griffiths, R., 47
Gross, R. T., 43
Grundfest, H., 288, 292, 329, 330
Grüneberg, H., 43
Grüsser, O. J., 116, 377, 378
Grützner, A., 377

Guild, J., 489n., **513**
Guilford, J. P., 297, **330**, 494n., **513**, **657**
Guillemin, E. A., **377**
Guthrie, E. R., 647, 648, **657**, **658**
Gutierrez-Costa, O., 348, 349
Guttman, N., xxxi, xxxii, xxxvii, 400, **413**, 542, **616**

Hagiwara, S., 390, **412**
Hagstrom, E. C., 400, 401, **413**
Haig, C., 445, **480**
Hake, H. W., 627, **656**
Haldane, J. B. S., **43**
Hall, C. S., 15, 35, **43**, 172, **235**
Hall, M., 213, **237**
Hall, V., **239**, **328**, **329**, **330**, **331**, **333**, **375**
Hallowell, A. I., xxxi, xxxiv, xxxvi, xxxvii, xxxviii
Hanbery, J., **237**
Hardy, A. C., 431n., **479**
Hare, C. C., **41**, **42**, **43**, **44**
Hari, Y., **241**
Harlow, H. F., 96, 97, **238**, **239**, 240, 275n., **278**, **333**, **413**, **617**, **618**
Harmon, P. J., **235**
Harriman, A. E., **413**
Harris, D. B., **48**
Harris, H., **43**
Hartline, H. K., **330**, **377**, 437, 438n., 439, 440, 441, 442, 444, 445, 447, 449, 450, 451, 453, 454, 455, **479**, **480**, **481**, **513**
Harvald, B., **43**, **44**
Harvey, W., 174
Hasegawa, Y., **241**
Haslerud, G. M., **155**
Hastorf, A. H., 684, 693, 696, **703**
Hauge, M., **41**, **43**
Haugen, F. P., **98**
Hayek, F. A., **116**
Hayhow, W. R., **235**
Head, H., 188, 199, **235**, 410, **413**
Hearst, E., **235**, **330**
Heath, P., **618**
Hebb, D. O., **43**, 167, **235**, 255, 266, 267, 268, 269, 270, 271, 272, 273, **278**, 409, **413**, 522, 539, 540, **616**, 642, 643, 648, 649, 655, **657**
Hecht, S., **116**, 438n., 444, 445, **480**, 487, 488, 506, 510, **513**, 525, 559, **616**
Heidbreder, E., 642, **657**
Heider, F., **616**
Heisenberg, W., 96, 114
Held, R., 536, 537, **616**

Helm, C., 315, **330**
Helmholtz, H. von, 58, 263, 380, 382, 434, 435, 642, **657**
Helson, H., 309, **330**, **411**, 489n., **513**, 640, **657**
Hendrix, C. E., **155**, **375**
Hensel, H., **413**
Henson, C. O., **377**
Hernández-Peón, R., 97, **330**, 360, **377**, 643, 649, **657**
Herndon, C. N., **43**
Heron, W. T., 14, **43**
Herrick, C. J., 64, 77, **97**, 119, 154, 178, 179, 184, 186, 187, **235**
Herrick, R. M., **513**
Herschel, J. F. W., 428, 429
Hertz, P., 431
Hess, E. H., **235**, 645, **657**
Hick, W. E., **377**
Hilgard, E. R., xxxiv, 137, **155**, 460n., **480**
Hirsch, J., **43**
Hirszfeld, H., 4
Hirszfeld, L., 4
Hoch, P. H., **44**
Hochberg, J. E., 629, 637, 646, **657**
Hodgkin, A. L., **480**
Hodgson, E. S., **235**
Hogben, L., **43**
Hollaender, A., **481**
Holmes, G., 410, **413**
Hook, S., **617**
Hooker, D., **41**, **42**, **43**, **44**, **97**
Horowitz, L., **413**
Horowitz, N. H., **235**, 409, **414**
Howard, M., **40**
Howes, D. H., 502, **513**
Hsia, D. Y-Y., **43**, **44**
Hubel, D. H., **330**, 359, **377**
Hufschmidt, H. J., 112, **118**
Hughes, J. R., **329**, **377**, **618**
Hughes, L. H., **413**
Hull, C. L., 485, **513**, 525, 540n., **616**, 623, 648, **657**
Hume, D., 381
Hunt, C. C., **413**, **658**
Hunt, H. F., **155**
Hunter, W. S., 484n., 501, **513**, 644, **657**
Hurwitz, R. E., **43**
Hutt, P. J., 211, **233**
Huxley, A. F., **480**
Huxley, J., **241**
Hyman, R., 371, **377**, 397, **415**

Iarbus, A. L., **480**
Ingram, W. R., **232**
Inkeles, A., xxxvii

Ittelson, W. H., xxx, xxxii, xxxiv, xxxvi, 657, 660, 682, 683, 684, 685, 686, 688, 693, 694, 695, **702, 703, 704**

Jackson, J. H., 65, 67, 78, **97**
Jacobs, P. A., **44**
Jacobsen, C. F., **155**
Jaederholme, G. A., 21, **46**
Jahn, T. L., 510, **513**
James, W., 196, 199, 206, 213, **235**, 649
Jasper, H. H., 64, 67, **96, 97, 98, 157,** 182, 183, 217, 220, 221, **235, 237, 239, 330, 332, 378, 412, 618**
Jeans, J. H., 430
Jeffress, L. A., **117, 278, 657**
Jenkins, F. A., 431*n.*, **480**
Jennings, H. S., 460
Jensen, B. T., **616**
Jervis, G. A., **44**
Johannsen, W., 168, **235**
Johansson, G., **616,** 637, **657**
John, E. R., **41**, 134, **156**, 218, **235**, 271, **377**
Johnson, E. P., 353
Johnson, H. M., 297, **331**
Jones, A. D., **412**
Jones, E., **156**
Jones, M. R., **413, 616**
Jouvet, M., 360, **377, 657**
Juel-Nielsen, N., **44**
Jung, R., **97,** 108, **116, 378**
Just, G., **40, 45**

Kaada, B. P., **116**
Kaij, L., **41**
Kalish, H. I., 542, **616**
Kallmann, F. J., 26, 27, 28, **44**
Kantor, J. R., 250, **278**
Kaplan, A. R., **44**
Kaplan, O. J., **44**
Kare, M., **414**
Karon, B. P., **44**
Katona, G., xxxiv, xxxvi, xxxvii
Kaufer, G., 686, 687, **703**
Kaufman, E. L., **513, 657**
Kaven, A., **44**
Keller, F. S., **156,** 460*n.*, **480**
Keller, M., 507, **513**
Kellogg, W. N., **331**
Kelly, G. A., 644, **657**
Kemp, E. H., 506, **513**
Kendler, H. H., vi, vii
Kepler, J., 422
Kesson, M. L., 255, **279**
Kety, S. S., **44,** 76, **97**
Kiang, N. Y-S., 351, 352, 354, **377, 378**
Killam, E. K., **97**

Killam, K. F., **97,** 134, **156,** 218, **235, 377**
Kilpatrick, F. P., **658,** 688, 690, 695, **702, 703, 704**
Kim, C., **156**
Kimura, K., 385, **413**
Kirk, R. L., **44**
Kirkman, B. H., **40**
Kirkman, H. N., **44**
Kishimoto, K., **45**
Kistler, J. C., **42**
Kitai, S. T., **329**
Klein, D., **42**
Klein, S. J., **43**
Kleist, K., **116**
Klemmer, E. T., **378**
Kley, I. B., **46**
Kling, A., **157, 415**
Kling, J. W., **413**
Klose, R., **116**
Klüver, H., 109, 129, **117,** 164, 202, 210, 225, **235, 413,** 540, **616**
Knighton, R. S., **378, 412**
Knox, W. E., **44**
Koch, S., vi, vii, **116, 155, 330, 331, 332,** 512, 513, 514, 540*n.*, **615, 616, 617**
Koffka, K., 197, **236,** 525, 538, **617**
Kohler, I., 536, 537, 590, **617,** 646, 647, 648, 654, **658**
Köhler, W., 114, 115, **117,** 197, **236,** 263, 264, 265, 266, 273, **278,** 519, 533, 535, 538, 552, 553, **617,** 648, 654, **658**
Kolle, K., **44**
Komai, T., **45**
Konorski, J., 61, **97**
Kooi, K. A., 219, **232**
Kramrisch, S., **617**
Kraus, M., **44**
Krauskopf, J., **481**
Krech, D., 31, 32, **45, 47, 236**
Krechevsky, I., **45**
Krogh, A., 226, **236**
Krueckel, B., **45, 236**
Kruger, L., **156, 157, 618**
Kuffler, S. W., **97, 328, 331, 413,** 453, 478, 481, **658**
Kuhlenbeck, H., **117**
Kutash, S. B., **702, 703**
Kuypers, H. G. J. M., 186, 187, 190, **237**

Lacey, J. I., 135, **156**
Lacey, O. L., 502, **514**
Lambert, J. H., 426
Lambert, W. W., xxxiii, xxxvii
Landauer, W., **45**
Lane, R. E., xxxiv, xxxvii

Langley, A. G., 429
Lanier, L. H., vi, vii, xv
Lansing, R. W., 378
Lapras, C., 360, 377
Larson, R. M., 221, 234
Lashley, K. S., 74n., 110, 113, 117, 175, 176, 178, 207, 208, 209, 212, 215, 225, 227, 236, 263, 264, 265, 266, 273, 278, 344, 378
Laughlin, W. S., 49
Lawrence, D. H., xxxi, xxxii, xxxiv, xxxvii
Lawrence, L., 616, 656
Leeper, R., xxxi, xxxii, xxxiv, xxxvi, xxxvii
Le Grand, Y., 438n., 481
Lehrman, D. S., 164, 165, 166, 236
Lejeune, J., 45
Le Magnen, J., 413
Lerner, I. M., 45
Lettvin, J. Y., 378, 532, 617
Lewin, K., 137, 156
Li, C. C., 45
Li, C.-L., 331
Licklider, J. C. R., 325, 331, 538, 617
Liddell, H. S., 61n., 263
Lidz, R. W., 45
Lidz, T., 45
Liepmann, H., 111, 117
Liljestrand, G., 388, 413
Lilly, J. C., 97
Lindsley, D. B., 156, 278, 378, 409, 414
Liu, C. N., 409, 415
Livingston, R. B., xxxiv, 51, 97, 98, 617
Livingston, W. K., 98
Lloyd, D. P. C., 433n., 481
Locke, J., 381
Loeb, J., 460
Loevinger, J., 20, 45
Lombroso, C. T., 236
Long, G. E., 442, 481
Long, L., 642, 658
Lord, M. W., 513, 657
Lorente de No, R., 117, 331
Lorenz, K. Z., 163, 164, 174, 237, 558, 617
Loucks, R. B., 221, 237
Lounsbury, F. G., xxxvi
Lowenstein, O., 331
Lubbock, J., 460
Lucas, K., 436
Luce, R. D., 314n., 316, 317, 326, 331
Luciani, L., 196
Ludwig, C., 58
Ludwig, W. I., 45
Luxemburger, H., 45

McCarthy, G., 692, 704
McClearn, G. E., 45
McCleary, R. A., 399, 414
McCulloch, W. S., 259, 260, 261, 262, 263, 265, 269, 273, 278, 378, 617, 647
McDonald, P. R., 445, 480
McDougall, W., 162, 164, 170, 237
McElroy, W. D., 45
McFalls, V. W., 43
McGarry, J. J., 46
McGinnies, E., 502, 514
Mach, E., 420n., 481
Mack, J. D., 492n., 625, 659
MacLean, P. D., 52, 87, 89n., 98, 156, 408, 409, 414
McLeish, J., 99
MacLeod, R. B., vii, 413, 617
MacLeod, S., 414
MacNichol, E. F., 439, 480
McWhirter, K. G., 40
Macy, J., Jr., 375
Maddox, H., 45
Magoun, H. W., 64, 67, 97, 98, 103, 117, 183, 239, 328, 329, 330, 332, 333, 375, 414, 534, 615, 617, 618
Malis, L. I., 156, 618
Malus, 424, 425
Maneo, S., 241
Margaria, R., 330, 442, 479, 513
Marks, P. A., 43
Marquis, D. G., 460n., 480
Marriott, F. H. C., 332, 514
Marshall, W. A., 239
Marshall, W. H., 64, 98, 237, 331
Maruhashi, J., 98, 331, 393, 414
Masland, R. L., 98
Mather, K., 45
Matteucci, C., 434
Matthews, R., 437, 477, 478
Maturana, H. R., 378, 617
Mauro, A., 293, 331
Maxwell, G., 618
Maxwell, J. C., 430
Maynard, E. M., 118
Mayne, S., 478
Mead, M., 18, 45
Meikle, T. H., 378
Melton, A. W., 275n.
Mendel, G., 160, 169, 173
Menger, K., 504, 514
Merlis, J. K., 236
Merton, R. K., 41
Messick, S., 315, 329, 330
Messinger, E. C., 44
Metzger, W., 567, 571, 573, 617
Meyer, D. R., 202, 237, 278

Meyers, R., 117
Meyerson, B., 688, 704
Michotte, A., 553n., 617
Mickle, W. A., 237
Miles, C. C., 49
Miller, D. R., xxxi, xxxiv, xxxvii
Miller, G. A., 156, 331, 340, 378, 642, 658
Miller, H., 415
Miller, N. E., 98, 255, 279, 414, 540, 617, 648, 656
Miller, W. H., 447, 481
Milne, L. J., 444, 480
Milner, B., 156, 536, 617
Milner, P., 414
Miner, N., 74n., 279
Minturn, A. L., 658
Mishkin, M., 212, 213, 237, 238, 240
Mitchell, H. K., 49
Mizuguchi, K., 98, 331, 414
Moncrieff, R. W., 414
Monnier, M., 378
Morgan, C. L., 460
Morgan, C. T., 279, 333
Morison, R. S., 64, 182, 237
Morrell, F., 220, 221, 237
Morrissette, J. R., 157
Morton, N. E., 41, 45
Moruzzi, G., 67, 98, 329
Mosbeck, J., 46
Moss, F. A., 240
Mosteller, F., 485, 512
Mountcastle, V. B., 117, 155, 188, 191, 238, 239, 331, 332, 345, 346, 378, 411
Mueller, C. G., vi, vii, 481, 492, 493, 494, 514
Müller, J., 55, 58, 343, 380, 381, 394
Munk, H., 196
Murchison, C., 236, 414, 617
Murdock, G. P., 46
Murphy, D., 46
Murray, H., 554, 617
Myers, R. E., 74n., 279
Myro, G., 703

Nachmansohn, D., 284, 331
Nafe, J. P., 391, 414
Nagel, E., 331
Nashold, B. S., 237
Natsumoto, J., 241
Nauta, W. J. H., 186, 187, 190, 237, 240
Neel, J. V., 41, 46
Neff, W. D., 193, 194, 205, 232, 234, 617
Newcomer, H. S., 479
Newell, F. W., 233
Newman, H. H., 46

Newton, I., 54, 55, 57, 229, 423, 428
Nielsen, J. M., 199, 237
Nissen, H. W., 176, 234, 237
Norman, R. M., 47
Noshay, W. C., 378, 412

O'Connor, C. M., 330
Oersted, H. C., 434
Ogle, K. N., 494n., 514
Oldfield, R. C., 642, 658
Olds, J., 70, 98, 271, 272, 279, 414
O'Leary, J. L., 188, 233
Olszewski, J., 107, 117, 237
Oltman, J. E., 46
Oppenheimer, J., 415
Orbach, J., 214, 233, 238
Orrego, F., 118
Osgood, C. E., xxxii, xxxiv, xxxvii, 619, 633, 644, 648, 650, 651, 658
Øster, J., 46
Owen, R. D., 49
Ozaki, Y., 45

Palestini, M., 357, 378
Panse, F., 46
Papez, J. W., 113, 117, 184, 238, 408
Pasik, P., 156, 212, 214, 238
Pasik, T., 156, 238
Patton, R. A., 156, 279
Pavlov, I. P., 57, 59, 60, 206, 207, 229, 253, 458n., 459n., 460
Peake, W. T., 352, 378
Pearson, J. S., 46
Pearson, K., 21, 46
Pease, D. C., 118
Pender, C. B., 46
Penfield, W., 103, 117, 156, 414, 615, 617
Penrose, L. S., 24, 46
Perrin, F. H., 431n., 479
Peterson, I., 116
Petrullo, L., 703
Pettigrew, T. F., 690, 702, 704
Pfaffmann, C., xxxvii, 198, 238, 332, 380, 385, 386, 387, 389, 396, 401, 413, 414, 416
Picasso, P., 663
Pick, H., 414
Pickering, G. W., 46
Pilgrim, F. J., 415
Pincus, G., 41
Pintler, M. H., 48
Pirenne, M. H., 332, 438n., 444, 480, 481, 487, 488, 513, 514, 616
Pitts, W. H., 260, 262, 278, 378, 617
Planansky, K., 46
Planck, M., 431
Plato, 54n., 89, 90, 91, 94

Platt, R., 46
Platzmann, R. L., 329, 376
Plummer, G., 46
Poggio, A. F., 117
Poggio, G. F., 191, 238
Pollack, I., 658
Polly, E. H., 118
Polyak, S., 420n., 438n., 481
Postman, L., xxx, xxxi, xxxii, xxxiv, xxxvii, 544, 615, 617, 640n., 656
Pouillet, C. S. M., 435
Powell, T. P. S., 331
Pratt, C. C., 519, 556, 617
Prell, D. B., 42
Pribram, H. B., 238
Pribram, K. H., xxxvii, 119, 156, 157, 185, 237, 238, 269, 270, 272, 279, 643, 658
Price, B., 46
Pritchard, R. M., 478
Proctor, L. D., 378, 412
Purdy, J., 616, 656
Purkinje, J. E., 428
Purpura, D. P., 98, 292, 332
Putschar, E., 235

Quastler, H., 329, 376
Quillian, J. P., 658

Rabinovich, M. Y., 239
Race, R. R., 46
Radcliffe, K. B., 691, 704
Randall, W., 188
Ranson, S. W., 186, 232, 238, 332
Rao, C. R., 46
Rashevsky, N., 257, 258, 259, 266, 279
Rasmussen, G. L., 379
Ratliff, F., xxxii, xxxiv, xxxvii, 330, 417, 447, 449, 450, 453, 456, 463, 480, 481
Ratoosh, P., xxxii, xxxiv, xxxvii, 483, 514
Rayleigh (Lord), 430
Razran, G., 98, 238
Reed, S. C., 40
Reed, T. E., 46
Reese, T. W., 513, 644, 657, 658
Reeve, E. C. R., 41, 50
Reichenbach, H., 157
Rembrandt, 594, 598, 602, 663
Renard, G., 42
Restle, F., 639, 658
Reymond, D. B., 434
Rhines, K., 117
Ricci, G. F., 330
Rich, D. C., 481
Richardson, L. F., 489n., 513, 514

Richardson, M. W., 631, 658
Richter, C. P., 399, 400, 415
Riesen, A. H., 109, 118, 167, 168, 177, 233, 238, 645, 658
Riggs, L. A., 353, 438n., 456, 481
Rioch, D. McK., 238
Riopelle, A. J., 238, 239
Ripps, H., 490
Ritter, J. W., 429
Roberts, J. A. F., 47
Roberts, L., 117, 221, 237
Robinovich, M. Y., 216
Robinson, F., 157, 409, 414
Robinson, G. M., 232
Robinson, R., 232
Robson, K., 409, 415
Roby, T. B., 415
Roderick, T. E., 47
Rodnick, E. H., vii, xxxvii
Roe, A., 41, 238
Rogers, C. R., 547, 618
Rohracher, H., 118
Rohrer, J. H., 47
Roig, J. A., 222, 239
Romanes, G. J., 459
Rorschach, H., 673
Rose, J. E., 180, 181, 182, 187, 188, 190, 238, 239, 329, 332, 345, 346, 378, 533, 618
Rosenblatt, F., 619, 652, 653, 654, 658
Rosenblith, W. A., xxxvii, 329, 330, 332, 334, 361, 371, 375, 376, 377, 378, 416
Rosenmeyer, T. G., 99
Rosenthal, D., 28, 47
Rosenzweig, M. R., 45, 47, 236, 332
Rosner, B. S., xxxiv, xxxvii, 280, 332
Ross, S., 35, 47
Rossi, G. F., 357, 378, 379
Rosvold, H. E., 223, 239
Roth, A., 692, 704
Rothenbuhler, W. C., 47
Rotter, J. B., xxxvii
Royce, J. R., 47
Rubin, E., 572
Ruch, T. C., 97, 206, 239, 332
Rüdin, E., 25
Rundquist, E. A., 47
Rupert, A., 377
Rushton, W. A. H., 496, 514
Rusinov, V. S., 216, 239
Russell, B., 90, 98
Russell, J. T., 544, 618
Russell, L. B., 47
Russell, W. L., 35, 47
Rutledge, L. T., 221, 222, 234

Samet, S., 397, **415**
Samuels, J., **44**
Sand, A., **331**
Sanford, N., xxxi, xxxiv, xxxvii
Sanger, R., 46
Sarason, S. B., 98
Sashin, D., 375
Saslow, M. G., **379**
Saunders, D. R., **44**
Schäfer, E. A., 98
Schaltenbrand, G., 112, **116, 118**
Scheibel, A. B., 107, **118, 332**
Scheibel, M. A., 107, **118**
Scheibel, M. E., **332**
Scherrer, H., **97**, 330, **377, 657**
Schlosberg, H., **333, 379**, 409, **415**
Schmitt, J. R., 40
Schneirla, T. C., **47, 48**
Schoenfeld, W. N., xxxi, xxxii, xxxiv, xxxvii, 156, 460n., **480**
Schreiner, L., **157, 415**
Schull, W. J., **41, 46**
Schultz, R. L., 105, **118**
Schulz, B., 48
Schut, J. W., 40
Schwartzbaum, J. S., 129n., **157**
Scott, J. P., 15, 30, **40, 42, 48**, 173, **239**
Scott, O. L. S., 48
Scott, W. A., 48
Scott-Moncrieff, R., **232**
Scriven, M., **618**
Sears, P. S., 48
Sears, R. R., 48
Sechenov, I. M., 57, 58, 458, 459, 460
Sechzer, J. A., **378**
Segundo, J. P., 222, **239**
Seidenberg, B., 694, **703, 704**
Selfridge, O. G., **643, 658**
Semmes, J., 74n.
Shagass, C., **235**
Shakespeare, W., 474
Sharpless, S., **157**, 217, **239, 332, 618**
Shaw, T., 97
Sheatz, G., **97**, 234, **235**, 329, 330, 332, 377, **656**
Sheer, D. E., **332**
Sheffield, F. D., **415**
Shell, W. F., **239**
Sheppard, P. M., **48**
Sherif, C. W., **47, 48**
Sherif, M., xxxiv, xxxvii, **47, 48**
Sherrington, C. S., 55, 57, 83, 84, **99**, 207, 221, 225, 227, 228, 229, **239**, 406, **415**
Shickman, G. M., **333**
Shields, J., **48**
Shimokochi, M., **241**

Shlaer, S., 444, **480**, 487, 488, **513, 616**
Sholl, D. A., 105, 106, **118**, 342n., **379**
Shuford, E. H., Jr., **415, 416**
Siebert, N., **328**
Sigler, M., 501, **513**, 644, **657**
Simon, E., **99**
Simon, H. A., xxxiv, xxxvii
Simpson, G. G., **41, 238**
Sindberg, R. M., **240**
Sinnott, E. W., 48
Siskel, M., Jr., 402, **412**
Sjögren, T., 48
Skinner, B. F., 137, **155**, 227, 229, **239**, 255, **279**, 463, **482**, 486, **514**
Slack, C. W., 670, 682, 685, 690, 693, 695, **703, 704**
Slater, E., 26, 28, **48**
Slater, P., 46
Slome, D., 48
Smirnov, G., **235**
Smith, C. J., **329**
Smith, G. H., 687, **704**
Smith, H. W., **118**
Smith, M., **415**, 496, **514**
Smith, M. B., vii
Smith, R. L., **156**
Smith, S., 647, **658**
Smith, T., 489n., **514**
Smith, W. M., 684, **704**
Smithies, O., 49
Snell, B., **99**
Snell, W. 422
Snyder, L. H., xxxi, xxxiv, 1, **41, 49**
Sokoloff, L., **99**
Sokolov, E. N., 134, **155**, 157, **379**
Solomon, H., **615, 617**
Solomon, R. L., 502, **513**
Sommer-Smith, J. A., 222, **239**
Sophocles, 51
Sorsby, A., **41, 42, 48, 49**
Soulairac, A., 402, **415**
Spence, K. W., **279**, 297, 310, **328**, 460n., **482**, 487, 498, 504, 506, **512**
Sperling, G., **618**
Sperry, R. W., 74n., 79, **99, 118**, 208, **239**, 255, 272, **279**, 537, **618**, 645, **659**
Spiegel, E., **415**
Spindler, G., xxxiv, xxxvii
Spindler, L., xxxiv, xxxvii
Sprague, J. M., 409, **415**
Springer, L., **188**
Spuhler, J. N., **49**
Srb, A. M., **49**
Stamm, J. S., **49**
Steinberg, A. G., **49**

Stellar, E. L., **157, 279,** 397, 409, **415**
Stenhouse, N. S., **44**
Stenstedt, Å., **49**
Stevens, J. C., 492n., **625, 659**
Stevens, J. R., **156**
Stevens, K. N., **378**
Stevens, S. S., **43, 99, 157, 235, 237, 278,**
297, 307, 313, 314, 317, 318, 326,
332, 333, 379, 414, 415, 416, **478,**
484, 489n., 490, 492n., **505, 513,**
514, 556, 623, 624, **625, 626, 627,**
639, **657, 659, 669, 704**
Stratton, G. M., 646, **659**
Strong, J., 420n., 431n., **482**
Strong, J. A., **44**
Strong, P. N., **238**
Survis, J., **233**
Sutton, W. S., **239**
Svaetichin, G., 437, **479**
Swets, J. A., **333**
Szafran, J., **376**

Taguiri, R., **703**
Talbot, S. A., **237, 239**
Tanner, W. P., Jr., **333**
Tasaki, I., 81, **98, 99, 118,** 284, 331, 333,
414, 415
Taylor, F., xxxiv, xxxvii
Taylor, J., **97, 513**
Terman, L. M., **49**
Teuber, H. L., **157,** 199, 200, 210, **239,**
240, 279, 618
Thacher, C., **479**
Thompson, R. F., 202, **240**
Thompson, W., Jr., 370, **379**
Thompson, W. R., 33, 35, **42, 49**
Thorndike, E. L., **460**
Thorndike, R., vii, 57
Thorpe, W. H., 177, **240**
Thurstone, L. L., 306, **333**
Tinbergen, N., 164, **240**
Titchener, E. B., 198, 213, **240,** 500,
514, 519, 525, 612, **618**
Toch, H. H., **695, 704**
Tolman, E. C., **279, 617**
Toraldo di Francia, C., **482**
Torgerson, W. S., 314n., **333,** 632, **659**
Tower, D. B., 272, **279**
Troland, L. T., 407, **415**
Tryon, R. C., 14, 32, **49,** 172, **240**
Tucker, D., **415**
Tucker, L., 315, **330**
Tunturi, A. R., 203, **240**
Turpin, R., **45**
Twain, M., **460**
Tyler, L. E., **49**

Ukhtomsky, A. A., **59**
Urban, F. M., **333**
Utley, J., **189**

Van Gogh, V., **607**
Velasco, M., **97**
Velter, E., **42**
Vernier, V. G., **97, 234, 329, 377, 656**
Vernon, M. D., 464, 470, 471, **478**
Verplanck, W. S., **333,** 466, 482
Verzeano, M., **97, 329**
Verzilova, O. V., 219, **240**
Vidale, E. B., xxxvii, 334, 348, 349, 353
Vinci, Leonardo da, 661
Volkmann, J., **333, 513,** 644, **657**
Volta, A., **434**
von Békésy, G., **328, 416,** 464, **478**
von Bonin, G., xxxiv, 100, **115, 118**
von Frey, M., 380, 382
von Holst, E., 112, **118,** 535, **618**
von Monakow, C., 111, **118, 618**
von Senden, M., 109, **118, 618**
Von Weizsäcker, V., 110, **118**

Waardenburg, P. J., **49**
Waddington, C. H., **41, 49, 50,** 170, **240**
Waelsch, H., **39**
Wagman, I. H., **444, 480**
Wagner, H. G., **439,** 447, **480**
Wagner, R. P., **49**
Wald, G., 438n., **482, 514**
Walker, A. E., **240**
Wallace, B., **41**
Wallach, H., **117, 538, 617, 618**
Walsh, E. G., **392**
Walter, H. J., **375**
Walzl, E. M., **241**
Warner, L., **482**
Warren, K. B., **49**
Warren, R. P., **416**
Washburn, S., 165
Watson, J. B., 163, 168, 209, 227, 229,
240, 459, 460, **482,** 525, 538, 539,
618
Weber, E. H., 439n., **506**
Weddell, G., 391, **416**
Wedensky, N. Y., **59**
Weinberg, W., 8
Weiskrantz, L. A., **157**
Weiss, P., **79, 99**
Welch, L., 642, **658, 659**
Wernicke, 129
Wertheimer, M., **333, 538,** 636, 647
Wever, E. G., **333, 416, 546, 547, 618**
White, B., **616**
White, H. E., 431n., **480**

Whitehead, A. N., 698
Whitfield, I. C., 240
Whitlock, D. G., 240
Wiener, N., 260, 261, **279, 659**
Williams, C. D., **41**
Williams, C. E., **40**
Wilska, A., 438, **482**
Wilson, E. A., 496, **514**
Wilson, J. T., vii
Wilson, M., **240**
Wilson, W. A., **157**, 212, **240**
Windle, W. F., **99, 379**
Winters, R. W., **43**
Wittreich, W. J., 691, **704**
Wölfflin, N., 602, **618**
Wolfle, D., vii, xv
Wolstenholme, G. E. W., **330**
Woodger, J. H., **50**
Woodworth, R. S., 243, **279, 333, 379,** 642, 649, **659**
Woolf, B., **50**
Woolsey, C. N., 64, **96, 97, 98,** 180, 181, 182, 187, 189, 190, 202, **237, 238,**

239, 240, **241, 278, 333,** 354, 355, 379, 413, 533,, **617, 618**
Worden, F. G., 218, **241**
Wright, S., **50, 241**
Wright, W. D., 441, **482**
Wulfeck, J. W., **513**
Wulff, V. J., 438n., **482**
Wundt, W., 213, 243, **279,** 380
Wyckoff, L. B., 643, **659**

Yamaguchi, Y., **241**
Yamazaki, H., **241**
Yerkes, R. M., 460
Yockey, H. P., **329, 376**
Yoshii, N., 216, 219, **241**
Young, P. T., 399, 407, **416**
Young, T., 423

Zanchetti, A., 357, **378, 379**
Zener, K. E., vi, vii, xxxii, xxxiv, xxxvi, xxxvii, 515, **615, 618**
Zotterman, Y., **333,** 390, **412, 413, 416**
Zubin, J., **44**

SUBJECT INDEX

Ablation experiments, 68–70, 83–85, 146, 202–206, 209ff., 215–216, 224, 250, 255, 324, 340, 373, 533
Abnormal psychology, 14, 21–29, 35–38
  (*See also* Psychopathology and perception; Psychotherapy)
Absolute judgments, 488–492
Absolute threshold, 319–320, 442–443, 469–470
Absorption factor, 510
Abstraction, loss of capacity for, 199
Acceptance as basic response to taste, 396
Accommodation, 685–686
Acetylcholine metabolism, 32–33
Action and perception, 697
Action potential, 62, 282ff., 347, 366, 434–436
  compound, 392, 435
  (*See also* Response, evoked, single-unit)
Acute preparations, 296–297
Adaptive behavior, 633–634
Affective responses, 68, 87, 113–114, 268, 407, 410
  (*See also* Emotional significance and perception)
Afferent code, 383
Afferent fibers, 81–82, 146–147
Afferent input patterns, 391
Afterdischarge, 223
Agnosia, 199–201
All-or-nothing principle, 62–64, 80–81, 101, 260, 284, 288, 337, 343, 345, 365, 384–385
  (*See also* Single-unit response)
Amacrine cells, 447–448
Amaurotic idiocy, 16, 22
Ameaningful thinking, xxxix
American Psychological Association, vi, xv
America's Psychologists, vi, xv
Amnesia for visual tasks, 210, 213
Amplitude of neuroelectric responses, 294–296, 325–327, 345, 347–348, 350

Amygdalectomy, 126ff., 145–146
Analogue computers, 64
Analysis of cues in perception, 499–500
Anesthesia, 64–65, 67, 76, 87, 296–297, 350–352, 358, 360, 364–367
Animal electricity, 55, 433–434
Animal psychophysics, 463ff.
Aniseikonic lenses, 690–692
Anisotropy of visual perception, 562ff., 573–602, 606–607
Anterior nuclei, 184–185
Anxiety, 76, 691–692
Aphasia, 113, 196, 199
Apparent distance, 594ff., 682–689
Apparent movement, 695
Apparent slant, 550, 551
Appetitive mechanisms, 85, 87, 124, 151
Apriorism, 667
Arousal, 68–69, 103, 107
Association areas of cortex, 68, 86, 195ff., 206
Associationism, 648–649
Assumed size, 683ff.
Assumptive world, 678–679
Astrocytes, 82–83
Attention, 75, 113, 123, 134, 135, 137, 198, 359–360, 468
Attitude, 123
Audiogenic seizures, 33–34, 37, 171–172
Audiometry, 464
Audition, 106, 202–206
Auditory response areas, cortical, 354–355
Autocorrelation, 361–365
Autonomic ganglia, 85
Autosomes, 6, 11–12
Averaged neural responses, 341, 345, 347–354, 356, 364–365
Aversive stimulus, 403
Axon, 282ff.
  and all-or-nothing response, 62–64, 80–81
  conduction rate, 101
  giant motor, of squid, 282–283, 433

717

Baltimore cats, 145
Basal forebrain, 124, 126–129, 133
Behavior, adaptive, 633–634
   brain and, 52–53, 71
   critical neural variables, 123–124, 334–337, 348, 368–374
   genetics, 224
   lawfulness, 633–642
   phylogeny, 163, 175, 215–216
   "ready-made," 248–249
   science of, 458–460, 553
   status of concept, 538–541
   voluntary, 124ff.
Behavior sequences, 124
Behaviorism, xx, xxxii, 149–153, 227–229, 297–299, 458–460, 484, 494, 521–522, 538–541, 648ff.
Bell-Magendie Law, 147
Bewegungsentwurf, 111
Bias, sampling, of microelectrodes, 289–290
Binary system and brain function models, 81, 259–263
   (See also Computers as brain models)
Binocular rivalry, 692–694
Biochemical genetics, 3, 4
Biological basis of taste reactions, 403
Biological psychology, 158–231
   EEG and learning, 216–224
      conditioning EEG, 220–221
   evolution of cortex and thalamus, 178–195
   introduction to article, 159–161
   and learning psychology, 224–231
   place of learning in comparative psychology, 161–178
      behavior as species character, 161–166
      comparative method, 174–178
      genetics of behavior, 170–173
      individual differences, 166–170
   sensation and learning, 195–216
      electrophysiology and sensory quality, 197–198
      experimental studies of sensation and perception, 200–206
      Lashley's study, 207–210
Biological sciences, 225–227, 458
Biophysics, mathematical, 257–259
"Black-body" concept, 430
Blindness and recovery of vision, 109
Blood-brain barrier, 77, 82
Boolean algebra, 259–260
Brain, architecture of cortex, 104–106
   attention, 113
   character and, 102
   consciousness, 102–103

Brain, emotions, 113–114
   free will, 114–115
   introduction to article, 100
   and mind, 89–96, 100–115
   motor output, 110–112
   nerve cells, 100–102
   neurological and psychological studies, 51–96, 119–154
   optic sensations, 107–110
   and personality, 102
   sensorium commune, 110
   sensory input, 106–107
   speech, 113
   summary, 115
Brain circuitry, 83–89, 114, 184, 338–339
Brain stem, 64ff., 69, 71, 86, 87, 107, 133, 269
   (See also Reticular formation)
Brain waves (see EEG)
Breeding, selective, 14–15, 30ff., 165–166, 168–170, 172–174
Bridging laws, xix
Brightness, 497
Brightness contrast, 453–454, 466–469, 582–584
Brightness discrimination, 202, 208–209, 464–466, 505–510
Brightness vs. texture organizations, 570–572
Broca's area, 113
Bunsen-Roscoe law, 501, 506–507, 644

Calculus of potential, 71n.
Cats, Baltimore vs. Washington, 145
Caudate nucleus, 223
Causation, 555, 649
   multiple, 16–17, 151
   of neuropsychological phenomena, 121–124
   of physiological phenomena, 55ff., 59, 70, 103–104
   (See also Explanation; Reductionism)
Cellular change, 223
Central control of sensory signals, 72–73, 86–87, 91, 394–395, 533
Central nervous system (see Nervous system)
Cerebellum, 68
Change, perceptual, 674, 678–679, 699–701
Channeling, neuronal, 71–72
Character and brain, 102
Chemical transmitters, 61, 85–89, 287
Chemoreception, 178
Choice response, 399
Cholinesterase activity of brain tissue, 32–33

Chorda tympani nerve, 386, 397
Chromaticness, 497, 499
Chromosome theory of heredity, 2
Chromosomes, 2, 5ff.
  translocation, 24n.
Chunking, 642, 650
Circuitry, brain, 83–89, 114, 184, 338–339
Circulation, 76–77
Classical physics, 70n.–71n., 93–94
Classical psychophysics, 311–312, 487–488, 621–622
Clinical neurology, 122
Closure, 115
Coding in nervous system, 338, 344, 351, 356, 383
Coenotropes, 647
Cognitive and conative dispositions, 162–163
Cognitive vs. phenomenal reports, 552–554
Cognitive relationships in perception, 517, 535, 543–545, 551, 633–645
Cold fibers, 82
Color, 497–499
Color contrast, 454
Color correction, 428
Color naming, 488–492
Common path, 453
Comparative neurophysiology, 77–78, 299
Comparative physiology, 174–178
Comparative psychology, 15, 29–34, 224, 457ff.
Complimentarity principle, 104
Compound response, 290–291
Computational routines for limens, 305
Computers as brain models, 55, 64, 80–81
Concept formation, 642
Concepts, behavioral and introspective, 150, 472–473, 477
Conceptual nervous system, 227
Concordance-discordance studies, 26–29, 38
Conditional probability, 298
Conditioning, 133, 220–222
  Pavlovian, 57, 60, 206–207, 254
Cones, 107–108
Conflict, 268
Consciousness, 53, 59, 66–68, 87, 102–103, 115, 119, 472–473, 665, 667
  (See also Experience; Experiential factors)
Consensual validation, 149ff.
Conservation of energy, 435
Constancy, 108, 109, 263, 374, 446, 525, 531, 544–545, 580, 653–655

Constancy-learning, 646–647, 654–655
Constructs, 276
  hypothetical, 637
  intervening, 142
  space-time, 53
Consummatory behavior, 399, 407
Context, 531
Contingent conditions of perception, 527–530
Contour, 550, 630
Contrast effects, 450–451, 453–454, 532
Control, behavior, perception as, 517
  central, of sensory signals, 72–73, 86–87, 91, 394–395, 533
  stimulus, of behavior, 462–463
Convergence, 686
Convergent operations, 627
Copulation, 87
Corpus callosum, 108
Cortex, 59–60, 68ff., 140, 178–179, 185ff.
  architecture, 104–106
  as forecasting mechanism, 112
Cortical mapping, 354–355
Cortical representation of visceral and somatic mechanism, 59
Criterion response, 335
  for neuroelectric data, 340
Critical-value function, 492n.
Cross-correlation, 362–364
Cue variables in perception, 499–500
Cultural differences, 17
Cutaneous modalities, 391–393
Cytogenetics, 2ff.
Cytology, 2

Dark adaptation, 443, 469–471
Data and theory, xxxiii-xxxiv, 141ff., 258ff., 270–278, 495
Data processing, of neuroelectric activity, 337–339
  sensory, 633–642
Deafness, 113
Decerebration studies, 83–84
Deficit method, 210
Delayed response, 211
Dendrites, 282, 292
Depolarization, 283, 286ff., 384
Deprivation, 461, 466
  of food, 126ff.
  of visual experience, 167–168
Desynchronization of electrical activity, 133–135, 221
Determinism, 59, 114–115
  (See also Causation; Explanation; Reductionism)
Development study, 165, 170
Developmental neurophysiology, 78–80

Diagonal, descending, "causal," 605–606
Diencephalon, 179
Difference method, 227
Differential psychology, 15–21
Differential reinforcement, 302–303, 462–465, 468
Differential sensitivity, 321
Diffraction, 423–425
Discrimination, perceptual, 517, 542–543, 622
  sequential, 131ff.
  of taste, 389–391
Disease, genetic factors in, 14, 30
Disinhibition, 450
Disorganized behavior, 268
Dispersion, 419–420, 422–423
Dissolution of function, 67, 84
Distal stimulus, 527
Distance, apparent, 594ff., 682–689
Distribution, of intelligence, 21–25
  of responses, 125ff., 138
Doctrine of levels, 65–72
Dogs, behavior genetics, 30
Dorsal- and lateral-column systems, 186–188
Dorsal thalamus, 180–181
Double dissociation, 210
Dove prism, 455
Drive reduction, 406
Drives, 124, 128, 461–462
Drosophila, 3, 4, 6
  Bar gene, 19
  behavior genetics, 29, 31
  major gene effects in, 7–8, 19
Dualistic vs. monistic views, 60–61, 89ff., 152
  (See also Mind-body relations; Psychophysical parallelism)
Duration, visual, 500–503, 507–510

Eating, 124, 151
  food deprivation, 126ff.
EEG, 17, 59, 62, 135, 183, 216–224, 250, 361–364
Efferent fibers, 146–147
Electrical activity, desynchronization, 133–135, 221
Electrical stimulation and recording, 85, 221–223, 282ff.
Electricity, animal, 55
Electroconvulsive shock, 250
Electromagnetic theory, 430–431
Electrophysiology, 197–198, 216ff., 325–327, 334–375
  of taste, 384–395, 410–411
  (See also Neuroelectric responses)
Electroretinogram, 353

Electrotonic field forces, 73–74, 80
Elementarism, 669
Emotional experience, 68, 87, 113–114, 268, 407, 410
Emotional significance and perception, 687–688, 693
  (See also Affective responses)
Environment and gene interaction, 10ff., 17ff., 38, 39, 166ff.
Epicritic sense, 188
Epistemology, 418
Epithalamus, 179, 180
Equal-interval method, 624
Equipotentiality, 208, 266, 340
Equivalent stimuli, 164, 225
Error sensing, 136, 140
Ethology, 163, 548
Evoked neuroelectric responses, 324, 341–342, 345, 347–354, 356, 359–360, 364–365
Evolution of nervous system, 177–178
Evolution genetics, 4, 161–162
Excitation, 58, 60, 74, 80, 261ff.
Excitatory and inhibitory influences in retina 447ff., 455–456
Experience, scientific status, 517–523
Experiential factors, 154, 165, 265, 310ff., 474, 517–614, 664–667, 677
  (See also Introspection)
Experimental design in physiological psychology, 249–250
  (See also Psychophysical experiment)
Experimental psychology, 15
Experimental science, 57, 95, 119
Explanation, 55, 57, 70, 95, 225ff., 259, 497–499
  (See also Causation)
Externalization, 674, 677–678
Exteroceptive systems, 179, 409
Extinction, 467–468
Extirpation experiments (see Ablation experiments)
Extracellular records, 288ff.
Extrapyramidal system, 111, 112, 536
Extrinsic nuclei, 180ff., 185, 188–194

Factor analysis, 637
Familial incidence of schizophrenia, 25–29, 37
Familiarity and size-distance relationships, 682ff.
Fechner's law, 316, 318, 321, 326, 381
Feeblemindedness, mental deficiency, 21–25
  test intelligence, 18–21
  (See also Idiocy)
Feedback, 531

Feeling, quantitative theory, 391
Fibers, afferent, 81–82, 146–147
  cortical, 104–105, 185ff.
  efferent, 146–147
  nociceptive, 82, 106, 186
  pressure, 82
  temperature, 106, 321
  touch, 82, 106, 186
Fields of psychology, xvi–xvii, xxxvii–xxxviii
Figure-ground reversals, 570ff.
Final common path, 207
First-order invariances, 308
Fissure of Rolando, 79, 199
Fixed-interval reinforcement, 125ff., 137
Food deprivation, 126ff.
Forecasting, 110, 112
Form constancy, 653–655
Fornix, 78
Foster-child investigations in schizophrenia studies, 37–38
Fractionation method, 624
Free will, 59, 114–115
Frequency codes, 394
Frequency discrimination, 202–206
Friedreich's ataxia, 16
Frontal cortex, 138ff.
Functional approach to perception, 671–674
Functional neuroanatomy, 359
Fundamental measurement, 504–505

Game, operant as, 139
Gating action, 133
Gene effects, 1–39
Generalization, 222
Generalization gradient, 136
"Generator potentials," 319
Genes, 6ff., 79, 165ff.
  and animal behavior, 29–34
  effects of, diversity, 7–10, 12–14
    major, in man, 9–10, 22ff.
    multiple, 12
  interaction, 10ff.
  mimic, 11–22
Genetics, of behavior, 224
  biochemical, 3, 4
  definition, 1
  developmental, 3, 4
  of evolution, 4
  human, 8–10, 16
  physiological, 3, 31–34
  of populations, 4, 15, 30
  and psychology, 1–39
    interrelations, 14–34
      genetics, and abnormal psychology, 21–29

Genetics, and psychology, interrelations,
    genetics, and comparative
      psychology, 29–34
    and differential psychology, 15–21
    introduction, 14–15
    methodologic, 34–39
  metatheoretic note, 39
  principles of gene action, 5–14
    different genes and indistinguishable effects, 11–12
    gene-and-environment interaction, 10–11
    gene interaction, 10
    introduction, 5–7
    major genes and polygenes, 12–14
    multiple effects of genes, 12
    phenocopies, 11
    variety of gene effects, 7–10
  scope, 1–5
  subdivisions, 1–5
Genic balance, 7
Genotype, 6, 7, 16, 31ff., 34ff., 165–166, 168–170
Genotypical functions, 625ff., 650
Gestalten, 107
Giant motor axon of squid, 282–283, 433
"Glance curve," 604
Glia, 82–83
Graded potentials, 286–288, 290–293, 343, 345, 384–385
Grooming, 87
Gustatory afferent nerve discharges, 385–388

Habit, 161–162
Habituation processes, 129, 134, 135, 137, 204, 217ff., 297, 359–360
Hair fibers, 82
Hedonic responses (see Affective responses)
Heisenberg indeterminacy principle, 96, 114
Heredity, 1–39, 166ff.
  and environment, 19–21, 39
  (See also Genes; Genetics)
Heterozygous dosage, 6, 30
Hierarchical analysis of perception, 639–642
Hippocampal region, 133, 134, 179, 184
Hollywood cats, 145
Homeostasis, 72n., 136, 269, 532
Homologies, 163, 181
Homosexual behavior, 18
Homozygous dosage, 6, 30
Honeybee, behavior genetics, 30
Horizontal cells, 447–448

Horseshoe crab, 438ff., 443, 456
Hue, 497–498
  (*See also* Color contrast; Color correction; Color naming)
Hunger, 151
Huntington's chorea, 16, 25
"Hybrid" sciences, 473
Hypermetamorphotic reaction, 129
Hypothalamus, 89*n*., 136, 179, 184, 228–229
Hypotheses, 142, 149, 257ff.
Hypothetical constructs, 637
Hysteresis, 258, 626

Idiocy, amaurotic, 16, 22
  genetics, 21–24
  microcephalic, 22–23
  mongoloid, 23–24
Illuminated object, 527
Imbecility, genetics, 21–24
Imprinting, 170
Inbred strains, genetic differentiation among, 31, 34–35, 170–171
Incidence, familial, of schizophrenia, 25–29, 37
Incongruity, 136, 140
Indeterminacy, 96, 114
Individual differences, and heredity, 5ff., 9–10, 15–21, 38, 39, 166–170
  in psychophysics, 298–299
  (*See also* Population genetics; Twin studies; Variability)
Individuation, 78–79
Information theory, 260–263, 644
Infrared portion of spectrum, 428
Inheritance, 161
  (*See also* Genetics)
Inhibition, 58, 60, 72, 80, 467
Inhibitory and excitatory influences in retina, 447ff., 455–456
Injury potential, 434
Input, 106–107, 134–135
  afferent, pattern, 391
Insects, behavior genetics, 29–31
Instinct, 161–162, 164–165
Instructions, 559, 561
  in psychophysical experiments, 299, 302–303, 310ff., 463, 486, 496–497
Intact electrophysiological preparations, 322
Intelligence, distribution, 21–25
  and genes, 16, 18–21, 171
  test, 18–21
Intensity, 345–352
  psychophysics, 313–318, 466–467
Intention, 124ff.
Interaction of genes, 10ff.

Interdisciplinary programs, xviii–xix, xxv
Interference, 419–420, 423–425
Intervening constructs, 142
Intracellular recording, 282ff.
Intralaminar nuclei, 182–183
Intrinsic nuclei, 180ff., 185, 188–194
Introspection, 149ff., 167, 198, 304, 457, 485–487, 495, 519ff., 558–559, 628–629, 675
Invariance hypothesis and size-distance relationships, 688–689
Invariances, first-, and second-order, in psychophysics, 308–309
Invariant recurrent properties, 124, 262–263
Inversion, perceptual effects, 562ff.
Involutional melancholia, 29
IQ (test intelligence), 18–21
Irradiation injury, 82
Isocortex, 133–135
Isomorphism, 64–65, 108, 265, 394, 528, 531, 535, 630–631, 638*n*.

James-Lange theory of emotion, 114
Judgment, 123

Kirchhoff's law, 430

Lange-James theory of emotion, 114
Language, 150, 457, 472, 487, 498, 558–559
Latency, 294–296, 335, 341–342, 345–350, 356, 369–370, 372
  (*See also* Reaction time)
Lateral geniculate body, 180
Laterality and perspective perception, 603, 606*n*.
Law of regression, 169
Laws of perceptual grouping, 636–637, 647
Learning, biological psychology and, 224–231
  and instinct, 164–165, 167ff.
  Lashley's study, 207–210
  and neuronal channeling, 71
  and perception, xxxi–xxxii, 645–655
  physiological correlates, 216ff.
  Sechenov's view, 58–59
  and sensation, 195–216
  tasks for comparative studies, 175–177, 211
Learning ability, inheritance, 172
Learning set, 212–213
Level of analysis, xvi–xx, 223–224, 243–244
Levels of function, 65–72
Lewinian theory, 137

Life principles, 87
Light, nature, 419–432
  wave theory, 425–426
Light adaptation, 443
Light deprivation, 167–168
Limbic lobe, 68, 86, 87, 89n., 269, 408–409
Limulus, 438ff., 443, 456
Linearity assumption, 325–327
Localization, functional, 218–219
Locus of chromosomes, 6, 10, 13
Looking behavior, 562ff., 577, 580, 602–608
Luminance, 498, 502–508, 508–510
Luminous and nonluminous objects, 419–420, 428ff.

Mach's bands, 453–454
Macroelectrodes, chronically implanted, 322
  recording with, 341–342, 345, 347–354, 356, 359–365
Magnitude estimations, 313ff., 623–627
Major genes, 12–14, 16, 22
  and animal behavior, 29–30
Mammalian thalamus, 180–185
Manic-depressive psychosis, 29
Mass action, 78–79, 111, 208
Material vs. mental world, 53, 59, 89ff., 119–124, 243, 476–477
Mathematical biophysics, 257–259
Mathematical models (see Models)
Matter and sensation, 53, 59, 90, 152
Maturation, 78, 168, 177
Meaning, connotative and denotative, 142, 310ff.
  empirical vs. theoretical, 268, 497–499
  of "O perceives X," 542–549
  of objectivity, 474–475
  of objects, 682–689, 693
Measurement, in all disciplines, 473, 475–477
  psychophysical, 304–307, 503–505, 623ff., 638–639
  (See also Autocorrelation; Boolean algebra; Models; Psychophysical experiment; Quantification; Scale value)
Measures of neuroelectric responses, 293–296, 336–343
Mechanistic psychology, 55
Medial geniculate body, 180
Medium world, 524, 526–528
Membrane, 282
  postsynaptic, 287–288
Memory, 110, 199
Memory trace, 58, 109, 196, 206ff., 214

Mendelian laws, 1, 2, 35, 165ff., 226
Mental deficiency, 21–25
Mental disease and genetics, 25–29
Mental vs. material world, 53, 59, 89ff., 119–124, 243, 476–477
Mentalism, 121, 484
  (See also Mind-body relations)
Metabolism, 76–77
Metaphysics, 119
Metatheory, 39
Metathetic continua, 326, 344, 639
Methodology, interrelations of psychology and genetics in, 34–39
  (See also Experimental design; Measurement; Psychophysical experiment)
Microcephaly, 22–23
Microdissection, 436
Microelectrode recording, 284, 289–290, 341–342, 345–346, 352, 357, 359, 365–367, 390, 437–438
Microglia, 83
Midline nuclei, 182–183
"Mimic" genes, 11–12
Mind and brain, 59, 66–67, 89–96, 100–115, 119–124, 149ff., 433, 539
Mind-body relations, xviii, 53, 55, 58ff., 67, 100–115, 119–124, 198, 243
Models, 147–149, 152–153, 630
  biophysical, 257–259
  of brain function, 55, 64, 80–81, 125, 216
  classical psychophysical, 311–312
  factor analysis, 637
  mathematical, electrophysiological, 338–339, 342
Modes of confirmation, 311
Modulation in central nervous system, 72, 87, 91ff., 394
Molar levels, 226, 243–244, 533, 630
Molecular levels, 226, 243–244, 630
Mongolism, 23–24
Monistic vs. dualistic views, 60–61, 89ff., 149, 152
  (See also Mind-body relations; Psychophysical parallelism)
Moron, 24–25
Morphogenesis, 226
Motivation, 68–70
  and perception, 686–688, 691–692
Motor cortex, precentral, 140
Motor fibers, 146–147
Motor-nerve endings, 82
Motor output, 110–112
Mouse, major gene effects in, 8, 11
Movement perception, 694–695

Multidimensional psychophysics, 631–633, 638–639
Mutation, 3ff., 12–14, 30

Naming behavior, 488–492
National Science Foundation, vi, vii, xv
Nativism, 645ff., 666–667
Necker cube, 589
Negative reinforcement, 70, 71, 87
Neocortex, 179, 184
Nerve cell, 100ff.
Nerve impulse, 432–437
Nerve-muscle preparation, 228, 435
Nerve transmission, 54ff., 62–64, 80–82, 101–102, 228
Nerve trunks, 228
Nervous system, 54ff., 72ff., 83ff., 101, 177–178, 215–216, 227–228
Neural correlates of behavioral events, 123–124, 334–337, 348, 368–374
Neural integration in retina, 443, 446–457
Neural patterns, 336, 345, 356, 373
Neuroelectric events related to sensory communication, 334–375
concluding remarks, 373–375
introduction to article, 334–336
measurement and analysis in electrophysiology, 336–343
statistical view of neuroelectric phenomena, 339–343
neural representation of stimulus variables, 343–357
intensity, 345–352
localizable representations, 354–357
time, 352–354
preliminaries to assessment of state variables, 357–367
temporal aspects of responses to discrete stimuli, 367–373
Neural representation, 125, 134, 136, 139, 343–357
Neuraxis, 65, 67ff., 296
Neurobehavioral data, 121, 141, 144
Neurobiotaxis, 79
Neurochemistry, 61, 85–89, 287
Neuroelectric responses, 293–296, 325–327
(See also Electrophysiology)
Neuroglia, 82–83
Neurological disciplines and psychology, 119–154
interrelations among methods, 141–154
bridging laws and systematizing, 146–149
data gathering, 143–146
fact and fantasy, 141–143
psychological subjective behaviorism, 149–153

Neurological disciplines and psychology, introduction, 120–121
mind-brain relationship, 121–124
neural variables critical to behavior, 123–124
what is neuropsychology? 121–123
neurology of intention and will, 124–141
execution of intentions, 137–141
initiation of intentions, 125–137
where the neuropsychologist? 153–154
Neuron, 54ff., 62–64, 80–82, 100ff., 282ff.
single recordings from, 325, 341–342, 345–346, 352, 357, 359, 365–367
Neuronal integration, 62
Neuropharmacology, 61, 85–89
Neurophysiological function, 295, 318ff.
Neurophysiological preparations, 296–297
Neurophysiological and psychological studies of man's brain, 51–96
changing concepts pertinent to psychology, 61–75
all-or-nothing principle, 62–64
central control of sensory signals, 72–73
doctrine of levels, 65–72
nervous system as "reactor," 73–75
specific point-to-point relations, 64–65
conceptual and experimental domains of neurophysiology, 75–89
biophysics and physiology of neuron, 80–82
circulation and metabolism, 76–77
comparative neurophysiology, 77–78
developmental neurophysiology, 78–80
physiology of neuroglia, 82–83
techniques applied to brain circuitry, 83–89
introduction to article, 52–53
mind and brain, 89–96
neurophysiology in historical perspective, 54–61
boundaries, 61
Russian tradition, 58–61
Western tradition, 54–58
Neurophysiology, 51–96, 100–115, 280–328, 334–375
Neuropil, 64
Neuropsychology, 120–124, 145, 153–154
Neurospora, 3, 4
Neurosurgery, 122
Nociceptive fibers, 82, 106, 186
Nonlinearity in psychophysics, 326–327
Nuclear region, 292
Nucleus medialis dorsalis, 184–185

Nucleus ventralis posterior, 180
Number of nerve cells, 75, 105
Numbers assigned to continuous phenomena, 475–477, 489

Object-event-world, 524–526, 537
Object-oriented approach, 668
Object recognition, 199–200, 525ff.
Objectivism, 669
Objectivity, 431, 473–475, 521, 538ff., 552–556
(*See also* Behaviorism)
Observer, 558–559, 676–677
"Off" response, 453, 455–456
Old cortex, 184
Olfaction, 107, 394–395
Olfactory cortex, 179, 184
Oligodendrocytes, 82–83
"On-off" responses, 455–456
Operant behavior, 124, 125, 137, 139, 462–463
Operational definitions, 142–143, 458
Opossum, 181
Optic array, 527–529
Optic nerve, 75, 79, 106ff., 185, 191–194, 432, 437–445
Optics, physical, 428–431
physiological, 690
"Organ level" of analysis, 223–224
Organization of Behavior, 266
Orienting reaction, 134, 135
Orienting reflex, 133, 135, 335
Origin of Species, 161–162
Outcome, 124–125, 140

Pacemaking, 81
Pain impulses, 82, 106, 186
Palatability, 407
Paranoia, 29
Pattern, afferent input, 391
of behavior, 462–463
Pattern discrimination, 206, 209, 632–633
Pattern theory, 263–266
Patterning, neural, 336, 345, 356, 373
Pedigree method, 171
Percept, 666
Perception, xxxi–xxxii, 93, 225, 446, 483–512, 515–614, 619–655, 660–702
classical cognitive view, 528–529
in decerebrate preparations, 84
definition, 619–621, 662ff.
distorted, 57, 87, 91, 646, 682ff.
and psychophysics, 621–633
and related areas, 619–655
introduction to article, 619–621
perception and learning, 645–655

Perception, and related areas, perception and learning, toward adequate theory of perceptual learning, 647–655
efforts to determine facts, 645–647
perception and psychophysics, 621–633
systematic study of subjective variables, 623–633
two approaches, 621–623
perceptual and cognitive mechanism, 633–645
convergent views, 642–644
processing of sensory data, 633–642
relationship between perception and cognition, 644–645
of relations, 176, 203–206
(*See also* Size-distance relationships)
and sensation, 195–197, 200–206, 483–512
and transactional psychology, 660–702
concluding note, 701–702
empirical generalizations, 696–697
experiments deriving from transactional approach, 680–696
historical introduction, 661–662
interrelationship issue, 697–701
major approaches toward definition, 664–674
problem of definition, 662–664
transactional approach to perception, 674–680
"Perception curve," 604
Perceptron, 652–653
Perceptual change, 674, 678–679, 699–701
Perceptual experience, relations to external world through internal processings, 515–614
concluding statement, 608–614
experiential events and properties, 517–523
experiential report, methodological comments, 556–562
and scientific objectivity, 552–556
implications of phase analysis and of discrimination of specific meanings of perceiving, 549–552
interrelations among phases, 537–538
introduction to article, 516–517
multiple meanings of "*O* perceives *X,*" 542–549
phase analysis of perceiving, 523–537
phenomenal properties and perceptual organizations, 562–608
scientific status of concept of behavior, 538–541

Perceptual function, 492–493
Perceptual hierarchy, 639–642
Personality, and brain, 102
  and perception, 672–673, 686–688, 697–701
Personality development and genes, 15–18, 20–21
Perspective, perceptual, shifts in, 562ff., 589
Phantom sensations, 57
Phenocopies, 11
Phenomenal interrelations, 150
Phenomenological approach (*see* Experience; Experiential factors; Introspection; Verbal reports)
Phenotype, 6, 7, 10, 31, 166ff., 224
Phenotypical functions, 625ff., 650
Phenylketonuric amentia, 16, 22, 24, 36
Phi-gamma hypothesis, 305–306
Philosophers of science, xviii, 119, 149ff.
Philosophy of science, 230
Photic driving, 218, 221
Photolysis rate, 506ff.
Photometry, 426–428, 439*n.*, 510
Photopic luminosity function, 471
Photopigments, 440
Physical optics, 428–431
Physics, physiology, and psychology in study of vision, 417–477
  behavioral aspects of vision, 457–473
    behavioral studies, 463–473
    fundamental concepts, 460–463
    science of behavior, 458–460
  and biology, 229
  classical, 70*n.*–71*n.*, 93–94
  discussion, 473–477
    meaning of objectivity, 474–475
    measurement, 475–477
  introduction to article, 418–419
  nature of light, 419–432
    concepts based on direct visual observations, 420–426
    development of physical measures, 428–432
    quantitive visual photometry, 426–428
  and psychology, 518–520, 539, 552–554
  transmission and integration in visual system, 432–457
    activity of optic nerve, 437–457
    nerve impulse, 432–437
Physiological genetics, 165ff.
Physiological optics, 690
Physiological psychology, 15, 104, 242–246
  experimental work, 246–256
  introduction to article, 242

Physiological psychology, theorists, 256–270
  binary digital theory, 259–263
  Hebb's theory, 266–269
  mathematical biophysics, 257–259
  pattern theory, 263–266
  Pribram's synthesis, 269–270
  theory and experiment, 270–278
  what is "physiological psychology"? 242–246
Physiology, physics, and psychology in study of vision, 417–477
  and psychology, 103–104
Pigeon, visual processes in, 464ff.
Pineal gland, 54
Pinhole camera, 420
Place perception, 645–646
  (*See also* Size-distance relationships)
Plans, 140
Plasticity in nervous system, 62, 64
Plexus, 447
Pointer readings, 519, 520, 553, 554
Poisson distribution, 443
Polarization, 419–420, 425
Polygenes, 12–14
  and behavior, 16–17, 19, 30–34
Population genetics, 4, 15, 30, 35, 168–169, 226
Positive reinforcement (*see* Reinforcement)
Positivism, xviii
  (*See also* Operational definitions)
Postingestion factor, 399
Posture, 83
Potential, evoked, from somatosensory cortex, 292
  resting, 283, 284, 286, 289, 434
  (*See also* Action potential)
Power law, 313ff.
Precentral motor cortex, 140
Prediction, 358
  and cortex, 112
  (*See also* Probability theory)
Preexposure luminance, 502–503
Preference, relative, 402
Preference curve, 404ff.
Presentation of stimuli, 301–302
Preservation, of self, 87, 89*n.*
  of species, 87, 89*n.*
Pressure fibers, 82
Prevost's law of exchange, 430
Primary attention, 135
Primary sensory modalities, 81–82
Probabilistic functionalism, 678–679
Probability theory, 70*n.*–71*n.*, 298, 304ff.
Problem-solving situation, 134
Process, xxxv–xxxvi

Programing of stimuli, 139, 301–302
Projection system of brain, 64, 68ff., 72, 86, 188ff.
Prothetic continua, 326, 344, 639
Protopathic sense, 188, 391–392
Proximal stimulus, 527
Pseudohermaphrodites, 18
Psyche, 54
Psychoanalytic concepts, 459, 673
Psychology, biological, 158–231
   fields, xvi–xvii, xxxvii–xxxviii
   and genetics, 1–39
   and neurology, 119–154
   and neurophysiology, 51–96, 100–115, 280–328, 334–375
   and physics, 518–520, 539, 552–554
   and physiology, 103–104
   relations to biological and social sciences, xviii–xix
   of personality, 14
Psychometric function, 305–306
Psychon, 650n.–651n.
Psychoneuroses and genetics, 25
Psychopathology and perception, 698–701
Psychopharmacology, co-twin control method in, 38
   in studies of animal behavior, 33–34
Psychophysical experiment, 297–298, 360, 404ff., 487–488, 519, 546–547, 621–622, 631–633
   with animals, 463ff.
Psychophysical function, 492, 546, 624ff.
Psychophysical parallelism, 152, 198, 243, 528
Psychophysics, classical, 311–312, 487–488, 621–622
   and neurophysiology, 280–328
   concluding remarks, 327–328
   interrelationships between psychophysics and neurophysiology, 318–327
   empirical relations, 318–321
   measurement, theory, and linearity assumption, 325–327
   psychophysiological preparation, 321–325
   introduction to article, 281
   neurophysiology, 282–297
   electrical properties of single neurons, 282–290
   extracellular records from neuronal pools, 290–293
   independent variables in neurophysiology, 296–297
   measures of neuroelectric responses, 293–296
   psychophysics, 297–318

Psychophysics, and neurophysiology, psychophysics, behavioral definition, 297–299
   computational devices, 304–307
   empirical variables, 299–304
   experiential terminology, 310–318
   forms of psychophysical functions, 307–309
   and perception, 621–633, 668
Psychophysiological preparation, 321–325
Psychoses and gentics, 25–29, 35–38
Psychotherapy, 547, 678, 698–701
Public events, 474–475, 490, 538ff., 553
Pulvinar, 181, 191, 211
Punctate distribution of skin sensitivity, 382, 391–393
Punishment, 70, 71, 87
Pure line, 168–169
"Pure" science, 473
Pyramidal system, 78, 93n., 111–112, 536
Pyriform area, 184

Quanta and visual response, 442–443
Quantification of continuous phenomena, 475–477, 638–639
   (See also Probability theory; Psychophysical experiment; Scale value)
Quantitative methods in psychophysics, 304–307, 503–505, 638–639
Quantitative theory of feeling, 391
Quantum concept, 431
Quasi-state variables, 358, 360

R statistics, 306–307
Rabbit, 181
   Himalayan, 10–11
Radiant thermal properties of luminous objects, 428ff.
Radiation effects on embryos, 23
Rat, 181
Rate of response, 125ff., 138, 140, 468
Ratio judgments, 316
Reaction time, 307, 335, 337, 345, 368–373, 501
   (See also Latency)
"Ready-made" behavior, 248–249
Receptive field, 451–453
Receptor, analysis, 198, 530–532
   grouping, 636–638
   mosaic, 446, 450, 530
   potentials, 384–385
Receptor-states, 634–636
Reciprocity law, 440–441
Recruiting response, 182–183
Rectilinear propagation, 419–421
Reductionism, xviii, 121–123, 143, 153–154, 225ff., 245–246, 325, 394

Reference direction, 585–586
Reflection, 419–420, 422, 527
Reflex, 57, 79, 207, 221, 433
  conduction, 228
  orienting, 133, 135, 335
  stretch, 286
Reflexology, 224–225
Refraction, 419–420, 422, 429
Refractive index, 423
Refractory period, 284, 436
Reinforcement, 70, 71, 87, 125, 137, 271,
    407, 461–462, 464, 468
  differential, 302–303, 462–465, 468
  fixed-interval, 125ff., 137
  function of stimuli, 395
Rejection as basic response to taste, 396
Relationism, 667
Relative preference, 402, 404ff.
Releaser, social, 164
Relevancy, 632–633, 641, 643
Reliability in nervous system, 64, 80
Reorganization, perceptual, 562–608
Reproduction, 87
Response, averaged neural, 341, 345, 347–
    354, 356, 364–365
  compound, 290–291
  evoked, 324, 341–342, 345, 347–354,
    356, 359–360, 364–365
  graded, 286–288, 290–293, 343, 345
  measures, 293–296, 336–343, 461
  nonindependence of successive, 466
  rate, 125ff., 138, 140, 468
  restriction, 304
  single-unit, 341–342, 345–346, 352,
    357, 359, 365–367
  specification, 335–336, 338, 547–548
  units, 461
  (*See also* All-or-nothing principle)
Response chaining, 140
Response-response relations, 335–336, 374
Responses, sets, 303–304
Resting potential, 283, 284, 286, 289, 434
Restriction of response, 304
Reticular formation, 64ff., 86, 87, 103,
    107, 115, 133, 134, 183, 187, 270ff.,
    409, 534
Retina, 86, 106, 107–110, 438, 443, 446–
    457, 530ff.
Retinal ganglion cells, 79, 107
Retinal image, 446ff., 530
Reversals, perceptual, 562ff., 589
Reward (*see* Reinforcement)
Rhinencephalon, 409
Rods, 107–108
Roles, 17–18
Rotating trapezoid, 689–690
Rückmeldung, 112

Russian tradition and nervous system, 58–
  61

S statistics, 305–306
Saccharin, responses to, 399–403
Saltatory conduction, 80
Sampling of brain, 324
Sampling biases of microelectrodes, 289–
  290
Satiation, 129, 137
Saturation, 497, 498
Scale value, 306–307, 313ff., 485ff., 496–
    497, 505ff., 623ff., 643
  (*See also* Measurement; Psychophysical
    experiment)
Scalloped response curves, 125, 138
Schedules of reinforcement (*see* Rate of
  response; Reinforcement)
Schizophrenia and genetics, 25–29, 35–38
Science, of behavior, 458–460, 553
  experimental, 57, 119
Scientific universe of discourse, 120–121,
  149ff.
Scotoma, 200, 212
Scotopic luminosity function, 471
Scratch fibers, 82
Searching, 135
Second-order invariances, 309
Secondary attention, 135
Seizures, audiogenic, biochemical and
  genetic studies, 33–34, 37, 171–172
Selection, 161
Selective breeding, 14–15, 30ff., 165–
  166, 168–170, 172–174
Self-stimulation, 70, 408–409
Semantic differential, 633
Semantics, 146, 310ff.
Sensation, 382ff.
  and learning, 195–216
  and matter, 53
  and perception, 195–197, 200–206,
    483–512
  phantom, 57
  unlearned, 167–168
Sensationism, 669
Sensorium commune, 110
Sensory acuity, 177, 212
Sensory core, 188–189
Sensory data processing, 633–642
Sensory deprivation, 409–410
Sensory fibers (*see* Fibers)
Sensory input, 106–107, 134–135, 183,
  187–188
Sensory modalities, primary, 81–82, 393
Sensory performance of organisms, 339–
  340

Sensory processes and behavior, taste as model S-R system, 380–411
  behavioral consequences of gustatory stimulation, 395–410
    afferent discharge and behavior, 396–399
    biological basis of taste reactions, 403
    hedonic responses, 403–408
    physiological mechanisms in reinforcement, 408–410
    reinforcing functions of stimuli, 395
    responses to sugar and saccharin, 399–403
  electrophysiology of taste, 384–395
    afferent pattern and taste qualities, 389–391
    central control of receptors, 394–395
    cutaneous modalities, 391–393
    gustatory afferent nerve discharges, 385–388
    other senses and quality, 393–394
    receptor potentials, 384–385
  introduction to article, 380–383
  summary, 410–411
Sensory psychology, perception, and behavior, 483–512
  description and explanatory terminology, 497–499
  formal properties of psychophysical measurement, 503–505
  introduction to article, 483–485
  rational accounts of sensory relations, 505–510
  relations of sensation and perception, 499–503
  summary, 510–512
  types of stimulus-response relations, 485–497
    absolute judgments, 488–492
    experiment involving introspection, 485–487
    psychophysical experiment, 487–488
    symbolic formation, 493–497
    thresholds and perceptual functions, 492–493
Sensory quality, 197–198, 383
Sensory relations, 505–510
Sensory responses, 64–65, 71ff., 106ff., 195ff., 397–399
Sensory stimulation of mouth receptors, 403
Sensory systems, phylogeny of, 185–188
Sequential discrimination, 131ff.
Set, behavioral, 65

Set theory, 643
Sets, of responses, 299, 303–304
  of stimuli, 299–301
Sex differences, 17–18
Sham rage, 229
Sherrington's methods, 228–229, 324
Signaling system, cortex as, 59–60, 71ff., 86–87
Silver chloride, 429
Simultaneous brightness contrast, 455, 466–469
Single-unit response, 341–342, 345–346, 352, 357, 359, 365–367, 385–386, 435–437
Single visual elements, 437ff.
Situational variables, 125
Size, assumed, 683ff.
  of nerve cells, 105
  of nerve fibers, 185–188
Size constancy, 108, 109, 544–545, 653
Size-distance relationships, 682–689
  (See also Place perception)
Skilled behavior, 125, 140
Sleep, 74, 76, 183
Smell, 107, 394–395
Snell's law of refraction, 429
Social perception, 695–696
Social psychology, 14
Social roles, 17–18
Socioenvironmental factors, 154
Solar spectrum, 428
Somatic-visceral relations, 60–61
Soul, 54, 90, 119, 433
  (See also Mind)
Space-time constructs, 53
Spatial relationships, 594ff., 682–689
Spatial vs. visual responders in rats, 31–33
Spatiotemporal patterns of neuroelectric activity, 336, 345, 373
Species character, 161–166
Species differences in psychophysics, 298–299
Specific nerve energy, 186, 381–382, 533
Spectral sensitivity, 440, 469, 471–473
Speech, 113
Spike potential, 283, 286, 288, 345ff.
  (See also Single-unit response)
Spinal animal, 83, 111–112
Spinal cord, 65, 73, 111–112, 186, 221
Spontaneous activity, neural, 338, 342, 360, 366–367
Spontaneous perceptual reorganizations, 564–573
Squid, giant axon, 282–283, 433
Startle reaction, 133
Stationary image, 455

Statistics, S and R in psychophysics, 304–307
Stefan-Boltzmann law, 430
Stereoscopic vision, 494*n*., 691
Stimulus, distal and proximal, 527
  equivalence, 164, 225
  measurement, 336–337
  novel intense, 133, 135, 395, 467, 468
  programing, 139, 301–302
  specification, 300–301, 335–336, 373–374
  variables in psychophysics, 299ff.
Stimulus control of behavior, 462–463
Stimulus determination, 669–670
Stimulus error, 492*n*., 544–546, 552
Stimulus-response paradigm, 74, 225, 267, 357–358, 380ff., 621–622, 648–649, 670–671
Stimulus-response relations, 335–336, 338, 368, 374, 485–497, 667–670
Stimulus substitution, 225
Strategy, 139, 140
Stress and perception, 691–692
Stretch reflex, 286
Striate area, 108–109
Stroboscopic movement, 695
Structure, and function, 198, 220, 228–229
  inheritance, 163
Study of psychology, Project A, v–vii
  conceptual and systematic (Study I), v–vi, xi–xiii
  coverage, contributor group, and working atmosphere, xxi–xxx
  empirical substructure and relations with other sciences (Study II), vi, xi–xxxix
  panel of consultants, vi
  steering committee, vi–vii
Subcutaneous fibers, 82
Subjective magnitude, 314ff.
Subthreshold responses of axonal membrane, 280
Sugar, responses to, 399–403
Summation of potentials, 290
Supraliminal psychophysics, 313ff.
Surface, and interior, 526, 593
  slant, 550, 551, 593
  visible and nonvisible, 525–526
Survey, perceptual, 602–608
  (*See also* Looking behavior)
Sweet taste, 402, 403
Synaptic transmission, 55, 62–64, 80, 101, 228, 285ff.
Systematic formulations, v–vi, xi–xiv
Systems neurophysiology, 338

Taste, 107, 198, 380–411
Taste buds, 385
Tautology, 261
Taxonomic studies, 164
Teleological mechanism, 72, 86–87, 93ff.
Temperature impulses, 106, 321
Temporal aspects of electrophysiology, 294–296, 325–327, 352–354, 367–373
Temporal interactions, 320
Temporal lobe, 78, 138, 210–215
Test intelligence, 18–21
Texture, 570–572, 591, 592, 630
Thalamic syndrome, 410
Thalamocortical relations in cats, 193–194
Thalamus, 179–185
Themes of analysis, xii–xiv, xxvi–xxviii
Theory, binary digital, 259–263
  and data, 141ff., 258ff., 270–278, 495
  vs. empiricism, xxxiii–xxxiv, 505ff.
  of evolution, 161–162
  Hebb's, 266–269
  of knowledge, 418
  of light, 419–420
  pattern, 263–266
  of perceptual learning, 647–655
  in physiological psychology, 256ff.
  Pribram's, 269–270
Therapy (*see* Psychotherapy)
Therapy tests, value of co-twin control in, 38
Thereness-thatness apparatus, 682
Thermal properties of luminous objects, 428ff.
Thermocouple, 429
Thermoelectric current, 429
Thermopile, 429
Thought, 123
Threshold, 305–306, 319–320, 442–443, 469–470, 487, 492–493
Tiger moth mating preferences, 29
Time-space constructs, 53
Topographic organization of cortex, 189ff.
Touch fibers, 82, 106, 186
Touch threshold, 199–200
Training of subjects, 558ff.
Trait, Darwin's approach, 162
  development, 165
  Watson's approach, 163
Transactional mechanisms, 66, 68, 70, 93*n*.
Transactional psychology, 660–702
Transactionalists, 636
Transducers, 81, 82
Transfer of training, 222

Transitional cortex, 184
Transmembrane events, 284, 288
Transmission, neural, 55ff., 62ff., 80–82, 101–102, 285ff.
  (*See also* Action potential)
Transmission process in perception, 529–530
Transposition, 129ff., 197
Trapezoid, rotating, 689–690
Trends, of Study I, xi–xiii
  of Study II, xi–xxxix
Twin studies, values, limitations, and basic postulates, 26–29, 37
Twins, incidence of schizophrenia in, 26–29, 38
  monozygotic, 14, 17

Ultraviolet region, 429
Unconscious inference, 263, 642
Unit characters, 7, 10
Universe of discourse, 120–121, 149ff.
Unmyelinated fibers, 82

Validation, consensual, 149ff.
  perceptual, 674, 679–680
Value and brain activities, 87, 91, 114–115
Variability, in neuroelectric responses, 341–342
  normal, genetics, 9–10, 13–14, 17, 30ff., 39
  (*See also* Individual differences)
Variable-interval reinforcement, 464
Variables, continuous vs. discrete, 638–639
  dependent, in vision, 432ff.
  independent, in perception, 529–530, 548, 622
  in physiological psychology, 248–256
  in psychophysics, 299–304, 493–497, 499ff., 622ff.
  quasi-state, 358, 360
  situational, 125
  in transactional approach, 680–682
Variation, 161, 162, 166ff.

Velocity of light, 420–421
Verbal instructions, 559, 561
  in psychophysical experiments, 299, 302–303, 310ff., 463, 486, 496–497
Verbal reports, 486–487, 490, 552–562, 622–623, 627
  and nonverbal behaviors in psychotherapy, 547
Vertebrate retina, 451–453
Viability, effects of genes on, 12, 13
Vigilance, 199
Visceral-somatic relations, 60–61
Visible and nonvisible object surfaces, 525–526
Vision, 106–110, 191–194, 200, 209ff., 417–477
Visual deprivation, 167–168
Visual duration, 500–503, 507–510
Visual field, 143, 212, 509–510, 560
Visual photometry, 426–428, 439n.
Visual vs. spatial responders in rats, 31–33
Visual surface (*see* Surface)
Visual threshold, absolute, 469–470
Vitalism, 55, 120–121
Volition, 58, 124ff., 140
  (*See also* Free will)
Voluntary movement, 124

Wakefulness, 183
Waking brain, 54, 55
Washington cats, 145
Wave theory, 425–426
Weber's law, 314, 316–318, 381, 439n.
Weighting process, 678–679
Wernicke's area, 113
Wheatstone bridge, 429
Wholism, 667
Wide-receptive fibers, 82
Wien's displacement law, 430
Will (*see* Free will; Volition)
Wisconsin General Testing Apparatus, 129

X chromosomes, 6